Elizabethan Prose Fiction

Elizabethan Prose Fiction

EDITED BY Merritt Lawlis

INDIANA UNIVERSITY

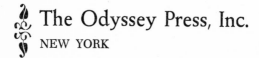

The Odyssey Press, Inc.
NEW YORK

For
Naomi, Marcia, Barb, and Abby

◊ Preface

The nine works included in this volume represent, in my judgment, the different kinds of prose fiction published in the age of Elizabeth I, 1558–1603. Implicit in such a judgment is the acknowledgment that other works could have been chosen just as well. My attempt has been to represent the different kinds in the right proportion. Since romance was the most popular form among the Elizabethans, five of the nine works have elements of romance or anti-romance in them. Regretfully, I have had to omit Sidney's *Arcadia;* a responsible abridgment would run to at least 100 pages.

With one exception, all nine works are complete. I have edited only the first half of *Euphues: The Anatomy of Wit;* but that half constitutes all the narrative part, to which Lyly gave a sense of finality. I have included all prefatory material to each work; occasionally in a preface or dedication an author reveals his intentions, which the close reader may want to take into account.

I should like to thank the following libraries for giving me permission to use their early editions as copytexts: the Bodleian Library, Oxford University (for *Farewell to the Military Profession* and *A Notable Discovery of Cozenage*); the British Museum (for *Pandosto*); the Folger Shakespeare Library (for *The Adventures of Master F. J.*); the Henry E. Huntington Library (for *The Sackful of News, The Unfortunate Traveler,* and *Thomas of Reading*); the Carl H. Pforzheimer Library (for *Rosalind*); and the Trinity College Library, Cambridge University (for *Euphues: The Anatomy of Wit*).

I am grateful to the University of Pittsburgh, and especially to the members of the English Department, for a very pleasant and profitable nine months in 1965–66 as an Andrew Mellon Fellow. For the two months in the same year as a Folger Shakespeare Library Fellow I wish to thank the entire Folger staff; such a scholarly, efficient, and yet relaxed atmosphere (the third element, alas, not available in universities), I had never encountered before and will remember fondly. A grant from the Graduate School of Indiana University paid for much of the necessary materials and assistance in the preparation of this edition.

To the revisers of the *Short-Title Catalogue . . . 1475–1640,* especially the late Professor William A. Jackson and Miss Katharine F. Pantzer of Houghton Library, I am indebted for a great deal of the information about early editions that appears in the Textual Notes and in several of the footnotes.

Several of my friends and colleagues have read various parts of the manuscript. For their many helpful questions, suggestions, and corrections, I wish to thank Professors Gates K. Agnew, Frederick L. Beaty, Georges R. Edelen, Charles R. Forker, Rudolf B. Gottfried, Lewis H. Miller, Jr., Charles D. Peet, Jr., William H. Wiatt, and Malvin R. Zirker, Jr., all of Indiana University; and Alan M. Markman, University of Pittsburgh.

For their careful work in helping me with the collation and copying, I wish to thank the following graduate students at Indiana University: Miss Danna D'Esopo, Mr. Martin Green, Mrs. Barbara S. Hillenbrand, Mr. Samuel Longmire, Mrs. Elizabeth B. Pontius, and Mr. Keith Schap.

Unlike many preface wives, mine did no typing; nor did she, so far as I know, contribute anything directly to this volume. She is merely the best of wives.

M. L.

Bloomington, Indiana

℘ Contents

Elizabethan Prose Fiction

Key to Abbreviations and Short References in the Footnotes

DNB   *Dictionary of National Biography*
ELH   *[Journal of] English Literary History*
HLQ   *Huntington Library Quarterly*
N&Q   *Notes and Queries*
OED   *Oxford English Dictionary*
PMLA   *Publications of the Modern Language Association of America*
PQ   *Philological Quarterly*
RLC   *Revue de Littérature Comparée*
SJ   *Shakespeare-Jahrbuch*
SP   *Studies in Philology*
SSF   *Studies in Short Fiction*
TLS   *[London] Times Literary Supplement*

If an article or book is listed in the Select Bibliography, it is referred to in the footnotes as briefly as possible (last name only of the author and a short title); but if it is not listed in the Select Bibliography, then the reference is complete (full name of the author, all the title unless it is unusually long, as well as the place and date of publication).

⚘ Introduction

1. *Elizabethan Prose Fiction*

The modern reader who approaches Elizabethan prose fiction for the first time may expect to have a certain amount of difficulty, just as he would if he were having his first experience with the Greek romance of the second and third centuries or the Renaissance Italian *novella* beginning with Boccaccio in the fourteenth century. Or perhaps a more relevant analogy, since it does not involve translation from a foreign language, is Elizabethan drama, for which modern drama is only a slight preparation. Any reading of a much earlier literature requires certain imaginative adjustments, most of them rather easy but some of them extremely difficult to make. The purpose of this section of the general introduction to Elizabethan prose fiction is to isolate briefly a few of the troublesome areas and suggest possible ways of adjusting to them. One hardly need add that the process of going back into another age, and trying to think and feel as men and women did then, can be an intellectual pleasure of an exceptionally rewarding kind.

Perhaps the most obvious difference between Elizabethan fiction and our own has to do with the changes in the meanings of words and idioms. Many sixteenth-century expressions are no longer used at all, while others do not mean what we may think they do. The Elizabethan word "bravery" means "finery" now. A few other random examples are "incontinent" (immediately), "meat" (dairy products), "lewd" (ignorant), "artificial" (made by art), and "corn" (grain). Hopefully, the footnotes in the present volume will help explain both archaic and misleading expressions; but it will be necessary to some extent for the reader to build up gradually an Elizabethan vocabulary. He should be prepared to see a great deal of what we now call slang, for which the Elizabethans had a special fondness, even in otherwise serious and dignified contexts. A related problem is their

1

robust tendency to use four-letter words, referred to in our dictionaries as vulgar. Usually the precise meaning is all too clear; the difficult part is adjusting our sensibilities, learning not to be shocked by mere frankness and openness.

The language of Deloney, Greene, and Nashe is full of concrete references to contemporary places and persons. Some of the places, like "Paris Garden" (mentioned in footnote 219 of *The Unfortunate Traveler*), scholars have been able to trace fairly well. But "Galino" (mentioned in footnote 54 of *Thomas of Reading*) does not turn up in other works of the time; and therefore we have no idea what, if anything, the word conjured up in the Elizabethan imagination. Generally speaking, a great deal of modesty on our part is appropriate; often we are not able to say exactly and fully what the Elizabethans meant by a word.

We know that many Elizabethan writers loved puns. Miss M. M. Mahood has estimated that there are some 3,000 of them in Shakespeare's plays and poems, 175 in *Romeo and Juliet* alone.[1] Nashe used puns as much as Shakespeare did, and there are probably at least 175 in *The Unfortunate Traveler*. But we cannot possibly recognize them all, for on one level they refer to contemporary gossip and other tidbits of information that are lost to us. Where the present-day student recognizes a simple pun and the present-day scholar a double pun, the ordinary Elizabethan reader may have understood a triple and the Elizabethan scholar a quadruple pun.

Elizabethan religious and political biases are particularly interesting. Adjustments to them will be easy for some modern readers and difficult for others. "Fortunately," we are all biased one way or another; and we are at least acquainted with prejudices of many kinds, some of them probably unknown to the Elizabethans. But the trouble is that the prejudices of one age seem amusing, and also stupid, to another. When Barnaby Rich in one of his dedications links together "the pope, the Turk, and the devil" (p. 202), our disposition is to laugh. It is difficult for us to imagine that particular

---

[1]*Shakespeare's Wordplay* (London, 1957), pp. 56, 164. If we look beyond the puns to rhetoric generally, we find that Elizabethan writers, generally speaking, were more interested in exploiting rhetorical devices than our writers are now. That Elizabethan readers were themselves interested both in the theory and the practice of rhetoric would seem to be indicated by the unusual popularity of Thomas Wilson's *Art of Rhetoric* (eight editions between 1553 and 1585) and John Lyly's *Euphues: The Anatomy of Wit* (thirteen editions between 1578 and 1597).

triumvirate as "the enemy." But in fact a fairly large proportion of Europeans in the late sixteenth century agreed with Rich. To Lyly, Nashe, and a great many other Elizabethans the Puritan was a fourth menace. As explained in the Biographical Sketches, Lyly and Nashe defended the *via media*, Queen Elizabeth's version of the Reformation; in her hands the Establishment became neither Catholic nor Puritan, but a middle way between the two.

By our standards Elizabeth's methods of obtaining a compromise were cruel, tyrannical, and most undemocratic while, at the same time, they were efficient, orderly, and resourceful. In Deloney there is a strong undercurrent of disguised protest, but most of the other writers of the period seem to go along with Elizabeth's tactics. Occasionally one senses a wartime psychology, a complex of emotional responses that spring from a conviction that only strong measures will combat real and present dangers.

Different as many Elizabethan works are from each other, they are closer to each other in form than they are to modern works. To a large extent the reason is what we may term "formal convention" (or "conventional form," depending on the emphasis). Creative writers in the English Renaissance tend to agree, as a matter of course and probably without fully realizing it, that certain aspects of a story should be rendered in a particular way—a way that now, 400 years later, seems not only foreign but arbitrary and artificial. An example is the long monologue, sometimes coming in the middle of a stretch of dialogue and sometimes given as a soliloquy (a series of private thoughts of a rather general nature.) Either way—as an interruption of dialogue (see the speech by the "old gentleman" beginning on p. 129 in *Euphues*) or as a soliloquy (see Margaret's toward the beginning of Chapter 3 in *Thomas of Reading*)—the monologue in Elizabethan fiction is a little oration, a set piece, often with beginning, middle, and end. To our charge that no one ever thought or talked as the "old gentleman" does, the Elizabethan writer probably would raise an eyebrow: after all, the chaos of people's real thoughts is hardly worth recording. Unlike us, the Elizabethans often read aloud to each other; and in a work of prose fiction the monologue, careful in thought and pleasing in rhythm and sound effects, may very well have been one of the choice oral selections. Ideally, our response should be a pause while we fully appreciate the set piece, the marble inlay, suspending in the meantime our natural desire to get on with the story-line. But if we find the pace unbearably slow, then our next best response is to read the mono-

logue faster than we do other parts of the story. Certainly we should
not let it spoil the whole work for us.[2]

In modern fiction we are used to seeing the action strictly related
to character and theme; and when we read Lodge, Greene, and
Deloney, we sense familiar patterns of narrative structure. But when
we read Lyly and Nashe, we discover an unfamiliar use of action.
Euphues is really a series of dialogues with little movement in time
or space. *The Unfortunate Traveler* is full of movement; but the
narrator constantly interrupts it to give us what matters to him much
more—an incisive attack on some person, group, or place. Our
proper response when we read Lyly or Nashe is to enjoy the dialogue
or attack for its own sake. All we can require of any work is that it
have an inner integrity; in an individual case the development of
theme or character may not be important.

A good guess is that *The Unfortunate Traveler* struck the Elizabethan reader the same way that it strikes us—as a bold and confident mixture of disparate forms. It embraces within a loose structure
all four of the classical genres (lyric, epic, comedy, and tragedy); and
then, impishly juxtaposed with these highly respected forms, are such
"base" forms as jests, "outlandish chronicle" (as the narrator calls it),
and inverted medieval romance told with Rabelaisian gusto. The
resulting medley surely was intended to be a *tour de force*. We
should regard it as an extreme example, but at the same time it is
symptomatic of a general Elizabethan confidence in mixing seemingly
unmixable elements. Greene, Nashe, and Deloney find uses of the
lowly jestbook in almost anything they write, no matter how serious
its main emphasis. Lyly places slang and a homely proverb alongside
the most dignified reference to the classics. Deloney captures the
rhythms of actual speech such as few writers have ever done; and
then he gives, quite straightforwardly, a fairly long stretch of euphuistic dialogue. Our difficulty is in recognizing how the mixtures are
appropriate. The introductions to the individual works attempt to
provide solutions to this and other problems, but one general point
may be made here: the mixing of forms in Elizabethan literature,
including Shakespeare's plays, is a source of tremendous vitality; it is
one of the main reasons why the sparks fly.

What terms shall we use in describing the nine works included

[2]Another conventional aspect of form is the interpolated poem; if the poem
contributed to the tone of the story, Elizabethan writers and readers apparently were content with it. Strict relevance to the action, and what we now
call unity, seem not to have been primary aims of Elizabethan fiction.

in the present anthology? Our main concern should be to describe accurately and not worry very much about applying names and labels. Yet we can see that the works are different from each other in fundamental ways; and in our desire to compare only the comparable, we will want to divide them into meaningful groups. Two modern critics, Henry James and Northrop Frye, have provided a few helpful terms. In using these terms we should remember that they are only roughly accurate, that they are merely convenient in a preliminary grouping and placing.

In his preface to the New York edition of *The American*, Henry James considers the art of prose fiction in relation to the nature of our everyday experience. When we read any work of fiction, he suggests, we are projected out into imaginative space in a balloon. James' metaphor is apt, for no work of fiction is entirely earthbound: there is always something—pattern of organization, selectivity, omniscience on the part of the narrator—that makes the most realistic story different from real life. In the form of prose fiction that we call "novel," the rope attached to our balloon is always in evidence. As we sit in the balloon, we can and do look down and observe *terra firma*, where the other end of our rope leading from the balloon is fastened; that is, the narrator of a novel constantly "asks" us to observe real life and make comparisons between it and the characters and actions of his story. But the form that we call "romance" is quite different; the art of it, according to James, consists in the narrator's ability to cut the rope without our detecting him in the act. By various means he in effect gives us a drug that makes us concentrate strongly on some things while ignoring others. All the while he communicates an "air of truth" so strong that we are lulled into the feeling that there is no need to check on reality by looking down at the rope and the earth. Of course, if we *were* to look down, we should notice that the rope has been cut; we are, in James' phrase, "at large and unrelated."

James' metaphor is helpful in placing all the works in this anthology. "Apolonius and Silla," *Pandosto, Rosalind,* and *Thomas of Reading* are all romances, though at least two of them are strongly mixed with other kinds. For these four works the cable has been cut, though the distance of the balloon from the earth varies considerably from work to work, or even within the same work. In *Master F. J.*, a novel, the cable has not been cut; we maintain at all times a close contact with the earth. In *The Sackful of News, A Notable Discovery,* and *The Unfortunate Traveler* the cable remains not only intact but is rather short, so that we must see a great deal of the earth every time we look out (and we are never disposed to look up). *Euphues* presents a special case. To modern readers the rope probably is not cut. Yet as we look down from the balloon, we do not see the earth; we see some other planet of Lyly's creation. To certain Elizabethan readers, probably, on the other hand, the rope is not cut and is attached to what the Elizabethans regarded as one area of our own planet, earth.

In his book *The Anatomy of Criticism*, Northrop Frye recognizes the differences between "novel" and "romance" and adds two more forms, "confession" and "anatomy." "Confession" applies to some of the pamphlets that Greene wrote late in his career—*The Repentance of Robert Greene*, for example—but generally speaking it is a form rarely encountered in the sixteenth century. "Anatomy," on the other hand, is a particularly useful term in describing Elizabethan prose fiction, in which there is a strong tendency to take apart and analyze in a manner that is both "extroverted and intellectual." *Euphues* is almost pure anatomy; and we will have occasion to notice elements of it in *Pandosto, A Notable Discovery,* and *The Unfortunate Traveler.*

Related to the analytical nature of much Elizabethan prose fiction is a cluster of other characteristics—a tendency to be objective and outward in the presentation of character, loose in the structuring of action, and openly didactic in the comments of the narrator and the characters. Rarely do we see a character in a strictly personal or intimate light. The soliloquies express general feelings of mankind, not the idiosyncratic feelings of a particular man or woman. Occasionally Deloney's scenes bring us up close to warm and friendly persons, but even in Deloney the principal scenes are often quite objective and external. The murder scene in Chapter 10 of *Thomas of Reading* is a good example. Chapter 9 of *Jack of Newbury* is another: Jack's great generosity toward Randoll Pert is essentially a personal act; but Deloney's method is to arrange the scene to express a general truth ("the honesty of a man is all") before a whole crowd of onlookers, who prevent Jack and Randoll from saying anything personal to each other. Yet Deloney's technique is like Gascoigne's in that his outward and spare presentation suggests and implies a vague and pervasive inwardness; we sense the nature of Jack's generosity and Randoll's gratitude without ever getting their thoughts apart from what they say in dialogue.

To the looseness of structure the present-day reader will have no difficulty in adjusting, for the mid- and later-twentieth century novel, at least in the United States and Europe, is no longer the "well-made novel" of Galsworthy and Bennett, who are currently out of favor.

But the didacticism is something else. Many modern readers will have difficulty giving it the serious consideration that its emphasis and sheer quantity seem to demand. Particularly striking is the narrator's apparent certainty about life. In Elizabethan prose fiction, in Shakespeare's *Lucrece,* in Spenser's *Faerie Queene,* the narrator gives every impression that he knows what the eternal verities are; he rarely communicates any sense of doubt or groping such as the narrators of twentieth-century fiction communicate in various ways. The Elizabethans tended to have strong faiths—in the Bible, in the Establishment, in the classics, and (often above all) in man himself. Sometimes their belief in man and their love of the Greek and Roman classics, all pagan, had a way of contradicting their sense of Christianity. Our problem, then, is not only to empathize with an age of faith but with the contradictory faiths of that age.

One last note. I have said that the Elizabethans *tended* to have strong faiths, and my implication was that they were "sincere." On the whole, that probably is an accurate generalization. But we should also take into account the Elizabethan practice of official licensing and censoring of books. Unfortunately, our information is incomplete; probably an author then could get almost anything by the licensers if he was clever enough, and probably the licensers occasionally winked at a book in which the author attacked the English monarch or church in a thinly disguised allegory. In view of these and other probabilities, our response to the problem should not be unqualified suspicion. We need not turn every episode around, or over, or inside out before we get at the author's true meaning. In sixteenth-century England most artists apparently believed in, or took for granted, the system under which they lived their whole lives. It would be odd if they did not, for it was the only system they knew much about. Most of them probably were neither devoutly Christian nor vehemently atheistical, and in their works they usually give every appearance of saying what they had to say in the form in which they wanted to say it.

On the other hand, we should be prepared for the maverick, the unexpected and unusual case. It is not enough to rest content with what *most* Elizabethans did (even if we knew for certain what most of them did). If we attend to the evidence all round us now, we realize that ours is not completely an age of skepticism and protest;

it is not completely anything. Neither was the Renaissance entirely an age of faith and conformity. Regardless of what the age was like generally, our immediate task, as we approach Elizabethan prose fiction, is to read accurately each individual work, one at a time, beginning with the surface and then proceeding to whatever emphases, silences, beliefs, and insincerities to which the surface points.

2. *Preparation of the Texts*

In the paragraphs that follow, in several of the footnotes to the individual texts, and in a section toward the back of this volume called "Textual Notes," I have assumed that textual matters are relevant to criticism. For the most part I have addressed not the expert but the student who is ready to begin appreciating how and why editorial decisions inevitably affect the way in which an author's words are transmitted to the reader.

In preparing each text my first concern was to discover which of the early editions is authoritative. Having chosen an authoritative edition, I copied from it (used it as my copytext). But as the discussions in the Textual Notes section will make clear, using the copytext is not always a simple matter, especially if there is some question whether the author made revisions; *Master F. J., Euphues,* and *The Unfortunate Traveler* all presented special problems that seemed to me to call for solutions out of the ordinary. The other six texts were comparatively trouble free; for one reason or another, in each case the earliest extant edition was also the authoritative edition. I have collated line by line each copytext with other early editions, though in some cases I have not been able to see all the early editions; but I have collated all the standard modern editions, such as Bond's edition of Lyly and McKerrow's of Nashe.

Listed in the Textual Notes are the "substantive emendations"—that is, corrections of the copytext that have to do with the author's meaning and not merely with "accidentals," the simple variations of spelling and punctuation that to some extent were introduced by the printer. Evident misprints—accidents that occurred during the printing, such as turned, damaged, or transposed letters—I have corrected silently when there is no ambiguity. The emendation list, however, is on the inclusive side; when there is any question whether an apparent misprint or a change of spelling or punctuation involves a change of meaning, then I include it in the list (the accepted reading to the left of the bracket and the rejected reading to the right).

My intent has been to prepare a careful text, modernizing the original spelling and punctuation only when the original meaning or effect will remain essentially unchanged. In *The Sackful of News,* "Fryer" may be modernized to "friar," "cloathes" to "clothes," and "Summers" to "summer's" without loss. In *Euphues,* however, as I have explained in footnote 107, "rise" may not be changed to the modern equivalent, "risen." Lyly probably is using "rise" to rhyme with "paradise"; but, in any case, it is not the function of an editor to bring an author's grammar up-to-date. For dozens of words in each of the longer works there are no modern spellings. "Appeach" in *Master F. J.* should not be changed to its modern equivalent, "impeach"; that would be a kind of translation, which I have tried to avoid. In such cases I leave the original expression and give the modern sense in a footnote.

For the benefit of the modern reader I have tried to "normalize"— to introduce a certain amount of consistency in the spelling. My method was not to impose arbitrarily a modern usage, but to choose one of the variants actually given in the copytext and then use it throughout. The Elizabethan printer used "&" or "and," whichever at the moment helped him justify a line of type; he also used "S.," "St.," or "Saint" interchangeably, as well as "q.," "quod," or "quoth." I have used only "and," "St.," and "quoth" throughout. Variant spellings probably offered no special difficulty to the Elizabethan reader. But the modern reader is used to consistency; when he sees the same words spelled differently, he wonders if there is some reason for it. Unless in my judgment the author actually had a reason, my plan has been to normalize.

I have referred to the author of "Apolonius and Silla" as "Barnaby Rich," but on title pages and other records of the time his first name is spelled four different ways and his last name nine.[3] In his dedication, "To the Noble Soldiers of England," Rich begins a paragraph with these words; "for first the military profession, by means whereof men were advanced to the greatest renown. . . ." Yet the title of the book that includes seven other *novelle* besides "Apolonius" reads *"Farewell to Military Profession."* Either expression—"the military profession" (with the article) or *"Military Profession"* (without the article) was idiomatic at the time. But since only the former is idiomatic now, I have consistently referred to the title as *Farewell to the Military Profession.*

[3]See Cranfill, *Rich's Farewell to Military Profession,* p. 228.

With some misgivings I have normalized the title of Lodge's work to "*Rosalind.*" Previously, even in modernized editions, the title has been "*Rosalynde.*" In the first edition (1590) the heroine's name appears three ways—"Rosalynde," "Rosalynd," and "Rosalind." "Rosalynd" is the most common spelling and "Rosalind" the least, but we cannot be sure that Lodge had any more to do with the frequency of a particular spelling than the compositor did. Lodge seems to have consistently pronounced the name "roz'-ə-lind." In Rosader's "Second Sonetto" the verses are in couplets, the heroine's name rhyming with "kind"; and in several other poems it is clear that her name is to rhyme either with "kind" or "unkind." Some readers of Lodge's romance have found the final "e" in "Rosalynde" a little ambiguous, especially after they learn that Lodge's story is based on a medieval tale. The final "e" should not be pronounced, and perhaps the best way to make that absolutely clear is for the editor to omit it.

With regard to punctuation, in some original passages sentence patterns are broken up by heavy stops, while in other passages of exactly the same nature the comma serves both as a light and a heavy stop. It is difficult to know whether the author or the compositor is responsible for the inconsistency; but I did not hesitate to change the comma to a period or semicolon when the sense required it, though in each case I usually found a precedent in the work itself. The aim was not to force a modern usage; but if the original offered a precedent in the direction of modern usage, I accepted it. When I had any doubt about the sense, I called attention to the original punctuation in a footnote.

Elizabethan compositors occasionally set two or three solid pages without paragraphing. I have taken the liberty of starting new paragraphs, hopefully making the sense clearer without introducing any break in thought. For each new speech in dialogue I have started a new paragraph and added quotation marks.

In the footnotes to the text my aim has been to help the close reader, the reader who wants to get something more than a hazy idea of what the stories are about. Usually my notes are strictly informational, but occasionally they have to do with analyzing the form and content. I have tried to keep in mind what Lyly said in his dedication of *Euphues* to Sir William West: "When the matter itself bringeth credit, the man with his gloss winneth small commendation." Since this edition contains about 900 footnotes, I may deserve small commendation. But the amount of glossing depends on the audience and the author. For the freshman in college Deloney requires only an occasional note, while almost every sentence in Nashe contains word-play or an allusion that needs explaining. On the other hand, for the scholar very little, even in Nashe, needs glossing. I have tried to aim between the freshman and the scholar at the upperclassman in college and the first-year graduate student.

One way I have reduced the number of footnotes is to avoid glossing words that can be found in an ordinary abridged dictionary. I happen to have used the College Edition of *Webster's New World Dictionary of the American Language* (New York, 1964), which includes a number of words that were used repeatedly in Elizabethan prose fiction but are no longer in common usage, at least in the United States. A few examples are "hobby" (small hawk), "stews" (brothel), "fere" (companion), and "discovert" (having no husband). Previous editors have glossed these words, but it seems to me reasonable (especially now that I am giving fair warning!) to expect the reader to look them up for himself. Expressions not to be found in *Webster's New World Dictionary* I have glossed, unless their sense is made clear by the context; my principal source was the *Oxford English Dictionary* (Oxford, 1888–1933).

Another way I have reduced the number of footnotes is to avoid (with a few exceptions) supplying encyclopedia information when it is not strictly relevant. An example in Nashe is "Epimenides," who appears on p. 450 of the text. According to the encyclopedias, Epimenides was a philosopher who lived in the sixth century B.C.; presumably a great deal more can be found out about him in special studies of early Greek and Cretan philosophers, and the motif of a nap lasting many years can be traced down to Rip van Winkle. Any reader who wants to conduct a further investigation will no doubt find it rewarding, but it will not help him understand what is going on in *The Unfortunate Traveler*. I should add one point: Nashe spells the name "Epemenides"; I have altered his spelling (without affecting the pronunciation) so that the reader may look up the name quickly, without having to wonder whether he is looking up the right man. For all such references to Greek and Roman names I have used either *Webster's New World Dictionary* or Catherine B. Avery's *The New Century Classical Handbook* (New York, 1962).

Place names I try to handle in the same way: the object is to give the correct modern spelling, if the place can be located at all, but explain where and what the place is only if it is important to the context. Footnote 15 in *The Unfortunate Traveler* is justifiable, in my judgment, for two reasons: Turney and Turwin are important to the story, and Nashe's anglicization of the French place names is a stylistic trait to which the reader should be alerted. My main source of information about place names was Leon F. Seltzer's *The Columbia Lippincott Gazetteer of the World* (New York, 1952). I have also used Edward H. Sugden's *A Topographical Dictionary to the Works of Shakespeare and His Fellow Dramatists* (Manchester, 1925), the index to McKerrow's edition of Nashe, the index to the Bohn edition of Pliny, and various encyclopedias.

One of the more vexing problems in the footnotes was deciding when to translate foreign expressions. One cannot assume that the present-day reader knows Latin, French, Spanish, and Italian, the languages quoted more or less frequently in the works included in this collection. But, interestingly enough, with the exception of Latin, the authors themselves did not know foreign languages very well either, though they sometimes wanted to give a contrary impression. What I tried to do was help the reader in any way I could without distracting him unnecessarily. Although I am quite sure that I have not been perfectly consistent, my aim was to translate a foreign passage only when it is in some way important to the context, and not just a trivial expression. Certainly if I had translated every single foreign expression, this edition would have contained several hundred more footnotes than it does. Fortunately, Nashe often translates his own Latin; and the sense of many foreign expressions is clear enough from the context. If one phrase, like *"alla Napolatana"* in *Master F. J.*, is translated in a footnote, then a similar phrase, *"alla Piedmontese,"* will not need translating when it appears later in the novel.

In writing the footnotes I have tried to resist the temptation to draw parallels of thought or expression between the works in this collection and Chaucer, Shakespeare, and others. It is sometimes revealing to know that Shakespeare used such-and-such a phrase or incident from "Apolonius" or *Pandosto;* but in this edition I wanted primarily to encourage, at long last, the reading of Elizabethan prose fiction for its own sake.

The Sackful of News

(*c.* 1558)

ANONYMOUS

The *Sackful of News* may be what we call "subliterary." Where the point is for separating literature from subliterature, no one knows for sure; and yet we all may come close to agreeing that *Sackful* is hardly within the pale. On the other hand, it is not for that reason an object of contempt, any more than a popular ballad, a folk tale, or a comic strip is. We need not demand sophistication from everything we read. Furthermore, if we are interested in trying to see how a work of prose fiction is put together—how the different springs and wheels make it tick—the lowly *Sackful* can be a good place to begin; its very simplicity will prove an advantage.

Ernst Schulz and F. P. Wilson have between them isolated and described three forms of the jestbook—collections of detached jests, jest-biographies, and collections of comic *novelle*.[1] The last of these forms had no particular vogue in England, though it is interesting to

[1] "*Novella*" in Italian means "short story"; its use as a critical term helps us remember that the art of the short tale in the Renaissance had its beginnings in the middle of the fourteenth century with Boccaccio. See Wilson's article "The English Jestbooks of the Sixteenth and Early Seventeenth Centuries." See also Schulz's book *Die englischen Schwankbücher bis herab zu "Dobson's Drie Bobs."* Incidentally, *Dobson's Drie Bobs* is a first-rate jest-biography; it was edited by E. A. Horsman for Oxford Univ. Press in 1955.

note that Thomas Deloney probably was the translator of one collection of comic *novelle* from French into English.[2] But the other two forms of the jestbook were very popular. They are also historically important. They derive from the medieval *exemplum* and *fabliau,* and they lead directly into sixteenth-century "criminal fiction," represented in this volume by Greene's *A Notable Discovery of Cozenage;* they also seem to have been models for Nashe and Deloney when a short, boisterous scene was called for.[3] The only essential difference between a "collection of detached jests" and a "jest-biography" is that in the jest-biography one person, usually the principal character, is a character in all the jests, thus binding the whole collection rather loosely together. For example, in *The Merry, Conceited Jests of George Peele* (1607) all the individual stories are nominally about the Elizabethan actor and playwright George Peele (1558?–1597?).[4]

The Sackful of News is a collection of detached jests, the simplest of the three jestbook forms. Each jest is a separate tale, completely detached from the others before and after it. There happen to be twenty-two tales in *Sackful;* there could have been any number at all. *The Fables of Alphonsus and Poggio,* published in 1484 by William Caxton on the first printing press in England, contained only thirteen tales, and *A Hundred Merry Tales* (1526) contained, as the title indicates, an even hundred. But the form of the individual tale is roughly the same in all the collections of detached jests. It is short, sometimes only half a page, and never running to more than a few pages. The presentation is basically scenic. There is usually some dialogue, and it is often crisp and colloquial. The reader is placed fairly close to the action (close enough to hear the dialogue); but sensory details of the kind that we get on every page in Deloney—the particular material and cut of a person's jacket, the taste of a certain kind of wine—are not usually given by the narrator or by any of the characters.

[2]Bonaventure Des Périers' *The Mirror of Mirth and Pleasant Conceits.* See J. Woodrow Hassell, Jr., "An Elizabethan Translation of the Tales of Des Périers: *The Mirrour of Mirth,* 1583 and 1592," *SP,* LII (1955), 172–185.

[3]For a fuller discussion of the jestbook and an approach to Elizabethan prose fiction from "a social point of view," see Schlauch, *Antecedents of the English Novel, 1400–1600,* especially pp. 85–99, 240. See also Baker, *The History of the English Novel,* I, 288–294; II, 168, 170, 174 and 186.

[4]Peele probably did live somewhat merrily, though we should not take all the exploits in *Conceited Jests* as literally biographical. See David H. Horne, *The Life and Minor Works of George Peele* (New Haven, Conn., 1952), pp. 110–126.

Sackful in many ways is like other jestbooks of its type. But it is unusual in its moral neutrality. Many collections of detached jests reveal more obviously their origin in the *exemplum*. The last sentence of the third "fable" in *The Fables of Alphonsus and Poggio* reads: "For there is no sin or misdeed done but that once it shall be known and manifested."[5] Almost all the jests in *A Hundred Merry Tales* end with "By this tale a man may learn . . ." or words to that effect (and without irony).

One suspects that the narrator of *Sackful* finds life considerably more complex. Certainly he does not harbor grudges against women, friars, or Welshmen, who, in many of the sixteenth-century jestbooks, come in for a great deal of satire, some of it bitter. In tale No. 3 of *Sackful* the young wife thinks up a scheme to cuckold her husband. The point of view, that of the wife and her "servant," has a bearing on the way we are to take the ending. When the husband thinks he has a chaste wife and a loyal servant, we are not asked to approve of the wife and her lover, but we are asked to appreciate their ingenuity. In several other jestbooks such tales are more plentiful and the wife is clearly blamed; taken together, these jestbooks contribute a sizable body of material to what the Renaissance called "the woman question." Does a woman have any sense of right and wrong? Does she have a mind or soul? Should a man marry? It is difficult now for us to realize with what anxiety perfectly intelligent men of the Renaissance argued these questions.[6]

Friars had been fair game for a long time, as one may note in *The Decameron* and in countless medieval *fabliaux*. "Friar John" or "Prester John" is one of the best known jestbook types, with two inevitable characteristics, lechery and gluttony. Often the humor consists in an elaboration of his ingenuity in satisfying one or the other of his appetites. Sometimes the humor involves "poetic justice," the friar being trapped by the husband while the whole neighborhood laughs. But the narrator of *Sackful* prefers a more disinterested presentation. Priests enter into four of the tales (Nos. 1, 2, 6, and 19), but neither separately nor together do these tales amount to any satire of the clergy. Since priests in *Sackful* are quite different from each other, the

[5]See *A Hundred Merry Tales and Other English Jestbooks of the Fifteenth and Sixteenth Centuries*, ed. Zall, p. 22.

[6]Anyone interested in the phenomenon would do well to begin with Samuel Putnam's translation of Rabelais' *Pantagruel*, Book III (1546). See *The Portable Rabelais* (New York, 1946); Putnam's discussion of the "querelle des femmes" begins on p. 369.

implication is that they are much like other men, lecherous or greedy only in particular instances.

What strikes us immediately in tale No. 1 is that it is only one remove from oral tradition. There is a kind of incremental repetition about it that we observe in many popular ballads. Occasionally a pronoun has an ambiguous reference; but if the tale were told orally, the proper gesture and inflection would remove all ambiguity. Vague reference is also a clue to the essential careless and offhand nature of the jest; we may be sure that the unknown author spent little time in polishing the language. Yet on the whole each tale is clarity itself, colloquial expressions like "foxed" in tale No. 6 yielding their meanings in context even after 400 years.

The humor in *Sackful* is of two general kinds, verbal and situational. Tales No. 13, 14, and 16 are completely centered on puns; that is, the whole point to each of them is that a word has two widely different meanings. In No. 13 it is "sallet," which means both "helmet" and "salad." When the boy brings a helmet and sets it on the dinner table, we laugh because a helmet on the table is as incongruous as a salad hanging on the wall.

Another kind of tale in *Sackful* that involves verbal humor is the statement that can be taken two ways, the *double entendre*, as in Nos. 15 and 22. When the widow says to her servant, "Thou shalt go from one whore to another," she probably means that after she dismisses him from her service, he will go begging in the streets and will be lucky if he finds even whores to serve. But the servant takes her statement in a different way when he says, "Then I will go from you to your sister."

No. 18 is a good example of situational humor. We are to visualize three young men trying unsuccessfully to retrieve their caps from the water by making a human chain suspended from a tree limb. No. 1 is a combination of verbal and situational humor with a lightness of touch that precludes any anger at the priest. The longest speech in the dialogue, a speech containing the "punch lines" of the tale, comes from the miller, whose little allegory about heaven and hell is easily translatable in sexual terms (as in Boccaccio's tale in *The Decameron,* the tenth story of the third day). The miller establishes, to the bishop's satisfaction, that an ass is wiser than the priest (a kind of mock riddle or paradox).

No. 3 may have seemed a mock romance to Elizabethan readers. In bare outline it is like a chivalric romance, with secret lovers and a husband none the wiser, only we are to see nothing ideal in the love and nothing discreet in the secrecy. The narrator writes bluntly: "there came the servant to his mistress when she lay in bed and did what he would with her, and she was content." That is all, as if to say that people have appetites, and they satisfy them; it is what goes on in the real world every day. The word "servant" is perhaps to be taken two ways; the young man is clearly an indentured servant, but he seems also to be described as his mistress' lover in a low-life version of "courtly love."

The range of subject matter in *The Sackful of News* is fairly wide. As we have seen, there are tales about priests, about masters and servants, and about love in the lower or middle classes. Two stories, Nos. 4 and 5, deal specifically with city people and their relationship with country people. It would seem that the narrator himself is from London, which he describes as "here" in No. 4; but he is sensitive to the simplicity of the "man in the country" who goes to the chapel in St. Paul's Church in London and hears voice and organ music for the first time in his life. It is a little ridiculous that the country man could have been immured for so long from an experience so accessible to Londoners; yet the experience is wonderful and worth waiting for. "Oh, Lord, shall I go to heaven presently?" is an ecstatic response that the Londoner could never have, for he has taken church music for granted all his life. Although we are on the edge of sentimentality here, as we are occasionally in the stories of Deloney, we have no difficulty in appreciating the narrator's respect for the attitudes and intentions of common, ordinary people.

In No. 5 we see the "Essex man" clumping along Cheapside in his hobnailed shoes until a young city man in mock seriousness tells him that the nails are ruining London streets. When the country man takes off his shoes and carries them, we are not entirely sure why. Is it because he is afraid the young man will tell the lord mayor, or is it because he doesn't want to bruise the streets? Certainly he fails to see the joke until he hears the laughter. But his simplicity may be compounded of more than ignorance and fear; he seems to express also a certain awe and respect for London and Londoners.

Although as a whole *Sackful* may be subliterary, several of its tales are "imaginative"; the action suggests levels of meaning beyond itself. We suspect that the anonymous author possessed a certain amount of "art" after all, and it is not difficult to see that his technique leads naturally to a "scene" in a form of prose fiction that we now call the "novel."

The Sackful of News

The First Tale

In the country of Almaine, in a certain village, there was on a time a parson of a church which preached unto his parishioners, and thereby showed them the joys of heaven and the pains of hell, and many other things. And as he thus preached in the pulpit, among the people there was a miller which knew well that the priest had a concubine, and spake so loud that everybody did hear him.

"What, foolish priest," said he, "thou makest much babbling in the pulpit, and all thy wit is not worth a straw; for I have an ass that is far wiser than thou art, and thou makest here much ado of heaven and hell, and I may if I will have both heaven and hell at mine own house, wind and weather at mine own will, and as it pleaseth me."

Wherewith the priest was greatly displeased because he disturbed him in his sermon and said he would complain thereof to the bishop.

"Well," said the miller, "if thou dost complain, I will abide by that which I have said."

But as soon as the priest had done his sermon, he went to the bishop and complained unto him of all that which the miller had formerly spoken; whereupon the bishop incontinently[7] sent for the miller, and when the miller came, the bishop demanded if he could reasonably answer the complaint made against him by the priest.

"Yea, my lord," quoth the miller, "that I can."

"Well," said the bishop, "thou saidst that thou mightest have thy choice both of heaven and hell at home in thine own house when it pleaseth thee; and moreover thou saidst thou hadst both wind and weather at thine own pleasure; and also thou saidst thou hast an ass that is far wiser than the parish priest. If thou canst prove thy saying true, thou shalt go quit without danger."

"Indeed," quoth the miller, "I said that I had the choice of heaven and hell at mine own house, if I would, and so I have, for I have a

[7]*incontinently:* immediately.

mother of mine at home that is so old that she can neither go nor stand; and I trust as long as I keep her well and do her good, I shall, by the grace of God, have heaven at will; and if I do not that, I deserve perpetual damnation. And likewise I said that I had both wind and weather at will, and that is true, for if it be the Lord's will that I have good wind and weather, it is my will also and I am very well contented therewith; and if it be his will to send me otherwise, it is my will also, and I am pleased therewith. And whereas I said that I had an ass that was wiser than our priest, that is most true, for mine ass sometime when she stumbleth in a hole as she goeth, she will beware that she come no more that way, but looketh well before her, and will take heed that she do fall no more therein. But this priest hath had a maid this seven years and more, which he lieth withal, and falleth oft in her hole, and yet he cannot beware of it. And thus I hope I have sufficiently answered to this complaint."

"Well," said the bishop, "thou hast answered, and wisely, and therefore go thy ways."

And so he departed without any blame. But the priest was deprived of his benefice and so another was set in his place to his great rebuke and shame.

Another [2]

There was a friar in London which did use to go often to the house of an old woman; but ever when he came to her house, she hid all the meat[8] she had. On a time this friar came to her house, bringing certain company with him, and demanded of the wife if she had any meat. And she said, "Nay."

"Well," quoth the friar, "have you not a whetstone?"

"Yea," quoth the woman, "what will you do with it?"

"Marry," quoth he, "I would make meat thereof."

Then she brought a whetstone. He asked her likewise if she had not a frying pan. "Yea," said she, "but what the devil will ye do therewith?"

"Marry," said the friar, "you shall see by and by what I will do with it." And when he had the pan, he set it on the fire and put the whetstone therein.

"Cock's body,"[9] said the woman, "you will burn the pan."

"No, no," quoth the friar, "if you will give me some eggs, it will

[8]*meat:* whit meat (dairy products).
[9]*Cock's body:* a corruption of "God's body" (a popular oath).

not burn at all." But she would have had the pan from him when that she saw it was in danger; yet he would not let her but still urged her to fetch him some eggs, which she did.

"Tush," said the friar, "here are not enow;[10] go fetch ten or twelve." So the good wife was constrained to fetch more for fear lest the pan should burn. And when he had them, he put them in the pan.

"Now," quoth he, "if you have no butter, the pan will burn and the eggs too." So the good wife, being very loath to have her pan burnt and her eggs lost, she fetched him a dish of butter, the which he put into the pan and made good meat thereof and brought it to the table, saying, "Much good may it do you, my masters; now may you say you have eaten of a buttered whetstone."

Whereat all the company laughed, but the woman was exceeding angry because the friar had subtly beguiled her of her meat.

Another [3]

There was an old man that could not well see, who had a fair young wife, and with them dwelt a young man which had long wooed his mistress to have his pleasure of her, who at the last consented to him; but they knew not how to bring it to pass, for she did never go abroad but in her husband's company, and led him always. At last she devised a very fine shift, and bade her servant that he should that night about midnight come into her chamber where her husband and she lay, and she would find some device for him.

Night came, and the old man and wife went to bed, but she slept not a wink, but thought still upon her pretended purpose; but a little before the time prefixed, she awakened her husband and said thus unto him, "Sir, I will tell you a thing in secret which your servant was purposed to do; when I am alone, I can never be at quiet for him, but he is always enticing me to have me at his will; and so at the last to be quiet with him, I consented to meet him in the garden, but for mine honesty's sake I will not. Wherefore I pray you put on my clothes and go meet him; so when he comes to you, beat him well and chide him, for I know well he will not strike you because you are his master, and then he may amend himself and prove a good servant."

And the man was well pleased therewith. So the good man put on his wife's clothes and took a good cudgel in his hand and went into the garden. At length there came the servant to his mistress where

---

[10]*enow:* enough.

she lay in bed and did what he would with her, and she was content; and then she told him how she had sent her husband into the garden in her apparel, and wherefore, and to what purpose.

So her servant arose and, as she bade him, took a good staff with him and went into the garden, as though he knew not it was his master, and said unto him, "Nay, you whore, I did this but only to prove thee, whether thou wouldest be false to my good master, and not that I would do such a vile thing with thee." Whereupon he fell upon his master, giving him many sore stripes, and beating him most cruelly, still calling him nothing but, "Out, you whore, will you offer this abuse to my good master?"

"Alas," quoth his master, "good John, I am thy master; strike me no more, I pray thee."

"Nay, whore," quoth he, "I know who thou art well enough." And so he struck him again, beating him most grievously.

"Good John," said his master, "feel, I have a beard." Then the servant felt, knowing well who it was, who presently kneeled down and cried his master mercy. "Now thanks be to God," quoth his master, "I have as good a servant of thee as a man can have, and I have as good a wife as the world affords."

Afterwards the master went to bed and his servant also. When the old man came to bed to his wife, she demanded of him how he sped. He answered and said, "By my troth, wife, I have the trustiest servant in the world, and as faithful a wife; for my servant came thither with a great staff, and did beat me right sore, thinking it had been you; wherefore I was well pleased therewith."

But ever after the servant was well beloved of his master but better of his mistress; for his master had no mistrust of him, though he had made him a cuckold. So the poor man was cruelly beaten and made a summer's bird nevertheless.

Another [4]

There was a man in the country who had not been any far traveler and dwelt far from any church, except a church that was seven or eight miles from his house; and there they never sang mass nor evensong but did ever say it. And on a time he came to London, having never been here before; and being in London, he went to Paul's Church and went into the chapel where they sang mass with organs; and when he heard the melody of the organs and the singing together that he never heard before, he thought he should have gone to heaven by and by, and looked, and said aloud, that[11] everyone heard, "Oh, Lord, shall I go to heaven presently? I would thou wouldest let me alone till I might go home and fetch my white stick and black hood,[12] and then I would go gladly with thee." Whereat all the people laughed heartily.

Another [5]

There was an Essex man came to London who had a pair of shoes full of nails, and as he went along Cheapside he passed by a merchant's house where many young men were at the door; and among the rest one of them perceived that the man had nails in his shoes; whereupon he said to him, "Thou churl, why comest thou hither with thy nailed shoes, and breakest the stones of our streets? Indeed, I will show my lord mayor of it."

When the country man heard him, he put off his shoes and carried them in his hand and went in his hose[13] till he came to Paul's; whereat everybody laughed. And when he perceived that the people laughed at him, he put on his shoes again.

Another [6]

There was a priest in the country which had christened a child; and when he had christened it, he and the clerk were bidden to the drinking that should be there, and thither they went with other people; and being there, the priest drank and made so merry that he was quite foxed[14] and thought to go home before he laid him down to sleep; but having gone a little way, he grew so drowsy that he could go no further, but laid him down by a ditchside, so that his feet did hang in the water; and lying on his back, the moon shined in his face.

Thus he lay till the rest of the company came from drinking, who as they came home found the priest lying as aforesaid, and they thought to get him away; but do what they could he would not rise, but said, "Do not meddle with me, for I lie very well and will not

---

[11]*that:* so that.

[12]*white stick and black hood:* That is, if he is going to heaven, he wants to dress up in his best clothes—and especially carry his white walking stick and wear his black hood, probably of soft material, under his hat.

[13]*hose:* a combination of present-day socks and trousers; tights.

[14]*foxed:* stupefied by drink (with perhaps the implication that intoxicating liquor is crafty like a fox, creeping up on the unwary).

stir hence before morning; but I pray lay some more clothes on my feet and blow out the candle and let me lie and take my rest."

Another [7]

There was once a country man which came to London where he had never been before; and as he went over London Bridge, he saw certain ships sailing, being the first time he had seen any, and perceiving the sails made of cloth, he thought to assay if his plow would go so; and when he came home, he caused his wife to give him a large new sheet and went and set it on the plow like a sail, thinking the plow would go with the wind; but it removed not, which when he saw, he said, "What the devil, have I spoiled my sheet about nothing?" So he set his horses to the plow again.

Another [8]

A certain butcher was flaying a calf at night and had stuck a lighted candle upon his head, because he would be the quicker about his business; and when he had done, he thought to take the same candle to light him to bed, but he had forgot where he had set it and sought about the house for it; and all the while it stuck in his cap upon his head and lighted him in seeking it.

At the last one of his fellows came and asked him what he sought for. "Marry," quoth he, "I look for the candle which I did flay the calf withal."

"Why, thou fool," quoth he, "thou hast a candle in thy cap." And then he felt towards his cap and took away the candle burning; whereat there was great laughing, and he mocked[15] for his labor, as he was well worthy.

Another [9]

There was a man that had been drinking so hard that he could scarce stand upon his feet; yet at night he would go home; and as he went through a green meadow, near a hedgeside the briars held him by the clothes and the legs; and he had thought that one had holden him and would have had him to drink more, and he said, "Good fellow, let me go; by my troth, I can drink no more. I have drank so much already that I cannot go home." And there he abode all the same night and on the morrow went his ways.

[15]*mocked:* was mocked.

Another [10]

It happened not long since that upon Easterday two young fellows that had been at the plow all the days of their lives came into the church to hear mass both said and sung, as then it was accustomed to be; and there they saw the priest go censing with frankincense; and when they were both out of the church again and going home, one of them cried out to his fellow with a loud voice, saying "Lob,[16] I pray thee, what was that the priest went so whinging whanging[17] withal?"

"Why, Hob," quoth the other, "dost thou not know? It is frankincense."

"Is it frankincense? I am sure it stunk as if the devil had been in the church."

Another [11]

There were once two men that were both masterless and moneyless, and one said to the other, "What remedy canst thou now find out that we may either get some meat or money?"

"By my troth," quoth the other, "I do know a very fine shift." And being very early in the morning, they espied a man coming with hogs.

"Lo, yonder cometh a man with hogs, and I will tell him that they be sheep, and I will cause him to lay a wager with me whether they be sheep or hogs; and I will cause the matter to be judged by the next man that cometh; but then thou must go another way and meet with us; when we demand of thee whether they be sheep or hogs, thou must say that they be sheep."

Then they separated themselves the one from the other; and the one went to meet the man that had the swine, bidding him good morrow, the man doing the like to him again. Then he said to the old man, "Father, where had you your fair sheep?"

"What sheep?" quoth the man.

16*Lob:* In the sixteenth century "Lob" (or "Hob") was a name for "clown" or "country bumpkin"; but the two young farmers are aware only of speaking to each other familiarly, "Lob" meaning to them what "Bud" or "Buddy" means in the twentieth century.

17*whinging whanging:* moving about quite vigorously; apparently the priest's gestures are rather violent as he swings the censer in the incense ceremony. "Whanging" can also mean "whining" and may refer to the priest's tone of voice.

"These sheep that you drive before you."

"Why," quoth the old man, "they are swine."

"What," quoth the other, "will you make me a fool? Think you I know not sheep from swine?"

"Marry," quoth the old man, "I will lay one of my swine against what thou wilt that they be no sheep."

"I hold thee my coat against one of thy sheep," quoth the other.

"I am content," quoth the old man. "By whom shall we be tried?"

"By the next man that meets us."

"Content," said the old man.

And then they perceived the man coming, being the fellow of the young man. And when he came to them, the old man requested him to tell them what beasts those were.

"Why," quoth he, "they be sheep; do you not know sheep?"

"I told him so," quoth the other young man, "but he would not believe me, and so I laid my coat upon a wager that they were sheep, and he laid one of his sheep against my coat that they were swine; and I won it, have I not?"

"Yea," quoth the old man, "but, God help me, I bought them for swine."

And then the young man took one of the fattest hogs he could find amongst them all and carried him away, and his fellow went another way as though he had not known him; and the poor man returned again to the place where he had bought them. What became of him afterward I cannot tell. Only thus much I know, that he was deceived by those two crafty fellows of one of his hogs. But they immediately met one the other again and sold the hog for money and rejoiced that they fared so well, not knowing how to have otherwise sustained their wants.

Another [12]

There was a man born in Essex that had been brought up in Norfolk from a child, and on a time he was purposely minded to see his father and mother in Essex; and as he went, he heard a cow cry.

"Thanked be God," said he, "that once before I die, I hear my mother's tongue."

Another [13]

A man there was that had a child born in the north country, and upon a time this man had certain guests; and he prepared sallets[18] and other meat for them and bid his boy go into the cellar and take the sallet there, meaning the herbs, and lay them in a platter and put vinegar and oil thereto. Now the boy had never seen a sallet eaten in his country, but he went; and looking about the cellar, at last he espied a rusty sallet of steel, sticking on a wall, and said to himself, "What will my master do with this in a platter?" So down he took it and put it into a platter and put oil and vinegar unto it and brought it to the table.

"Why, thou knave," quoth his master, "I bade thee bring the herbs, which we call a sallet."

"Now, by my sire's sale,[19] master," said the boy, "I did never see such in my country." Whereat the guests laughed heartily.

Another [14]

There was a gentlewoman that had a French boy dwelling with her, and on a time she gave the boy a penny to fetch her some grains[20] for to eat, supposing that he would go to the apothecary's for them, but having the money, he went into the kitchen to the maid, requiring her to give him a basket; and then he went unto a brewhouse and fetched a pennyworth of grains. But the gentlewoman did greatly marvel where he tarried so long, supposing that he had been at the apothecary's; but at last he came home with the basket upon his shoulders full of grains. Then the gentlewoman asked him if he had brought her the grains.

"Yes, mistress," quoth he, "I have brought you a pennyworth of grains for your horse."

"Why, knave," quoth she, "I meant thou shouldst go to the apothecary's for them."

"By cock, mistress," quoth he, "I knew not that, but I have brought such as I could get." Whereupon the gentlewoman laughed heartily to see how he had served her through mere simplicity.

[18]*sallets:* The whole tale depends on a pun: a "sallet" is a kind of helmet, with a projection over the neck, worn during the fifteenth and sixteenth centuries in battle; but it is also a salad.

[19]*by my sire's sale:* The meaning of "sale" probably is "great hall" or "castle"; apparently the expression is a mild oath, chosen here for the alliteration with "sire's" (meaning "lord's" or "master's") and for the play on "sallet" in the previous line. But "sale" could be an error for "salt."

[20]*grains:* a pun. The boy interprets his mistress to mean grains of barley or wheat used to make malt in the brewhouse; but the gentlewoman actually means "grains of Paradise," a spice supposedly good medicinally for the stomach and also for making the breath smell sweet.

Another [15]

There was a widow in London that had a Dutchman to her servant before whom she set a rotten cheese and butter for his dinner; and he ate of the butter because he liked it, and his mistress bade him eat of the cheese.

"No, mistress," quoth he, "the butter is good enough."

She, perceiving he would eat none of the bad cheese, said, "Thou knave, thou art not to dwell with honest folks."

"By my troth, mistress," said he, "had I taken heed ere I came hither, I had never come here."

"Well, knave," quoth she, "thou shalt go from one whore to another."

"Then will I go," quoth he, "from you to your sister." And so departed.

Another [16]

There was an Italian which loved coleworts[21] well, and on a time he had his boy go fetch him some coleworts and set them over the fire against he came home; and the boy knew not the coleworts, but imagined thereby his master had meant coals and carried them into his master's chamber. But then he thought with himself that it would not be good for him to set the basket on the fire and let them burn. Now when his master came home, he went into the kitchen and demanded of the maid if the coleworts were ready; she said she saw none. Then he said no more but went to his chamber, and meeting the boy by the way, he asked him for his coleworts which he had him make ready.

"Marry, sir," said he, "they be almost enough, for they have lain roasting in the fire almost this hour."

"Where are they?" said the master.

"In your chamber, sir," quoth the boy.

So he went into his chamber and there he saw a great fire, and then he asked the boy again where the coleworts were.

"Why, master," quoth the boy, "I understood you that you bade me fetch coals and hang them over the fire in the basket, and if I should have done so the basket would have burned; wherefore I took the basket and poured the coals on the fire."

[21]*coleworts:* cabbages; the pun depends on the fact that cabbages were also called "coles," a word that sounds like "coals."

"Oh, whoreson," quoth his master, "I bade thee to fetch some cole-worts and hang them in a kettle over the fire." And he was angry with the boy, but the boy still said he did as he was bidden.

Another [17]

There was on a time a priest in the country that preached upon a holiday in his parish church; and as he stood in the pulpit, he perceived through a hole in the glass window that other men's swine were in his corn.[22]

"What the mischief," said he, "stand I here fading[23] the time to the devil and see yonder swine are spoiling my corn?" And then he leapt out of the pulpit and ran as if he had been mad and left all the people to stand there like a company of fools.

Another [18]

There was three young men going to Lambeth along by the water-side, and the one played with the other; and they cast each other's cap into the water in such sort as they could not get their caps again. But over the place where their caps were did grow a great old tree, the which did cover a great deal of the water. One of them said to the rest, "Sirs, I have found out a notable way to come by them. First I will make myself fast by the middle with one of your girdles[24] unto the tree, and he that is with you shall hang fast upon my girdle, and he that is last shall take hold on him that holds fast on my girdle; and so with one of his hands he may take up all our caps and cast them on the sand." And so they did.

But when they thought that they had been most secure and fast, he that was above felt his girdle slack[25] and said, "Soft, sirs, my girdle slacketh."

"Make it fast quickly," said they, but as he was untying it to make it faster, they fell all three into the water and were well washed for their pains.

Another [19]

On a time there was a priest in the country that was not very well learned and had but a small living, and he devised with himself how

---

[22]*corn:* grain (wheat, barley, etc., but not maize, as in the U.S. today).
[23]*fading:* passing away, wasting.
[24]*girdles:* belts.
[25]*slack:* come loose (that is, the knot in the belt).

he might get some money; and at last he bethought him that making of baskets was a good trade, and so he fell to it and took a servant. And so his servant and he made six baskets every week; and when he had made six baskets, then he knew it to be Sunday. And on a time he had made six baskets and knew it not and on the morrow began to make the seventh; but he had overlabored himself and forgot to ring to mass. Then the people resorting to church caused the bell to be rung. When the priest heard it, he bade his servant go up to his chamber and look how many baskets were made; and the servant went up and found six baskets.

"Cock's body, master," quoth he, "we have made six baskets already."

"What the devil," said the priest, "have we made six baskets already? Then do I know it is Sunday. Go therefore presently and help them ring to mass, for by my troth I had forgot myself."

Another [20]

There was a man and his wife lying in bed together, and the good man laid his buttocks on his wife's knees, and so they lay sleeping; and the man dreamed that he was dead and, as he thought, was carried into heaven; and being there, he dreamed that he did shit through the moon into the world, but he did shit into his wife's lap. And when he awaked, he told his wife his dream; and as she would have turned on the other side, she felt that she was all to-beshitten.

"Cock's body," quoth she, "you have dreamed fair, for you have all to-beshitten my knees." And so they were both fain to rise to make themselves clean.

Another [21]

There was a lady dwelt in the country which had a fool that did use to go with her to church; and on a time as his lady sat in the church, she let a great fart escape so that all the people heard it; and they looked on the fool that stood by her, thinking that it was he; which when the fool perceived, he said, "Truly, it was not I that let the fart; it was my lady." Whereat she was ashamed and went out of the church and chid the fool because he said it was not himself.

Then the fool ran into the church again and said aloud, "Masters, the fart which my lady let I will take it upon me, for she commanded me to say so." Whereat all the people laughed more than they did before, and the lady was much more ashamed.

Another [22]

In the country dwelt a gentlewoman who had a Frenchman dwelling with her, and he did ever use to go to church with her; and upon a time he and his mistress were going to church, and she bade him pull the door after him and follow her to the church; and so he took the door between his arms and lifted it from the hooks and followed his mistress with it.

But when she looked behind her and saw him bring the door upon his back, "Why, thou foolish knave," quoth she, "what wilt thou do with the door?"

"Marry, mistress," quoth he, "you had me pull the door after me."

"Why, whoreson," quoth she, "I did command thee that thou shouldest make fast the door after thee and not to bring it upon thy back after me."

But after this there was much good sport and laughing at his simplicity and foolishness therein.

⅜ The Adventures of
Master F. J.
(1573)

GEORGE GASCOIGNE

With George Gascoigne we enter the realm of "serious literature." *The Supposes* was Gascoigne's translation in 1566 of Ariosto's play, *I Suppositi*, for a select Gray's Inn audience. It was an unusual play for the Elizabethan period in that its medium was prose, which perhaps means that Gascoigne had a fuller appreciation of the uses of prose than other writers of his time. Yet he was also one of the two or three important English poets of the mid-sixteenth century; a few of his love lyrics have a light and felicitous touch. By 1575 Gascoigne showed that he was a critic with some important things to say about prosody. In "Certain Notes of Instruction" he comments intelligently on such matters as rhyme, accentual meter, and the caesura. Gascoigne was, in other words, a serious artist interested in the technical aspects of writing.

We may be fairly sure that when he sat down to write *Master F. J.*, he did not say to himself, "I am going to write a 'novel' and not a 'romance.'" The distinction was not made in the sixteenth century; and the creative writer, in any period, tends not to bother with external labels. Henry James probably was typical in that he never concerned himself with whether or not *The American* was a romance while he was writing it; his main problem then was to make the work consistent within itself. But as a critic, as a reader of that work some years after its original publication, James saw that *The American* was different from certain of his other works—that it was a romance and they were novels, and that there are fairly basic differences between the two forms.

Master F. J. is a novel according to James' criteria. It is closely related to everyday life. The hero is not, in James' phrase, a "lighted figure"; he does not stand out as being larger or more brilliant than other men, as heroes of romance do. The other characters are not deliberately "obscured"; we see them in their natural relations with the hero, and there is no attempt to play them down or to show their inferiority to the hero. To us the setting in a castle of northern England may at first seem "romantic"; but we soon realize that castles in sixteenth-century England are numerous and that this one is described simply as a large place where the characters happen to live (and is without any mysterious noises, haunting history, or terrible beauty).[1]

The aspect of Gascoigne's technique that immediately strikes us is a consistent attempt to suggest, without the aid of omniscience, the inner life of his characters. Not much actually happens in *Master F. J.*; what Gascoigne explores is his characters' *re*actions to the situation in which they find themselves. A gesture or a burst of laughter is a psychological clue that is to suggest hidden, but all-important, emotions. When at one point (p. 108) the secretary and Dame Pergo "burst out into open laughter," they reveal to us several things at the same time—Elinor's character, the nature of her "past," and F. J.'s innocence. It is an effective scene and works like another scene in which there is a similar occurrence: in Chapter XL of James' *Portrait of a Lady* Isabel perceives "like a sudden flicker of light" that between Osmond and Madame Merle there has been an intimate relationship for a long time.

Fundamentally, Gascoigne's method of suggesting his characters'

---

[1]See James' preface to *The American* in *The Art of the Novel*, ed. R. P. Blackmur (New York, 1937), pp. 20–39. It is interesting to note how well *Master F. J.* fits Frye's description of the novel form (*Anatomy of Criticism*, pp. 304–310). We may say with some assurance that *Master F. J.* is "extroverted and personal" in putting stress on "human character as it manifests itself in society"; it is about "real people," not archetypes or stylized figures of romance; and the world of *Master F. J.* implies a "stable society," in which we are to discern social contexts and roots. See also Richard Chase, *The American Novel and Its Tradition* (New York, 1957), pp. 12–28. Chase observes that the novel form "renders reality closely and in comprehensive detail" and presents the characters "in their real complexity of temperament and motive . . . . Character is more important than action and plot. . . . The events that occur will usually be plausible. . . ." *Master F. J.* is only about 32,000 words long, and some readers may not wish to call it a novel on that account. But substantively, qualitatively *Master F. J.* has the earmarks; and it may very well belong just before Richardson in one important "line" of English novelists: Gascoigne–Richardson–Fanny Burney–Austen–George Eliot–James –Conrad–Lawrence (with apologies to F. R. Leavis' *The Great Tradition*).

inner lives involves what we may call "authority." How do we know what we know? By what method does the author establish for the reader what is definitely true, what is probably true, what is possibly true, and what is not known? One of the central facts about *Master F. J.* is that the author has not taken the "privilege of omniscience"— has not taken the right he has as an author of knowing (and then telling the reader) the inner thoughts and feelings of one or more of his characters. When an author invents a story, and creates the characters in it, he can, if he so desires, tell us what each and every character is thinking and feeling, whether they are guilty or innocent of misdemeanors, whether their statements are truthful or untruthful. But Gascoigne chose not to tell his story from any superior advantage; his narrator, G. T., knows only what he sees and hears. G. T. passes on to us what the characters say about each other and themselves, and then we must assess the "evidence" ourselves.

The three prefaces to *Master F. J.* are much more important than prefaces usually are. They serve roughly the same purpose as the first few pages of Henry James' *The Turn of the Screw*; in James' story the reader gradually realizes that he is twice removed from the events of the governess' story. Douglas reads the governess' story, with approval of her motives; but both he and she are "now" dead, and there is no way of clearing up certain ambiguous matters. The three prefaces to *Master F. J.* remove us, in a similar way, from what happened to the hero in the north of England. They form a "frame" or outer story. If they are the frame, F. J.'s adventures form the picture itself. But we are not quite sure where the one leaves off and the other begins. The effect is something like the opening of Pirandello's *Six Characters in Search of an Author*. What Gascoigne evidently wants is complete authorial silence; he even leaves his name off the title page.

The central story of *Master F. J.* is almost as simple externally as one of the jests in *Sackful*. A young and inexperienced gentleman, while traveling in the north of England, falls in love with a woman who is married to the heir of a large castle and estate. Caught up into the private life of this estate, young F. J. finds himself in a situation that is simple in terms of outward events (as opposed, say, to Greene's *Pandosto* or Lodge's *Rosalind*) but rather complex in its emotional overtones. F. J. has his first love affair, and we are to watch his apprenticeship in love. Elinor, the married woman, has a "past," though we are not sure how shady it is. Frances, Elinor's sister-in-law, becomes F. J.'s most trusted companion from whom he gets a good bit of information about the household, most of it probably reliable.

Frances becomes a kind of *ficelle*, like Miss Stackpole in James' *Portrait of a Lady* or Miss Gostrey in *The Ambassadors*. She is the reader's friend as well as F. J.'s. We are not always aware of it, but her statements come to us thirdhand: F. J. reports what she says to G. T. who then tells us.

The brief summary given above reveals a story that could be told all sorts of ways. It could be a tragedy, a comedy, or a farce; it could be told straightforwardly or ironically. The tone of the story Gascoigne chose to tell stems from the attitude toward it by the narrator, G. T. He is an "older" man, perhaps middle aged, telling the story of his young friend, F. J. From G. T.'s point of view, the whole proceeding is somewhat amusing.[2] He sees and reports ("as my friend F. J. has declared unto me") F. J.'s private anguish, but he always gives it the perspective of his own broad experience. The effect is one of lightness and yet also of sympathy, tact, and delicacy. The technical name for the point of view is "first-person minor character,"[3] but it is an unusual handling of that point of view in that G. T. is not a character at all, not even a minor one, in the central events as they occurred.[4]

[2]Fieler, in "Gascoigne's Use of Courtly Love Conventions in 'The Adventures Passed by Master F. J.',", perhaps overemphasizes the comic aspects at the expense of Gascoigne's subtlety; yet *Master F. J.* is "comic" in the true sense, and Fieler has shown how Gascoigne refuses to take entirely seriously certain romance and courtly love elements.

[3]The expression used, along with "first-person observer," by Cleanth Brooks and Robert Penn Warren in *Understanding Fiction* (New York, 1959), pp. 660–664. See Norman Friedman's discussion of " 'I' as Witness" and " 'I' as Protagonist," in "Point of View in Fiction: The Development of a Critical Concept," *Approaches to the Novel*, ed. Scholes, pp. 130–132.

[4]For a number of years (since 1891 at least) critics have debated the question: how should we take the characters and events in *Master F. J.*? Adams, in "Gascoigne's 'Master F. J.' as Original Fiction," argues that *Master F. J.* is "original imaginative fiction," by which he means that the characters and events are not taken from "real life"; they are only made to *seem* real by Gascoigne's commendable art of verisimilitude. Adams thinks that Gascoigne's art was so successful that contemporary readers of the first edition of 1573 naïvely (and wrongly) came to the conclusion that Gascoigne wrote about a scandalous love affair in which he himself had taken part. Adams' article is a reaction against a long line of critics, including C. T. Prouty, who, in Adams' view, have reacted to Gascoigne's novel as naïvely as the readers of 1573. Prouty, in *George Gascoigne*, offers evidence from various records of the Elizabethan period to substantiate his belief that F. J. is Gascoigne himself and the events of the novel "actual events," possibly taking place in Barnard Castle, when Gascoigne visited northern England while a student at Cambridge.

The Printer to the Reader

It hath been an old saying that while two dogs do strive for a bone the third may come and carry it away. And this proverb may, as I fear, be well verified in me which take in hand the imprinting of this poetical posy. For the case seemeth doubtful, and I will disclose my conjecture.

Master H. W., in the beginning of this work, hath in his letter (written to the readers) cunningly discharged himself of any such misliking, as the graver sort of grayhaired judges might, perhaps, conceive in the publication of these pleasant pamphlets.[5] And next unto that learned preamble, the letter of G. T. (by whom, as seemeth, the first copy hereof was unto the same H. W. delivered) doth with no less clerkly cunning seek to persuade the readers that he also would by no means have it published. Now I fear very much, all these words notwithstanding, that these two gentlemen were of one assent, compact to have it imprinted. And yet, finding by experience that nothing is so well handled nowadays but that some malicious minds may either take occasion to mislike it themselves or else find means to make it odious unto others, they have, therefore, each of them, politicly prevented the danger of misreport, and suffered me, the poor printer, to run away with the palm of so perilous a victory.

Notwithstanding, having well perused the work, I find nothing therein amiss (to my judgment) unless it be two or three wanton places passed over in the discourse of an amorous enterprise. The which, forasmuch as the words are cleanly (although the thing meant be somewhat natural), I have thought good also to let them pass as they came to me, and the rather because (as Master H. W. hath well alleged in his letter to the reader) the well-minded man may reap some commodity out of the most frivolous works that are written. And as the venomous spider will suck poison out of the most wholesome herb, and the industrious bee can gather honey out of the most

---

[5] *these pleasant pamphlets: The Adventures of Master F. J.* was only one of several works included in the same volume, which bore the general title, *A Hundred Sundry Flowers Bound up in One Small Posy.* "The Printer to the Reader" and the two following dedications in the first edition of 1573 probably were written by Gascoigne himself as a part of his "mask of anonymity," to use the words of C. T. Prouty (whose biography, *George Gascoigne,* and whose edition of *A Hundred Sundry Flowers* give many further details).

stinking weed: even so the discreet reader may take a happy example by the most lascivious histories, although the captious and hare-brained heads can neither be encouraged by the good nor fore-warned by the bad. And thus much I have thought good to say in excuse of some savors, which may perchance smell unpleasantly to some noses, in some part of this poetical posy.

Now it hath with this fault a greater commodity than common posies have been accustomed to present, and that is this: you shall not be constrained to smell of the flowers therein contained all at once, neither yet to take them up in such order as they are sorted. But you may take any one flower by itself; and if that smell not so pleasantly as you would wish, I doubt not yet but you may find some other which may supply the defects thereof. As thus, he which would have good moral lessons clerkly handled, let him smell to the tragedy translated out of Euripides. He that would laugh at a pretty conceit closely conveyed, let him peruse the comedy translated out of Ariosto. He that would take example by the unlawful affections of a lover bestowed upon an unconstant dame, let them read the report in verse made by Dan Bartholomew of Bath, or the discourse in prose of the adventures passed by Master F. J., whom the reader may name Freeman Jones, for the better understanding of the same. He that would see any particular pang of love lively displayed, may here approve every pamphlet by the title, and so remain contented. As also divers godly hymns and psalms may in like manner be found in this record. To conclude, the work is so universal, as either in one place or other, any man's mind may therewith be satisfied. The which I adventure (under pretext of this promise) to present unto all indifferent eyes as followeth.

The Adventures of Master F. J.

H. W. to the Reader

In August last passed, my familiar friend, Master G. T., bestowed upon me the reading of a written book, wherein he had collected divers discourses and verses, invented upon sundry occasions, by sundry gentlemen (in mine opinion) right commendable for their capacity. And herewithal my said friend charged me that I should use them only for mine own particular commodity, and eftsoons safely deliver the original copy to him again; wherein I must confess myself but half a merchant, for the copy unto him I have safely redelivered. But the work (for I thought it worthy to be published) I have entreated my friend A. B. to imprint, as one that thought better to please a number by common commodity than to feed the humor of any private person[6] by needless singularity. This I have adventured for thy contentation[7] (learned reader). And further have presumed of myself to christen it by the name of *A Hundred Sundry Flowers*. In which poetical posy are set forth many trifling fantasies, humorous passions, and strange affects of a lover. And therein (although the wiser sort would turn over the leaf as a thing altogether fruitless) yet I myself have reaped this commodity, to sit and smile at the fond devices of such as have enchained themselves in the golden fetters of fantasy, and having bewrayed themselves to the whole world, do yet conjecture that they walk unseen in a net.

Some other things you may also find in this book which are as void of vanity as the first are lame for government. And I must confess that (what to laugh at the one and what to learn by the other) I have, contrary to the charge of my said friend G. T., procured for these trifles this day of publication. Whereat if the authors only repine, and the number of other learned minds be thankful, I may then boast to have gained a bushel of good will in exchange for one pint of peevish choler. But if it fall out contrary to expectation that the reader's judgments agree not with mine opinion in their commendations, I may then (unless their courtesies supply my want of discretion) with loss of some labor, accompt also the loss of my familiar friends, in doubt whereof, I cover all our names, and refer you to the well-written letter of my friend G. T. next following, whereby you may more at large consider of these occasions. And so I commend the praise of other men's travails, together with the pardon of mine own rashness, unto the well-willing minds of discreet readers. From my lodging near the Strand the twentieth of January, 1572.

H. W.

[6]*person:* The spelling of the 1573 edition is "parson," a sixteenth-century alternate spelling of "person," which is the intended sense.

[7]*contentation:* satisfaction, contentment.

The Letter of G. T. to His Very Friend H. W.
Concerning This Work

Remembering the late conference passed between us in my lodging, and how you seemed to esteem some pamphlets which I did there show unto you far above their worth in skill; I did straightway conclude the same your judgment to proceed of two especial causes: one (and principal), the steadfast good will which you have ever hitherto sithens our first familiarity borne towards me; another (of no less weight), the exceeding zeal and favor that you bear to good letters. The which (I agree with you) do no less bloom and appear in pleasant ditties or compendious sonnets, devised by green, youthful capacities, than they do fruitfully flourish unto perfection in the riper works of grave and grayhaired writers. For as in the last the younger sort may make a mirror of perfect life, so in the first the most frosty-bearded philosopher may take just occasion of honest recreation, not altogether without wholesome lessons, tending to the reformation of manners. For who doubteth but that poets in their most feigned fables and imaginations have metaphorically set forth unto us the right rewards of virtues and the due punishments for vices? Marry, indeed, I may not compare pamphlets unto poems, neither yet may justly advant[8] for our native countrymen that they have in their verses hitherto (translations excepted) delivered unto us any such notable volume, as have been by poets of antiquity, left unto the posterity. And the more pity that amongst so many toward wits, no one hath been hitherto encouraged to follow the trace of that worthy and famous knight, Sir Geoffrey Chaucer, and after many pretty devices spent in youth for the obtaining a worthless victory, might consume and consummate his age in describing the right pathway to perfect felicity with the due preservation of the same. The which although some may judge over grave a subject to be handled in style metrical, yet for that I have found in the verses of eloquent Latinists, learned Greeks, and pleasant Italians, sundry directions whereby a man may be guided toward the attaining of that unspeakable treasure. I have thus far lamented that our countrymen have chosen rather to win a passover praise by the wanton penning of a few loving lays than to gain immortal fame by the clerkly handling of so profitable a theme. For if quickness of inven-

---

[8]*advant:* boast.

tion, proper vocables, apt epithets, and store of monosyllables may help a pleasant brain to be crowned with laurel, I doubt not but both our countrymen and country language might be enthronized among the old foreleaders unto the mount Helicon.

But now let me return to my first purpose; for I have wandered somewhat beside the path, and yet not clean out of the way. I have thought good (I say) to present you with this written book, wherein you shall find a number of sonnets, lays, letters, ballads, rondelets, virelays, and verses; the works of your friend and mine, Master F. J., and divers others; the which when I had with long travail confusedly gathered together, I thought it then *opere pretium* to reduce them into some good order. The which I have done according to my barren skill in this written book, commending it unto you to read and to peruse, and desiring you as I only do adventure thus to participate the sight thereof unto your former good will, even so that you will by no means make the same common, but after your own recreation taken therein that you will safely redeliver unto me the original copy. For otherwise, I shall not only provoke all the authors to be offended with me, but further shall lose the opportunity of a greater matter, half and more granted unto me already by the willing consent of one of them. And to be plain with you, my friend, he hath written (which as far as I can learn did never yet come to the reading or perusing of any man but himself) two notable works, the one called *The Sundry Lots of Love,* the other of his own invention entitled *The Climbing of an Eagle's Nest.* These things, and especially the latter, doth seem by the name to be a work worthy the reading. And the rather I judge so because his fantasy is so occupied in the same as that, contrary to his wonted use, he hath hitherto withheld it from sight of any of his familiars until it be finished; you may guess him by his nature. And, therefore, I require your secrecy herein, lest if he hear the contrary, we shall not be able by any means to procure these other at his hands. So fare you well, from my chamber this tenth of August, 1572.

Yours or not his own,
G. T.

When I had with no small entreaty obtained of Master F. J. and sundry other toward young gentlemen the sundry copies of these sundry matters—then as well for that the number of them was great, as also for that I found none of them so barren but that (in my judgment) had in it *aliquid salis*,[9] and especially being considered by the very proper occasion whereupon it was written (as they themselves did always with the verse rehearse unto me the cause that then moved them to write)—I did with more labor gather them into some order and so placed them in this register. Wherein as near as I could guess, I have set in the first places those which Master F. J. did compile. And to begin with this, his history that ensueth, it was (as he declared unto me) written upon this occasion. The said F. J. chanced once in the north parts of this realm to fall in company of a very fair gentlewoman whose name was Mistress Elinor, unto whom bearing a hot affection, he first adventured to write this letter following.

G. T.

Mistress, I pray you understand that being altogether a stranger in these parties,[10] my good hap hath been to behold you to my (no small) contentation, and my evil hap accompanies the same with such imperfection of my deserts as that I find always a ready repulse in mine own frowardness. So that considering the natural climate of the country, I must say that I have found fire in frost. And yet comparing the inequality of my deserts with the least part of your worthiness, I feel a continual frost in my most fervent fire. Such is then the extremity of my passions, the which I could never have been content to commit unto this telltale paper, were it not that I am destitute of all other help. Acept, therefore, I beseech you, the earnest good will of a more trusty (than worthy) servant, who, being thereby encouraged, may supply the defects of his abilities with ready trial of dutiful loyalty. And let this poor paper (besprent with salt tears and blown over with scalding sighs) be saved of you as a safeguard for your sampler,[11] or a bottom to wind your sewing silk[12] that, when your last needleful is wrought, you may return to reading thereof and consider the care of him who is

More yours than his own,

F. J.

[9]*aliquid salis:* some wit.

[10]*these parties:* Apparently the sense is "these parts" or "this section of the country" (as in G. T.'s expression "the north parts" in the previous sentence).

[11]*safeguard for your sampler:* wrapper to protect your sewing work.

[12]*bottom to wind your sewing silk:* core around which to wind your silk thread.

This letter by her received (as I have heard him say), her answer was this: she took occasion one day, at his request, to dance with him; the which doing, she bashfully began to declare unto him that she had read over the writing which he delivered unto her, with like protestation that as at delivery thereof she understood not for what cause he thrust the same into her bosom, so now she could not perceive thereby any part of his meaning; nevertheless, at last seemed to take upon her the matter, and though she disabled herself, yet gave him thanks, as etc. Whereupon he broke the brawl[13] and, walking abroad, devised immediately these few verses following.

G. T.

Fair Bersabe,[14] the bright, once bathing in a well,
With dew bedimmed King David's eyes that ruled Israel.
And Solomon himself, the source of sapience,
Against the force of such assaults could make but small defense.
  To it the stoutest yield, and strongest feel like woe,
  Bold Hercules and Samson both, did prove it to be so.
What wonder seemeth then, when stars stand thick in skies,
If such a blazing star have power to dim my dazzled eyes?

L'envoy

To you these few suffice, your wits be quick and good;
You can conject by change of hue what humors feed my blood.

F. J.

I have heard the author say that these were the first verses that ever he wrote upon like occasion. The which considering the matter precedent may in my judgment be well allowed; and to judge his doings by the effects he declared unto me—that before he could put the same in legible writing, it pleased the said Mistress Elinor of her courtesy thus to deal with him. Walking in a garden among divers other gentlemen and gentlewomen, with a little frowning smile in passing by him, she delivered unto him a paper, with these words: "For that I understand not," quoth she, "th'intent of your letters, I pray you take them here again, and bestow them at your pleasure."

The which done and said, she passed by without change either of pace or countenance. F. J., somewhat troubled with her angry look, did suddenly leave the company and, walking into a park near

---

[13]*broke the brawl:* quit dancing; "brawl" meant a particular dance step resembling the cotillion.

[14]*Bersabe:* Bathsheba; see II Samuel, Chapter 11.

adjoining, in great rage began to wreak his malice on this poor paper and the same did rend and tear in pieces. When suddenly, at a glance, he perceived it was not of his own handwriting, and therewithal abashed, upon better regard he perceived in one piece thereof written (in Roman)[15] these letters, S H E; wherefore, placing all the pieces thereof as orderly as he could, he found therein written these few lines hereafter following.

G. T.

Your sudden departure from our pastime yesterday did enforce me for lack of chosen company to return unto my work, wherein I did so long continue till at the last the bare bottom did draw unto my remembrance your strange request. And although I found therein no just cause to credit your colored words, yet have I thought good hereby to requite you with like courtesy, so that at least you shall not condemn me for ungrateful. But as to the matter therein contained, if I could persuade myself that there were in me any coals to kindle such sparks of fire, I might yet peradventure be drawn to believe that your mind were frozen with like fear. But as no smoke ariseth where no coal is kindled, so without cause of affection the passion is easy to be cured. This is all that I understand of your dark letters. And as much as I mean to answer.

SHE

My friend F. J. hath told me divers times that immediately upon receipt hereof, he grew in jealousy that the same was not her own device. And therein I have no less allowed his judgment than commended his invention of the verses and letters before rehearsed. For as by the style, this letter of hers bewrayeth that it was not penned by a woman's capacity, so the sequel of her doings may decipher that she had more ready clerks than trusty servants in store. Well yet as the perfect hound, when he hath chased the hurt deer amid the whole herd, will never give over till he have singled it again, even so F. J., though somewhat abashed with this doubtful show, yet still constant in his former intention, ceased not by all possible means to bring this deer yet once again to the bows whereby she might be the more surely stricken, and so in the end enforced to

---

[15]*in Roman:* in the Roman style of handwriting—simple, smooth, and rounded—as opposed to the "secretary"—angular and descended from the Gothic style of handwriting. F. J.'s own handwriting probably was in the secretary.

yield. Wherefore he thought not best to commit the said verses willingly into her custody, but privily lost them in her chamber written in counterfeit. And after on the next day thought better to reply, either upon her or upon her secretary in this wise as here followeth.

G. T.

The much that you have answered is very much and much more than I am able to reply unto; nevertheless, in mine own defense, thus much I allege, that if my sudden departure pleased not you, I cannot myself therewith be pleased, as one that seeketh not to please many and more desirous to please you than any. The cause of mine affection I suppose you behold daily. For (self love avoided) every wight may judge of themselves as much as reason persuadeth: the which if it be in your good nature suppressed with bashfulness, then mighty love grant you may once behold my wan cheeks washed in woe, that therein my salt tears may be a mirror to represent your own shadow, and that like unto Narcissus you may be constrained to kiss the cold waves wherein your counterfeit is so lively portrayed. For if abundance of other matters failed to draw my gazing eyes in contemplation of so rare excellency, yet might these your letters both frame in me an admiration of such divine *esprit* and a confusion to my dull understanding which so rashly presumed to wander in this endless labyrinth. Such I esteem you, and thereby am become such, and even

HE. F. J.

This letter finished and fair written over,[16] his chance was to meet her alone in a gallery of the same house where (as I have heard him declare) his manhood in this kind of combat was first tried; and therein I can compare him to a valiant prince, who, distressed with power of enemies, had committed the safeguard of his person to treaty of *ambassade*[17] and suddenly (surprised with a *camisado*[18] in his own trenches) was enforced to yield as prisoner. Even so my

[16]*fair written over:* copied neatly.

[17]*treaty of ambassade:* Later (p. 97) the sense of the French word *ambassade* is simply "ambassador"; here the sense probably is "agreement made by ambassadors" of both camps, his and the enemy's.

[18]*camisado:* The literal meaning is "an attack in one's shirt." It was a fairly common Renaissance military term meaning a surprise night attack in which the attackers wear shirts over their armor to recognize each other.

friend F. J., lately overcome by the beautiful beams of this Dame Elinor, and having now committed his most secret intent to these late rehearsed letters, was at unawares encountered with his friendly foe and constrained either to prepare some new defense or else like a recreant to yield himself as already vanquished. Wherefore (as in a trance) he lifted up his dazzled eyes and so continued in a certain kind of admiration, not unlike the astronomer who (having after a whole night's travail, in the gray morning found his desired star) hath fixed his hungry eyes to behold the comet long looked for; whereat this gracious dame (as one that could discern the sun before her chamber windows were wide open) did deign to embolden the fainting knight with these or like words.

"I perceive now," quoth she, "how mishap doth follow me, that having chosen this walk for a simple solace, I am here disquieted by the man that meaneth my destruction"—and therewithal, as half angry, began to turn her back, when as my friend F. J., now awaked, gan thus salute her.

"Mistress," quoth he, "and I perceive now that good hap haunts me, for being by lack of opportunity constrained to commit my welfare unto these blabbing leaves of bewraying paper (showing that in his hand), I am here recomforted with happy view of my desired joy"—and therewithal reverently kissing her hand, did softly distrain her slender arm and so stayed her departure.[19]

The first blow thus proffered and defended, they walked and talked, traversing divers ways; wherein I doubt not but that my friend F. J. could quit himself reasonably well. And though it stood not with duty of a friend that I should therein require to know his secrets, yet of himself he declared thus much: that after long talk she was contented to accept his proffered service, but yet still disabling herself and seeming to marvel what cause had moved him to subject his liberty so wilfully, or at least in a prison (as she termed it) so unworthy. Whereunto I need not rehearse his answer, but suppose now that thus they departed, saving I had forgotten this: she required of him the last rehearsed letter, saying that his first was lost and now she lacked a new bottom for her silk; the which, I warrant you, he granted. And so proffering to take an humble *congé* by *bezo las manos*, she graciously gave him the *zuccado dez labros* and so for

---

[19]*kissing her hand . . . stayed her departure:* All three early editions read "his hand," but "his" would seem to be a mistake for "her" (spelled "hir" in the 1573 edition). The sense seems to be that F. J. kissed her hand and grasped ("did distrain") her arm softly, thus preventing her from leaving.

then departed. And thereupon recompting her words, he compiled these following, which he termed *terza sequenza*,[20] to sweet Mistress SHE.

G. T.

Of thee, dear dame, three lessons would I learn.
What reason first persuades the foolish fly
(As soon as she a candle can discern)
To play with flame till she be burnt thereby?
Or what may move the mouse to bite the bait
Which strikes the trap that stops her hungry breath?
What calls the bird where snares of deep deceit
Are closely couched[21] to draw her to her death?
Consider well what is the cause of this,
And though percase[22] thou wilt not so confess,
Yet deep desire to gain a heavenly bliss
May drown the mind in dole and dark distress.
Oft is it seen (whereat my heart may bleed)
Fools play so long till they be caught in deed.
        And then
It is a heaven to see them hop and skip,
And seek all shifts to shake their shackles off.
It is a world to see them hang the lip,[23]
Who (erst) at love were wont to scorn and scoff.
But as the mouse, once caught in crafty trap,
May bounce and beat against the boarden wall
Till she have brought her head in such misshape,
That down to death her fainting limbs must fall;
And as the fly, once singed in the flame,
Cannot command her wings to wave away
But by the heel she hangeth in the same
Till cruel death her hasty journey stay—
So they that seek to break the links of love
Strive with the stream, and this by pain I prove.

[20]*terza sequenza:* a poem in three stanzas. G. T.'s lightly mocking tone is emphasized in this and the previous sentence by his use of foreign phrases—*"congé"* is French for "leave" or "departure," and *"bezo las manos"* is bad Italian for "kissing her hands"; *"zuccado dez labros"* probably is supposed to mean "kiss on the lips," but it does not seem to be any language at all (which may be part of the humor).

[21]*couched:* The errata sheet at the beginning of *A Hundred Sundry Flowers* (sig. A3ᵛ) changes "caught" to "coucht" (here modernized to "couched").

[22]*percase:* perchance.

[23]*It is a world to see them hang the lip:* It is a marvel to see them pout.

                                        For when
I first beheld that heavenly hue of thine,
Thy stately stature, and thy comely grace,
I must confess these dazzled eyes of mine
Did wink for fear, when I first viewed thy face.
But bold desire did open them again,
And bade me look till I had looked too long;
I pitied them that did procure my pain,
And lov'd the looks that wrought me all the wrong.
And as the bird once caught (but works her woe)
That strives to leave the limed twigs[24] behind,
Even so the more I strave to part thee fro,
The greater grief did grow within my mind;
Remediless, then, must I yield to thee,
And crave no more, thy servant but to be
                    Till then and ever.   HE. F. J.

When he had well sorted this sequence, he sought opportunity to
leave it where she might find it before it were lost. And now the
coals began to kindle, whereof (but ere while) she feigned herself
altogether ignorant. The flames began to break out on every side;
and she, to quench them, shut up herself in her chamber solitarily.
But as the smithy gathers greater heat by casting on of water, even
so the more she absented herself from company, the fresher was the
grief which galled her remembrance. So that at last the report was
spread through the house that Mistress Elinor was sick. At which
news F. J. took small comfort; nevertheless, Dame Venus with good
aspect did yet thus much further his enterprise.

The dame (whether it were by sudden change, or of wonted
custom) fell one day into a great bleeding at the nose. For which
accident the said F. J., amongst other pretty conceits, hath a present
remedy, whereby he took occasion (when they of the house had all
in vain sought many ways to stop her bleeding) to work his feat in
this wise: First he pleaded ignorance, as though he knew not her
name, and therefore demanded the same of one other gentlewoman
in the house whose name was Mistress Frances, who, when she had
to him declared that her name was Elinor, he said these words, or
very like, in effect:

"If I thought I should not offend Mistress Elinor, I would not
doubt to stop her bleeding without either pain or difficulty."

[24]*twigs:* The *errata* sheet changes "wings" to "twigs." A "lime twig" was
a twig covered with birdlime, an extremely adhesive material that made the
bird, having once landed, cling to the tree limb and thus be caught.

This gentlewoman, somewhat tickled with his words, did incontinent[25] make relation thereof to the said Mistress Elinor, who immediately (declaring that F. J. was her late received servant) returned the said messenger unto him with especial charge that he should employ his *devoir* towards the recovery of her health. With whom the same F. J. repaired to the chamber of his desired and finding her set in a chair, leaning on the one side over a silver basin. After his due reverence, he laid his hand on her temples and, privily rounding[26] her in her ear, desired her to command a hazel stick and a knife. The which being brought, he delivered unto her, saying on this wise:

"Mistress, I will speak certain words in secret to myself, and do require no more; but when you hear me say openly this word, 'Amen,' that you with this knife will make a nick upon this hazel stick; and when you have made five nicks, command me also to cease."

The dame, partly of good will to the knight and partly to be stanched of her bleeding, commanded her maid and required the other gentles somewhat to stand aside; which done, he began his orisons, wherein he had not long muttered before he pronounced, "Amen," wherewith the lady made a nick on the stick with her knife. The said F. J. continued to another "Amen" when the lady, having made another nick, felt her bleeding begin to stanch, and so by the third "Amen" thoroughly stanched.

F. J., then changing his prayers into private talk, said softly unto her: "Mistress, I am glad that I am hereby enabled to do you some service, and as the stanching of your own blood may some way recomfort you, so if the shedding of my blood may any way content you, I beseech you command it, for it shall be ever more readily employed in your service," and therewithal with a loud voice pronounced "Amen!"

Wherewith the good lady, making a nick, did secretly answer thus: "Good servant," quoth she, "I must needs think myself right happy to have gained your service and good will; and be you sure that although there be in me no such desert as may draw you into this depth of affection, yet such as I am I shall be always glad to show myself thankful unto you. And now, if you think yourself assured that I shall bleed no more, do then pronounce your fifth "Amen."

[25]*incontinent:* immediately.
[26]*rounding:* whispering.

The which pronounced, she made also her fifth nick, and held up her head, calling the company unto her and declaring unto them that her bleeding was thoroughly stanched.

Well, it were long to tell what sundry opinions were pronounced upon this act, and I do dwell overlong in the discourses of this F. J., especially having taken in hand only to copy out his verses. But for the circumstance doth better declare the effect, I will return to my former tale.

F. J., tarrying awhile in the chamber, found opportunity to loose his sequence near to his desired mistress[27] and, after *congé* taken, departed.

After whose departure the lady arose out of her chair; and her maid, going about to remove the same, espied and took up the writing. The which her mistress perceiving, gan suddenly conjecture that the same had in it some like matter to the verses once before left in like manner, and made semblant to mistrust that the same should be some words of conjuration. And, taking it from her maid, did peruse it and immediately said to the company that she would not forgo the same for a great treasure. But, to be plain, I think that (F. J. excepted) she was glad to be rid of all company until she had with sufficient leisure turned over and retossed every card in this sequence. And not long after, being now tickled through all the veins with an unknown humor, adventured of herself to commit unto a like ambassador the deciphering of that which hitherto she had kept more secret, and thereupon wrote with her own hand and head in this wise.

G. T.

Good servant, I am out of all doubt much beholding unto you, and I have great comfort by your means in the stanching of my blood, and I take great comfort to read your letters, and I have found in my chamber divers songs which I think to be of your making, and I promise you they are excellently made, and I assure you that I will be ready to do for you any pleasure that I can, during my life. Wherefore, I pray you come to my chamber once in a day, till I come abroad again, and I will be glad of your company, and for because that you have promised to be my HE, I will take upon me this name, your SHE.

[27]*loose his sequence . . . mistress:* leave his verses, the three-stanza poem called *terza sequenza,* lying near Lady Elinor.

This letter I have seen, of her own handwriting; and as therein the reader may find great difference of style from her former letter, so may you now understand the cause. She had in the same house a friend, a servant, a secretary. What should I name him? Such one as she esteemed in time past more than was cause in time present, and to make my tale good, I will (by report of my very good friend F. J.) describe him unto you. He was in height the proportion of two pygmies; in breadth, the thickness of two bacon hogs; of presumption, a giant; of power, a gnat; apishly witted, knavishly mannered, and crabbedly favored. What was there in him, then, to draw a fair lady's liking? Marry, sir, even all in all, a well-lined purse, wherewith he could at every call provide such pretty conceits as pleased her peevish fantasy, and by that means he had thoroughly (long before) insinuated himself with this amorous dame. This manling, this minion, this slave, this secretary, was now by occasion ridden to London forsooth; and though his absence were unto her a disfurnishing of eloquence, it was yet unto F. J. an opportunity of good advantage. For when he perceived the change of her style, and thereby grew in some suspicion that the same proceeded by absence of her chief chancellor, he thought good now to smite while the iron was hot, and to lend his mistress such a pen in her secretary's absence as he should never be able at his return to amend the well writing thereof. Wherefore according to her command, he repaired once every day to her chamber, at the least, whereas he guided himself so well and could devise such store of sundry pleasures and pastimes, that he grew in favor, not only with his desired, but also with the rest of the gentlewomen.

And one day passing the time amongst them, their play grew to this end, that his mistress, being queen, demanded of him these questions:

"Servant," quoth she, "I charge you, as well upon your allegiance, being now my subject, as also upon your fidelity, having vowed your service unto me, that you answer me these three questions by the very truth of your secret thought. First, what thing in this universal world doth most rejoice and comfort you?"

F. J., abasing his eyes towards the ground, took good advisement in his answer, when a fair gentlewoman of the company clapped him on the shoulder, saying, "How now, sir, is your hand on your halfpenny?"[28]

[28]*is your hand on your halfpenny:* a proverb (Tilley, H315), the sense of which is "Do you have a selfish object in view?"

To whom he answered, "No, fair lady, my hand is on my heart, and yet my heart is not in mine own hands."

Wherewithal abashed, turning towards Dame Elinor, he said, "My sovereign and mistress, according to the charge of your command and the duty that I owe you, my tongue shall bewray unto you the truth of mine intent. At this present a reward given me without desert doth so rejoice me with continual remembrance thereof that, though my mind be so occupied to think thereon, as that day nor night I can be quiet from that thought, yet the joy and pleasure which I conceive in the same is such that I can neither be cloyed with continuance thereof, nor yet afraid that any mishap can countervail so great a treasure. This is to me such a heaven to dwell in as that I feed by day and repose by night upon the fresh record of this reward."

This (as he sayeth) he meant by the kiss that she lent him in the gallery, and by the profession of her last letters and words.

Well, though this answer be somewhat misty, yet let my friend's excuse be that, taken upon the sudden, he thought better to answer darkly than to be mistrusted openly.

Her second question was "What thing in this life did most grieve his heart and disquiet his mind?" Whereunto he answered that although his late rehearsed joy were incomparable, yet the greatest enemy that disturbed the same was the privy worm of his own guilty conscience, which accused him evermore with great unworthiness, and that this was his greatest grief.

The lady, biting upon the bit at his cunning answers made unto these two questions, gan thus reply: "Servant, I had thought to have touched you yet nearer with my third question, but I will refrain to attempt your patience; and now for my third demand, answer me directly in what manner this passion doth handle you and how these contraries may hang together by any possibility of concord, for your words are strange."

F. J., now rousing himself, boldly took occasion thus to handle his answer.

"Mistress," quoth he, "my words indeed are strange; but yet my passion is much stranger, and thereupon this other day to content mine own fantasy I devised a sonnet, which although it be a piece of cocklorel's[29] music, and such as I might be ashamed to publish in this company, yet because my truth in this answer may the better appear unto you, I pray you vouchsafe to receive the same in writing." And drawing a paper out of his pocket presented it unto her, wherein was written this sonnet.

[29]*cocklorel's:* rogue's.

G. T.

Love, hope, and death do stir in me such strife
As never man but I led such a life.
First burning love doth wound my heart to death,
And when death comes at call of inward grief,
Cold lingering hope doth feed my fainting breath
Against my will, and yields my wound relief;
So that I live, but yet my life is such
As death would never grieve me half so much.
No comfort, then, but only this I taste.
To salve such sore, such hope will never want,
And with such hope, such life will ever last,
And with such life, such sorrows are not scant.
O strange desire, O life with torments tossed!
Through too much hope, mine only hope is lost.

Even HE.   F. J.

This sonnet was highly commended, and in my judgment it deserveth no less. I have heard F. J. say that he borrowed the invention of an Italian, but were it a translation or invention (if I be judge) it is both pretty and pithy.

His duty thus performed, their pastimes ended; and at their departure for a watchword he counseled his mistress by little and little to walk abroad, saying that the gallery near adjoining was so pleasant, as if he were half dead, he thought that by walking therein he might be half and more revived.

"Think you so, servant?" quoth she. "And the last time that I walked there, I suppose I took the cause of my malady, but by your advice (and for you have so clerkly stanched my bleeding) I will assay to walk there tomorrow."

"Mistress," quoth he, "and in more full accomplishment of my duty towards you, and in sure hope that you will use the same only to your own private commodity, I will there await upon you, and between you and me will teach you the full order how to stanch the bleeding of any creature; whereby you shall be as cunning as myself."

"Gramercy, good servant," quoth she, "I think you lost the same in writing here yesterday; but I cannot understand it, and therefore tomorrow (if I feel myself anything amended) I will send for you thither to instruct me thoroughly."

Thus they departed. And at supper time the knight of the castle, finding fault that his guest's stomach served him no better, began to accuse the grossness of his viands; to whom one of the gentle-women which had passed the afternoon in his company, answered, "Nay, sir," quoth she, "this gentleman hath a passion, the which once in a day at the least doth kill his appetite."

"Are you so well acquainted with the disposition of his body?" quoth the lord of the house.

"By his own saying," quoth she, "and not otherwise."

"Fair lady," quoth F. J., "you either mistook me or overheard me then, for I told of a comfortable humor which so fed me with continual remembrance of joy, as that my stomach being full thereof, doth desire in manner none other vittles."

"Why, sir," quoth the host, "do you then live by love?"

"God forbid, sir," quoth F. J., "for then my cheeks would be much thinner than they be, but there are divers other greater causes of joy than the doubtful lots of love. And for mine own part, to be plain, I cannot love, and I dare not hate."

"I would I thought so," quoth the gentlewoman.

And thus with pretty nips, they passed over their supper; which ended, the lord of the house required F. J. to dance and pass the time with the gentlewoman, which he refused not to do. But suddenly, before the music was well tuned, came out Dame Elinor in her night attire and said to the lord that (supposing the solitariness of her chamber had increased her malady) she came out for her better recreation to see them dance.

"Well done, daughter," quoth the lord.

"And I, mistress," quoth F. J., "would gladly bestow the leading of you about this great chamber, to drive away the faintness of your fever."

"No, good servant," quoth the lady, "but in my stead, I pray you dance with this fair gentlewoman," pointing him to the lady that had so taken him up at supper. F. J., to avoid mistrust, did agree to her request without further entreaty.

The dance begun, this knight marched on with the image of St. Frances in his hand and St. Elinor in his heart. The violands at end of the pavion[30] stayed a while; in which time this dame said to F. J. on this wise:

"I am right sorry for you in two respects, although the familiarity have hitherto had no great continuance between us; and as I do lament your case, so do I rejoice (for mine own contentation) that

[30]*pavion:* pavan; a slow, stately court dance for couples.

I shall now see a due trial of the experiment which I have long desired."

This said, she kept silence. When F. J. (somewhat astonied with her strange speech) thus answered: "Mistress, although I cannot conceive the meaning of your words, yet by courtesy I am constrained to yield you thanks for your good will, the which appeareth no less in lamenting of mishaps than in rejoicing at good fortune. What experiment you mean to try by me, I know not, but I dare assure you that my skill in experiments is very simple."

Herewith the instruments sounded a new measure, and they passed forthwards, leaving to talk, until the noise ceased; which done, the gentlewoman replied.

"I am sorry, sir, that you did erewhile deny love and all his laws, and that in so open audience."

"Not so," quoth F. J., "but as the word was roundly taken, so can I readily answer it by good reason."

"Well," quoth she, "how if the hearers will admit no reasonable answer?"

"My reason shall yet be, nevertheless," quoth he, "in reasonable judgment."

Herewith she smiled, and he cast a glance towards Dame Elinor askances,[31] "Art thou pleased?" Again the viols called them forthwards, and again at the end of the brawl said F. J. to this gentlewoman:

"I pray you, mistress, and what may be the second cause of your sorrow sustained in my behalf?"

"Nay, soft," quoth she, "percase I have not yet told you the first; but content yourself, for the second cause you shall never know at my hands until I see due trial of the experiment which I have long desired."

"Why, then," quoth he, "I can but wish a present occasion to bring the same to effect to the end that I might also understand the mystery of your meaning."

"And so might you fail of your purpose," quoth she, "for I mean to be better assured of him that shall know the depth of mine intent in such a secret than I do suppose that any creature (one except) may be of you."

"Gentlewoman," quoth he, "you speak Greek, the which I have

---

[31]*askances:* "as who sayeth" is the marginal note in the 1575 edition; "as if to say" is perhaps better modern English.

now forgotten, and mine instructors are too far from me at this present to expound your words."

"Or else too near," quoth she, and so smiling stayed her talk, when the music called them to another dance. Which ended, F. J., half afraid of false suspect, and more amazed at this strange talk, gave over, and bringing Mistress Frances to her place was thus saluted by his mistress.

"Servant," quoth she, "I had done you great wrong to have danced with you, considering that this gentlewoman and you had former occasion of so weighty conference."

"Mistress," said F. J., "you had done me great pleasure, for by our conference I have but brought my brains in a busy conjecture."

"I doubt not," said his mistress, "but you will end that business easily."

"It is hard," said F. J., "to end the thing whereof yet I have found no beginning." His mistress with change of countenance kept silence; whereat Dame Frances rejoicing, cast out this bone to gnaw on.

"I perceive," quoth she, "it is evil to halt before a cripple."[32]

F. J., perceiving now that his mistress waxed angry, thought good on her behalf thus to answer: "And it is evil to hop before them that run for the bell."[33]

His mistress replied, "And it is evil to hang the bell at their heels which are always running."

The lord of the castle, overhearing these proper quips, rose out of his chair and, coming towards F. J., required him to dance a galliard.

"Sir," said F. J., "I have hitherto at your appointment but walked about the house; now if you be desirous to see one tumble a turn or twain, it is like enough that I might provoke you to laugh at

[32]Dame Frances slightly alters a proverb (Tilley, H60), which usually runs "It is hard (or ill) halting before a cripple." The proverb could be taken several ways. Here the primary sense seems to be that it is wrong of Elinor to pretend love (feign a limp) before one who really is in love (a cripple); since Frances is in love with F. J. and F. J. with Elinor, either of them may be the "cripple." Another sense, used by Lyly, is that a real cripple can easily spot a counterfeit cripple; and this sense, if also applied to love, is prophetic of the ending of *Master F. J.*

[33]*evil to hop . . . bell:* F. J. manages to continue the wit by using another proverb (Tilley, B275), which usually is worded "He bears away the bell" (wins the prize). F. J. seems to accuse Frances of leaping in front of Elinor in order to get a prize; but since the ultimate prize is F. J. himself, one wonders if he fully appreciates the meaning of his own remark.

me; but in good faith my dancing days are almost done, and therefore, sir," quoth he, "I pray you speak to them that are more nimble at tripping on the toe."

Whilst he was thus saying, Dame Elinor had made her *congé*, and was now entering the door of her chamber when F. J., all amazed at her sudden departure, followed to take leave of his mistress. But she, more than angry, refused to hear his good night and, entering her chamber, caused her maid to clap the door. F. J., with heavy cheer, returned to his company, and Mistress Frances, to touch his sore with a corrosive, said to him softly in this wise: "Sir, you may now perceive that this our country cannot allow the French manner of dancing, for they (as I have heard tell) do more commonly dance to talk than entreat to dance."

F. J., hoping to drive out one nail with another, and thinking this a mean most convenient to suppress all jealous supposes, took Mistress Frances by the hand and with a heavy smile answered: "Mistress, and I (because I have seen the French manner of dancing) will eftsoons entreat you to dance a bargenet."[34]

"What mean you by this?" quoth Mistress Frances.

"If it please you to follow," quoth he, "you shall see that I can jest without joy, and laugh without lust." And calling the musicians, caused them softly to sound the *tinternel*[35] when he, clearing his voice, did, *alla Napolitana,* apply these verses following unto the measure.

G. T.

In prime of lusty years, when Cupid caught me in,
And nature taught the way to love, how I might best begin.
To please my wandering eye, in beauty's tickle trade,
To gaze on each that passed by, a careless sport I made.

With sweet enticing bait, I fished for many a dame,
And warmed me by many a fire, yet felt I not the flame;
But when at last I spied the face that pleased me most,
The coals were quick, the wood was dry, and I began to toast.

And smiling yet full oft, I have beheld that face,
When in my heart I might bewail mine own unlucky case;
And oft again with looks that might bewray my grief,
I pleaded hard for just reward, and sought to find relief.

[34]*bargenet:* a pastoral or rustic song and dance.
[35]*tinternel:* apparently some kind of instrumental music, perhaps of a kind that rings out in some way (from the French *tinter,* to ring); "*alla Napolitana*" means "in the manner of people from Naples."

What will you more? So oft my gazing eyes did seek
To see the rose and lily strive upon that lively cheek;
Till at the last I spied, and by good proof I found,
That in that face was painted plain, the piercer of my wound.

Then (all too late) aghast, I did my foot retire,
And sought with secret sighs to quench my greedy, scalding fire;
But lo, I did prevail as much to guide my will,
As he that seeks with halting heel, to hop against the hill.

Or as the feeble sight, would search the sunny beam,
Even so I found but labor lost, to strive against the stream.
Then gan I thus resolve, since liking forced love,
Should I mislike my happy choice, before I did it prove?

And since none other joy I had but her to see,
Should I retire my deep desire? No, no, it would not be;
Though great the duty were, that she did well deserve,
And I, poor man, unworthy am so worthy a wight to serve.

Yet hope my comfort stayed, that she would have regard
To my good will, that nothing crav'd, but like for just reward;
I see the falcon gent[36] sometimes will take delight,
To seek the solace of her wing, and dally with a kite.

The fairest wolf will choose the foulest for her make,[37]
And why? Because he doth endure most sorrow for her sake.
Even so had I like hope, when doleful days were spent,
When weary words were wasted well, to open true intent.

When floods of flowing tears had washed my weeping eyes,
When trembling tongue had troubled her, with loud lamenting cries;
At last her worthy wit would pity this my plaint,
And comfort me her own poor slave, whom fear had made so faint.

  Wherefore I made a vow, the stony rock should start,
  Ere I presume, to let her slip out of my faithful heart.

L'envoy

And when she saw by proof, the pith of my good will,
She took in worth this simple song, for want of better skill;
And as my just deserts, her gentle heart did move,
She was content to answer thus: I am content to love.

                                                    F. J.

[36]*falcon gent:* gentle falcon; "one of the seven kinds of falcons, so called for her gentle disposition" (Prouty's edition, p. 247).
[37]*The fairest wolf . . . make:* "make" means "mate"; Prouty notes (p. 247) a romantic contemporary belief that the female wolf chose the male who, because he was the dirtiest of the pack, was therefore the one who had chased her longest and most ardently.

These verses are more in number than do stand with contentation of some judgments and yet, the occasion thoroughly considered, I can commend them with the rest; for it is (as may be well termed) *continua oratio,* declaring a full discourse of his first love. Wherein (over and besides that the epithets are aptly applied and the verse of itself pleasant enough) I note that by it he meant in clouds to decipher unto Mistress Frances such matter as she would snatch at, and yet could take no good hold of the same. Furthermore, it answered very aptly to the note which the music sounded, as the skillful reader by due trial may approve.

This singing dance or dancing song ended, Mistress Frances, giving due thanks, seemed weary also of the company and, proffering to depart, gave yet this farewell to F. J., not vexed by choler but pleased with contentation and called away by heavy sleep.

"I am constrained," quoth she, "to bid you good night." And so, turning to the rest of the company, took her leave.

Then the master of the house commanded a torch to light F. J. to his lodging, where (as I have heard him say) the sudden change of his mistress' countenance, together with the strangeness of Mistress Frances' talk, made such an encounter in his mind that he could take no rest that night.

Wherefore in the morning, rising very early (although it were far before his mistress' hour) he cooled his choler by walking in the gallery near to her lodging, and there in this passion compiled these verses following.   G. T.

> A cloud of care hath covered all my coast,
> And storms of strife do threaten to appear;
> The waves of woe, which I mistrusted most,
> Have broke the banks wherein my life lay clear;
> Chips of ill chance are fallen amid my choice,
> To mar the mind that meant for to rejoice.
>
> Before I sought, I found the haven of hap,
> Wherein (once found) I sought to shroud my ship;
> But low'ring love hath lift me from her lap,
> And crabbed lot begins to hang the lip;
> The drops of dark mistrust do fall so thick
> They pierce my coat, and touch my skin at quick.
>
> What may be said, where truth cannot prevail?
> What plea may serve, where will itself is judge?
> What reason rules, where right and reason fail?
> Remediless then must the guiltless trudge,
> And seek out care, to be the carving knife
> To cut the thread, that ling'reth such a life.   F. J.

This is but a rough meter—and reason, for it was devised in great disquiet of mind and written in rage. Yet have I seen much worse pass the musters, yea and where both the lieutenant and provost marshall were men of ripe judgment. And as it is, I pray you let it pass here; for the truth is that F. J. himself had so slender liking thereof, or at least of one word escaped therein, that he never presented it. But to the matter.

When he had long (and all in vain) looked for the coming of his mistress into her appointed walk, he wandered into the park near adjoining to the castle wall, where his chance was to meet Mistress Frances, accompanied with one other gentlewoman, by whom he passed with a reverence of courtesy; and so walking on, came into the side of a thicket, where he sat down under a tree to allay his sadness with solitariness.

Mistress Frances, partly of courtesy and affection, and partly to content her mind by continuance of such talk as they had commenced over night, entreated her companion to go with her unto this tree of reformation. Whereas they found the knight wth his arms folded in a heavy kind of contemplation, unto whom Mistress Frances stepped apace (right softly) and at unawares gave this salutation:

"I little thought, sir knight," quoth she, "by your evensong yesternight, to have found you presently at such a morrow mass, but I perceive you serve your saint with double devotion; and I pray God grant you treble meed for your true intent."

F. J., taken thus upon the sudden, could none otherwise answer but thus: "I told you, mistress," quoth he, "that I could laugh without lust and jest without joy." And therewithal starting up, with a more bold countenance, came towards the dames, proffering unto them his service, to wait upon them homewards.

"I have heard say ofttimes," quoth Mistress Frances, "that it is hard to serve two masters at one time, but we will be right glad of your company."

"I thank you," quoth F. J. And so, walking on with them, fell into sundry discourses, still refusing to touch any part of their former communication until Mistress Frances said unto him:

"By my troth," quoth she, "I would be your debtor these two days to answer me truly but unto one question that I will propound."

"Fair gentlewoman," quoth he, "you shall not need to become my debtor, but if it please you to quit question by question, I will be more ready to gratify you in this request than either reason requireth, or than you would be willing to work my contentation."

"Master F. J.," quoth she, and that sadly, "peradventure you know but a little how willing I would be to procure your contentation, but you know that hitherto familiarity hath taken no deep root betwixt us twain. And though I find in you no manner of cause whereby I might doubt to commit this or greater matter unto you, yet have I stayed hitherto so to do, in doubt lest you might thereby justly condemn me both of arrogancy and lack of discretion. Wherewith I must yet foolishly affirm that I have with great pain bridled my tongue from disclosing the same unto you. Such is then the good will that I bear towards you, the which if you rather judge to be impudence than a friendly meaning, I may then curse the hour that I first concluded thus to deal with you." Herewithal being now red for chaste bashfulness, she abased her eyes and stayed her talk.

To whom F. J. thus answered: "Mistress Frances, if I should with so exceeding villainy requite such and so exceeding courtesy, I might not only seem to degenerate from all gentry, but also to differ in behavior from all the rest of my life spent. Wherefore to be plain with you in few words, I think myself so much bound unto you for divers respects, as, if ability do not fail me, you shall find me mindful in requital of the same. And for disclosing your mind to me, you may, if so please you, adventure it without adventure. For by this sun," quoth he, "I will not deceive such trust as you shall lay upon me, and furthermore, so far forth as I may, I will be yours in any respect. Wherefore I beseech you accept me for your faithful friend, and so shall you surely find me."

"Not so," quoth she, "but you shall be my Trust, if you vouchsafe the name, and I will be to you as you shall please to term me."

"My Hope," quoth he, "if you so be pleased."

And thus agreed, they two walked apart from the other gentlewoman and fell into sad talk, wherein Mistress Frances did very courteously declare unto him that, indeed, one cause of her sorrow sustained in his behalf was that he had said so openly over night that he could not love. For she perceived very well the affection between him and Madame Elinor; and she was also advertised that Dame Elinor stood in the portal of her chamber, harkening to the talk that they had at supper that night. Wherefore she seemed to be sorry that such a word (rashly escaped) might become great hindrance unto his desire, but a greater cause of her grief was (as she declared) that his hap was to bestow his liking so unworthily; for she seemed to accuse Dame Elinor for the most unconstant woman living. In full proof whereof, she bewrayed unto F. J. how she, the same Dame

Elinor, had of long time been yielded to the minion secretary, whom I have before described.

"In whom though there be," quoth she, "no one point of worthiness, yet shameth she not to use him as her dearest friend, or rather her holiest idol." And that this notwithstanding, Dame Elinor had been also sundry times won to choice of change, as she named unto F. J. two gentlemen, whereof the one was named H. D. and that other H. K., by whom she was during sundry times of their several abode in those parties, entreated to like courtesy. For these causes the Dame Frances seemed to mislike F. J.'s choice and to lament that she doubted[38] in process of time to see him abused.

The experiment she meant was this: for that she thought F. J. (I use her words) a man in every respect very worthy to have the several use of a more commodious common, she hoped now to see if his enclosure thereof might be defensible against her said secretary, and such like. These things, and divers other of great importance, this courteous Lady Frances did friendly disclose unto F. J. and furthermore did both instruct and advise him how to proceed in his enterprise.

Now to make my talk[39] good and lest the reader might be drawn in a jealous suppose of this Lady Frances, I must let you understand that she was unto F. J. a kinswoman, a virgin of rare chastity, singular capacity, notable modesty, and excellent beauty; and though F. J. had cast his affection on the other (being a married woman) yet was there in their beauties no great difference. But in all other good gifts a wonderful diversity, as much as might be between constancy and flitting fantasy, between womanly countenance and girlish garishness, between hot dissimulation and temperate fidelity. Now if any man will curiously ask the question why F. J. should choose the one and leave the other, over and besides the common proverb (so many men, so many minds) thus may be answered: we see by common experience that the highest flying falcon doth more commonly prey upon the corn-fed crow and the simple, shiftless dove than on the mounting kite. And why? Because the one is overcome with less difficulty than that other. Thus much in defense of this Lady Frances, and to excuse the choice of my friend F. J. who thought himself now no less be-

[38]*doubted:* feared. For the sense of "parties," in the previous sentence, see note 10.

[39]*talk:* The 1587 edition emends "talk" to "tale," which makes good sense; but "talk" may be what G. T. intends—vaguely in the sense of "discourse," or specifically in the sense of "rumor" or "gossip."

holding to good fortune to have found such a trusty friend, than bounden to Dame Venus to have won such a mistress.

And to return unto my pretense, understand you that F. J. (being now with these two fair ladies come very near the castle) grew in some jealous doubt (as on his own behalf) whether he were best to break company or not. When his assured Hope, perceiving the same, gan thus recomfort him.

"Good sir," quoth she, "if you trusted your trusty friends, you should not need thus cowardly to stand in dread of your friendly enemies."

"Well said, in faith," quoth F. J., "and I must confess you were in my bosom before I wist, but yet I have heard said often that in Trust is treason."

"Well spoken, for yourself," quoth his Hope. F. J., now remembering that he had but erewhile taken upon him the name of her Trust, came home *per misericordiam,* when his Hope, entering the castle gate, caught hold of his lap[40] and half by force led him by the gallery unto his mistress' chamber. Whereas after a little dissembling disdain, he was at last by the good help of his Hope, right thankfully received; and for his mistress was now ready to dine, he was therefore for that time arrested there and a supersedeas[41] sent into the great chamber unto the lord of the house, who expected his coming out of the park.

The dinner ended, and he thoroughly contented both with welfare and welcome, they fell into sundry devices of pastime. At last F. J., taking into his hand a lute that lay on his mistress' bed, did unto the note of the Venetian galliard apply the Italian ditty written by the worthy Bradamant unto the noble Rugier, as Ariosto hath it, "Rugier qual semper fui, etc."[42] But his mistress could not be quiet until she heard him repeat the tinternel which he used over night. The which F. J. refused not, at end whereof his mistress, thinking now she had showed herself too earnest to use any further dissimulation, especially perceiving the toward inclination of her servant's Hope, fell to flat, plain dealing and, walking to the window, called her servant apart

[40]*lap:* coattail (or at least some part of F. J.'s clothing that hung down or lapped over); *"per misericordiam"* means "because of a tender heart."

[41]*supersedeas:* a suspending or halting (of the lord's plans in the great chamber); legally, a common-law writ commanding a stay of legal proceedings.

[42]*Rugier qual semper fui,* etc.: Bradamant and Ruggiero are the main characters in the Italian epic *Orlando Furioso* (1516) by Ludovico Ariosto. It was not translated into English until 1591.

unto her, of whom she demanded secretly and in sad earnest, "Who devised this tinternel?"

"My father's sister's brother's son," quoth F. J.

His mistress, laughing right heartily, demanded yet again by whom the same was figured. "By a niece to an aunt of yours, mistress," quoth he.

"Well, then, servant," quoth she, "I swear unto you here by my father's soul that my mother's youngest daughter doth love your father's eldest son above any creature living."

F. J., hereby recomforted, gan thus reply: "Mistress, though my father's eldest son be far unworthy of so noble a match, yet since it pleaseth her so well to accept him, I would thus much say behind his back that your mother's daughter hath done him some wrong."

"And wherein, servant?" quoth she.

"By my troth, mistress," quoth he, "it is not yet twenty hours since without touch of breast, she gave him such a nip by the heart as did altogether bereave him his night's rest with the bruise thereof."

"Well, servant," quoth she, "content yourself, and for your sake, I will speak to her to provide him a plaster, the which I myself will apply to his hurt. And to the end it may work the better with him, I will purvey a lodging for him where hereafter he may sleep at more quiet."

This said, the rosy hue distained her sickly cheeks and she returned to the company, leaving F. J. ravished between hope and dread as one that could neither conjecture the meaning of her mystical words nor assuredly trust unto the knot of her sliding affections.

When the Lady Frances, coming to him, demanded, "What? Dream you, sir?"

"Yea, marry, do I, fair lady," quoth he.

"And what was your dream, sir?" quoth she.

"I dreamt," quoth F. J., "that walking in a pleasant garden garnished with sundry delights, my hap was to espy, hanging in the air, a hope wherein I might well behold the aspects and face of the heavens; and calling to remembrance the day and hour of my nativity, I did thereby (according to my small skill in astronomy) try the conclusions of mine adventures."

"And what found you therein?" quoth Dame Frances.

"You awaked me out of my dream," quoth he, "or else peradventure you should not have known."

"I believe you well," quoth the Lady Frances and, laughing at his quick answer, brought him by the hand unto the rest of his company, where he tarried not long before his gracious mistress bade him to farewell[43] and to keep his hour there again when he should by her be summoned.

Hereby F. J. passed the rest of that day in hope, awaiting the happy time when his mistress should send for him. Supper time came and passed over, and not long after came the handmaid of the Lady Elinor into the great chamber, desiring F. J. to repair unto their mistress, the which he willingly accomplished. And being now entered into her chamber, he might perceive his mistress in her night's attire, preparing herself towards bed; to whom F. J. said, "Why how now, mistress? I had thought this night to have seen you dance (at least or at last) amongst us."

"By my troth, good servant," quoth she, "I adventured so soon unto the great chamber yesternight that I find myself somewhat sickly disposed and therefore do strain courtesy (as you see) to go the sooner to my bed this night. But before I sleep," quoth she, "I am to charge you with a matter of weight." And, taking him apart from the rest, declared that (as that present night) she would talk with him more at large in the gallery near adjoining to her chamber.

Hereupon F. J., discreetly dissimuling his joy, took his leave and returned into the great chamber, where he had not long continued before the lord of the castle commanded a torch to light him unto his lodging; whereas he prepared himself and went to bed, commanding his servant also to go to his rest. And when he thought as well his servant, as the rest of the household, to be safe, he arose again and, taking his nightgown, did under the same convey his naked sword, and so walked to the gallery where he found his good mistress walking in her nightgown and attending his coming.

The moon was now at the full, the skies clear, and the weather temperate, by reason whereof he might the more plainly and with the greater contentation behold his long desired joys. And spreading his arms abroad to embrace his loving mistress, he said: "Oh, my dear lady, when shall I be able with any desert to countervail the least part of this your bountiful goodness?"

The dame (whether it were of fear indeed, or that the wiliness of womanhood had taught her to cover her conceits with some fine dissimulation) stert[44] back from the knight, and shrieking (but softly)

---

[43]*to farewell:* not only "good-by" but literally to "fare well" (and therefore the "to" should not be dropped, as in the 1575 and 1587 editions).

[44]*stert:* started.

said unto him, "Alas, servant, what have I deserved that you come against me with naked sword as against an open enemy?"

F. J., perceiving her intent, excused himself, declaring that he brought the same for their defense and not to offend her in any wise. The lady, being therewith somewhat appeased, they began with more comfortable gesture to expel the dread of the said late affright, and sithens to become bolder of behavior, more familiar in speech, and most kind in accomplishing of common comfort.

But why hold I so long discourse in describing the joys which (for lack of like experience) I cannot set out to the full? Were it not that I know to whom I write, I would the more beware what I write. F. J. was a man and neither of us are senseless; and therefore I should slander him (over and besides a greater obloquy to the whole genealogy of Aeneas) if I should imagine that of tender heart he would forbear to express her more tender limbs against the hard floor. Sufficed that of her courteous nature, she was content to accept boards for a bed of down, mats for cambric sheets, and the night-gown of F. J. for a counterpoint to cover them. And thus with calm content, instead of quiet sleep, they beguiled the night until the proudest star began to abandon the firmament; when F. J. and his mistress were constrained also to abandon their delights and with ten thousand sweet kisses and straight embracings, did frame themselves to play loath to depart.

Well, remedy was there none, but Dame Elinor must return unto her chamber; and F. J. must also convey himself (as closely as might be) into his chamber, the which was hard to do, the day being so far sprung, and he having a large base court[45] to pass over before he could recover his stairfoot door. And though he were not much perceived, yet the Lady Frances, being no less desirous to see an issue of these enterprises than F. J. was willing to cover them in secrecy, did watch and, even at the entering of his chamber door, perceived the point of his naked sword glistering under the skirt of his nightgown; whereat she smiled and said to herself, "This gear goeth well about."

Well, F. J., having now recovered his chamber, he went to bed; and there let him sleep, as his mistress did on that other side. Although the Lady Frances, being thoroughly tickled now in all the veins, could not enjoy such quiet rest but, arising, took another gentle-woman of the house with her, and walked into the park to take the fresh air of the morning. They had not long walked there, but they returned, and though F. J. had not yet slept sufficiently, for one which

---

[45]*base court:* an outside courtyard, "base" probably in the sense of "low" (down a few steps).

had so far travailed[46] in the night past, yet they went into his chamber to raise him and, coming to his bedside, found him fast on sleep. "Alas," quoth that other gentlewoman, "it were pity to awake him."

"Even so it were," quoth Dame Frances, "but we will take away somewhat of his, whereby he may perceive that we were here." And looking about the chamber, his naked sword presented itself to the hands of Dame Frances, who took it with her and, softly shutting his chamber door again, went down the stairs and recovered her own lodging in good order and unperceived of anybody, saving only that other gentlewoman which accompanied her.

At the last, F. J. awaked and, appareling himself, walked out also to take the air. And being thoroughly recomforted as well with remembrance of his joys forepassed as also with the pleasant harmony which the birds made on every side, and the fragrant smell of the redolent flowers and blossoms which budded on every branch, he did in these delights compile these verses following. The occasion (as I have heard him rehearse) was by encounter that he had with his lady by light of the moon; and forasmuch as the moon in midst of their delights did vanish away or was overspread with a cloud, thereupon he took the subject of his theme. And thus it ensueth, called "A Moonshine Banquet."

G. T.

> Dame Cynthia herself (that shines so bright,
> And deigneth not to leave her lofty place
> But only then, when Phoebus shows his face,
> Which is her brother born and lends her light)
> Disdained not yet to do my lady right,
> To prove that in such heavenly wights as she,
> It sitteth best that right and reason be.
> For when she spied my lady's golden rays,
> Into the clouds,
> Her head she shrouds,
> And shamed to shine where she her beams displays.
>
> Good reason yet, that to my simple skill,
> I should the name of Cynthia adore.
> By whose high help I might behold the more
> My lady's lovely looks at mine own will,
> With deep content, to gaze and gaze my fill,
> Of courtesy and not of dark disdain,
> Dame Cynthia disclosed my lady plain.

[46]*far travailed:* "far" is to suggest "traveled," but the main reference in the pun is to the "travail" of F. J.'s affair with Elinor.

She did but lend her light (as for a light)
With friendly grace,
To show her face,
That else would show and shine in her despite.

Dan Phoebus he with many a low'ring look,
Had her beheld of yore in angry wise:
And when he could none other mean devise
To stain her name, this deep deceit he took
To be the bait that best might hide his hook:
Into her eyes his parching beams he cast,
To scorch their skins, that gaz'd on her full fast.
Whereby when many a man was sunburnt so
They thought my queen
The sun had been
With scalding flames, which wrought them all that woe.

And thus when many a look had look'd so long,
As that their eyes were dim and dazzled both,
Some fainting hearts that were both lewd[47] and loath
To look again from whence the error sprung,
Gan close their eye for fear of further wrong.
And some again, once drawn into the maze,
Gan lewdly blame the beams of beauty's blaze.
But I with deep foresight did soon espy,
How Phoebus meant
By false intent
To slander so her name with cruelty.

Wherefore at better leisure thought I best
To try the treason of his treachery,
And to exalt my lady's dignity
When Phoebus fled and drew him down to rest
Amid the waves that walter[48] in the west.
I gan behold this lovely lady's face,
Whereon Dame Nature spent her gifts of grace,
And found therein no parching heat at all,
But such bright hue
As might renew
An angel's joys in reign celestial.

The courteous moon that wish'd to do me good,
Did shine to show my dame more perfectly,
But when she saw her passing jollity,
The moon, for shame, did blush as red as blood,
And shrank aside and kept her horns in hood.

[47]*lewd:* ignorant.
[48]*walter:* roll to and fro.

So that now when Dame Cynthia was gone,
I might enjoy my lady's looks alone,
Yet honored still the moon with true intent,
Who taught us skill
To work our will
And gave us place till all the night was spent.

F. J.

This ballade, or howsoever I shall term it, percase you will not like, and yet in my judgment it hath great good store of deep invention; and for the order of the verse, it is not common. I have not heard many of like proportion; some will accompt it but a diddledum, but who so had heard F. J. sing it to the lute, by a note of his own device, I suppose he would esteem it to be a pleasant diddledum. And for my part, if I were not partial, I would say more in commendation of it than now I mean to do, leaving it to your and like judgments.

And now to return to my tale. By that time that F. J. returned out of the park it was dinner time, and at dinner they all met. I mean both Dame Elinor, Dame Frances, and F. J. I leave to describe that the Lady Frances was gorgeously attired and set forth with very brave apparel, and Madame Elinor only in her nightgown girt to her, with a coif trimmed *alla Piedmontese,* on the which she wore a little cap crossed over the crown with two bands of yellow sarcenet or cypress, in the midst whereof she had placed (of her own handwriting) in paper this word, "Contented." This attire pleased her then to use and could not have displeased Mistress Frances, had she not been more privy to the cause than to the thing itself. At least the lord of the castle of ignorance, and Dame Frances of great temperance, let it pass without offense. At dinner, because the one was pleased with all former reckonings, and the other made privy to the accompt, there passed no word of taunt or grudge, but *omnia bene.* After dinner Dame Elinor, being no less desirous to have F. J.'s company than Dame Frances was to take him in some pretty trip, they began to question how they might best pass the day. The Lady Elinor seemed desirous to keep her chamber, but Mistress Frances for another purpose seemed desirous to ride abroad, thereby to take the open air. They agreed to ride a mile or twain for solace and requested F. J. to accompany them, the which willingly granted.

Each one parted from other to prepare themselves, and now began the sport; for when F. J. was booted, his horses saddled, and he ready to ride, he gan miss his rapier. Whereat all astonied he began to blame his man; but blame whom he would, found it could not be.

At last the ladies going towards horseback, called for him in the base court and demanded if he were ready. To whom F. J. answered, "Madames, I am more than ready, and yet not so ready as I would be." And immediately taking himself in trip, he thought best to utter no more of his conceit, but in haste more than good speed mounted his horse and coming toward the dames, presented himself, turning, bounding, and taking up his courser to the uttermost of his power in bravery. After suffering his horse to breathe himself, he gan also allay his own choler and to the dames he said, "Fair ladies, I am ready when it pleaseth you to ride whereso you command."

"How ready soever you be, servant," quoth Dame Elinor, "it seemeth your horse is readier at your command than at ours."

"If he be at my command, mistress," quoth he, "he shall be at yours."

"Gramercy, good servant," quoth she, "but my meaning is that I fear he be too stirring for our company."

"If he prove so, mistress," quoth F. J., "I have here a soberer palfrey to serve you on."

The dames being mounted, they rode forthwards by the space of a mile or very near, and F. J. (whether it were of his horse's courage or his own choler) came not so near them as they wished. At last the Lady Frances said unto him, "Master F. J., you said that you had a soberer horse, which if it be so, we would be glad of your company, but I believe by your countenance, your horse and you are agreed."

F. J., alighting, called his servant, changed horses with him and, overtaking the dames, said to Mistress Frances, "And why do you think, fair lady, that my horse and I are agreed?"

"Because by your countenance," quoth she, "it seemeth your patience is stirred."

"In good faith," quoth F. J., "you have guessed aright, but not with any of you."

"Then we care the less, servant," quoth Dame Elinor.

"By my troth, mistress," quoth F. J. (looking well about him that none might hear but they two) "it is with my servant, who hath lost my sword out of my chamber."

Dame Elinor, little remembering the occasion, replied: "It is no matter, servant," quoth she, "you shall hear of it again, I warrant you, and presently we ride in God's peace, and I trust shall have no need of it."

"Yet, mistress," quoth he, "a weapon serveth both uses, as well to defend as to offend."

"Now by my troth," quoth Dame Frances, "I have now my dream, for I dreamt this night that I was in a pleasant meadow alone, where I met with a tall gentleman, appareled in a nightgown of silk all embroidered about with a guard[49] of naked swords; and when he came towards me, I seemed to be afraid of him, but he recomforted me saying, 'Be not afraid, fair lady, for I use this garment only for mine own defense. And in this sort went that warlike god, Mars, what time he taught Dame Venus to make Vulcan a hammer of the new fashion.' Notwithstanding these comfortable words, the fright of the dream awaked me, and sithens unto this hour I have not slept at all."

"And what time of the night dreamt you this?" quoth F. J.

"In the gray morning about dawning of the day. But why ask you?" quoth Dame Frances.

F. J., with a great sigh, answered, "Because that dreams are to be marked more at some hour of the night than at some other."

"Why, are you so cunning at the interpretation of dreams, servant?" quoth the Lady Elinor.

"Not very cunning, mistress," quoth F. J., "but guess, like a young scholar."

The dames continued in these and like pleasant talks; but F. J. could not be merry, as one that esteemed the preservation of his mistress' honor no less than the obtaining of his own delights. And yet to avoid further suspicion, he repressed his passions as much as he could. The Lady Elinor, more careless than considerative of her own case, pricking forwards said softly to F. J., "I had thought you had received small cause, servant, to be thus dumpish when I would be merry."

"Alas, dear mistress," quoth F. J., "it is altogether for your sake that I am pensive."

Dame Frances with courtesy withdrew herself and gave them leave, when as F. J. declared unto his mistress that his sword was taken out of his chamber, and that he dreaded much by the words of the Lady Frances that she had some understanding of the matter. Dame Elinor, now calling to remembrance what had passed the same night, at the first was abashed, but immediately (for these women be readily witted) cheered her servant and willed him to commit unto her the salving of that sore.

[49]*guard:* trimming or edging.

Thus they passed the rest of the way in pleasant talk with Dame Frances, and so returned towards the castle, where F. J. suffered the two dames to go together, and he alone unto his chamber to bewail his own misgovernment. But Dame Elinor (whether it were according to old custom or by wily policy) found mean that night that the sword was conveyed out of Mistress Frances' chamber and brought unto hers. And after redelivery of it unto F. J., she warned him to be more wary from that time forthwards.

Well, I dwell too long upon these particular points in discoursing this trifling history, but that the same is the more apt mean of introduction to the verses which I mean to rehearse unto you. And I think you will not disdain to read my conceit with his invention about declaration of his comedy. The next that ever F. J. wrote then upon any adventure happened between him and his fair lady was this, as I have heard him say, and upon this occasion. After he grew more bold and better acquainted with his mistress' disposition, he adventured one Friday in the morning to go unto her chamber, and thereupon wrote as followeth, which he termed "A Friday's Breakfast."

G. T.

> That selfsame day, and of that day that hour,
> When she doth reign that mock'd Vulcan the smith
> And thought it meet to harbor in her bower
> Some gallant guest for her to dally with.
> That blessed hour, that blest and happy day,
> I thought it meet, with hasty steps to go
> Unto the lodge, wherein my lady lay,
> To laugh for joy, or else to weep for woe.
> And lo, my lady of her wonted grace,
> First lent her lips to me (as for a kiss)
> And after that her body to embrace,
> Wherein Dame Nature wrought nothing amiss.
> What followed next, guess you that know the trade,
> For in this sort my Friday's feast I made.

F. J.

This sonnet is short and sweet, reasonably well, according to the occasion, etc. Many days passed these two lovers with great delight, their affairs being no less politickly governed than happily achieved. And surely I have heard F. J. affirm in sad earnest that he did not only love her, but was furthermore so ravished in ecstasy with continual remembrance of his delights that he made an idol of her in his inward conceit. So seemeth it by this challenge to beauty which he wrote in her praise and upon her name.

G. T.

Beauty, shut up thy shop and truss up all thy trash,
My Nell hath stolen thy finest stuff, and left thee in the lash.[50]
Thy market now is marred; thy gains are gone, God wot;
Thou hast no ware that may compare with this that I have got.
As for thy painted pale, and wrinkles surfled[51] up,
Are dear enough, for such as lust to drink of ev'ry cup:
Thy body's bolst'red out, with bombast and with bags,
Thy rolls,[52] thy ruffs, thy cauls,[53] thy coifs, thy jerkins, and thy
    jags.[54]
Thy curling and thy cost, thy frizzling and thy fare,
To court, to court with all those toys, and there set forth such ware
Before their hungry eyes, that gaze on every guest,
And choose the cheapest chaffare[55] still, to please their fancy
    best.
But I whose steadfast eyes could never cast a glance
With wandering look, amid the press, to take my choice by
    chance,
Have won by due desert, a piece that hath no peer,
And left the rest as refuse all, to serve the market there.
There let him choose that list, there catch the best who can.
A painted blazing bait may serve, to choke a gazing man.
But I have slipp'd[56] thy flower, that freshest is of hue.
I have thy corn, go sell thy chaff, I list to seek no new.
The windows of mine eyes are glaz'd with such delight,
As each new face seems full of faults, that blazeth in my sight.
And not without just cause, I can compare her so,
Lo here my glove I challenge him, that can, or dare say no.
Let thieves come with club, or Paris brag with brand,
To prove how fair their Helen was, that scourged the Grecian
    land.

[50]*lash:* lurch.
[51]*surfled:* painted (with a cosmetic).
[52]*rolls:* pads (of hair or cloth in a woman's headdress).
[53]*cauls:* close-fitting hairnets or caps for women; in this case they are richly ornamented.
[54]*jags:* notches or pointed slashes in cloth, especially in the sleeves.
[55]*chaffare:* The modern word is "chaffer," meaning "bargain" or "purchase"; F. J. may intend a rhyme with "fare" and "ware."
[56]*slipp'd:* cut.

Let mighty Mars himself come armed to the field
And vaunt Dame Venus to defend, with helmet, spear, and shield.
This hand that had good hap, my Helen to embrace,
Shall have like luck to foil her foes, and daunt them with disgrace.
And cause them to confess by verdict and by oath,
How far her lovely looks do stain[57] the beauties of them both.
And that my Helen is more fair than Paris' wife,
And doth deserve more famous praise than Venus for her life.
Which if I not perform, my life then let me leese,[58]
Or else be bound in chains of change to beg for beauty's fees.

F. J.

By this challenge I guess that either he was then in an ecstasy
or else sure I am now in a lunacy, for it is a proud challenge made
to Beauty herself, and all her companions. And imagining that
Beauty, having a shop where she uttered her wares of all sundry
sorts, his lady had stolen the finest away, leaving none behind her,
but painting, bolstering, forcing and such like, the which in his rage
he judgeth good enough to serve the court. And thereupon grew a
great quarrel. When these verses were, by the negligence of his
mistress, dispersed into sundry hands, and so at last to the reading
of a courtier—well, F. J. had his desire if his mistress liked them,
but as I have heard him declare, she grew in jealousy that the same
were not written by[59] her because her name was Elinor and not
Helen. And about this point have been divers and sundry opinions,
for this and divers other of his most notable poems have come to
view of the world, although altogether without his consent. And
some have attributed this praise unto a Helen, who deserved not so
well as this dame Elinor should seem to deserve by the relation of
F. J., and yet never a barrel of good herring between them both.[60]
But that other Helen, because she was and is of so base condition
as may deserve no manner commendation in any honest judgment,
therefore I will excuse my friend F. J. and adventure my pen in
his behalf that he would never bestow verse of so mean a subject.
And yet some of his acquaintance, being also acquainted (better
than I) that F. J. was sometimes acquainted with Helen, have stood
in argument with me that it was written by Helen, and not by
Elinor. Well, F. J. told me himself that it was written by this Dame

[57]*stain:* excel.
[58]*leese:* lose.
[59]*by:* about.
[60]*never a barrel of good herring between them both:* a proverb (Tilley,
B94); the sense is that there is little to choose between them, they are so
nearly equal.

Elinor, and that unto her he thus alleged that he took it all for one name, or at least he never read of any Elinor such matter as might sound worthy like commendation for beauty. And, indeed, considering that it was in the first beginning of his writings, as then he was no writer of any long continuance, comparing also the time that such reports do spread of his acquaintance with Helen, it cannot be written less than six or seven years before he knew Helen. Marry, peradventure if there were any acquaintance between F. J. and that Helen afterwards (the which I dare not confess) he might adapt it to her name, and so make it serve both their turns, as elder lovers have done before and still do and will do, world without end. Amen.

Well, by whom he wrote it I know not. But once[61] I am sure that he wrote it, for he is no borrower of inventions; and this is all that I mean to prove, as one that send you his verses by stealth, and do him double wrong to disclose unto any man the secret causes why they were devised. But this for your delight I do adventure. And to return to the purpose, he sought more certainly to please his Mistress Elinor with this sonnet written in her praise as followeth.

G. T.

> The stately dames of Rome their pearls did wear,
> About their necks to beautify their name.
> But she (whom I do serve) her pearls doth bear
> Close in her mouth and, smiling, shows the same.
> No wonder then, though ev'ry word she speaks,
> A jewel seems in judgment of the wise,
> Since that her sug'red tongue the passage breaks
> Between two rocks, bedeck'd with pearls of price.
> Her hair of gold, her front of ivory,
> (A bloody heart within so white a breast)
> Her teeth of pearl, lips ruby, crystal eye,
> Needs must I honor her above the rest.
> Since she is formed of none other mold
> But ruby, crystal, ivory, pearl, and gold.

F. J.

Of this sonnet I am assured that it is but a translation, for I myself have seen the invention of an Italian; and Master F. J. hath a little dilated the same, but not much besides the sense of the first, and the addition very aptly applied. Wherefore, I cannot condemn his doing therein, and for the sonnet, were it not a little too much praise (as the Italians do most commonly offend in the superlative)

---

[61] *once:* at any rate.

I could the more commend it. But I hope the party to whom it was dedicated had rather it were much more than anything less.

Well, thus these two lovers passed many days in exceeding contentation and more than speakable pleasures, in which time F. J. did compile very many verses according to sundry occasions proffered. Whereof I have not obtained the most at his hands, and the reason that he denied me the same was that (as he alleged) they were for the most part sauced with a taste of glory, as you know that in such cases a lover being charged with inexprimable[62] joys, and therewith enjoined both by duty and discretion to keep the same covert, can by no means devise a greater consolation than to commit it into some ciphered words and figured speeches in verse, whereby he feeleth his heart half (or more than half) eased of swelling. For as sighs are some present ease to the pensive mind, even so we find by experience that such secret intercommoning[63] of joys doth increase delight. I would not have you conster my words to this effect, that I think a man cannot sufficiently rejoice in the lucky lots of love unless he impart the same to others. God forbid that ever I should enter into such an heresy, for I have always been of this opinion: that as to be fortunate in love is one of the most inward contentations to man's mind of all earthly joys, even so if he do but once bewray the same to any living creature, immediately either dread of discovering doth bruise his breast with an intolerable burden, or else he loseth the principal virtue which gave effect to his gladness, not unlike to a pothecary's pot which being filled with sweet ointments or perfumes doth retain in itself some scent of the same, and being poured out doth return to the former state—hard, harsh, and of small savor. So the mind being fraught with delights, as long as it can keep them secretly enclosed may continually feed upon the pleasant record thereof as the well willing and ready horse biteth on the bridle, but having once disclosed them to any other, straightway we lose the hidden treasure of the same and are oppressed with sundry doubtful opinions and dreadful conceits. And yet for a man to record unto himself in the inward contemplation of his mind the often remembrance of his late received joys doth, as it were, ease the heart of burden, and add unto the mind a fresh supply of delight. Yea, and in verse principally (as I conceive) a man may best contrive this way of comfort in himself.

Therefore, as I have said, F. J., swimming now in delights, did

[62]*inexprimable:* inexpressible.
[63]*intercommoning:* sharing.

nothing but write such verse as might accumulate his joys to the extremity of pleasure. The which for that purpose he kept from me, as one more desirous to seem obscure and defective than overmuch to glory in his adventures, especially for that in the end his hap was as heavy as hitherto he had been fortunate.

Amongst other I remembered one happened upon this occasion. The husband of the Lady Elinor being all this while absent from her, gan now return and kept cut[64] at home, with whom F. J. found means so to insinuate himself that familiarity took deep root between them and seldom but by stealth you could find the one out of the other's company. On a time the knight riding on hunting desired F. J. to accompany him, the which he could not refuse to do, but like a lusty younker, ready at all assays, appareled himself in green, and about his neck a bugle, pricking and galloping amongst the foremost, according to the manner of that country. And it chanced that the married knight thus galloping lost his horn, which some divines[65] might have interpreted to be but molting[66] and that, by God's grace, he might have a new come up again shortly instead of that.

Well, he came to F. J., requiring him to lend him his bugle, for, said the knight, "I heard you not blow this day, and I would fain encourage the hounds if I had a horn."

Quoth F. J., "Although I have not been over lavish of my coming hitherto, I would you should not doubt but that I can tell how to use a horn well enough, and yet I may little do if I may not lend you a horn." And therewithal took his bugle from his neck and lent it to the knight, who, making in unto the hounds, gan assay to rechat.[67] But the horn was too hard for him to wind; whereat F. J. took pleasure and said to himself, "Blow till thou break that; I made thee one within these few days that thou wilt never crack whiles thou livest." And hereupon (before the fall of the buck) devised this sonnet following, which at his homecoming, he presented unto his mistress.

G. T.

---

[64]*kept cut:* Possibly the sense is "kept to himself" (despite the fact that he has just returned home and normally would be expected to enter into things); both the origin of the phrase and its meaning here are obscure.

[65]*divines:* diviners, seers.

[66]*molting:* the shedding of horns in certain animals; here the reference is to the horns of the cuckold.

[67]*to rechat:* to blow the horn (calling together the hounds—and encouraging them, as the knight says a few lines earlier).

As some men say, there is a kind of seed
Will grow to horns if it be sowed thick,
Wherewith I thought to try if I could breed
A brood of buds, well sharped on the prick.
And by good proof of learned skill I found,
(As on some special soil all seeds best frame)
So jealous brains do breed the battleground
That best of all might serve to bear the same.
Then sought I forth to find such supple soil,
And called to mind thy husband had a brain,
So that percase, by travail and by toil,
His fruitful front might turn my seed to gain.
And as I groped in that ground to sow it,
Start up a horn, thy husband could not blow it.

F. J.

This sonnet treateth of a strange seed, but it tasteth most of rye, which is more common amongst men nowadays. Well, let it pass amongst the rest and he that liketh it not, turn over the leaf to another; I doubt not but in this register he may find some to content him, unless he be too curious. And here I will surcease to rehearse any more of his verses until I have expressed how that his joys being now exalted to the highest degree, began to bend towards declination.

For now the unhappy secretary, whom I have before remembered, was returned from London, on whom F. J. had no sooner cast his eyes, but immediately he fell into a great passion of mind which might be compared unto a fever. This fruit grew of the good instructions that his Hope had planted in his mind; whereby I might take just occasion to forewarn every lover how they suffer this venomous serpent jealousy to creep into their conceits. For surely, of all other diseases in love, I suppose that to be incurable and would hold longer discourse therein were it not that both this tale and the verses of F. J. himself, hereafter to be recited, shall be sufficient to speak for me in this behalf.

The lover (as I say upon the sudden) was driven into such a malady as no meat might nourish his body, no delights please his mind, no remembrance of joys forepassed content him, nor any hope of the like to come might recomfort him. Hereat (some unto whom I have imparted this tale) have taken occasion to discommend his fainting heart; yet surely, the cause inwardly and deeply considered,

I cannot so lightly condemn him, for an old saying is that every man can give counsel better than follow it, and needs must the conflicts of his thoughts be strange between the remembrance of his forepassed pleasure and the present sight of this monster whom before (for lack of like instruction) he had not so thoroughly marked and beheld. Well, such was the grief unto him that he became sickly and kept his chamber.

The ladies, having received the news thereof, gan all at once lament his misfortune and of common consent agreed to visit him. They marched thither in good equipage, I warrant you, and found F. J. lying upon his bed languishing, whom they all saluted generally and sought to recomfort, but especially his mistress, having in her hand a branch of willow, wherewith she defended her from the hot air, gan thus say unto him. "Servant," quoth she, "for that I suppose your malady to proceed of none other cause but only slothfulness, I have brought this pretty rod to beat you a little, nothing doubting but when you feel the smart of a twig or twain, you will, like a tractable young scholar, pluck up your quickened spirits and cast this drowsiness apart."

F. J., with a great sigh, answered, "Alas, good mistress," quoth he, "if any like chastisement might quicken me, how much more might the presence of all you lovely dames recomfort my dulled mind, whom to behold were sufficient to revive an eye now dazzled with the dread of death, and that not only for the heavenly aspects which you represent, but also much the more for your exceeding courtesy, in that you have deigned to visit me, so unworthy a servant. But, good mistress," quoth he, "as it were shame for me to confess that ever my heart could yield for fear, so I assure you that my mind cannot be content to induce infirmity by sluggish conceit. But in truth, mistress, I am sick," quoth he. And therewithal the trembling of his heart had sent up such throbbing into his throat as that his voice (now deprived of breath) commanded the tongue to be still.

When Dame Elinor, for compassion, distilled into tears, and drew towards the window, leaving the other gentlewomen about his bed, who being no less sorry for his grief, yet for that they were none of them so touched in their secret thoughts, they had bolder spirits and freer speech to recomfort him.

Amongst the rest the Lady Frances (who indeed loved him deeply and could best conjecture the cause of his conceits) said unto him. "Good Trust," quoth she, "if any help of physic may cure your malady, I would not have you hurt yourself with these doubts which you seem to retain. If choice of diet may help, behold us here (your cooks) ready to minister all things needful. If company may drive away your annoy, we mean not to leave you solitary. If grief of mind be cause of your infirmity, we all here will offer our devoir to turn it into joy. If mishap have given you cause to fear or dread anything, remember Hope, which never faileth to recomfort an afflicted mind. And, good Trust," quoth she (distraining his hand right heartily) "let this simple proof of our poor good wills be so accepted of you as that it may work thereby the effect of our desires."

F. J. (as one in a trance) had marked very little of her courteous talk and yet gave her thanks, and so held his peace. Whereat the ladies (being all amazed) there became a silence in the chamber on all sides. Dame Elinor, fearing thereby that she might the more easily be espied, and having now dried up her tears, returned to F. J., recomforting him by all possible means of common courtesy, promising that since in her sickness he had not only stanched her bleeding, but also by his gentle company and sundry devices of honest pastime had driven away the pensiveness of her mind, she thought herself bound with like willingness to do her best in anything that might restore his health. And taking him by the hand, said further, "Good servant, if thou bear indeed any true affection to thy poor mistress, start upon thy feet again and let her enjoy thine accustomed service to her comfort; for sure," quoth she, "I will never leave to visit this chamber once in a day until I may have thee down with me."

F. J., hearing the hearty words of his mistress and perceiving the earnest manner of her pronunciation, began to receive unspeakable comfort in the same and said, "Mistress, your exceeding courtesy were able to revive a man half dead, and to me it is both great comfort, and it doth also gall my remembrance with a continual smart of mine own unworthiness. But as I would desire no longer life than till I might be able to deserve some part of your bounty, so I will endeavor myself to live, were it but only unto that end that I might merit some part of your favor with acceptable service and requite some deal the courtesy of all these other fair ladies, who have so far (above my deserts) deigned to do me good."

Thus said, the ladies tarried not long before they were called to evensong, when his mistress, taking his hand, kissed it, saying, "Farewell, good servant, and I pray thee suffer not the malice of thy sickness to overcome the gentleness of thy good heart."

F. J., ravished with joy, suffered them all to depart and was not able to pronounce one word. After their departure, he gan cast in his mind the exceeding courtesy used towards him by them all, but above all other the bounty of his mistress, and therewithal took a sound and firm opinion that it was not possible for her to counterfeit so deeply (as indeed I believe that she then did not) whereby he suddenly felt his heart greatly eased and began in himself thus to reason: "Was ever man of so wretched a heart? I am the most bounden to love," quoth he, "of all them that ever professed his service. I enjoy one the fairest that ever was found, and I find her the kindest that ever was heard of; yet in mine own wicked heart I could villainously conceive that of her which, being compared with the rest of her virtues, is not possible to harbor in so noble a mind. Hereby I have brought myself without cause into this feebleness, and good reason that for so high an offense I should be punished with great infirmity. What shall I then do? Yield to the same? No, but according to my late protestation I will recomfort this languishing mind of mine to the end I may live but only to do penance for this so notable a crime so rashly committed."

And thus saying, he start from his bed and gan to walk towards the window. But the venomous serpent which (as before I rehearsed) had stung him, could not be content that these medicines, applied by the mouth of his gentle mistress, should so soon restore him to guerison.[68] And although indeed they were such mithridate to F. J. as that they had now expelled the rancor of the poison, yet that ugly hellish monster had left behind her in the most secret of his bosom (even between the mind and the man) one of her familiars named Suspect, which gan work in the weak spirits of F. J. effects of no less peril than before he had received. His head swelling with these troublesome toys and his heart swimming in the tempests of tossing fantasy, he felt his legs so feeble that he was constrained to lie down on his bed again. And repeating in his own remembrance every word that his mistress had spoken unto him, he gan to dread that she had brought the willow branch to beat him with in token that he was of her forsaken, for so lovers do most commonly expound the willow garland. And this to think did cut his heart in twain.

A wonderful change. And here a little to stay you, I will describe (for I think you have not read it in Ariosto) the beginning, the fall, the return, and the being of this hellish bird, who indeed may well be counted a very limb of the Devil. Many years since, one of the

---

[68]*guerison:* health.

most dreadful dastards in the world, and one of them that first devised to wear his beard at length, lest the barber might do him a good turn sooner than he looked for it, and yet not so soon as he deserved, had builded for his security a pile on the highest and most inaccessible mount of all his territories. The which, being fortified with strong walls and environed with deep ditches, had no place of entry but one only door so straight and narrow as might by any possibility receive the body of one living man. From which he ascended up a ladder and so, creeping through a marvelous straight hole, attained to his lodging, the which was so dark and obscure as scarcely either sun or air could enter into it. Thus he devised to lodge in safety, and for the more surety gan trust none other letting down this ladder but only his wife, and at the foot thereof kept always by daylight a fierce mastiff, close enkenneled, which never saw nor heard the face or voice of any other creature but only of them two. Him by night he trusted with the scout of this pretty passage, having nevertheless between him and this dog a double door with treble locks, quadruple bars, and before all a port coulez[69] of iron. Neither yet could he be so hardy as to sleep until he had caused a guard of servants (whom he kept abroad for that purpose) to search all the corners adjoining to his fortress, and then between fearful sweat and shivering cold, with one eye open and the other closed, he stole sometimes a broken sleep divided with many terrible dreams.

In this sort the wretch lived all too long, until at last his wife, being not able any longer to support this hellish life, grew so hardy as with his own knife to dispatch his carcass out of this earthly purgatory. The which being done, his soul (and good reason) was quickly conveyed by Carone[70] unto hell. There Rhadamanthus, judge of that bench, commanded him quickly to be thrust into a boiling pool. And being therein plunged very often, he never shrieked nor cried, "I scald," as his other companions there cried, but seemed so lightly to esteem it that the judge thought meet to condemn him unto the most terrible place, where are such torments as neither pen can write, tongue express, or thought conceive. But the miser (even there) seemed to smile and to make small accompt of his punishment.

Rhadamanthus, hereof informed, sent for him and demanded the cause why he made so light of his durance. He answered that whiles

---

[69]*port coulez:* portcullis (a heavy gate moved up and down by chains).
[70]*Carone:* Charon, the boatman in Greek mythology who ferries dead souls across the river Styx.

he lived on earth, he was so continually afflicted and oppressed with suspicion as that now (only to think that he was out of those meditations) was sufficient armor to defend him from all other torments.

Rhadamanthus, astonied hereat, gan call together the senators of that kingdom and propounded this question: how and by what punishment they might devise to touch him according to his deserts? And hereupon fell great disputation, at last being considered that he had already been plunged in the most unspeakable torments and thereat little or nothing had changed countenance; therewithal that no soul was sent unto them to be relieved of his smart, but rather to be punished for his former delights. It was concluded by the general council that he should be eftsoons sent into the world and restored to the same body wherein he first had his resiance,[71] so to remain for perpetuity and never to depart nor to perish.

Thus this body and soul, being once again united and now eftsoons with the same pestilence infected, he became of a suspicious man, Suspicion itself. And now the wretch, remembering the treason of his wife, who had so willingly dispatched him once before, gan utterly abhor her and fled her company, searching in all countries some place of better assurance. And when he had in vain trod on the most part of the earth, he embarked himself to find some unknown island wherein he might frame some new habitation. And finding none so commodious as he desired, he fortuned (sailing along by the shore) to espy a rock more than six hundred cubits high which hung so suspiciously over the seas, as though it would threaten to fall at every little blast. This did Suspicion imagine to be a fit foundation whereon he might build his second bower. He forsook his boat and traveled by land to espy what entry or access might be made unto the same and found from land no manner of entry or access, unless it were that some courteous bird of the air would be ambassador, or convey some engines, as whilom the eagle did carry Ganymedes into heaven. He then returned to seas and, approaching near to this rock, found a small stream of fresh water issuing out of the same into the seas. The which, although it were so little and so straight as might uneathes[72] receive a boat of bigness to carry one living creature at once, yet in his conceit he thought it more large and spacious than that broad way called of our forefathers Via Appia, or than that other named Flaminia.

[71]*resiance:* abode, residence.
[72]*uneathes:* scarcely.

He abandoned his bark and, putting off his clothes, adventured (for he was now assured not to drown) to wade and swim against the stream of this unknown brook, the which (a wondrous thing to tell and scarcely to be believed) came down from the very top and height of this rock. And by the way he found six straight and dangerous places where the water seemed to stay his course, passing under six straight and low bridges, and hard by every of those places, a pile raised up in manner of a bulwark, the which were hollow, in such sort as lodgings and other places necessary might in them commodiously be devised by such one as could endure the hellishness of the place. Passing by these, he attained with much pain unto the top of the rock, the which he found hollowed as the rest, and far more fit for his security than otherwise apt for any commodity. There gan Suspicion determine to nestle himself, and having now placed six chosen porters—to wit, Dread, Mistrust, Wrath, Desperation, Frenzy, and Fury—at these six strange bulwarks, he lodged himself in that seven all alone, for he trusted no company. But ever mistrusting that his wife should eftsoons find him out, therein he shrieketh continually like to a screech owl to keep the watch waking, never content to sleep by day or by night. But to be sure that he should not oversleep himself, gan stuff his couch with porpentine's[73] quills, to the end that when heavy sleep overcame him, and he thereby should be constrained to charge his pallet with more heavy burden, those plumes might then prick through and so awake him.

His garments were steel upon iron, and that iron upon iron, and iron again; and the more he was armed, the less he trusted to be out of danger. He chopped and changed continually now this, now that— new keys, new locks, ditches new scoured, and walls newly fortified. And thus always uncontented liveth this wretched hellhound, Suspicion, in this hellish dungeon of habitation, from whence he never removeth his foot but only in the dead and silent nights when he may be assured that all creatures (but himself) are whelmed in sound sleep. And then with stealing steps he stalketh about the earth, infecting, tormenting, and vexing all kinds of people with some part of his afflictions, but especially such as either do sit in chair of greatest dignity and estimation, or else such as have achieved some dear and rare emprise. Those above all others he continually galleth with fresh wounds of dread, lest they might lose and forego the rooms whereunto with such long travail and good haps they had attained.

[73]*porpentine's:* porcupine's.

And by this means percase he had crept into the bosom of F. J. who (as is before declared) did erst swim in the deepest seas of earthly delights. Now, then, I must think it high time to return unto him, who, being now through feebleness eftsoons cast down upon his bed, gan cast in his inward meditations all things passed. And as one thoroughly puffed up and filled with one peevish conceit, could think upon nothing else, and yet, accusing his own guilty conscience to be infected with jealousy, did compile this translation of Ariosto's thirty-first song as followeth.

> What state to man, so sweet and pleasant were,
> As to be tied in links of worthy love?
> What life so blest and happy might appear,
> As for to serve Cupid, that god above?
> If that our minds were not sometimes infect
> With dread, with fear, with care, with cold suspect,
> With deep despair, with furious frenzy,
> Handmaids to her, whom we call jealousy.
>
> For ev'ry other sop of sour chance,
> Which lovers taste amid their sweet delight,
> Increaseth joy, and doth their love advance,
> In pleasure's place, to have more perfect plight.
> The thirsty mouth thinks water hath good taste,
> The hungry jaws are pleased with each repast.
> Who hath not prov'd what dearth by wars doth grow,
> Cannot of peace the pleasant plenties know.
>
> And though with eye we see not ev'ry joy,
> Yet may the mind, full well support the same.
> An absent life long led in great annoy,
> When presence comes, doth turn from grief to game.
> To serve without reward is thought great pain,
> But if despair do not therewith remain,
> It may be borne; for right rewards at last
> Follow true service, though they come not fast.
>
> Disdains, repulses, finally each ill,
> Each smart, each pain, of love each bitter taste,
> To think on them gan frame the lover's will,
> To like each joy, the more that comes at last.
> But this infernal plague if once it touch,
> Or venom once the lover's mind with grutch,[74]
> All feasts and joys that afterwards befall,
> The lover compts them light or nought at all.

[74]*grutch:* complaint, murmuring.

This is that sore, this is that poisoned wound,
The which to heal, nor salve, nor ointments serve,
Nor charm of words, nor image can be found,
Nor observance of stars can it preserve.
Nor all the art of magic can prevail,
Which Zoroastes[75] found for our avail.
Oh, cruel plague, above all sorrow's smart,
With desperate death thou slay'st the lover's heart.

And me even now, thy gall hath so infect,
As all the joys which ever lover found,
And all good haps, that ever Troilus' sect.[76]
Achieved yet above the luckless ground.
Can never sweeten once my mouth with mel,
Nor bring my thoughts again in rest to dwell.
Of thy mad moods, and of naught else I think,
In such like seas, fair Bradamant did sink.

F. J.

This is the translation of Ariosto, his thirty-first song,[77] all but the last staff, which seemeth as an allegory applied to the rest. It will please none but learned ears; he was tied to the invention, troubled in mind, etc. So I leave it to your judgment and return to F. J., who continued on his bed until his bountiful mistress with the company of the other courteous dames returned after supper to his chamber.

At their first entry, "Why, how now, servant," quoth Dame Elinor, "we hoped to have found you on foot."

"Mistress," quoth F. J., "I have assayed my feet since your departure, but I find them yet unable to support my heavy body, and therefore am constrained, as you see, to acquaint myself with these pillows."

"Servant," said she, "I am right sorry thereof, but since it is of necessity to bear sickness, I will employ my devoir to allay some part

---

[75]*Zoroastes:* Zoroaster (fl. 1000 B.C.) was founder of the ancient Persian religion in which the priests had occult powers; hence the reference to stars and magic.

[76]*Troilus' sect:* that all-too-large group of disappointed and jealous lovers; a reference to the story of Troilus and Criseyde, told by Boccaccio, Chaucer, and Robert Henryson (but not yet by Shakespeare).

[77]*translation of Ariosto, his thirty-first song:* F. J.'s first five stanzas are a free translation of the first five stanzas of Canto 31 in *Orlando Furioso.* F. J.'s sixth and last stanza is not from Ariosto; in it F. J. applies, in his own words, Ariosto's story (as well as the story of Troilus and Criseyde) to F. J.'s jealousy of Elinor. Incidentally, Ariosto's stanzas are *ottava rima* (abababcc); F. J. gives himself an extra rhyme (ababccdd).

of your pains, and to refresh your weary limbs with some comfortable matter." And therewithal, calling her handmaid, delivered unto her a bunch of pretty little keys and, whispering in her ear, dispatched her towards her chamber.

The maid tarried not long, but returned with a little casket, the which her mistress took, opened, and drew out of the same much fine linen, amongst the which she took a pillowbere[78] very fine and sweet, which, although it were of itself as sweet as might be, being of long time kept in that odoriferous chest, yet did she with damask water[79] (and that the best that might be, I warrant you) all to sprinkle it with her own hands, which in my conceit might much amend the matter. Then, calling for a fresh pillow, sent her maid to air the same and, at her return, put on this thus perfumed pillowbere.

In mean time also she had with her own hands attired her servant's head in a fair wrought kerchief taken out of the same casket, then laid him down upon this fresh and pleasant place, and prettily, as it were in sport, bedewed his temples with sweet water which she had ready in a casting bottle of gold, kissing his cheek and saying, "Good servant, be whole, for I might not long endure thus to attend thee, and yet the love that I bear towards thee cannot be content to see thee languish."

"Mistress," said F. J. (and that with a trembling voice) "assure yourself that if there remain in me any spark of life or possibility of recovery, then may this excellent bounty of yours be sufficient to revive me without any further travail or pain unto your person, for whom I am highly to blame in that I do not spare to put you unto this trouble. And better it were that such a wretch as I had died unknown than that by your exceeding courtesy you should fall into any malady, either by resorting unto me, or by these your pains taken about me."

"Servant," quoth she, "all pleasures seem painful to them that take no delight therein, and likewise all toil seemeth pleasant to such as set their felicity in the same. But for me be you sure I do it with so good a will that I can take no hurt thereby unless I shall perceive that it be rejected or neglected as unprofitable or uncomfortable unto you."

"To me, mistress," quoth F. J., "it is such pleasure as neither my feeble tongue can express nor my troubled mind conceive."

[78]*pillowbere:* pillowcase.
[79]*damask water:* rose water, which is distilled from damask roses (originally from Damascus).

"Why? Are you troubled in mind, then, servant?" quoth Dame Elinor.

F. J., now blushing, answered, "But even as all sick men be, mistress."

Herewith they stayed their talk a while, and the first that broke silence was the Lady Frances, who said, "And to drive away the troubles of your mind, good Trust, I would be glad if we could devise some pastime amongst us to keep you company, for I remember that with such devices you did greatly recomfort this fair lady when she languished in like sort."

"She languished indeed, gentle Hope," quoth F. J., "but God forbid that she had languished in like sort."

"Everybody thinketh their grief greatest," quoth Dame Elinor, "but indeed whether my grief were the more or the less, I am right sorry that yours is such as it is. And to assay whether our passions proceeded of like cause or not, I would we could (according to this lady's saying) devise some like pastimes to try if your malady would be cured with like medicines."

A gentlewoman of the company, whom I have not hitherto named —and that for good respects, lest her name might altogether disclose the rest—gan thus propound: "We have accustomed," quoth she, "heretofore in most of our games to choose a king or queen, and he or she during their government have charged every of us either with commandments or questions, as best seemed to their majesty. Wherein, to speak mine opinion, we have given overlarge a scope. Neither seemeth it reasonable that one should have the power to discover the thoughts or at least to bridle the affects of all the rest. And though indeed in questioning (which doth of the twain more nearly touch the mind?) everyone is at free liberty to answer what they list, yet oft have I heard a question demanded in such sort, and upon such sudden, that it hath been hardly answered without moving matter of contention. And in commands also sometimes it happeneth one to be commanded unto such service as either they are unfit to accomplish (and then the party's weakness is thereby detected) or else to do something that they would not, whereof ensueth more grutch than game. Wherefore in mine opinion, we shall do well to choose by lot amongst us a governor who, for that it shall be sufficient pre-eminence to use the chair of majesty, shall be bound to give sentence upon all such arguments and questions as we shall orderly propound unto them. And from him or her (as from an oracle) we will receive answer and deciding of our litigious causes."

This dame had stuff in her, an old courtier, and a wily wench whom for this discourse I will name Pergo, lest her name natural were too broad before[80] and might not drink of all waters. Well, this proportion of Pergo pleased them well and by lot it happened that F. J. must be moderator of these matters and collector of these causes.

The which being so constituted, the Lady Elinor said unto this Dame Pergo, "You have devised this pastime," quoth she, "and because we think you to be most expert in the handling thereof, do you propound the first question, and we shall be the more ready and able to follow your example."

The Lady Pergo refused not, but began on this wise: "Noble governor," quoth she, "amongst the adventures that have befallen me, I remember especially this one, that in youth it was my chance to be beloved of a very courtlike young gentleman who abode near the place wherein my parents had their resiance. This gentleman, whether it were for beauty or for any other respect that he saw in me I know not, but he was enamored of me, and that with an exceeding vehement passion. And of such force were his affects that notwithstanding many repulses which he had received at my hands, he seemed daily to grow in the renewing of his desires. I, on the other side, although I could by no means mislike of him by any good reason—considering that he was of birth no way inferior unto me, of possessions not to be disdained, of person right comely, of behavior courtly, of manners modest, of mind liberal, and of virtuous disposition—yet such was the gaiety of my mind as that I could not be content to lend him over-large thongs of my love, but always dangerously[81] behaved myself towards him and in such sort as he could neither take comfort of mine answers nor yet once find himself requited with one good look for all his travail. This notwithstanding, the worthy knight continued his suit with no less vehement affection than erst he had begun it, even by the space of seven years. At the last, whether discomfited by my dealings or tired by long travail, or that he had percase light upon the lake that is in the Forest of Ardena,[82] and so, in haste and all thirsty, had drunk some drops of

[80]*lest her name natural were too broad before:* lest Dame Pergo's real name be too well known.

[81]*dangerously:* coyly.

[82]*the Forest of Ardena:* In *Orlando Furioso,* I, 78, there are two fountains in the Forest of Ardennes (in modern France and Belgium); Rinaldo drinks from the Fountain of Love and immediately feels the power of love, but Angelica drinks from the Fountain of Hate. G. T. suggests that F. J. may have drunk from the latter fountain.

disdain. Whereby his hot flames were quenched, or that he had undertaken to serve no longer but his just term of apprenticehood, or that the teeth of time had gnawn and tired his dulled spirits in such sort as that, all benumbed, he was constrained to use some other artificial balm[83] for the quickening of his senses, or by what cause moved I know not. He did not only leave his long continued suit, but (as I have since perceived) grew to hate me more deadly than before I had disdained him.

"At the first beginning of his retire I perceived not his hatred but imagined that, being over wearied, he had withdrawn himself for a time. And considering his worthiness, therewithal his constancy of long time proved, I thought that I could not in the whole world find out a fitter match to bestow myself than on so worthy a person. Wherefore I did by all possible means procure that he might eftsoons use his accustomed repair unto my parents. And, further, in all places where I happened to meet him, I used all the courtesies towards him that might be contained within the bounds of modesty. But all was in vain, for he was now become more dangerous[84] to be won than the haggard falcon.[85] Our lots being thus unluckily changed, I grew to burn in desire; and the more dangerous that he showed himself unto me, the more earnest I was by all means to procure his consent of love. At the last, I might perceive that not only he disdained me but, as methought, boiled in hatred against me. And the time that I thus continued tormented with these thoughts was also just the space of seven years.

"Finally, when I perceived no remedy for my perplexities, I assayed by absence to wear away this malady, and therefore utterly refused to come in his presence, yea, or almost in any other company. Whereby I have consumed in lost time the flower of my youth and am become as you see (what with years and what with the tormenting passions of love) pale, wan, and full of wrinkles. Nevertheless, I have thereby gained thus much, that at last I have wond[86] myself clear out of Cupid's chains, and remain careless at liberty.

---

[83]*artificial balm:* balm skilfully made.

[84]*dangerous:* difficult to deal with.

[85]*haggard falcon:* a falcon captured after reaching maturity and therefore difficult to train; it has remained wild too long.

[86]*wond:* Apparently the modern word is "wound" (past tense of "to wind"); but the sense is really "*un*wound."

"Now mark to what end I tell you this. First, seven years passed in the which I could never be content to yield unto his just desires; next, other seven years I spent in seeking to recover his lost love; and sithens both those seven years, there are even now on St. Valentine's day last, other seven years passed in the which neither I have desired to see him nor he hath coveted to hear of me. My parents now perceiving how the crow's foot is crept under mine eye, and remembering the long suit that this gentleman had in youth spent on me, considering therewithal that green youth is well mellowed in us both, have of late sought to persuade a marriage between us. The which the knight hath not refused to hear of, and I have not disdained to think on. By their mediation we have been eftsoons brought to parley. Wherein over and besides the ripping up of many old griefs, this hath been chiefly rehearsed and objected between us: what wrong and injury each of us hath done to other, and hereabouts we have fallen to sharp contention. He alleged that much greater is the wrong which I have done unto him than that repulse which he hath sithens used to me. And I have affirmed the contrary; the matter yet hangeth in variance. Now, of you, worthy governor, I would be most glad to hear this question decided, remembering that there was no difference in the times between us. And surely, unless your judgment help me, I am afraid my marriage will be marred, and I may go lead apes in hell."[87]

F. J. answered, "Good Pergo, I am sorry to hear so lamentable a discourse of your luckless love, and much the sorrier in that I must needs give sentence against you. For surely great was the wrong that either of you have done to other, and greater was the needless grief which causeless each of you hath conceived in this long time. But greatest, in my judgment, hath been both the wrong and the grief of the knight, in that notwithstanding his deserts (which yourself confess) he never enjoyed any guerdon of love at your hands. And you (as you allege) did enjoy his love of long time together, so that by the reckoning it will fall out (although being blinded in your own conceit, you see it not) that of the one and twenty years, you enjoyed his love seven at the least, but that ever he enjoyed yours we cannot perceive. And much greater is the wrong that rewardeth evil for good

---

[87]*lead apes in hell:* a proverb (Tilley, M37), according to which an old maid who never had children in life is condemned to leading apes in hell.

than that which requireth tip for tap. Further, it seemed that whereas you went about in time to try him, you did altogether lose time which can never be recovered—and not only lost your own time, whereof you would seem now to lament, but also compelled him to lose his time which he might (be it spoken without offense to you) have bestowed in some other worthy place. And therefore, as that grief is much greater which hath no kind of comfort to allay it, so much more is that wrong which altogether without cause is offered."

"And I," said Pergo, "must needs think that much easier is it for them to endure grief which never tasted of joy, and much less is that wrong which is so willingly proffered to be by recompense restored. For if this knight will confess that he never had cause to rejoice in all the time of his service, then with better contentation might he abide grief than I, who having tasted of the delight which I did secretly conceive of his deserts, do think each grief a present death by the remembrance of those forepassed thoughts. And less wrong seemeth it to be destitute of the thing which was never obtained than to be deprived of a jewel whereof we have been already possessed, so that under your correction I might conclude that greater hath been my grief and injury sustained than that of the knight."

To whom F. J. replied, "As touching delight, it may not be denied but that every lover doth take delight in the inward contemplation of his mind to think of the worthiness of his beloved, and therefore you may not allege that the knight had never cause to rejoice unless you will altogether condemn yourself of unworthiness. Marry, if you will say that he tasted not the delights that lovers seek, then mark who was the cause but yourself? And if you would accuse him of like ingratitude for that he disdained you in the latter seven years, whenas he might, by accepting your love, have recompensed himself of all former wrongs, you must remember therewithal that the cruelty by you showed towards him was such that he could by no means perceive that your change proceeded of good will, but rather eftsoons to hold him enchained in unknown links of subtle dealings, and therefore not without cause he doubted you, and yet without cause you rejected him. He had often sought occasion, but by your refusals he could never find him. You having occasion fast by the foretop did dally with him so long till at last he slipped his head from you and then catching at the bald noddle, you found yourself the cause, and yet you would accuse another. To conclude, greater is the grief that is sustained without desert, and much more is the wrong that is offered without cause."

Thus F. J. decided the question propounded by Pergo and expected that some other dame should propound another, but his mistress (having her hand on another halfpenny)[88] gan thus say unto him: "Servant, this pastime is good and such as I must needs like of to drive away your pensive thoughts. But sleeping time approacheth, and I fear we disquiet you. Wherefore the rest of this time we will (if so like you) bestow in trimming up your bed, and tomorrow we shall meet here and renew this new begun game with Madame Pergo."

"Mistress," quoth F. J., "I must obey your will and most humbly thank you of your great goodness, and all these ladies for their courtesy. Even so, requiring you that you will no further trouble yourselves about me, but let my servant alone with conducting me to bed."

"Yes, servant," quoth she, "I will see if you can sleep any better in my sheets." And therewith commanded her handmaid to fetch a pair of clean sheets. The which being brought (marvelous fine and sweet) the Ladies Frances and Elinor did courteously unfold them and laid them on the bed. Which done, they also entreated F. J. to unclothe him and go to bed.

Being laid, his mistress dressed and couched the clothes about him, sithens moistened his temples with rose water, gave him handkerchiefs and other fresh linen about him. In doing whereof, she whispered in his ear, saying, "Servant, this night I will be with thee." And after with the rest of the dames gave him good night and departed, leaving F. J. in a trance between hope and despair, trust and mistrust.

Thus he lay ravished, commanding his servant to go to bed and saying that himself would assay if he could sleep. About ten or eleven of the clock came his mistress in her nightgown, who, knowing all privy ways in that house very perfectly, had conveyed herself into F. J.'s chamber unseen and unperceived. And being now come unto his bedside kneeled down and, laying her arm over him, said these or like words: "My good servant, if thou knewest what perplexities I suffer in beholding of thine infirmities, it might then suffice either utterly to drive away thy malady or much more to augment thy griefs, for I know thou lovest me and I think also that

---

[88]*having her hand on another halfpenny:* based on two similar proverbs (Tilley, H80 and H315); as Tilley explains, the sense is "to have a selfish object in view" (though perhaps "having other fish to fry" or "having some different purpose of her own" is a little closer to the exact sense).

thou hast had sufficient proof of mine unfeigned good will, in remembrance whereof I fall into sundry passions. First, I compt the happy lots of our first acquaintance, and therein I call to mind the equality of our affections, for I think that there were never two lovers conjoined with freer consent on both parties. And if my over-hasty delivery of yielding words be not wrested hereafter to my condemnation, I can then assure myself to escape forever without desert of any reproof. Herewithal I cannot forget the sundry adventures happened since we became one heart divided in two bodies, all which have been both happily achieved and delectably enjoyed. What resteth then to consider but this, thy present state? The first corrosive that I have felt and the last cordial that I look for, the end of my joys, and the beginning of my torments."

And hereat her salt tears gan bathe the dying lips of her servant, who, hearing these words and well considering her demeanor, began now to accuse himself of such and so heinous treason as that his guilty heart was constrained to yield unto a just scourge for the same. He swooned under her arm, the which when she perceived, it were hard to tell what fears did most affright her.

But I have heard my friend F. J. confess that he was in a happy trance and thought himself for divers causes unhappily revived. For surely I have heard him affirm that to die in such a passion had been rather pleasant than like to pangs of death. It were hard now to rehearse how he was revived, since there were none present but he, dying, who could not declare, and she, living, who would not disclose so much as I mean to bewray. For my friend F. J. hath to me imported that, returning to life, the first thing which he felt was that his good mistress lay pressing his breast with the whole weight of her body and biting his lips with her friendly teeth. And peradventure she refrained (either of courtesy towards him or for womanish fear to hurt her tender hand) to strike him on the cheeks in such sort as they do that strive to call again a dying creature, and therefore thought this the aptest mean to reduce him unto remembrance.

F. J., now awaked, could no less do than of his courteous nature receive his mistress into his bed. Who, as one that knew that way better than how to help his swooning, gan gently strip off her clothes and, lovingly embracing him, gan demand of him in this sort: "Alas, good servant," quoth she, "what kind of malady is this that so extremely doth torment thee?"

F. J. with fainting speech answered, "Mistress, as for my malady, it hath been easily cured by your bountiful medicines applied. But I must confess that in receiving that guerison at your hands, I have been constrained to fall into an ecstasy through the galling remembrance of mine own unworthiness. Nevertheless, good mistress, since I perceive such fidelity remaining between us as that few words will persuade such trust as lovers ought to embrace, let these few words suffice to crave your pardon and do eftsoons power upon me (your unworthy servant) the abundant waves of your accustomed clemency. For I must confess that I have so highly offended you as (but your goodness surpass the malice of my conceits) I must remain (and that right worthily) to the severe punishment of my deserts, and so should you but lose him who hath cast away himself and neither can accuse you nor dare excuse himself of the crime."

Dame Elinor, who had rather have found her servant perfectly revived than thus with strange conceits encumbered and, musing much at his dark speech, became importunate to know the certainty of his thoughts. And F. J., as one not master of himself, gan at the last plainly confess how he had mistrusted the change of her vowed affections. Yea, and (that more was) he plainly expressed with whom, of whom, by whom, and to whom she bent her better liking.

Now, here I would demand of you and such other as are expert: is there any greater impediment to the fruition of a lover's delights than to be mistrusted? Or, rather, is it not the ready way to rase[89] all love and former good will out of remembrance, to tell a guilty mind that you do mistrust it? It should seem yes, by Dame Elinor, who began now to take the matter hotly. And of such vehemency were her fancies that she now fell into flat defiance with F. J., who although he sought by many fair words to temper her choleric passions, and by yielding himself to get the conquest of another, yet could he by no means determine the quarrel.

The soft pillows, being present at all these hot words, put forth themselves as mediators for a truce between these enemies and desired that (if they would needs fight) it might be in their presence but only one push of the pike, and so from thenceforth to become friends again forever. But the dame denied flatly, alleging that she found no cause at all to use such courtesy unto such a recreant, adding further many words of great reproach, the which did so enrage[90] F. J. as that, having now forgotten all former courtesies, he

[89]*rase:* erase.
[90]*enrage:* The *errata* sheet changes "encourage" to "enrage."

drew upon his new professed enemy, and bare her up with such a violence against the bolster, that before she could prepare the ward, he thrust her through both hands, and etc.

Whereby the dame, swooning for fear, was constrained (for a time) to abandon her body to the enemy's courtesy. At last when she came to herself, she rose suddenly and determined to save herself by flight, leaving F. J. with many despiteful words and swearing that he should never (eftsoons) take her at the like advantage, the which oath she kept better than her former professed good will. And having now recovered her chamber (because she found her hurt to be nothing dangerous) I doubt not but she slept quietly the rest of the night, as F. J., also persuading himself that he should with convenient leisure recover her from this hagger conceit,[91] took some better rest towards the morning than he had done in many nights forepast.

So let them both sleep whiles I turn my pen unto the before-named secretary, who, being (as I said) come lately from London, had made many proffers to renew his accustomed consultations. But the sorrow which his mistress had conceived in F. J. his sickness, together with her continual repair to him during the same, had been such lets unto his attempts as it was long time before he could obtain audience. At the last these new accidents fell so favorably for the furtherance of his cause that he came to his mistress' presence and there pleaded for himself. Now, if I should at large write his allegations, together with her subtle answers, I should but cumber your ears with unpleasant rehearsal of feminine frailty. To be short, the late disdainful mood which she had conceived against F. J., together with a scruple which lay in her conscience touching the eleventh article of her belief,[92] moved her presently with better will to consult with this secretary, as well upon a speedy revenge of her late-received wrongs as also upon the reformation of her religion. And in very deed, it fell out that the secretary, having been of long time absent and thereby his quills and pens not worn so near as they were wont to be, did now prick such fair large notes that his mistress

[91]*hagger conceit:* haggard or wild, unruly thought.
[92]*eleventh article of her belief:* a reference to the *Thirty-Nine Articles,* a body of doctrinal statements issued by the Church of England in 1563. The eleventh article had to do with justification of man only by faith in Christ, not by "works or deservings." Elinor's "belief" and "religion" are made all the more physical and worldly by G. T.'s humorous analogy.

liked better to sing faburden[93] under him than to descant any longer upon F. J.'s plain song.

And thus they continued in good accord until it fortuned that Dame Frances came into her chamber upon such sudden as she had like to have marred all the music. Well, they covered their clefs as closely as they could, but yet not altogether without some suspicion given to the said Dame Frances, who, although she could have been content to take any pain in F. J.'s behalf, yet otherwise she would never have bestowed the watching about so worthless a prize.

After womanly salutations they fell into sundry discourses, the secretary still abiding in the chamber with them. At last two or three other gentlewomen of the castle came into Madame Elinor's chamber, who, after their "*bon jour*," did all (*una voce*) seem to lament the sickness of F. J. and called upon the Dames Elinor and Frances to go visit him again. The Lady Frances courteously consented, but Madame Elinor first alleged that she herself was also sickly, the which she attributed to her late pains taken about F. J., and said that only for that cause she was constrained to keep her bed longer than her accustomed hour.

The dames (but especially the Lady Frances) gan straightways conjecture some great cause of sudden change and so, leaving Dame Elinor, walked altogether into the park to take the air of the morning. And as they thus walked, it chanced that Dame Pergo heard a cuckoo chant, who (because the pride of the spring was now past) cried, "Cuck, cuck, cuckoo," in her stammering voice.

"Aha," quoth Pergo, "this foul bird begins to fly the country, and yet before her departure, see how spitefully she can devise to salute us."

"Not us," quoth Dame Frances, "but some other whom she hath espied."

Wherewith Dame Pergo, looking round about her and espying none other company, said, "Why here is nobody but we few women," quoth she.

"Thanks be to God, the house is not far from us," quoth Dame Frances.

Hereat the wily Pergo, partly perceiving Dame Frances' meaning, replied on this sort: "I understand you not," quoth she, "but to leap out of this matter, shall we go visit Master F. J. and see how he doth this morning?"

[93]*faburden:* literally, an undersong; but we are to catch the sexual implication. In the 1573 edition "pens" is spelled "pennes."

"Why?" quoth Dame Frances. "Do you suppose that the cuckoo called unto him?"

"Nay, marry," quoth Pergo, "for (as far as I know) he is not married."

"As who should say," quoth Dame Frances, "that the cuckoo envieth none but married folks?"

"I take it so," said Pergo.

The Lady Frances answered, "Yes, sure I have noted as evil luck in love (after the cuckoo's call) to have happened unto divers unmarried folks as ever I did unto the married, but I can be well content that we go unto Master J., for I promised on the behalf of us all that we would use our best devoir to recomfort him until he had recovered health. And I do much marvel that the Lady Elinor is now become so unwilling to take any travail in his behalf, especially remembering that but yesternight she was so diligent to bring him to bed. But I perceive that all earthly things are subject unto change."

"Even so they be," quoth Pergo, "for you may behold the trees which but even this other day were clad in gladsome green, and now their leaves begin to fade and change color."

Thus they passed, talking and walking, until they returned unto the castle, whereas they went straight unto F. J.'s chamber and found him in bed.

"Why, how now, Trust," quoth Dame Frances, "will it be no better?"

"Yes, shortly, I hope," quoth F. J.

The ladies all saluted him, and he gave them the gramercy. At the last, Pergo popped this question unto him: "And how have you slept in your mistress' sheets, Master F. J.?" quoth she.

"Reasonable well," quoth F. J. "but, I pray you, where is my mistress this morning?"

"Marry," said Pergo, "we left her in bed scarce well at ease."

"I am the more sorry," quoth F. J.

"Why, Trust," said Mistress Frances, "be of good comfort and assure yourself that here are others who would be as glad of your well doing as your mistress in any respect."

"I ought not to doubt thereof," quoth F. J., "having the proof that I have had of your great courtesies. But I thought it my duty to ask for my mistress, being absent."

Thus they passed some time with him until they were called away unto prayers. And that being finished, they went to dinner, where they met Dame Elinor, attired in a night kerchief after the soolenest[94] (the *solemnest* fashion, I should have said) who looked very drowsily upon all folks—unless it were her secretary, unto whom she deigned sometime to send a friendly glance. The lord of the castle demanded of her how F. J. did this morning. She answered that she knew not, for she had not seen him that day.

"You may do well, then, daughter," quoth the lord, "to go now unto him and to assay if he will eat anything. And if there be no meats that like him,[95] I pray you command (for him) anything that is in my house."

"You must pardon me, sir," quoth she, "I am sickly disposed and would be loath to take the air."

"Why, then, go you, Mistress Frances," quoth he, "and take somebody with you. And, I charge you, see that he lack nothing."

Mistress Frances was glad of the *ambassade* and, arising from the table with one other gentlewoman, took with her a dish of chickens boiled in white broth, saying to her father, "I think this meat meetest for Master F. J. of any that is here."

"It is so," quoth he, "daughter; and if he like not that, cause somewhat else to be dressed for him according to his appetite."

Thus she departed and came to F. J., who, being plunged in sundry woes and thrilled with restless thoughts, was now beginning to arise. But seeing the dames, couched down again and said unto them, "Alas, fair ladies, you put yourselves to more pains than either I do desire or can deserve."

"Good Trust," quoth Dame Frances, "our pains are no greater than duty requireth, nor yet so great as we could vouchsafe in your behalf. And presently my father hath sent us unto you," quoth she, "with this pittance, and if your appetite desire any one thing more than other, we are to desire likewise that you will not refrain to call for it."

"Oh, my good Hope," quoth he, "I perceive that I shall not die as long as you may make me live."

And being now somedeal recomforted with the remembrance of his mistress' words, which she had used overnight at her first coming—and also thinking that although she parted in choler, it was but justly provoked by himself, and that at leisure he should find some salve for that sore also—he determined to take the comfort of his assured Hope and so to expel all venomness of mistrust before received. Wherefore raising himself in his bed, he cast a nightgown about his shoulders, saying, "It shall never be said that my fainting

[94]*soolenest:* probably "sullenest."   [95]*that like him:* that he likes.

heart can reject the comfortable cordials of so friendly physicians."

"Now, by my troth, well said, gentle Trust," quoth Dame Frances, "and in so doing assure yourself of guerison with speed."

This thus said, the courteous dame became his carver, and he with a bold spirit gan taste of her cookery. But the late conflicts of his conceits had so disacquainted his stomach from repasts that he could not well away with meat, and yet nevertheless by little and little received some nurture. When his Hope had crammed him as long as she could make him feed, they delivered the rest to the other gentlewoman, who, having not dined, fell to her provender. In which meanwhile the Lady Frances had much comfortable speech with F. J. and declared that she perceived very well the cause of his malady.

"But, my Trust," quoth she, "be all whole, and remember what I foretold you in the beginning. Nevertheless, you must think that there are remedies for all mischiefs. And if you will be ruled by mine advice, we will soon find the mean to ease you of this mishap."

F. J. took comfort in her discretion and, friendly kissing her hand, gave her a cartload of thanks for her great good will, promising to put to his uttermost force and evermore to be ruled by her advice. Thus they passed the dinner while, the Lady Frances always refusing to declare her conceit of the late change which she perceived in his mistress, for she thought best first to win his will unto conformity by little and little and then in the end to persuade him with necessity. When the other gentlewoman had vittled her, they departed, requiring F. J. to arise and boldly to resist the faintness of his fever, the which he promised and so bade them *a Dio*.

The ladies at their return found the court in Dame Elinor's chamber, who had there assembled her secretary, Dame Pergo, and the rest. There they passed an hour or twain in sundry discourses wherein Dame Pergo did always cast out some bone for Mistress Frances to gnaw upon, for that indeed she perceived her hearty affection towards F. J. Whereat Mistress Frances changed no countenance, but reserved her revenge until a better opportunity.

At last quoth Dame Frances unto Mistress Elinor: "And when will you go unto your servant, fair lady?"

"When he is sick and I am whole," quoth Dame Elinor.

"That is even now," quoth the other, "for how sick he is yourself can witness, and how well you are we must bear record."

"You may as well be deceived in my disposition," quoth Dame Elinor, "as I was overseen[96] in his sudden alteration. And if he be

[96]*overseen:* deceived.

sick, you are meetest to be his physician, and you saw yesterday that my pains did little profit towards his recomfort."

"Yes, surely," said the other, "not only I but all the rest had occasion to judge that your courtesy was his chief comfort."

"Well," quoth Dame Elinor, "you know not what I know."

"Nor you what I think," quoth Dame Frances.

"Think what you list," quoth Elinor.

"Indeed," quoth Frances, "I may not think that you care; neither will I die for your displeasure."[97] And so, half angry, she departed.

At supper they met again, and the master of the house demanded of his daughter Frances how F. J. did.

"Sir," quoth she, "he did eat somewhat at dinner, and sithens I saw him not."

"The more to blame," quoth he, "and now I would have all you gentlewomen take of the best meats and go sup with him, for company driveth away carefulness, and leave you me here with your leavings alone."

"Nay, sir," quoth Mistress Elinor, "I pray you give me leave to bear you company, for I dare not adventure thither."

The lord of the castle was contented and dispatched away the rest, who, taking with them such viands as they thought meetest, went unto F. J.'s chamber, finding him up and walking about to recover strength. Whereat Dame Frances rejoiced and declared how her father had sent that company to attend him at supper. F. J. gave great thanks and, missing now nothing but his mistress, thought not good yet to ask for her. But because he partly guessed the cause of her absence, he contented himself, hoping that when his lure was new garnished, he should easily reclaim her from those coy conceits.

They passed over their supper all in quiet and, soon after, Mistress Frances, being desirous to requite Dame Pergo's quips, requested that they might continue the pastime which Dame Pergo had begun over night. Whereunto they all consented and the lot fell unto Dame Frances to propound the second question, who, addressing her speech unto F. J., said in this wise:

"Noble governor, I will rehearse unto you a strange history, not feigned, neither borrowed out of any old authority, but a thing done indeed of late days and not far distant from this place where we now remain. It chanced that a gentleman, our neighbor, being married to a very fair gentlewoman, lived with her by the space of four or

<hr />

[97]*displeasure:* The *errata* sheet changes "pleasure" to "displeasure."

five years in great contentation, trusting her no less than he loved her, and yet loving her as much as any man could love a woman. On that other side the gentlewoman had won (unto her beauty) a singular commendation for her chaste and modest behavior. Yet it happened in time that a lusty young gentleman (who very often resorted to them) obtained that at her hands which never any man could before him attain. And, to be plain, he won so much in her affections that, forgetting both her own duty and her husband's kindness, she yielded her body at the commandment of this lover, in which pastime they passed long time by their politic government.

"At last the friends of this lady (and especially three sisters which she had) espied overmuch familiarity between the two lovers and, dreading lest it might break out to their common reproach, took their sister apart and declared that the world did judge scarce well of the repair of that gentleman unto her house, and that if she did not foresee it in time, she should not only lose the good credit which she herself had hitherto possessed, but furthermore should distain their whole race with common obloquy and reproach. These and sundry other godly admonitions of these sisters could not sink in the mind of this gentlewoman, for she did not only stand in defiance what any man could think of her, but also seemed to accuse them, that because they saw her estimation (being their younger) to grow above their own, they had therefore devised this means to set variance between her husband and her.

"The sisters, seeing their wholesome counsel so rejected, and her continue still in her obstinate opinion, addressed their speech unto her husband, declaring that the world judged not the best, neither they themselves did very well like of the familiarity between their sister and that gentleman, and therefore advised him to forecast all perils and in time to forbid him his house. The husband (on that other side) had also conceived such a good opinion of his guest and had grown into such a strict familiarity with him that you might with more ease have removed a stone wall than once to make him think amiss, either of his wife or of her lover. Yea, and immediately after this conference, he would not stick thus to say unto his wife: 'Bess,' (for so indeed was her name), 'thou hast three such busy-brained sisters as I think shortly their heads will break. They would have me to be jealous of thee. No, no, Bess,' etc. So that he was not only far from any such belief, but furthermore did every day increase his courtesies towards the lover. The sisters, being thus on all sides rejected, and yet perceiving more and more an unseemly behavior between their sister and her minion, began to melt in their own grease. And such was their enraged pretense of revenge that they suborned divers servants in the house to watch so diligently as that this treason might be discovered.

"Amongst the rest, one maid of subtle spirit had so long watched them that at last she espied them go into a chamber together and lock the door to them. Whereupon she ran with all haste possible to her master and told him that if he would come with her, she would show him a very strange sight. The gentleman (suspecting nothing) went with her until he came into a chamber near unto that wherein they had shut themselves, and she, pointing her master to the keyhole, bade him look through, where he saw the thing which most might mislike him to behold. Whereat he suddenly drew his dagger and turned towards the maid, who fled from him for fear of mischief. But when he could not overtake her in the heat of his choler, he commanded that she should forthwith truss up that little which she had and to depart his service. And before her departure he found means to talk with her, threatening that if ever she spake any word of this mystery in any place where she should come, it should cost her life. The maid for fear departed in silence, and the master never changed countenance either to his wife or to her paramour, but feigned unto his wife that he had turned away the maid upon that sudden for that she had thrown a kitchen knife at him whiles he went about to correct a fault in her, etc.

"Thus the good gentleman drank up his own sweat unseen every day, increasing courtesy to the lover and never changing countenance to his wife in anything, but only that he refrained to have such knowledge of her carnally as he in times past had, and other men have of their wives. In this sort he continued by the space almost of half a year, nevertheless lamenting his mishap in solitary places. At last (what moved him I know not) he fell again to company with his wife as other men do, and, as I have heard it said, he used this policy: every time that he had knowledge of her, he would leave either in the bed or in her cushion-cloth, or by her looking glass, or in some place where she must needs find it, a piece of money which then was fallen to three halfpence. And I remember they called them 'slips.'[98] Thus he dealt with her continually by the space of four or five months, using her, nevertheless, very kindly in all other respects, and providing for her all things necessary at the first call. But unto

[98]*slips:* practically worthless coins (fitting payment and punishment for the "slips" of which the wife has been guilty with her lover).

his guest he still augmented his courtesy in such sort that you would have thought them to be sworn brothers.

"All this notwithstanding, his wife, much musing at these three halfpenny pieces which she found in this sort—and, furthermore, having sundry times found her husband in solitary places making great lamentation—she grew inquisitive what should be the secret cause of these alterations. Unto whom he would none otherwise answer but that any man should find occasion to be more pensive at one time than at another. The wife notwithstanding, increasing her suspect, imparted the same unto her lover, alleging therewithal that she doubted very much lest her husband had some vehement suspicion of their affairs. The lover encouraged her and likewise declared that if she would be importunate to inquire the cause, her husband would not be able to keep it from her; and having now thoroughly instructed her, she dealt with her husband in this sort:

"One day when she knew him to be in his study alone, she came in to him and, having fast locked the door after her and conveyed the key into her pocket, she began first with earnest entreaty and then with tears to crave that he would no longer keep from her the cause of his sudden alteration. The husband dissimuled[99] the matter still. At last she was so earnest to know for what cause he left money in such sort at sundry times that he answered on this wise:

"'Wife,' quoth he, 'thou knowest how long we have been married together and how long I made so dear accompt of thee as ever man made of his wife. Since which days thou knowest also how long I refrained thy company and how long again I have used thy company, leaving the money in this sort. And the cause is this: so long as thou didst behave thyself faithfully towards me, I never loathed thy company. But sithens I have perceived thee to be a harlot, and therefore did I for a time refrain and forbear to lie with thee. And now I can no longer forbear it, I do give thee every time that I lie with thee a slip, which is to make thee understand thine own whoredom. And this reward is sufficient for a whore.'

"The wife began stoutly to stand at defiance, but the husband cut off her speech and declared when, where, and how he had seen it. Hereat the woman, being abashed and finding her conscience guilty of as much as had alleged, fell down on her knees and, with most bitter tears, craved pardon, confessing her offense. Whereat her husband (moved with pity) and melting likewise in floods of lamen-

---

[99]*dissimuled:* dissembled; practiced dissimulation.

tation, recomforted her, promising that if from that day forwards she would be true unto him, he would not only forgive all that was past, but become more tender and loving unto her than ever he was.

"What do I tarry so long? They became of accord and, in full accomplishment thereof, the gentlewoman did altogether eschew the company, the speech, and (as much as in her lay) the sight of her lover, although her husband did continue his courtesy towards him, and often charged his wife to make him fair semblant. The lover was now only left in perplexity, who knew nothing what might be the cause of all these changes; and that most grieved him, he could by no means obtain again the speech of his desired. He watched all opportunities; he suborned messengers; he wrote letters. But all in vain. In the end she caused to be declared unto him a time and place where she would meet him and speak with him.

"Being met, she put him in remembrance of all that had passed between them. She laid also before him how trusty she had been unto him in all professions. She confessed also how faithfully he had discharged the duty of a friend in all respects, and therewithal she declared that her late alteration and pensiveness of mind was not without great cause, for that she had of late such a mishap as might change the disposition of any living creature. Yea, and that the case was such, as unless she found present remedy, her death must needs ensue and that speedily. For the preventing whereof, she alleged that she had beaten her brains with all devices possible and that in the end she could think of no redress but one, the which lay only in him to accomplish. Wherefore she besought him for all the love and good will which had ever passed between them now to show the fruits of true friendship and to gratify her with a free grant to this request. The lover, who had always been desirous to pleasure her in anything, but now especially to recover her wonted kindness, gan frankly promise to accomplish anything that might be to him possible—yea, though it were to his great detriment—and therewithal did deeply blame her in that she would so long torment herself with any grief, considering that it lay in him to help it. The lady answered that she had so long kept it from his knowledge because she doubted whether he would be contented to perform it or not, although it was such a thing as he might easily grant without any manner of hurt to himself, and yet that now in the end she was forced to adventure upon his courtesy, being no longer able to bear the burden of her grief. The lover solicited her most earnestly to disclose it, and she (as fast) seemed to mistrust that he would not accomplish it.

"In the end she took out a book (which she had brought for the nonce) and bound him by oath to accomplish it. The lover mistrusting nothing less than that ensued, took the oath willingly. Which done, she declared all that had passed between her and her husband—his grief, her repentance, his pardon, her vow, and in the end of her tale enjoined the lover that from thenceforthwards, he should never attempt to break her constant determination. The lover replied that this was unpossible, but she plainly assured him that if he granted her that request, she would be his friend in all honest and godly wise. If not, she put him out of doubt that she would eschew his company and fly from his sight as from a scorpion.

"The lover, considering that her request was but just, accusing his own guilty conscience, remembering the great courtesies always used by her husband, and therewithal seeing the case now brought to such an issue as that by none other means than by this it could be concealed from knowledge of the world—but most of all being urged by his oath—did at last give an unwilling consent and yet a faithful promise to yield unto her will in all things. And thus being become of one assent, he remaineth the dearest friend and most welcome guest that may be, both to the lady and her husband, and the man and wife so kind (each to other) as if there never had been such a breach between them.

"Now, of you, noble governor, I would fain learn whether the perplexity of the husband when he looked in at the keyhole, or of the wife when she knew the cause why the slips were so scattered, or of the lover when he knew what was his mistress' charge, was greater of the three? I might have put in also the troubled thoughts of the sisters and the maid when they saw their good will rejected. But let these three suffice."

"Gentle Hope," quoth F. J., "you have rehearsed (and that right eloquently) a notable tale, or rather a notable history, because you seem to affirm that it was done indeed of late and not far hence. Wherein I note five especial points: that is, a marvelous patience in the husband, no less repentance in the wife, no small boldness of the maid, but much more rashness in the sisters, and last of all a rare tractability in the lover. Nevertheless, to return unto your question, I think the husband's perplexity greatest because his losses abounded above the rest and his injuries were uncomparable."

The Lady Frances did not seem to contrary him, but rather smiled in her sleeve at Dame Pergo, who had no less patience to hear the tale recited than the Lady Frances had pleasure in telling of it. But I may not rehearse the cause why unless I should tell all.

By this time the sleeping hour approached and the ladies prepared their departure, whenas Mistress Frances said unto F. J., "Although percase I shall not do it so handsomely as your mistress, yet, good Trust," quoth she, "if you vouchsafe it, I can be content to trim up your bed in the best manner that I may, as one who would be as glad as she to procure your quiet rest."

F. J. gave her great thanks, desiring her not to trouble herself, but to let his man alone with that charge. Thus they departed and how all parties took rest that night I know not. But in the morning F. J. began to consider to himself that he might lie long enough in his bed before his mistress would be appeased in her peevish conceits. Wherefore he arose and, being appareled in his nightgown, took occasion to walk in the gallery near adjoining unto his mistress' chamber. But there might he walk long enough ere his mistress would come to walk with him.

When dinner time came, he went into the great chamber, whereas the lord of the castle saluted him, being joyful of his recovery. F. J., giving due thanks, declared that his friendly entertainment, together with the great courtesy of the gentlewomen, was such as might revive a man although he were half dead.

"I would be loath," quoth the host, "that any gentleman coming to me for good will should want any courtesy of entertainment that lieth in my power."

When the meat was served to the table, the gentlewomen came in, all but Dame Elinor and Mistress Pergo, the which F. J. marked very well and it did somewhat abate his appetite. After dinner his Hope came unto him and demanded of him how he would pass the day for his recreation. To whom he answered, "Even as it best pleased her." She devised to walk into the park and so by little and little to acquaint himself with the air. He agreed and they walked together, being accompanied with one or two other gentlewomen.

Here (lest you should grow in some wrong conceit of F. J.) I must put you out of doubt that although there were now more cause that he should mistrust his mistress than ever he had before received, yet the vehement passions which he saw in her when she first came to visit him—and, moreover, the earnest words which she pronounced in his extremity—were such a refreshing to his mind as that he determined no more to trouble himself with like conceits, concluding, further, that if his mistress were not faulty, then had he committed a foul offense in needless jealousy, and that if she were faulty (especially with the secretary) then no persuasion could amend her nor any passion help him. And this was the cause that enabled him after such passing pangs to abide the doubtful conclusion, thus manfully and valiantly to repress faintness of his mind, nothing doubting but that he should have won his mistress to pardon his presumption and lovingly to embrace his service in wonted manner. But he was far deceived, for she was now in another tune, the which Mistress Frances began partly to discover unto him as they walked together. For she burdened him that his malady proceeded only of a disquiet mind.

"And if it did so, my gentle Hope," quoth he, "what remedy?"

"My good Trust," quoth she, "none other but to plant quiet where disquiet began to grow."

"I have determined so," quoth he, "but I must crave the help of your assured friendship."

"Thereof you may make accompt," quoth she, "but wherein?"

F. J., walking apart with her, began to declare that there was some contention happened between his mistress and him. The lady told him that she was not ignorant thereof. Then he desired her to treat so much in the cause as they might eftsoons come to parley.

"Thereof I dare assure you," quoth Mistress Frances.

And at their return, she led F. J. into his mistress' chamber, whom they found lying on her bed, whether galled with any grief or weary of the thing (which you wot of) I know not, but there she lay. Unto whom F. J. gave two or three salutations before she seemed to mark him.

At last said the Lady Frances unto her, "Your servant, hearing of your sickness, hath adventured thus far into the air to see you."

"I thank him," quoth Dame Elinor, and so lay still, refusing to give him any countenance.

Whereat F. J., perceiving all the other gentlewomen fall to whispering, thought good boldly to plead his own case and, approaching the bed, began to enforce his unwilling mistress unto courtesy. Wherein he used such vehemence as she could not well by any means refuse to talk with him. But what their talk was I may not take upon me to tell you unless you would have me fill up a whole volume only with his matters, and I have dilated them over largely already. Sufficeth this to be known: that in the end she pretended to pass over all old grudges, and thenceforth to pleasure him as occasion might serve. The which occasion was so long in happening that in the end F. J., being now eftsoons troubled with unquiet fantasies, and forced to use his pen again as an ambassador between them, one day amongst the rest found opportunity to thrust a letter into her bosom, wherein he had earnestly requested another moonshine banquet or Friday's breakfast to recomfort his dulled spirits. Whereunto the dame yielded this answer in writing, but of whose inditing judge you.

G. T.

I can but smile at your simplicity, who burden your friends with an impossibility. The case so stood as I could not though I would. Wherefore from henceforth either learn to frame your request more reasonably or else stand content with a flat repulse.

SHE

F. J. liked this letter but a little and, being thereby driven into his accustomed vein, he compiled in verse this answer following, upon these words contained in her letter: "I could not though I would."

G. T.

"I could not though I would." Good Lady, say not so,
Since one good word of your good will might soon redress my woe.
Where "would" is free before, there "could" can never fail;
For proof, you see how galleys pass where ships can bear no sail.
The weary mariner when skies are overcast,
By ready will doth guide his skill and wins the haven at last.
The pretty bird, that sings with prick against her breast,[100]
Doth make a virtue of her need to watch when others rest.
And true the proverb is, which you have laid apart,
There is no hap can seem too hard unto a willing heart.
Then lovely lady mine, you say not as you should,
In doubtful terms to answer thus: "I could not though I would."
Yes, yes, full well you know, your "can" is quick and good;
And wilfull "will" is eke[101] too swift to shed my guiltless blood.
But if good will were bent, as press'd as power is,
Such will would quickly find the skill to mend that is amiss.
Wherefore if you desire to see my true love spilt,
Command and I will slay myself, that yours may be the guilt,
But if you have no power to say your servant nay,
Write thus: "I may not as I would, yet must I as I may."

F. J.

Thus F. J. replied upon his mistress' answer, hoping thereby to recover some favor at her hands, but it would not be; so that now he

---

[100]*with prick against her breast:* According to a proverb (Tilley, N183), the nightingale sang with a thorn in her breast in order to keep awake at night.

[101]*eke:* also.

had been as likely (as at the first) to have fretted in fantasies, had not the Lady Frances continually comforted him. And by little and little she drove such reason into his mind that now he began to subdue his humors with discretion and to determine that if he might espy evident proof of his mistress' frailty, he would then stand content, with patience perforce, and give his mistress the *bezo las manos*.

And it happened one day amongst others that he resorted to his mistress' chamber and found her (*alla solito*)[102] lying upon her bed, and the secretary with Dame Pergo and her handmaid keeping of her company. Whereat F. J., somewhat repining, came to her and fell to dalliance, as one that had now rather adventure to be thought presumptuous than yield to be accompted bashful. He cast his arm over his mistress and began to accuse her of sluggishness, using some other bold parts, as well to provoke her as also to grieve the other. The lady seemed little to delight in his dallying, but cast a glance at her secretary and therewith smiled, whenas the secretary and Dame Pergo burst out into open laughter. The which F. J. perceiving, and disdaining her ingratitude, was forced to depart, and in that fantasy compiled this sonnet.

G. T.

> With her in arms that had my heart in hold,
> I stood of late to plead for pity so;
> And as I did her lovely looks behold,
> She cast a glance upon my rival foe.
> His fleering face provoked her to smile,
> When my salt tears were drowned in disdain;
> He glad, I sad, he laughed (alas the while)
> I wept for woe; I pined for deadly pain.
> And when I saw none other boot prevail,
> But reason's rule must guide my skilful mind,
> Why then (quoth I) old proverbs never fail,
> For yet was never good cat out of kind;[103]
> Nor woman true but, even as stories tell,
> Won with an egg, and lost again with shell.

F. J.

This sonnet declareth that he began now to accompt of her as she deserved, for it hath a sharp conclusion, and it is somewhat too general. Well, as it is he lost it where his mistress found it, and she im-

[102]*bezo las manos . . . alla solito:* kiss on the hands . . . in her usual manner.

[103]*was never good cat out of kind:* part of a proverb (Tilley, C167): "That cat is out of kind that sweet milk will not lap."

mediately imparted the same unto Dame Pergo, and Dame Pergo unto others, so that it quickly became common in the house. Amongst others, Mistress Frances, having recovered a copy of it, did seem to pardon the generality and to be well pleased with the particularity thereof, the which she bewrayed one day unto F. J. in this wise:

"Of all the joys that ever I had, my good Trust," quoth she, "there is none wherein I take more comfort than in your conformity. And although your present rage is such that you can be content to condemn a number unknown for the transgression of one too well known, yet I do rather rejoice that you should judge your pleasure over many than to be abused by any."

"My good Hope," quoth he, "it were not reason that after such manifold proofs of your exceeding courtesies, I should use strange or contentious speech with so dear a friend. And indeed I must confess that the opinion which I have conceived of my mistress hath stirred my pen to write very hardly against all the feminine gender, but I pray you pardon me," quoth he, "and if it please you I will recant it. As also (percase) I was but cloyed with surquedry[104] and presumed to think more than may be proved."

"Yea, but how if it were proved?" quoth Dame Frances.

"If it were so (which God forbid)," quoth he, "then could you not blame me to conceive that opinion."

"Howsoever I might blame you," quoth she, "I mean not to blame you. But I demand further if it be as I think and you suspect, what will you then do?"

"Surely," quoth F. J., "I have determined to drink up mine own sorrow secretly and to bid them both *a Dieu.*"

"I like your farewell better than your fantasy," quoth she, "and whensoever you can be content to take so much pains as the knight (which had a nightgown guarded with naked swords) did take, I think you may put yourself out of doubt of all these things."

By these words and other speech which she uttered unto him, F. J. smelt how the world went about, and therefore did one day in the gray morning adventure to pass through the gallery towards his mistress' chamber, hoping to have found the door open. But he found the contrary and there, attending in good devotion, heard the parting of his mistress and her secretary with many kind words. Whereby it appeared that the one was very loath to depart from the other. F. J. was enforced to bear this burden, and after he had attended there as long as the light would give him leave, he departed also to his

104*surquedry:* arrogance.

chamber and, appareling himself, could not be quiet until he had spoken with his mistress, whom he burdened flatly with this despiteful treachery. And she as fast denied it, until at last being still urged with such evident tokens as he alleged, she gave him this bone to gnaw upon.

"And if I did so," quoth she, "what then?"

Whereunto F. J. made none answer but departed with this farewell: "My loss is mine own, and your gain is none of yours; and sooner can I recover my loss than you enjoy the gain which you gape after." And when he was in place solitary, he compiled these following for a final end of the matter.

G. T.

> And if I did what then?
> Are you aggriev'd therefore?
> The sea hath fish for every man,
> And what would you have more?
>
> Thus did my mistress once
> Amaze my mind with doubt,
> And popp'd a question for the nonce,[105]
> To beat my brains about.
>
> Whereto I thus replied,
> Each fisherman can wish
> That all the sea at every tide
> Were his alone to fish.
>
> And so did I (in vain),
> But since it may not be,
> Let such fish there as find the gain,
> And leave the loss for me.
>
> And with such luck and loss,
> I will content myself;
> Till tides of turning time may toss
> Such fishers on the shelf.
>
> And when they stick on sands,
> That every man may see;
> Then will I laugh and clap my hands,
> As they do now at me.

F. J.

It is time now to make an end of this thriftless history, wherein although I could wade much further, as to declare his departure, what

---

[105]*for the nonce:* expressly, on purpose.

thanks he gave to his Hope, etc., yet I will cease, as one that had rather leave it unperfect than make it too plain. I have passed it over with "quoth he" and "quoth she," after my homely manner of writing, using sundry names for one person, as "the dame," "the lady," "mistress," etc., "the lord of the castle," "the master of the house," and "the host." Nevertheless, for that I have seen good authors term every gentlewoman a lady and every gentleman *domine*, I have thought it no greater fault that petty treason thus to intermingle them, nothing doubting but you will easily understand my meaning. And that is as much as I desire. Now henceforwards I will trouble you no more with such a barbarous style in prose, but will only recite unto you sundry verses written by sundry gentlemen, adding nothing of mine own, but only a title to every poem, whereby the cause of writing the same may the more evidently appear. Neither can I declare unto you who wrote the greatest part of them, for they are unto me but a posy presented out of sundry gardens; neither have I any other names of the flowers, but such short notes as the authors themselves have delivered thereby. If you can guess them, it shall no way offend me. I will begin with this translation as followeth.

G. T.

ℰ Euphues: The Anatomy of Wit

(1578)

JOHN LYLY

In proceeding from *The Sackful of News* and *Master F. J.* to John Lyly's first and most popular work, *Euphues: The Anatomy of Wit* (first edition, 1578; second and revised edition, 1579), the modern reader is impressed by the unusually wide variety of fiction available to the Elizabethan public. If *Sackful* is cruder than any work that could become popular today, *Euphues* is more refined. Yet if we bear with *Euphues* long enough to see what Lyly was trying to do, then we also place ourselves in a position to better understand the Elizabethans and their literature. Hunter has observed that *Euphues* is "above all, a triumph of style."[1] Yes, and the whole age shared in that triumph, first imitating it and then building on it, but never entirely leaving it behind. It is as "Elizabethan" as Elizabeth herself.

One admission we should make about *Euphues* is that it may not be primarily a work of prose fiction so much as a tract of some kind. The story is very simple; like *Master F. J.*, it can be summarized in one short paragraph. As we have noted, Gascoigne's bare story-line enabled him to concentrate on the subtle reactions of his characters to their situation. But Lyly is hardly any more interested in character

[1] *John Lyly*, p. 133.

analysis than he is in constructing a full story-line.[2] He seems to be interested primarily in how his characters express themselves.

The narrator refers to his narration as a "history," a "discourse," a "tale," and a "pamphlet." *Euphues* is all these things, but basically it is what Northrop Frye (and Lyly himself, in his subtitle) calls "anatomy." It is one of the best examples we shall ever find of the "extroverted and intellectual" work of verbal art.[3] In *Master F. J.* the leisurely and witty conversation of the kind we have in Castiglione's *The Courtier* is subordinate; in *Euphues* it becomes the whole *raison d'être*. The scenes are built round topics for conversation; "Education vs. Nature" is what the first scene, involving Eubulus and Euphues, is all about. That topic prepares us for another on "Love"; and once the action disposes of Lucilla, we are ready for "Friendship."

The narrator makes use of several kinds of knowledge or experience. One is science. The Elizabethan, no less than the average person living today, was impressed by anything scientific. The main encyclopedia of the time was Pliny the Elder's *Natural History,* a learned and well-organized compendium of information from Absci to Zythum. We are not to think, however, that Lyly always takes his sources of information seriously, or that he is asking us to; on the contrary, he is occasionally careless in his references, and one of the few ways in which he shows a sense of humor is to invent a Pliny-like bit of information and pass it off as authoritative. Generally speaking, the reference to science is either sheer ornament or merely a specific example; the main emphasis falls on the argument that the narrator or one of the characters is presenting.

In the first page or two the narrator refers to Aristippus, Lycurgus, Tully (Cicero), Ovid, Aristotle, the Epicureans, the Stoics, and various ancient Greek and Roman myths. Each reference is made easily and almost casually, as though any number of others could have been cited. Perhaps the intended effect is one of overwhelming authority; the reader is to feel that if all these great men of antiquity thought something true, then it must be true. Our response is to be a feeling as much as a thinking; we are to be convinced, but not through

[2]One should add, however, that although the strictly narrative elements are understated (as opposed to the overstatement that is characteristic of the style), they are not completely neglected. There are a surprising number of fine details just when they are most needed; we are told, for example, exactly why Lucilla is left behind with Euphues and why Philautus happens to accompany Ferardo on a business trip.

[3]*Anatomy of Criticism*, pp. 308 ff.

closely reasoned and well-documented scholarship. Most of the references will not bear close checking, and on occasion Lyly invents an ancient-sounding name and an authoritative-sounding idea to go with it.

Lyly is typical of Renaissance writers in that his knowledge is of the Roman classics rather than of the Greek; the Greek language made some headway in sixteenth-century England—Queen Elizabeth was an apt student of it—but few of the texts were available. Lyly is also typical in that he cites biblical texts along with the Roman and sees no particular conflict between Hebrew and Hellenic world views. In the same sentence will come references to Solomon and Tully, David and Ovid.

One gradually realizes, however, that *Euphues* is not concerned primarily with ideas in the classics or the Bible. Lyly is not interested, as some English humanists were, in finding a common ground between classical and biblical thought. On the contrary, he mentions so many authors that it would be impossible to find any philosophical basis that they have in common. What appears to interest him is not ideas so much as the process of reasoning, not the ideas themselves but the manipulation of them. The reader's attention is to be drawn only slightly to the authors of the ancient world; if the reader recognizes them, there will be some pleasure in recognition. But the main object is to follow the lines of argument that the narrator and his characters present. The appeal is to contemporary man's gift of reason, to be employed upon perennial topics.

Early in *Euphues* the narrator remarks that "an old-said saw [is] not of less truth than antiquity," and such an attitude continues all through the narrative. Proverbs are at least as important a source of Lyly's "content" as science, antiquity, and the Bible; and they do much more in accounting for *Euphues'* tremendous popularity. Lyly's essential conservatism, his medieval world picture, are nowhere more copiously illustrated than in his constant use of proverbs—those brief, anonymous insights, most of them centuries old, that form the popular wisdom of all classes. But he uses proverbs the way he uses antiquity and science, with a good deal of freedom. He adapts each proverb to his own sentence rhythms, though a surprising number of them fit nicely with but little change (for his style is naturally proverbial). Sometimes he strings two or three of them together so easily that the modern reader may not even recognize them as proverbs; they seem an integral part of Lyly's style.

His use of proverbs may be illustrated by one that appears on p. 149: "the broken bone, once set together, is stronger than ever it was." The line is given to Lucilla and is adapted from the proverb (Tilley, B515): "a broken bone is the stronger when it is well set." One is reminded of Hemingway's use of the same proverb in Chapter 34 of *Farewell to Arms*: "The world breaks every one and afterward many are strong at the broken places." This sentence, given to the narrator, Frederic Henry, is an integral part of the central idealism regarding courage and defiance. But Lyly makes no attempt to work the proverb into a theme; he uses it to help him analyze and illustrate wit. On p. 149 the proverb of the broken bone is merely the fourth of seven parallel examples.

A surprising aspect of Lyly's style is the lack of irony in it, whether verbal or situational. At one point Philautus ironically doubts Ferardo when he should doubt Lucilla (p. 170), and there are a few other examples; but for a work so full of subtle distinctions it is relatively free of both irony and ambiguity. As Hunter observes (p. 60): "Looked at one way [*Euphues*] is sophisticated and flippant; looked at from another angle it is seriously concerned with conduct." But the two aspects do not produce much tension, and perhaps that is the reason why *Euphues* contains so little irony.

Comparison with Nashe's style is revealing. Nashe's unit is the individual word while Lyly's is the clause. In *The Unfortunate Traveler* there are countless puns; many words have double meanings, and a sizable number have triple or even quadruple meanings. Lyly is not nearly so interested in words, and his vocabulary is considerably smaller. For all his audacity in balancing and counterbalancing clauses, Lyly is content to use fairly plain and common words. Unlike Nashe, he hardly ever needs to invent a new word in order to say precisely what he wants to say. On the other hand, Lyly seems more aware of usage and the changes in primary sense that usage brings. He uses "curious" and "lewd" in their old senses of "intricate" and "ignorant," but then in a different context he uses the same words in the modern senses in which they were just beginning to be used.

The word "euphuism" derives from the style of *Euphues*, but most of the obvious elements of euphuism existed before *Euphues* appeared in 1578. As William Ringler has shown, Lyly's style probably owes much to John Rainolds, a lecturer at Oxford while Lyly was a student there. Rainolds delivered his Latin lectures, based on Cicero's style, in a euphuistic manner.[4] Lyly's special contribution, as Hunter notes,

[4]See Ringler, and Allen, *Oratio in Laudem Artis Poeticae by John Rainolds*, pp. 10–23. The origin of euphuism can be traced all the way back to Gorgias in the fourth century B.C. if all we mean is a tendency to use

was a shortening of the clause, which he reduces to a "small number of easily recognized patterns, rhythmic and syntactic, repeated over and over again" (p. 264). Although it seems unusually complex to us, the style of *Euphues* was actually much simpler to the Elizabethan than the predominantly Ciceronian style that he was used to.

If Lyly's brand of euphuism seems to us unduly elegant, it is not blindly idealistic or sentimental. His diction, though not nearly so colloquial as Nashe's, has a number of four-letter words in it; and the tone keeps the reader at arm's length from the characters, with whom there is never any question of identification.

"Euphues" is a Greek word meaning "well grown" or "symmetrical" as well as "clever" or "witty." It applies in at least three ways—to Euphues as a person, to the language he and other characters use, and to the narrator's language. One should not fail to catch this last element, for *Euphues* is an unusually self-conscious book, though at the same time it is also unusually objective and impersonal. The language everywhere calls attention to itself as an object that is to be considered for its own sake, without telling us anything personal about the narrator or author and even without individualizing the characters except in a very general way.[5] There is little difference

---

symmetry and parallelism in clause structure and sound effects. Even in Lyly's own time there were several books in English—such as William Painter's *Palace of Pleasure* (1566), George Pettie's *A Petite Palace of Pettie His Pleasure* (1576), and John Grange's *Golden Aphroditis* (1577)— from which he doubtless learned something. But Lyly's book was much more popular at the time than any of the three, and it is a great deal more significant today. It has more integrity; the euphuistic elements are part of the book's very fabric: they *are* the book. We cannot use Pettie's *Petite Palace* to illustrate anything more than a few superficial elements; nor can we use Rainolds' *Oratio*, though his lectures may very well have been Lyly's most immediate source. *Euphues* is a great deal more than a sum of all its sources, direct and indirect. By "euphuism" we should mean no less than "the style of *Euphues*," though of course we can say that a number of Elizabethan works—including the three prefaces to *Master F. J.*— have euphuistic elements in them. (For other works on Lyly's style, in addition to Hunter and Ringler, see "A Select Bibliography," especially the article by Barish, who corrects Croll's still valuable analysis.)

[5] The narrator occasionally uses "I" in the course of the narrative, as on pp. 140 and 164; and on p. 138 he talks directly to the gentlemen readers on the limitations of wit. But there is no attempt to make his personality, whatever it is, have an effect on *Euphues* (the way G. T. has an effect on *Master F. J.*). "Self-conscious" is not the right expression to use in describing the narrator, for he has no "self" except as a user of language. The only real "self" in *Euphues* is wit.

between the language the narrator uses to comment on the characters and the language the characters use in their conversations with each other. Usually in a work of prose fiction one expects a plain, modest, neutral style from the narrator; and then one expects each character to speak "like himself," revealing his own peculiar nature. *Master F. J.* follows the usual pattern in this regard, but not *Euphues.*

Every part or section of *Euphues* has its individual topic, like "Friendship." But there is only one subject throughout, and that is wit. Lyly's full title, *Euphues: The Anatomy of Wit,* is unlike most book titles in that it is perfectly accurate. Lyle delineates wit the way another writer delineates character, and his single-minded preoccupation with his subject may be all that unifies his work in any meaningful sense.[6]

In the early part of *Love's Labor's Lost* (II, i, 64 ff.) Rosaline describes Berowne's wit:

> Another of these students at that time
> Was there with him, if I have heard a truth.
> Berowne they call him; but a merrier man,
> Within the limit of becoming mirth,
> I never spent an hour's talk withal.
> His eye begets occasion for his wit;
> For every object that the one doth catch
> The other turns to a mirth-moving jest,
> Which his fair tongue, conceit's expositor,
> Delivers in such apt and gracious words,
> That agèd ears play truant at his tales,
> And younger hearings are quite ravishèd,
> So sweet and voluble is his discourse.

When we hear Berowne perform, we find that Rosaline is right about him: he *is* witty—and Shakespeare must have been confident of his ability to write witty dialogue. Lyly is in roughly the same position; he has announced his subject, and now he must deliver. He does not merely analyze wit; he demonstrates it in his characters' dialogue and monologue and in the narrator's comments. To some extent he means by "wit" what Rosaline means—a liveliness and quickness of fancy, as well as apt, graceful, and sweet-sounding expressions. But he also means something that Rosaline does not

[6]Hunter's contention, in *John Lyly,* pp. 56 ff., that the narrative part of *Euphues* may be divided into a "five-act structure" is not entirely convincing (though, like all Hunter's judgments, it is worth serious consideration).

entirely imply—intellectual capacity, the ability to see very fine distinctions (and in the process to take all knowledge for one's province and to make appropriate analogies within that knowledge). On the other hand, Rosaline means something that Lyly makes little attempt to achieve—"mirth-moving jest." Occasionally, as on p. 185, "wit" means the same thing that we mean by "I. Q."; but the connotation is favorable or derogatory, depending on the context. *Euphues* is a truly intellectual work in that it considers also the limitations of intellectuality. The mind, according to Euphues, is "the grand captain" (p. 156), or at least it should be. But the fact is that wit often keeps company with folly and operates against both wisdom and happiness; Euphues asks himself:

> What is he, Euphues, that knowing thy wit and seeing thy folly, but will rather punish thy lewdness than pity thy heaviness? Was there ever any so fickle, so soon to be allured, any ever so faithless to deceive his friend, ever any so foolish to bathe himself in his own misfortune? Too true it is that as the sea crab swimmeth always against the stream, so wit always striveth against wisdom; and as the bee is oftentimes hurt with her own honey, so is wit not seldom plagued with his own conceit.

In the end, a "simple mind" is the best (p. 168); "simplicity" and "truth" go together (p. 168), just as "simplicity" and "deceit" are opposites (p. 175); "sincerity of the heart" is necessary (p. 178). The "obstinate will" (p. 184) is a distinct handicap, to be contested by reason and to some extent by knowledge, though knowledge is not emphasized. "Love knoweth no laws," writes Euphues to Philautus; Euphues is more comfortable with whatever is predictable, like friendship. Honor, honesty, duty, and constancy (especially the last) round out the list of verities in *Euphues*. The imagery often runs to blemishes, to physical or moral imperfections. With reason we are to perceive defects, no matter how deceptive the appearances ("outward talk . . . inward treachery" [p. 184]). But reason itself may also be deceived.

There may be a fairly simple explanation for all Lyly's rhetorical gymnastics and for the general popularity of his style in the 1580's. The Elizabethans were passing through a stage of being in love with language. We may see this love in Shakespeare's plays, especially the early ones in which Lyly's influence is deep and pervasive. We may see it also in the rhetoric books of the time; Henry Peacham, Richard Sherry, and Thomas Wilson were just as excited by the

English language as the poets were. They were all in love because they regarded discourse as man's own peculiar and natural endowment. If verbal expression is the most important means of exercising God-given reason, and reason is nothing without the ability to use it in speaking and writing, then it follows that a complete exercise of reason may involve fine rhetorical flourishes.

Alliteration is a flourish that has to do with the initial consonants of words ("more wit than wisdom"). Assonance has to do with the agreement of vowel sounds, as in the following example: "a liking every way to the eyes, than a loathing any way to the mind," where in both "eyes" and "mind" the vowel sound is approximately the same. But this last example is a typical instance of Lyly's attempting a number of his little tricks at the same time. In addition to assonance, we are to notice alliteration, internal rhyme ("liking" and "loathing"), isocolon (the clauses are of equal length), and antithesis (the clauses are balanced against each other). Lyly seems to be saying, in effect, "Look what I can do!" or, more accurately, since Lyly leaves himself out of his work, "Look what can be done with our wonderfully plastic English language!" If that is what he is saying, he certainly makes his point.[7]

⁌⧉⧉⧉⧉⧈⧉

To the Right Honorable, My Very Good Lord and Master, Sir William West, Knight, Lord de la Warr,[8] John Lyly Wisheth Long Life with Increase of Honor

Parrhasius, drawing the counterfeit of Helen, right honorable, made the attire of her head loose; who, being demanded why he did so, he answered she was loose. Vulcan was painted curiously,[9] yet with

[7]For a large perspective, in which Lyly may be seen with Sidney, Spenser, and others as realizing the potentialities of English rhetoric in the latter quarter of the sixteenth century, see Richard Foster Jones, *The Triumph of the English Language* (Stanford, Calif., 1952), especially Chapters I and VI.

[8]*Sir William West, Knight, Lord de la Warr:* We still know practically nothing about Sir William West, the tenth Baron de la Warr (1519?–1595), whose descendants, incidentally, gave the state of Delaware its name; see Hunter, *John Lyly*, pp. 67–68, 79. *Euphues and His England* (1580) is dedicated to Edward de Vere, the seventeenth Earl of Oxford.

[9]*curiously*: with careful art.

a poltfoot;[10] Leda cunningly, yet with her black hair.[11] Alexander, having a scar in his cheek, held his finger upon it, that Apelles might not paint it. Apelles painted him with his finger cleaving to his face.

"Why," quoth Alexander, "I laid my finger on my scar because I would not have thee see it."

"Yea," said Apelles, "and I drew it there because none else should perceive it; for if thy finger had been away, either thy scar would have been seen or my art misliked."

Whereby I gather that in all perfect works as well the fault as the face is to be shown. The fairest leopard is made with his spots, the finest cloth with his list, the smoothest shoe with his last.[12] Seeing, then, that in every counterfeit as well the blemish as the beauty is colored, I hope I shall not incur the displeasure of the wise, in that in the discourse of Euphues I have as well touched the vanities of his love as the virtues of his life.

The Persians, who above all their kings most honored Cyrus, caused him to be engraven as well with his hooked nose as his high forehead. He that loved Homer best concealed not his flattering, and he that praised Alexander most bewrayed his quaffing. Demonides must have a crooked shoe for his wry foot, Damocles a smooth glove for his straight hand. For as every painter that shadoweth a man in all parts giveth every piece his just proportion, so he that deciphereth the qualities of the mind ought as well to show every humor in his kind, as the other doth every part in his color. The surgeon that

[10]*poltfoot*: clubfoot.

[11]*Leda ... hair*: This reference to Leda in the second edition (1579) replaced the following reference to Venus that had appeared in the first edition (1578): "Venus cunningly, yet with her mole." Lyly himself very likely is responsible for the revision. One possible reason for it may be that a reference to Venus' mole appears later on in the second paragraph of the story proper, and Lyly may not have wanted a repetition. It may be relevant to add that "yet with her mole" does not exactly balance "yet with a poltfoot"; the new phrase, "yet with her black hair," with five syllables instead of four, does balance.

[12]*the finest cloth ... last*: These two examples in the second edition replaced the following in the first edition: "the sweetest rose with his prickles, the finest velvet with his brack." In this case we may be fairly certain of the main reason for the emendation: "the sweetest rose ... brack" appears word for word in the second paragraph of the story proper. Lyly's style is based on certain kinds of repetition, but an exact repetition of this kind would show a painful lack of "wit" on his part. It may be relevant to add that "prickles" and "brack" do not sound alike, while "list" and "last" in the revised phrasing do.

maketh the anatomy showeth as well the muscles in the heel as the veins of the heart.

If, then, the first sight of Euphues shall seem too light to be read of the wise, or too foolish to be regarded of the learned, they ought not to impute it to the iniquity of the author, but to the necessity of the history. Euphues beginneth with love as allured by wit, but endeth not with lust as bereft of wisdom. He wooeth women, provoked by youth, but weddeth not himself to wantonness as pricked by pleasure. I have set down the follies of his wit without breach of modesty and the sparks of his wisdom without suspicion of dishonesty. And, certes, I think there be more speeches which for gravity will mislike the foolish, than unseemly terms which for vanity may offend the wise.

Which discourse, right honorable, I hope you will the rather pardon for the rudeness, in that it is the first, and protect it the more willingly if it offend, in that it may be the last. It may be that fine wits will descant upon him that, having no wit, goeth about to make the anatomy of wit; and certainly their jesting, in my mind, is tolerable. For if the butcher should take upon him to cut the anatomy of a man because he hath skill in opening an ox, he would prove himself a calf; or if the horseleech[13] would adventure to minister a potion to a sick patient, in that he hath knowledge to give a drench to a diseased horse, he would make himself an ass. The shoemaker must not go above his latchet,[14] nor the hedger meddle with anything but his bill.[15] It is unseemly for the painter to feather a shaft, or the fletcher to handle the pencil. All which things make most against me in that a fool hath intruded himself to discourse of wit. But as I was willing to commit the fault, so am I content to make amends. Howsoever the case standeth, I look for no praise for my labor, but pardon for my good will; it is the greatest reward that I dare ask, and the least that they can offer. I desire no more, I deserve no less.

Though the style nothing delight the dainty ear of the curious sifter, yet will the matter recreate the mind of the courteous reader. The variety of the one will abate the harshness of the other. Things of greatest profit are set forth with least price. Where the wine is

[13]*horseleech*: veterinarian.
[14]*The shoemaker ... latchet*: See footnote 9 in Lodge's *Rosalind*, where something is made of a shoemaker who does "go above his latchet."
[15]*bill*: hedging bill (an implement with a curved blade and a long handle used to trim hedges and trees).

neat, there needeth no ivy bush.[16] The right coral needeth no coloring. Where the matter itself bringeth credit, the man with his gloss winneth small commendation. It is therefore, methinketh, a greater show of a pregnant wit than perfect wisdom, in a thing of sufficient excellency, to use superfluous eloquence. We commonly see that a black ground doth best beseem a white counterfeit. And Venus, according to the judgment of Mars, was then most amiable when she sat close by Vulcan. If these things be true which experience trieth—that a naked tale doth most truly set forth the naked truth, that where the countenance is fair there need no colors,[17] that painting is meeter for ragged walls than fine marble, that verity then shineth most bright when she is in least bravery[18]—I shall satisfy mine own mind, though I cannot feed their humors which greatly seek after those that sift the finest meal and bear the whitest mouths.[19]

It is a world to see how Englishmen desire to hear finer speech than the language will allow, to eat finer bread than is made of wheat, to wear finer cloth than is wrought of wool. But I let pass their fineness which can no way excuse my folly. If your lordship shall accept my good will, which I have always desired, I will patiently bear the ill will of the malicious, which I never deserved.

Thus committing this simple pamphlet to your lordship's patronage and your honor to the Almighty's protection, for the preservation of the which, as most bounden, I will pray continually, I end.

Your lordship's servant to command,

J. Lyly

---

[16]*wine is neat . . . ivy bush*: The sense probably is "where the wine is unadulterated (not mixed with water), no advertising sign is necessary." The ivy bush (the sign or symbol for a tavern in the sixteenth century) will not be necessary after the tavern gets the reputation for serving good wine; people will find their way without a sign.

[17]*where the countenance . . . no colors*: a slight variation of a proverb (Tilley, F7): "A good face needs no paint." *Euphues* is full of proverbs, but there will be no attempt to call attention to any more than the small fraction of them that need explaining.

[18]*bravery*: finery.

[19]*the whitest mouths*: used figuratively to indicate the elegance and fastidiousness discussed further in the next paragraph. Literally, as Bond suggests (I, 328), it was a term applied to horses that did not bloody their mouths champing at the bit.

To the Gentlemen Readers

I was driven into a quandary, gentlemen, whether I might send this my pamphlet to the printer or to the peddler. I thought it too bad for the press and too good for the pack.[20] But seeing my folly in writing to be as great as others', I was willing my fortune should be as ill as any's. We commonly see the book that at midsummer lieth bound on the stationer's stall at Christmas to be broken in the haberdasher's shop; which, since it is the order of proceeding, I am content this summer to have my doings read for a toy, that in winter they may be ready for trash.[21]

It is not strange, whenas the greatest wonder lasteth but nine days, that a new work should not endure but six months. Gentlemen use books as gentlewomen handle their flowers, who in the morning stick them in their heads and at night strew them at their heels. Cherries be fulsome when they be through ripe because they be plenty, and books be stale when they be printed in that they be common. In my mind, printers and tailors are bound chiefly to pray for gentlemen: the one hath so many fantasies to print, the other such divers fashions to make, that the pressing iron of the one is never out of the fire, nor the printing press of the other any time lieth still. But a fashion is but a day's wearing and a book but an hour's reading; which,

[20]*pack*: Croll and Clemons probably are right (p. 8) that "peddler" and "pack" do not refer to the peddling of ballads, for, after all, ballads were printed; "pack" would seem to mean a collection of odds and ends of little value, sold by a peddler.

[21]*We commonly . . . for trash*: To keep up with Lyly one must not neglect small details. Notice the parallelism in this sentence—"midsummer" and "Christmas" in the early part of the sentence paralleling "summer" and "winter," respectively, in the later part. In the first edition the wording is the same, except that "Christmas" and "Easter" are the key words in the first part of the sentence, and "winter" and "summer" are the matching words in the second part. There would seem to be two reasons for the emendations of the second edition: (1) The simple reflection that Easter does not come in the summer, and that the Christmas–winter, Easter–summer parallelism of the 1578 edition is not accurate; the change in the second edition to midsummer–summer and Christmas–winter removes the difficulty. (2) Midsummer (around 21 June) probably is the approximate date in 1579 when the second edition actually appeared ("at midsummer lieth bound") and was ready for sale. The first edition probably had been published late in December, 1578, and hence the phrase "at Christmas lieth bound." After making these changes in the second edition, Lyly forgot, however, to change "three months" to "six months" at the end of the first sentence of the next paragraph. The present editor has taken the liberty of making that change.

seeing it is so, I am of the shoemaker's mind, who careth not so the shoe hold the plucking on, nor I so my labors last the running over.[22]

He that cometh in print because he would be known is like the fool that cometh into the market because he would be seen. I am not he that seeketh praise for his labor, but pardon for his offense; neither do I set this forth for any devotion in print, but for duty which I owe to my patron. If one write never so well, he cannot please all; and write he never so ill, he shall please some. Fine heads will pick a quarrel with me if all be not curious, and flatterers a thank if anything be current.[23]

But this is my mind: let him that findeth fault amend it, and him that liketh it use it. Envy braggeth but draweth no blood; the malicious have more mind to quip than might to cut. I submit myself to the judgment of the wise and little esteem the censure of fools. The one will be satisfied with reason, the other are to be answered with silence. I know gentlemen will find no fault without cause and bear with those that deserve blame; as for others, I care not for their jests, for I never meant to make them my judges.

Farewell

To My Very Good Friends, the Gentlemen Scholars of Oxford[24]

There is no privilege that needeth a pardon, neither is there any remission to be asked where a commission is granted. I speak this, gentlemen, not to excuse the offense which is taken, but to offer a defense where I was mistaken. A clear conscience is a sure card. Truth hath the prerogative to speak with plainness and the modesty to bear with patience.

It was reported by some and believed of many that in the education of Ephebus, where mention was made of universities, that Oxford was too much either defaced or defamed.[25] I know not what the envious have picked out by malice, or the curious by wit, or the

---

[22]*plucking on ... running over:* "plucking on" means "pulling on" (which is actually the emendation of the 1953 edition); "running over" apparently means "skimming through."

[23]*pick ... a thank ... current:* To "pick a thank" means "to flatter," and "current" means "in vogue" or "generally accepted."

[24]*To My Very Good Friends ... Oxford:* This dedication was omitted in the 1578 edition.

[25]*Ephebus ... Oxford ... defaced or defamed:* In his section of *Euphues* called "Euphues and His Ephebus" (a section omitted in the present edition, which includes only the first and narrative half of *Euphues*), Euphues has a few sharp things to say about Oxford in the guise of Athens. See Bond's edition, I, 273–5, and also Hunter's *John Lyly*, p. 42.

guilty by their own galled consciences; but this I say, that I was as far from thinking ill as I find them from judging well. But if I should now go about to make amends, I were then faulty like Apelles' prentice, who, coveting to mend the nose, marred the cheek; and not unlike the foolish dyer,[26] who never thought his cloth black until it was burned. If any fault be committed, impute it to Euphues, who knew you not—not to Lyly, who hates you not.

Yet may I of all the rest most condemn Oxford of unkindness—of vice I cannot—who seemed to wean me before she brought me forth and to give me bones to gnaw before I could get the teat to suck. Wherein she played the nice mother in sending me into the country to nurse, where I tired[27] at a dry breast three years and was at the last enforced to wean myself. But it was destiny, for if I had not been gathered from the tree in the bud, I should, being blown, have proved a blast; and as good it is to be an addle-egg as an idle bird.[28]

Euphues at his arrival, I am assured, will view Oxford, where he will either recant his sayings or renew his complaints. He is now on the seas, and how he hath been tossed I know not; but whereas I had thought to receive him at Dover, I must meet him at Hampton. Nothing can hinder his coming but death, neither anything hasten his departure but unkindness.

Concerning myself, I have always thought so reverently of Oxford, of the scholars, of the manners, that I seemed to be rather an idolater than a blasphemer. They that invented this toy were unwise, and they that reported it unkind, and yet none of them can prove me unhonest.

But suppose I glanced at some abuses. Did not Jupiter's egg bring forth as well Helen, a light huswife[29] in earth, as Castor, a light star

---

[26]*dyer:* In the second edition the spelling is "Diar," which presumably may be modernized to "dyer," a person who dyes fabrics (but not the name of a person).

[27]*tired:* tugged.

[28]*in the bud ... idle bird:* A paraphrase will bring out Lyly's gift for compression. A bud is like an egg, the beginning of something; and a bud picked too early never blooms, just as an addled egg is rotten and produces no chicken. But if the bud, though it fully blossoms, becomes diseased, it still is not beautiful; similarly, if the egg is not addled but develops into an idle bird, it really is not any more of an ideal bird than an addled egg is.

[29]*huswife:* Lyly uses "huswife," the spelling in all the early editions, in two different senses—a woman who manages a household, and a hussy. The latter sense will be indicated by the original spelling "huswife," and the former by the modern spelling "housewife."

in heaven? The ostrich that taketh the greatest pride in her feathers picketh some of the worst out and burneth them. There is no tree but hath some blast, no countenance but hath some blemish; and shall Oxford, then, be blameless? I wish it were so, yet I cannot think it is so. But as it is, it may be better, and were it badder it is not the worst. I think there are few universities that have less faults than Oxford, many that have more, none but hath some.

But I commit my cause to the consciences of those that either know what I am, or can guess what I should be; the one will answer themselves in construing friendly, the other, if I knew them, I would satisfy reasonably. Thus loath to incur the suspicion of unkindness in not telling my mind, and not willing to make any excuse where there need no amends, I can neither crave pardon lest I should confess a fault, nor conceal my meaning lest I should be thought a fool. And so I end, yours assured to use.

John Lyly

Euphues: The Anatomy of Wit

There dwelt in Athens a young gentleman of great patrimony and of so comely a personage that it was doubted whether he were more bound to nature for the lineaments of his person or to fortune for the increase of his possessions. But nature, impatient of comparisons, and, as it were, disdaining a companion or copartner in her working, added to this comeliness of his body such a sharp capacity of mind that not only she proved fortune counterfeit, but was half of that opinion that she herself was only current. This young gallant, of more wit than wealth and yet of more wealth than wisdom, seeing himself inferior to none in pleasant conceits, thought himself superior to all in honest conditions, insomuch that he thought himself so apt to all things that he gave himself almost to nothing but practicing of those things commonly which are incident to these sharp wits—fine phrases, smooth quips, merry taunts, jesting without mean, and abusing mirth without measure.

As therefore the sweetest rose hath his prickle, the finest velvet his brack, the fairest flour his bran,[30] so the sharpest wit hath his wanton will and the holiest head his wicked way. And true it is that some men write, and most men believe, that in all perfect shapes a blemish bringeth rather a liking every way to the eyes than a loathing any way to the mind. Venus had her mole in her cheek which made her more amiable; Helen her scar in her chin which Paris called *cos amoris*, the whetstone of love; Aristippus his wart; Lycurgus his wen. So likewise in the disposition of the mind, either virtue is overshadowed with some vice or vice overcast with some virtue: Alexander valiant in war, yet given to wine; Tully eloquent in his glozes, yet vainglorious;[31] Solomon wise, yet too, too wanton; David holy, but yet an homicide; none more witty than Euphues,[32] yet at the first none more wicked.

The freshest colors soonest fade, the teenest[33] razor soonest turneth his edge, the finest cloth is soonest eaten with moths, and the cambric sooner stained than the coarse canvas. Which appeared well in this Euphues, whose wit being, like wax, apt to receive any impression, and bearing the head in his own hand,[34] either to use the rein or the spur, disdaining counsel, leaving his country, loathing his old acquaintance, thought either by wit to obtain some conquest or by shame to abide some conflict; who, preferring fancy before friends and his present humor before honor to come, laid reason in water,

[30]*brack . . . bran:* A "brack" is a flaw that may be found in cloth—in the weaving, through hard or careless use, or because of moths; "bran" (husk of the grain) is a different kind of flaw: since it is an excrescence, it should be removed from the grain to produce pure flour. In each example Lyly establishes an implied contrast between the ideal state of things and the flawed reality that we must accept.

[31]*Tully . . . glozes . . . vainglorious:* The sense is that although Tully (Cicero) makes flattering speeches (glozes) about others, he is at the same time boastful (vainglorious) about himself.

[32]*Euphues:* The hero's name is a Greek word meaning "well endowed," mentally and physically.

[33]*teenest:* probably, as Bond notes (I, 329), a popular corruption of "keenest"; in another work Lyly writes "setting a teen edge." The usual sense of "teen" (angry, vexed) does not fit.

[34]*bearing the head in his own hand:* The 1578 edition reads "having the bridle in his own hands," the sense of which is not greatly different, though in the revised phrasing there is more of a continuation of the metaphor having to do with "wax" and "impression." Compare a similar expression on p. 134: "The similitude you rehearse of the wax argueth your waxing and melting brain. . . ."

being too salt for his taste, and followed unbridled affection, most pleasant for his tooth.

When parents have more care how to leave their children wealthy than wise, and are more desirous to have them maintain the name than the nature of a gentleman; when they put gold into the hands of youth where they should put a rod under their girdle; when instead of awe they make them past grace and leave them rich executors of goods and poor executors of godliness—then is it no marvel that the son, being left rich by his father's will, become retchless[35] by his own will.[36]

But it hath been an old-said saw, and not of less truth than antiquity, that wit is the better if it be the dearer bought, as in the sequel of this history[37] shall most manifestly appear. It happened this young imp to arrive at Naples—a place of more pleasure than profit and yet of more profit than piety—the very walls and windows whereof showed it rather to be the tabernacle of Venus than the temple of Vesta. There was all things necessary and in readiness that might either allure the mind to lust or entice the heart to folly—a court more meet for an atheist than for one of Athens, for Ovid than for Aristotle, for a graceless lover than for a godly liver, more fitter for Paris than Hector, and meeter for Flora than Diana. Here my youth—whether for weariness he could not, or for wantonness would not, go any farther—determined to make his abode; whereby it is evidently seen that the fleetest fish swalloweth the delicatest bait, that the highest soaring hawk traineth to the lure, and that the wittiest brain is inveigled with the sudden views of alluring vanities.

Here he wanted no companions which courted him continually with sundry kinds of devices whereby they might either soak his

[35]*retchless:* reckless; the first syllable is to sound like "rich" in "being left rich."

[36]*who, preferring fancy before friends ... by his own will:* These lines, amounting to almost half a page, were inserted in the second edition. Very likely Lyly himself is responsible for the insertion, though no external proof exists. Whoever added the passage also had a little revising to do: after "conflict" and before "who, preferring fancy" he cut out the following clause from the 1578 edition: "and leaving the rule of reason, rashly ran into destruction." Then after "by his own will" he inserted "But" before "It hath been" to start the new paragraph.

[37]*sequel of this history:* The sense of "sequel" is "end" or "issue"; the reference is not to *Euphues and His England* (1580), but simply to how the present story "comes out."

purse to reap commodity or soothe his person to win credit, for he had guests and companions of all sorts. There frequented to his lodging as well the spider to suck poison of his fine wit, as the bee to gather honey, as well the drone as the dove, the fox as the lamb, as well Damocles to betray him as Damon to be true to him. Yet he behaved himself so warily that he singled[38] his game wisely. He could easily discern Apollo's music from Pan his pipe, and Venus' beauty from Juno's bravery, and the faith of Laelius from the flattery of Aristippus. He welcomed all but trusted none. He was merry but yet so wary that neither the flatterer could take advantage to entrap him in his talk nor the wisest any assurance of his friendship. Who, being demanded of one what countryman he was, he answered, "What countryman am I not? If I be in Crete I can lie, if in Greece I can shift, if in Italy I can court it.[39] If thou ask whose son I am also, I ask thee whose son I am not. I can carouse with Alexander, abstain with Romulus, eat with the Epicure, fast with the Stoic, sleep with Endymion, watch with Chrysippus"—using these speeches and other like.[40]

An old gentleman in Naples, seeing his pregnant wit, his eloquent tongue somewhat taunting yet with delight, his mirth without measure yet not without wit, his sayings vainglorious yet pithy, began to bewail his nurture and to muse at his nature, being incensed against the one as most pernicious and inflamed with the other as most precious. For he well knew that so rare a wit would in time either breed an intolerable trouble or bring an incomparable treasure to the commonweal; at the one he greatly pitied, at the other he rejoiced. Having, therefore, gotten opportunity to communicate with him his mind, with watery eyes (as one lamenting his wantonness) and smiling face (as one loving his wittiness) encountered him on this manner:

"Young gentleman, although my acquaintance be small to entreat you and my authority less to command you, yet my good will in

---

[38]*singled:* a hunting term, meaning to pick out and chase one animal (a deer, for example) from the herd. In the revised edition of 1579 "out" is omitted after "single," perhaps to eliminate an extra syllable: after the omission "singled his game" balances "behaved himself." Both "singled" and "singled out" were good usage.

[39]*lie ... shift ... court it:* To "court it" was to act the courtier, which, by implication, has a relationship with telling lies and living by fraud (shifting).

[40]*He could easily discern ... and other like:* These lines, amounting to about half a page, were inserted in the second edition.

giving you good counsel should induce you to believe me and my hoary hairs (ambassadors of experience) enforce you to follow me; for by how much the more I am a stranger to you, by so much the more you are beholding to me. Having, therefore, opportunity to utter my mind, I mean to be importunate with you to follow my meaning.

"As thy birth doth show the express and lively image of gentle blood, so thy bringing up seemeth to me to be a great blot to the lineage of so noble a brute. So that I am enforced to think that either thou didst want one to give thee good instructions, or that thy parents made thee a wanton with too much cockering; either they were too foolish in using no discipline, or thou too froward in rejecting their doctrine; either they willing to have thee idle, or thou willful to be ill employed. Did they not remember that which no man ought to forget, that the tender youth of a child is like the tempering of new wax—apt to receive any form? He that will carry a bull with Milo must use to carry him a calf also. He that coveteth to have a straight tree must not bow him being a twig. The potter fashioneth his clay when it is soft, and the sparrow is taught to come when he is young. As therefore the iron being hot receiveth any form with the stroke of the hammer, and keepeth it, being cold, forever, so the tender wit of a child, if with diligence it be instructed in youth, will with industry use those qualities in his age.

"They might also have taken example of the wise husbandmen who, in their fattest and most fertile ground, sow hemp before wheat, a grain that drieth up the superfluous moisture and maketh the soil more apt for corn; or of good gardeners who, in their curious knots,[41] mix hyssop with thyme as aiders the one to the growth of the other, the one being dry, the other moist; or of cunning painters who, for the whitest work, cast the blackest ground, to make the picture more amiable. If, therefore, thy father had been as wise an husbandman as he was a fortunate husband, or thy mother as good a housewife as she was a happy wife—if they had been both as good gardeners to keep their knot as they were grafters to bring forth such fruit, or as cunning painters as they were happy parents—no doubt they had sowed hemp before wheat (that is, discipline before affection), they had set hyssop with thyme (that is, manners with wit, the one to aid the other), and—to make thy dexterity more—they had cast a black

---

[41]*curious knots:* A "knot" was a flower bed or garden plot arranged in some complicated design; "curious" reinforces the central idea and means "ingenious" or "beautiful" (or both)·

ground for their white work (that is, they had mixed threats with fair looks).

"But things past are past calling again: it is too late to shut the stable door when the steed is stolen. The Trojans repented too late when their town was spoiled. Yet the remembrance of thy former follies might breed in thee a remorse of conscience and be a remedy against farther concupiscence. But now to the present time. The Lacedaemonians were wont to show their children drunken men and other wicked men, that, by seeing their filth, they might shun the like fault and avoid the like vices when they were at the like state. The Persians, to make their youth abhor gluttony, would paint an Epicure sleeping with meat in his mouth and most horribly overladen with wine, that, by the view of such monstrous sights, they might eschew the means of the like excess. The Parthians, to cause their youth to loathe the alluring trains of women's wiles and deceitful enticements, had most curiously carved in their houses a young man blind, besides whom was adjoined a woman so exquisite that, in some men's judgment, Pygmalion's image was not half so excellent —having one hand in his pocket as noting her theft, and holding a knife in the other hand to cut his throat.

"If the sight of such ugly shapes caused a loathing of the like sins, then, my good Euphues, consider their plight and beware of thine own peril. Thou art here in Naples a young sojourner, I an old senior; thou a stranger, I a citizen; thou secure, doubting no mishap; I sorrowful, dreading thy misfortune. Here mayest thou see that which I sigh to see, drunken sots wallowing in every house, in every chamber, yea, in every channel.[42] Here mayest thou behold that which I cannot without blushing behold nor without blubbering utter: those whose bellies be their gods, who offer their goods as sacrifice to their guts, who sleep with meat in their mouths, with sin in their hearts, and with shame in their houses. Here, yea, here, Euphues, mayest thou see, not the carved vizard of a lewd woman, but the incarnate visage of a lascivious wanton; not the shadow of love, but the substance of lust. My heart melteth in drops of blood to see a harlot with the one hand rob so many coffers and with the other to rip so many corses. Thou art here amidst the pikes between Scylla and Charybdis, ready if thou shun Syrtis to sink into Symplegades. Let the Lacedaemonian, the Persian, the Parthian, yea, the

---

[42]*channel:* gutter. Incidentally, "house" was changed to "corner" in the sixth edition of 1585. "Corner" goes better with "channel," but "house" fits better with "chamber."

Neapolitan, cause thee rather to detest such villainy at the sight and view of their vanity.

"Is it not far better to abhor sins by the remembrance of others' faults than by repentance of thine own follies? Is not he accounted most wise whom other men's harms do make most wary? But thou wilt haply say that although there be many things in Naples to be justly condemned, yet there are some things of necessity to be commended; and as thy will doth lean unto the one, so thy wit would also embrace the other.

"Alas, Euphues, by how much the more I love the high climbing of thy capacity, by so much the more I fear thy fall. The fine crystal is sooner crazed than the hard marble, the greenest beech burneth faster than the driest oak, the fairest silk is soonest soiled, and the sweetest wine turneth to the sharpest vinegar. The pestilence doth most rifest[43] infect the clearest complexion, and the caterpillar cleaveth unto the ripest fruit. The most delicate wit is allured with small enticement unto vice and most subject to yield unto vanity. If, therefore, thou do but hearken to the Sirens, thou wilt be enamored; if thou haunt their houses and places, thou shalt be enchanted. One drop of poison infecteth the whole tun of wine, one leaf of coloquintida marreth and spoileth the whole pot of porridge, one iron-mole defaceth the whole piece of lawn.[44]

"Descend into thine own conscience and consider with thyself the great difference between staring and stark blind, wit and wisdom, love and lust. Be merry but with modesty, be sober but not too sullen, be valiant but not too venturous. Let thy attire be comely but not costly, thy diet wholesome but not excessive. Use pastime as the word importeth—to pass the time in honest recreation. Mistrust no man without cause, neither be thou credulous without proof; be not light to follow every man's opinion, nor obstinate to stand in thine own conceit. Serve God, love God, fear God, and God will so bless thee as either thy heart can wish or thy friends desire. And so I end my counsel, beseeching thee to begin to follow it."

This old gentleman having finished his discourse, Euphues began to shape him answer in this sort:

[43]*most rifest:* "Rife" (readily occurring) is still good usage, but only the Elizabethans would think of putting it in the superlative and then reinforcing it with "most." A few pages below we find "more easier" and "solitarily alone."

[44]*iron-mole . . . lawn:* An "iron-mole" was a discolored spot or blemish, presumably the color of iron—like the mole on Venus' cheek. In this case the spot is on a fine piece of linen cloth (lawn).

"Father and friend—your age showeth the one, your honesty the other—I am neither so suspicious to mistrust your good will nor so sottish to mislike your good counsel; as I am, therefore, to thank you for the first, so it stands me upon to think better on the latter. I mean not to cavil with you as one loving sophistry, neither to control you as one having superiority; the one would bring my talk into the suspicion of fraud, the other convince me of folly.

"Whereas you argue, I know not upon what probabilities, but sure I am upon no proof, that my bringing-up should be a blemish to my birth. I answer, and swear, too, that you were not therein a little overshot; either you gave too much credit to the report of others, or too much liberty to your own judgment. You convince my parents of peevishness[45] in making me a wanton, and me of lewdness in rejecting correction. But so many men, so many minds: that may seem in your eye odious which in another's eye may be gracious. Aristippus a philosopher, yet who more courtly? Diogenes a philosopher, yet who more carterly?[46] Who more popular than Plato, retaining always good company? Who more envious than Timon, denouncing all human society? Who so severe as the Stoics, which like stocks[47] were moved with no melody? Who so secure as the Epicures, which wallowed in all kind of licentiousness? Though all men be made of one metal, yet they be not cast all in one mold. There is framed of the selfsame clay as well the tile to keep out water, as the pot to contain liquor, the sun doth harden the dirt and melt the wax, fire

[45]*convince my parents of peevishness:* The sense of "convince" here, and usually in Lyly, is "convict"; "peevishness" means "folly," though of what kind of folly the parents are guilty it is difficult to say. Apparently it is not mere neglect, for the end of the sentence seems to imply that the parents have tried to correct Euphues but in some unacceptable way.

[46]*courtly . . . carterly:* The sense of "carterly" (chosen because it sounds a little like "courtly") was "rude" or "ill-bred," though why the carter rather than, say, the tinker must contribute his trade name is not clear. As Clemons and Croll point out, Lyly does not deserve credit for the clever antithesis of courtly-carterly; Sir Thomas Wilson in *The Art of Rhetoric* (1553) already had used it.

[47]*Stoics . . . stocks:* The meaning of "stocks," a word then and now with many different meanings, is perhaps explained by another pun in *Euphues:* "Thought he him a Stoic that he would not be moved, or a stock that he could not?" (p. 154). In other words, a "stock" is a "stump" or a "block of wood" (though if the reader happens to think of the pillory, or "stockfish," or even "laughingstock," the latter used by Lyle on p. 181, the association may not be entirely off the mark). A "stock dove" (p. 179) is a wild pigeon that lives in a hollow tree.

maketh the gold to shine and the straw to smother, perfumes doth refresh the dove and kill the beetle, and the nature of the man disposeth that consent of the manners.

"Now whereas you seem to love my nature and loathe my nurture, you bewray your own weakness in thinking that nature may any ways be altered by education; and you have examples to confirm your pretense, so I have most evident and infallible arguments to serve for my purpose. It is natural for the vine to spread; the more you seek by art to alter it, the more in the end you shall augment it. It is proper for the palm tree to mount; the heavier you load it, the higher it sprouteth. Though iron be made soft with fire, it returneth to his hardness. Though the falcon be reclaimed to the fist, she retireth to her haggardness. The whelp of a mastiff will never be taught to retrieve the partridge. Education can have no show where the excellency of nature doth bear sway. The silly mouse will by no manner of means be tamed; the subtle fox may well be beaten, but never broken, from stealing his prey. If you pound spices, they smell the sweeter. Season the wood never so well, the wine will taste of the cask. Plant and translate the crab tree where and whensoever it please you, and it will never bear sweet apple—unless you graft by art, which nothing toucheth nature.[48] Infinite and innumerable were the examples I could allege and declare to confirm the force of nature and confute these, your vain and false forgeries, were not the repetition of them needless, having showed sufficient or bootless (seeing those alleged will not persuade you).[49] And can you be so unnatural, whom Dame Nature hath nourished and brought up so many years, to repine, as it were, against nature?

"The similitude you rehearse of the wax argueth your waxing and melting brain, and your example of the hot and hard iron showeth in you but cold and weak disposition. Do you not know that which all men do affirm and know, that black will take no other color? That the stone abeston,[50] being once made hot, will never be made cold? That fire cannot be forced downward? That nature will have course

---

[48]*unless you graft ... toucheth nature:* This line was added in the revised second edition.

[49]*having showed sufficient or bootless ... persuade you:* that is, the examples that I have given (showed) already are either convincing (sufficient) or not, and there is no point (bootless) in offering any more of them.

[50]*abeston:* asbestos (which, however, does not have the rhyme with "stone" that Lyly probably wants).

after kind? That everything will dispose itself according to nature? Can the Ethiop change or alter his skin, or the leopard his hue? Is it possible to gather grapes of thorns, or figs of thistles? Or to cause anything to strive against nature?

"But why go I about to praise nature, the which as yet was never any imp so wicked and barbarous, any Turk[51] so vile and brutish, any beast so dull and senseless, that could, or would, or durst, dispraise or contemn? Doth not Cicero conclude and allow that if we follow and obey nature we shall never err? Doth not Aristotle allege and confirm that nature frameth or maketh nothing in any point rude, vain, or unperfect? Nature was had in such estimation and admiration among the heathen people that she was reputed for the only goddess in heaven.

"If nature, then, have largely and bountifully endued me with her gifts, why deem you me so untoward and graceless? If she have dealt hardly with me, why extol you so much my birth? If nature bear no sway, why use you this adulation? If nature work the effect, what booteth any education? If nature be of strength or force, what availeth discipline or nurture? If of none, what helpeth nature? But let these sayings pass as known evidently and granted to be true, which none can or may deny, unless he be false or that he be an enemy to humanity.

"As touching my residence and abiding here in Naples, my youthly affections, my sports and pleasures, my pastimes, my common dalliance, my delights, my resort and company which daily use to visit me—although to you they breed more sorrow and care than solace and comfort because of your crabbed age, yet to me they bring more comfort and joy than care and grief, more bliss than bale, more happiness than heaviness, because of my youthful gentleness. Either you would have all men old as you are, or else you have quite forgotten that you yourself were young or ever knew young days; either in your youth you were a very vicious and ungodly man, or now (being aged) very superstitious and devout above measure.

"Put you no difference between the young flourishing bay tree and the old withered beech? No kind of distinction between the waxing and the waning of the moon? And between the rising and the setting of the sun? Do you measure the hot assaults of youth by the cold

---

[51]*Turk:* The example may seem odd to the modern reader, to whom a "Turk" is just a person from Turkey; but to the Elizabethan a "turk" (sometimes capitalized and sometimes not) was an infidel (non-Christian) and thus an object of scorn; the word also meant "dwarf" or "misshaped person."

skirmishes of age, whose years are subject to more infirmities than our youth? We merry, you melancholy; we zealous in affection, you jealous in all your doings; you testy without cause, we hasty for no quarrel; you careful, we careless; we bold, you fearful—we in all points contrary unto you, and you in all points unlike unto us.

"Seeing, therefore, we be repugnant each to the other in nature, would you have us alike in qualities? Would you have one potion ministered to the burning fever and to the cold palsy, one plaster to an old issue and a fresh wound, one salve for all sores, one sauce for all meats? No, no, Eubulus! But I will yield to more than either I am bound to grant, either thou able to prove. Suppose that which I never will believe, that Naples is a cankered storehouse of all strife, a common stews for all strumpets, the sink of shame, and the very nurse of all sin. Shall it therefore follow of necessity that all that are wooed of love should be wedded to lust? Will you conclude, as it were, *ex consequenti*, that whosoever arriveth here shall be enticed to folly and, being enticed, of force shall be entangled? No, no, it is the disposition of the thought that altereth the nature of the thing. The sun shineth upon the dunghill and is not corrupted, the diamond lieth in the fire and is not consumed, the crystal toucheth the toad and is not poisoned, the bird trochilus liveth by the mouth of the crocodile and is not spoiled, a perfect wit is neither bewitched with lewdness neither enticed with lasciviousness.

"Is it not common that the holm tree springeth amidst the beech? That the ivy spreadeth upon the hard stones? That the soft feather bed breaketh the hard blade? If experience have not taught you this, you have lived long and learned little, or if your moist brain have forgot it, you have learned much and profited nothing. But it may be that you measure my affections by your own fancies, and knowing yourself either too simple to raise the siege by policy or too weak to resist the assault by prowess, you deem me of as little wit as yourself or of less force, either of small capacity or of no courage. In my judgment, Eubulus, you shall as soon catch a hare with a tabor[52] as you shall persuade youth with your aged and overworn eloquence to such severity of life, which as yet there was never Stoic so strict nor Jesuit so superstitious neither votary so devout but would[53]

---

[52]*catch a hare with a tabor:* a proverb (Tilley, H160); "with a tabor" means "by playing a drum." Or perhaps we are to take the drum as a container, as in another proverb (Tilley, W416): "He catches the wind in a net."

[53]*never Stoic ... devout but would:* The wording of this clause remains

rather allow it in words than follow it in works, rather talk of it than try it. Neither were you such a saint in your youth that, abandoning all pleasures, all pastimes, and delights, you would choose rather to sacrifice the first fruits of your life to vain holiness than to youthly affections. But as to the stomach quatted[54] with dainties, all delicates seem queasy, and as he that surfeiteth with wine useth afterward to allay with water, so these old huddles[55] having overcharged their gorges with fancy, account all honest recreation mere folly and, having taken a surfeit of delight, seem now to savor it with despite.

"Seeing, therefore, it is labor lost for me to persuade you, and wind vainly wasted for you to exhort me, here I found you and here I leave you, having neither bought nor sold with you, but changed ware for ware. If you have taken little pleasure in my reply, sure I am that by your counsel I have reaped less profit. They that use to steal honey burn hemlock to smoke the bees from their hives, and it may be that to get some advantage of me, you have used these smoky arguments, thinking thereby to smother me with the conceit of strong imagination. But as the chameleon though he have most guts draweth least breath, or as the elder tree though he be fullest of pith is farthest from strength, so though your reasons seem inwardly to yourself somewhat substantial and your persuasions pithy in your own conceit, yet being well weighed without, they be shadows without substance and weak without force. The bird taurus hath a great voice but a small body, the thunder a great clap yet but a little stone,[56] the empty vessel giveth a greater sound than the full barrel. I mean not to apply it, but look into yourself and you shall certainly find it. And thus I leave you seeking it; but were

---

the same through the first two editions, but in the third it reads as follows: "never Stoic in precepts so strict, neither any in life so precise, but would. ..." It is possible that Lyly may be responsible for this elimination of a derogatory reference to Jesuits; but usually the third edition follows the second very closely, and one suspects that Lyly had nothing to do with the printing as a whole or with this particular passage.

[54]*quatted:* glutted.

[55]*huddles:* The primary sense seems to be "miserly and gluttonous old people"; but there may be a hint of two other senses of "huddle"— "confusion" and "group" (in this case the tendency for old people to be found together in a group).

[56]*thunder ... little stone:* Pliny the Elder in his *Natural History* (Book XXXVII, chapter 55) reports, with commendable skepticism, the popular belief not only that the stone brontea falls with thunder, but that it also has the power to quench fire started by lightning.

it not that my company stay my coming I would surely help you to look it, but I am called hence by my acquaintance."

Euphues, having thus ended his talk, departed, leaving this old gentleman in a great quandary; who, perceiving that he was more inclined to wantonness than to wisdom, with a deep sigh, the tears trickling down his cheeks, said:

"Seeing thou wilt not buy counsel at the first hand good cheap, thou shalt buy repentance at the second hand, at such an unreasonable rate, that thou wilt curse thy hard pennyworth and ban thy hard heart. Ah, Euphues, little dost thou know that if thy wealth waste, thy wit will give but small warmth, and if thy wit incline to willfulness that thy wealth will do thee no great good. If the one had been employed to thrift, the other to learning, it had been hard to conjecture whether thou shouldest have been more fortunate by riches or happy by wisdom, whether more esteemed in the commonweal for wealth to maintain war or for counsel to conclude peace. But, alas, why do I pity that in thee which thou seemest to praise in thyself?"

And so saying,[57] he immediately went to his own house, heavily bewailing the young man's unhappiness.

Here ye may behold, gentlemen, how lewdly[58] wit standeth in his own light, how he deemeth no penny good silver but his own, preferring the blossom before the fruit, the bud before the flower, the green blade before the ripe ear of corn, his own wit before all men's wisdoms. Neither is that geason,[59] seeing for the most part it is proper to all those of sharp capacity to esteem of themselves as most proper. If one be hard in conceiving, they pronounce him a dolt;[60] if given to study, they proclaim him a dunce; if merry, a jester; if sad, a saint; if full of words, a sot; if without speech, a cipher. If one argue with them boldly, then is he impudent; if coldly, an innocent. If there be reasoning of divinity, they cry *quae supra nos, nihil ad*

[57]*Ah, Euphues, little dost thou know . . . And so saying:* These lines, amounting to something less than half a page, appeared for the first time in the second edition. "And so saying" apparently was added to provide a smooth transition back into the text of the first edition.

[58]*lewdly:* Here the sense is "ignorantly," "clumsily," and perhaps "selfishly." But later (p. 164) the sense of "lewdness" is "lasciviousness."

[59]*geason:* uncommon (with perhaps a hint of another sense—barren).

[60]*hard in conceiving . . . a dolt:* Compare the passage early in *The Schoolmaster* (1570) where Roger Ascham discusses "hard wits" and "quick wits"; the former "proveth always the best," for they are "hard to receive but sure to keep." With "hard" Ascham associates "rough" and "staffish" (rigid, stubborn).

nos; if of humanity, *sententias loquitur carnifex.* Hereof cometh such great familiarity between the ripest wits when they shall see the disposition the one of the other, the *sympathia* of affections and, as it were, but a pair of shears to go between their natures;[61] one flattereth another in his own folly and layeth cushions under the elbow of his fellow when he seeth him take a nap with fancy, and as their wit wresteth them to vice, so it forgeth them some feat excuse to cloak their vanity.

Too much study doth intoxicate their brains, "For," say they, "although iron the more it is used the brighter it is, yet silver with much wearing doth waste to nothing; though the cammock the more it is bowed the better it serveth,[62] yet the bow the more it is bent and occupied,[63] the weaker it waxeth; though the camomile the more it is trodden and pressed down the more it spreadeth, yet the violet the oftener it is handled and touched the sooner it withereth and decayeth. Besides this, a fine wit, a sharp sense, a quick understanding, is able to attain to more in a moment or a very little space than a dull and blockish head in a month. The scythe cutteth far better and smoother than the saw, the wax yieldeth better and sooner to the seal than the steel to the stamp, the smooth and plain beech is easier to be carved than the knotty box. For neither is there anything but that hath his contraries."

Such is the nature of these novices that think to have learning without labor and treasure without travail—either not understanding, or else not remembering, that the finest edge is made with the blunt whetstone and the fairest jewel fashioned with the hard hammer. I go not about, gentlemen, to inveigh against wit, for then I were witless, but frankly to confess mine own little wit. I have ever thought so superstitiously of wit, that I fear I have committed idolatry against wisdom; and if nature had dealt so beneficially with me to have given me any wit, I should have been readier in the defense of it to

---

[61]*pair of shears . . . their natures:* a proverb (Tilley, P36), meaning that the ripest wits draw together and become alike (as though they were pieces of the same cloth cut by shears). The first Latin quotation, above (*"quae supra . . . ad nos"*) Lyly himself apparently translated "Things above us are not for us" (see Bond, II, 41.31); the second Latin quotation translates "The sentence is pronounced by the executioner."

[62]*cammock . . . bowed the better it serveth:* The cammock is a naturally curved or crooked stick, and the implication probably is that it therefore serves well in a game in which one needs to drive a ball with a stick (one thinks now of golf or hockey).

[63]*occupied:* used.

have made an apology, than any way to turn to apostasy. But this I
note, that, for the most part, they stand so on their pantofles[64] that
they be secure of perils, obstinate in their own opinions, impatient of
labor, apt to conceive wrong, credulous to believe the worst, ready
to shake off their old acquaintance without cause, and to condemn
them without color. All which humors are by so much the more
easier to be purged by how much the less they have festered the
sinews. But return we again to Euphues.

Euphues having sojourned by the space of two months in Naples,
whether he were moved by the courtesy of a young gentleman
named Philautus or enforced by destiny, whether his pregnant wit
or his pleasant conceits wrought the greater liking in the mind of
Euphues, I know not for certainty; but Euphues showed such entire
love towards him that he seemed to make small account of any
others, determining to enter into such an inviolable league of friendship with him as neither time by piecemeal should impair, neither
fancy utterly dissolve, nor any suspicion infringe.

"I have read," saith he, "and well I believe it, that a friend is in
prosperity a pleasure, a solace in adversity, in grief a comfort, in joy
a merry companion, at all times another I, in all places the express
image of mine own person—insomuch that I cannot tell whether the
immortal gods have bestowed any gift upon mortal men either more
noble or more necessary than friendship. Is there anything in the
world to be reputed—I will not say compared—to friendship? Can
any treasure in this transitory pilgrimage be of more value than a
friend, in whose bosom thou mayest sleep secure without fear, whom
thou mayest make partner of all thy secrets without suspicion of
fraud and partaker of all thy misfortune without mistrust of fleeting,[65]
who will account thy bale his bane, thy mishap his misery, the
pricking of thy finger the piercing of his heart? But whither am I
carried? Have I not also learned that one should eat a bushel of salt
with him whom he meaneth to make his friend,[66] that trial maketh
trust, that there is falsehood in fellowship? And what then? Doth

[64]*they stand . . . pantofles:* a proverb (Tilley, P43); "they" refers back
to "novices." The idiom is similar to the present-day idiom, "to stand
on one's own hind legs, " except that the Elizabethan expression is derogatory, involving vanity or pretension. Pantofles were indoor slippers.

[65]*fleeting:* unfaithfulness, fickleness (applied later, p. 182 to Lucilla).

[66]*eat a bushel of salt . . . friend:* that is, eat together, have meals together,
at his house; since salt is necessary to food, the word "salt" can stand for
the word "food"; "bushel," often omitted from the idiom, is to imply an
eating together many times.

not the sympathy of manners make the conjunction of minds? Is it not a byword, like will to like? Not so common as commendable it is to see young gentlemen choose them such friends with whom they may seem, being absent, to be present; being asunder, to be conversant; being dead, to be alive. I will, therefore, have Philautus for my fere, and by so much the more I make myself sure to have Philautus, by how much the more I view in him the lively image of Euphues."

Although there be none so ignorant that doth not know, neither any so impudent that will not confess friendship to be the jewel of human joy, yet whosoever shall see this amity grounded upon a little affection will soon conjecture that it shall be dissolved upon a light occasion, as in the sequel of Euphues and Philautus you shall see whose hot love waxed soon cold. For as the best wine doth make the sharpest vinegar, so the deepest love turneth to the deadliest hate. Who deserved the most blame? In mine opinion it is doubtful, and so difficult that I dare not presume to give verdict. For love being the cause for which so many mischiefs have been attempted, I am not yet persuaded whether[67] of them was most to be blamed, but certainly neither of them was blameless. I appeal to your judgment, gentlemen, not that I think any of you of the like disposition able to decide the question, but being of deeper discretion than I am, are more fit to debate the quarrel. Though the discourse of their friendship and falling out be somewhat long, yet being somewhat strange, I hope the delightfulness of the one will attenuate the tediousness of the other.

Euphues had continual access to the place of Philautus and no little familiarity with him; and finding him at convenient leisure, in these short terms unfolded his mind unto him:

"Gentleman and friend, the trial I have had of thy manners cutteth off divers terms which to another I would have used in the like matter. And since a long discourse argueth folly, and delicate words incur the suspicion of flattery, I am determined to use neither of them, knowing either of them to breed offense. Weighing with myself the force of friendship by the effects, I studied ever since my first coming to Naples to enter league with such a one as might direct my steps, being a stranger, and resemble my manners, being a scholar; the which two qualities as I find in you able to satisfy my desire, so I hope I shall find a heart in you willing to accomplish my request. Which if I may obtain, assure yourself that Damon to his

[67]*whether:* which of the two.

Pythias, Pylades to his Orestes, Titus to his Gysippus, Theseus to his Pirithoüs, Scipio to his Laelius, was never found more faithful than Euphues will be to Philautus."

Philautus by how much the less he looked for this discourse, by so much the more he liked it, for he saw all qualities both of body and mind in Euphues; unto whom he replied as followeth:

"Friend Euphues—for so your talk warranteth me to term you—I dare neither use a long process, neither a loving speech, lest unwittingly I should cause you to convince me of those things which you have already condemned. And verily I am bold to presume upon your courtesy, since you yourself have used so little curiosity, persuading myself that my short answer will work as great an effect in you as your few words did in me. And seeing that we resemble, as you say, each other in qualities, it cannot be that the one should differ from the other in courtesy. Seeing the sincere affection of the mind cannot be expressed by the mouth and that no art can unfold the entire love of the heart, I am earnestly to beseech you not to measure the firmness of my faith by the fewness of my words, but rather think that the overflowing waves of good will leave no passage for many words. Trial shall prove trust. Here is my hand, my heart, my lands, and my life at thy commandment. Thou mayest well perceive that I did believe thee that so soon I did love thee, and I hope thou wilt the rather love me in that I did believe thee."

Either Euphues and Philautus stood in need of friendship or were ordained to be friends. Upon so short warning to make so soon a conclusion might seem, in mine opinion, if it continued, miraculous; if shaken off, ridiculous. But[68] after many embracings and protestations one to another, they walked to dinner, where they wanted neither meat, neither music, neither any other pastime; and having banqueted, to digest their sweet confections, they danced all that afternoon. They used not only one board, but one bed, one book—if so be it they thought not one too many. Their friendship augmented every day, insomuch that the one could not refrain the company of the other one minute. All things went in common between them, which all men accounted commendable.

Philautus being a town-born child, both for his own countenance and the great countenance[69] which his father had while he lived,

---

[68]*Either Euphues . . . ridiculous. But:* These two sentences plus "But" first appeared in the second edition.

[69]*own countenance . . . great countenance:* The first "countenance" seems to mean "conduct" and the second, referring to the father, "reputation."

crept into credit with Don Ferardo, one of the chief governors of the city. Who, although he had a courtly crew of gentlewomen sojourning in his palace, yet his daughter, heir to his whole revenues, stained the beauty of them all; whose modest bashfulness caused the other[70] to look wan for envy; whose lily cheeks, dyed with a vermilion red, made the rest to blush for shame. For as the finest ruby staineth the color of the rest that be in place, or as the sun dimmeth the moon that she cannot be discerned, so this gallant girl, more fair than fortunate, and yet more fortunate than faithful, eclipsed the beauty of them all and changed their colors. Unto her had Philautus access, who won her by right of love and should have worn her by right of law had not Euphues by strange destiny broken the bonds of marriage and forbidden the banns of matrimony.

It happened that Don Ferardo had occasion to go to Venice about certain his own affairs, leaving his daughter the only steward of his household, who spared not to feast Philautus, her friend, with all kinds of delights and delicates, reserving only her honesty[71] as the chief stay of her honor. Her father being gone, she sent for her friend to supper; who came not, as he was accustomed, solitarily alone, but accompanied with his friend, Euphues. The gentlewoman, whether it were for niceness or for niggardness of courtesy, gave him such a cold welcome that he repented that he was come.

Euphues, though he knew himself worthy every way to have a good countenance, yet could he not perceive her willing any way to lend him a friendly look. Yet, lest he should seem to want gestures or to be dashed out of conceit with her coy countenance, he addressed him to a gentlewoman called Livia, unto whom he uttered this speech:

"Fair lady, if it be the guise of Italy to welcome strangers with strangeness, I must needs say the custom is strange and the country barbarous; if the manner of ladies to salute gentlemen with coyness, then I am enforced to think the women without courtesy to use such welcome, and the men past shame that will come. But hereafter I will either bring a stool on mine arm for an unbidden guest, or a vizard on my face for a shameless gossip."

Livia replied, "Sir, our country is civil and our gentlewomen are courteous; but in Naples it is counted a jest at every word to say, 'In faith, you are welcome.'"

[70]*the other:* the others (plural), perhaps thought of as a single group ("courtly crew").
[71]*honesty:* chastity.

As she was yet talking, supper was set on the board. Then Philautus spake thus unto Lucilla: "Yet,[72] gentlewoman, I was the bolder to bring my shadow with me (meaning Euphues), knowing that he should be the better welcome for my sake."

Unto whom the gentlewoman replied, "Sir, as I never when I saw you thought that you came without your shadow, so now I cannot a little marvel to see you so overshot in bringing a new shadow with you."

Euphues, though he perceived her coy nip, seemed not to care for it but, taking her by the hand, said, "Fair lady, seeing the shade doth often shield your beauty from the parching sun, I hope you will the better esteem of the shadow; and by so much the less it ought to be offensive, by how much the less it is able to offend you; and by so much the more you ought to like it, by how much the more you use to lie in it."

"Well, gentleman," answered Lucilla, "in arguing of the shadow we forego the substance. Pleaseth it you, therefore, to sit down to supper."

And so they all sat down. But Euphues fed of one dish which ever stood before him—the beauty of Lucilla. Here Euphues at the first sight was so kindled with desire that almost he was like to burn to coals.

Supper being ended, the order was in Naples that the gentlewomen would desire to hear some discourse, either concerning love or learning. And although Philautus was requested, yet he posted it over to Euphues, whom he knew most fit for that purpose. Euphues, being thus tied to the stake by their importunate entreaty, began as followeth:

"He that worst may is alway enforced to hold the candle; the weakest must still to the wall.[73] Where none will, the devil himself must bear the cross. But were it not, gentlewomen, that your lust[74]

---

[72]*Yet, lest he should seem to want . . . Lucilla: "Yet:* These lines, amounting to half a page, appeared for the first time in the second edition.

[73]*He that worst may . . . to the wall:* two proverbs back to back (Tilley, C40 and W185). Apparently the sense of the first one is that when a person is in a subordinate position, then he is the one who has to hold the candle for another to see by.

[74]*lust:* Perhaps one should return to "list" (wishes or desires of a rather general nature), the reading of the first edition. "Lust," the emended reading of the second edition, has several senses, including the one just given for "list"; if Lyly made the emendation, the reason may have been that he wanted the word to be ambiguous.

stands for law, I would borrow so much leave as to resign mine office to one of you, whose experience in love hath made you learned and whose learning hath made you so lovely; for me to entreat of the one, being a novice, or to discourse of the other, being a truant, I may well make you weary but never the wiser, and give you occasion rather to laugh at my rashness than to like my reasons. Yet I care the less to excuse my boldness to you who were the cause of my blindness. And since I am at mine own choice either to talk of love or of learning, I had rather for this time be deemed an unthrift in rejecting profit than a Stoic in renouncing pleasure.

"It hath been a question often disputed, but never determined, whether the qualities of the mind or the composition of the man cause women most to like, or whether beauty or wit move men most to love. Certes, by how much the more the mind is to be preferred before the body, by so much the more the graces of the one are to be preferred before the gifts of the other; which if it be so, that the contemplation of the inward quality ought to be respected more than the view of the outward beauty, then doubtless women either do or should love those best whose virtue is best, not measuring the deformed man with the reformed mind. The foul toad hath a fair stone in his head, the fine gold is found in the filthy earth, the sweet kernel lieth in the hard shell, virtue is harbored in the heart of him that most men esteem misshapen.

"Contrariwise, if we respect more the outward shape than the inward habit, good God, into how many mischiefs do we fall! Into what blindness are we led! Do we not commonly see that in painted pots is hidden the deadliest poison, that in the greenest grass is the greatest serpent, in the clearest water the ugliest toad? Doth not experience teach us that in the most curious sepulcher are enclosed rotten bones, that the cypress tree beareth a fair leaf but no fruit, that the estridge[75] carrieth fair feathers but rank flesh? How frantic are those lovers which are carried away with the gay glistering of the fine face, the beauty whereof is parched with the summer's blaze and chipped[76] with the winter's blast; which is of so short continuance that it fadeth before one perceive it flourish, of so small profit that it poisoneth those that possess it, of so little value with the wise that they account it a delicate bait with a deadly hook, a sweet panther with a devouring paunch, a sour poison in a silver pot.

[75]*estridge:* ostrich (also spelled "estrich").

[76]*chipped:* The sense is "chapped" (the actual spelling of the 1587 edition); but the vowel sound in "chipped" may be important to Lyly.

"Here I could enter into discourse of such fine dames as, being in love with their own looks, make such coarse account of their passionate lovers; for commonly if they be adorned with beauty, they be so strait-laced and made so high in the instep that they disdain them most that most desire them. It is a world to see the doting of their lovers and their dealing with them, the revealing of whose subtle trains[77] would cause me to shed tears, and you, gentlewomen, to shut your modest ears. Pardon me, gentlewomen, if I unfold every wile and show every wrinkle of women's disposition. Two things do they cause their servants to vow unto them, secrecy and sovereignty— the one to conceal their enticing sleights, by the other to assure themselves of their only service. Again—but, ho there! If I should have waded any further and sounded the depth of their deceit, I should either have procured your displeasure, or incurred the suspicion of fraud; either armed you to practice the like subtlety, or accused myself of perjury. But I mean not to offend your chaste minds with the rehearsal of their unchaste manners, whose ears I perceive to glow and hearts to be grieved at that which I have already uttered; not that amongst you there be any such, but that in your sex there should be any such.

"Let not gentlewomen, therefore, make too much of their painted sheath;[78] let them not be so curious in their own conceit or so currish to their loyal lovers. When the black crow's foot shall appear in their eye or the black ox tread on their foot;[79] when their beauty shall be like the blasted rose, their wealth wasted, their bodies worn, their faces wrinkled, their fingers crooked, who will like of them in their age who loved none in their youth? If you will be cherished when you be old, be courteous while you be young; if you look for comfort in your hoary hairs, be not coy when you have your golden locks; if

[77]*subtle trains:* traps or lures of no ordinary kind. In hunting, the word "train" meant something fairly concrete—a lure consisting of bait laid in a line or trail to attract a wild animal into a trap.

[78]*painted sheath:* showy exterior (of their bodies and clothing), an aspect of women's "subtle trains." Literally, "sheath" referred to a case for a sword or dagger, and the proverb-minded Lyly probably assumes that his reader will be reminded of the proverb (Tilley, S1048): "A leaden sword in a golden (painted) sheath."

[79]*black crow's foot . . . black ox tread on their foot:* Two symptoms of old age are wrinkles around the eyes and an infirm step. The black ox is the subject of a proverb (Tilley, O103); Tilley's quotations show that some users of the proverb have in mind not old age but marriage and family responsibility.

you would be embraced in the waning of your bravery, be not squeamish in the waxing of your beauty; if you desire to be kept like the roses when they have lost their color, smell sweet as the rose doth in the bud; if you would be tasted for old wine, be in the mouth a pleasant grape—so shall you be cherished for your courtesy, comforted for your honesty, embraced for your amity; so shall you be preserved with the sweet rose, and drunk with the pleasant wine.

"Thus far I am bold, gentlewomen, to counsel those that be coy, that they weave not the web of their own woe nor spin the thread of their own thralldom by their own overthwartness.[80] And seeing we are even in the bowels of love, it shall not be amiss to examine whether man or woman be soonest allured, whether be most constant the male or the female. And in this point I mean not to be mine own carver, lest I should seem either to pick a thank with men or a quarrel with women. If, therefore, it might stand with your pleasure, Mistress Lucilla, to give your censure, I would take the contrary; for sure I am though your judgment be sound, yet affection will shadow it."

Lucilla, seeing his pretense, thought to take advantage of his large proffer; unto whom she said, "Gentleman, in mine opinion, women are to be won with every wind, in whose sex there is neither force to withstand the assaults of love, neither constancy to remain faithful. And because your discourse hath hitherto bred delight, I am loath to hinder you in the sequel of your devices."

Euphues, perceiving himself to be taken napping, answered as followeth: "Mistress Lucilla, if you speak as you think, these gentlewomen present have little cause to thank you; if you cause me to commend women, my tale will be accounted a mere trifle and your words the plain truth. Yet knowing promise to be debt, I will pay it with performance. And I would the gentlemen here present were as ready to credit my proof as the gentlewomen are willing to hear their own praises, or I as able to overcome as Mistress Lucilla would be content to be overthrown. Howsoever the matter shall fall out, I am of the surer side: for if my reasons be weak, then is our sex strong; if forcible, then your judgment feeble; if I find truth on my side, I hope I shall, for my wages, win the good will of women; if I want proof, then, gentlewomen, of necessity you must yield to men. But to the matter.

"Touching the yielding to love, albeit their hearts seem tender, yet

[80]*overthwartness:* perversity, obstinate contrariness. Literally, "overthwart" means "crosswise" or "oblique."

they harden them like the stone of Sicilia, the which the more it is beaten the harder it is; for being framed, as it were, of the perfection of men, they be free from all such cogitations as may any way provoke them to uncleanness, insomuch as they abhor the light love of youth which is grounded upon lust and dissolved upon every light occasion. When they see the folly of men turn to fury, their delight to doting, their affection to frenzy; when they see them, as it were, pine in pleasure and to wax pale through their own peevishness, their suits, their service, their letters, their labors, their loves, their lives seem to them so odious that they harden their hearts against such concupiscence to the end they might convert them from rashness to reason, from such lewd disposition to honest discretion. Hereof it cometh that men accuse women of cruelty because they themselves want civility, they account them full of wiles in not yielding to their wickedness, faithless for resisting their filthiness. But I had almost forgot myself. You shall pardon me, Mistress Lucilla, for this time, if thus abruptly, I finish my discourse. It is neither for want of good will or lack of proof, but that I feel in myself such alteration that I can scarcely utter one word. Ah, Euphues, Euphues."

The gentlewomen were struck into such a quandary with this sudden change that they all changed color. But Euphues, taking Philautus by the hand and giving the gentlewomen thanks for their patience and his repast, bade them all farewell and went immediately to his chamber.

But Lucilla, who now began to fry in the flames of love, all the company being departed to their lodgings, entered into these terms and contrarieties:

"Ah, wretched wench, Lucilla, how art thou perplexed! What a doubtful fight dost thou feel betwixt faith and fancy, hope and fear, conscience and concupiscence. Oh, my Euphues, little dost thou know the sudden sorrow that I sustain for thy sweet sake. Whose wit hath bewitched me, whose rare qualities have deprived me of mine old quality, whose[81] courteous behavior without curiosity,

---

[81]*whose:* The 1578 reading, "whose," seems to be what Lyly intended; and the emended reading of both 1579 editions, "most," seems to be a mistake of some kind, perhaps by the compositor. The break in strict parallelism within the sentence is not perhaps the main issue, for similar breaks may be found throughout. What seems unlikely is that, by changing one word, Lyly would want the whole clause, "most courteous behavior without curiosity," to refer not to Euphues, as in the 1578 phrasing, but to Lucilla—and yet that is what the change would seem to involve.

whose comely feature without fault, whose filed speech without fraud, hath wrapped me in this misfortune.

"And canst thou, Lucilla, be so light of love in forsaking Philautus to fly to Euphues? Canst thou prefer a stranger before thy countryman, a starter[82] before thy companion? Why, Euphues doth perhaps desire my love, but Philautus hath deserved it. Why, Euphues' feature is worthy as good as I, but Philautus his faith is worthy a better. Aye, but the latter love is most fervent; aye, but the first ought to be most faithful. Aye, but Euphues hath greater perfection; aye, but Philautus hath deeper affection.

"Ah, fond wench, dost thou think Euphues will deem thee constant to him, when thou hast been unconstant to his friend? Weenest thou that he will have no mistrust of thy faithfulness, when he hath had trial of thy fickleness? Will he have no doubt of thine honor, when thou thyself callest thine honesty in question? Yes, yes, Lucilla, well doth he know that the glass once crazed will with the least clap be cracked, that the cloth which staineth with milk will soon lose his color with vinegar, that the eagle's wing will waste the feather as well of the phoenix as of the pheasant, that she that hath been faithless to one will never be faithful to any.

"But can Euphues convince me of fleeting, seeing for his sake I break my fidelity? Can he condemn me of disloyalty, when he is the only cause of my disliking? May he justly condemn me of treachery who hath this testimony as trial of my good will? Doth not he remember that the broken bone, once set together, is stronger than ever it was? That the greatest blot is taken off with the pumice? That though the spider poison the fly, she cannot infect the bee? That although I have been light to Philautus, I may be lovely to Euphues? It is not my desire but his deserts that moveth my mind to this choice, neither the want of the like good will in Philautus but the lack of the like good qualities that removeth my fancy from the one to the other.

"For as the bee that gathereth honey out of the weed, when she

[82]*starter:* The *OED* quotes this very passage to illustrate the following sense: "one given to wandering; one who cannot stay long in one place." If Lucilla is referring to Euphues' past (his leaving Athens), then the *OED* sense is correct, and the implication then would be that the wandering Euphues may therefore leave Naples and Lucilla in the near future. But it seems more likely that she is thinking of the present and Euphues' position in Naples; in that case the sense of "starter" is "upstart," "newcomer."

espieth the fair flower flieth to the sweetest; or as the kind[83] spaniel, though he hunt after birds yet forsakes them to retrieve the partridge; or as we commonly feed on beef hungerly at the first, yet seeing the quail more dainty change our diet—so I, although I loved Philautus for his good properties, yet seeing Euphues to excel him, I ought by nature to like him better. By so much the more, therefore, my change is to be excused, by how much the more my choice is excellent; and by so much the less I am to be condemned, by how much the more Euphues is to be commended. Is not the diamond of more value than the ruby because he is of more virtue? Is not the emerald preferred before the sapphire for his wonderful property? Is not Euphues more praiseworthy than Philautus, being more witty?

"But fie, Lucilla, why dost thou flatter thyself in thine own folly? Canst thou feign Euphues thy friend, whom by thine own words thou hast made thy foe? Didst not thou accuse women of inconstancy? Didst not thou account them easy to be won? Didst not thou condemn them of weakness? What sounder argument can he have against thee than thine own answer, what better proof than thine own speech, what greater trial than thine own talk? If thou hast belied women, he will judge thee unkind; if thou have revealed the truth, he must needs think thee unconstant; if he perceive thee to be won with a nut, he will imagine that thou wilt be lost with an apple;[84] if he find thee wanton before thou be wooed, he will guess thou wilt be wavering when thou art wedded.

"But suppose that Euphues love thee, that Philautus leave thee: will thy father, thinkest thou, give thee liberty to live after thine own lust? Will he esteem him worthy to inherit his possessions whom he accounteth unworthy to enjoy thy person? Is it like that he will match thee in marriage with a stranger, with a Grecian, with a mean man? Aye, but what knoweth my father whether he be wealthy, whether his revenues be able to countervail my father's lands, whether his birth be noble, yea or no? Can anyone make doubt of his gentle blood that seeth his gentle conditions? Can his honor be called into question whose honesty is so great? Is he to be thought thriftless who in all qualities of the mind is peerless? No, no, the tree

[83]*kind:* "kindly" or "gentle" may possibly be a secondary meaning, but the primary sense is "acting according to the nature of" a spaniel (which just happens to prefer partridges).

[84]*won with a nut . . . lost with an apple:* a proverb (Tilley, A295) that is usually expressed the other way round: "Won with an apple and lost with a nut." Possibly the reversal is deliberate, and not just a failure to remember correctly, to emphasize all the more the central idea.

is known by his fruit, the gold by his touch, the son by the sire. And as the soft wax receiveth whatsoever print be in the seal and showeth no other impression, so the tender babe being sealed with his father's gifts representeth his image most lively.

"But were I once certain of Euphues' good will, I would not so superstitiously account of my father's ill will. Time hath weaned me from my mother's teat, and age rid me from my father's correction. When children are in their swath-clouts,[85] then are they subject to the whip and ought to be careful of the rigor of their parents. As for me, seeing I am not fed with their pap, I am not to be led by their persuasions. Let my father use what speeches he list, I will follow mine own lust.

"Lust, Lucilla? What sayest thou? No, no, mine own love I should have said; for I am as far from lust as I am from reason, and as near to love as I am to folly. Then stick to thy determination and show thyself what love can do, what love dares do, what love hath done.[86] Albeit I can no way quench the coals of desire with forgetfulness, yet will I rake them up in the ashes of modesty. Seeing I dare not discover my love for maidenly shamefastness, I will dissemble it till time I have opportunity. And I hope so to behave myself, as Euphues shall think me his own and Philautus persuade himself I am none but his. But I would to God Euphues would repair hither, that the sight of him might mitigate some part of my martyrdom."

She, having thus discoursed with herself her own miseries, cast herself on the bed. And there let her lie. And return we to Euphues, who was so caught in the gin of folly that he neither could comfort himself nor durst ask counsel of his friend, suspecting that which indeed was true, that Philautus was corrival with him and cookmate[87] with Lucilla. Amidst, therefore, these his extremities between hope and fear, he uttered these or the like speeches:

"What is he, Euphues, that knowing thy wit and seeing thy folly, but will rather punish thy lewdness than pity thy heaviness? Was there ever any so fickle so soon to be allured, any ever so faithless to deceive his friend, ever any so foolish to bathe himself in his own misfortune? Too true it is that as the sea crab swimmeth always

---

[85]*swath-clouts:* swaddling (baby) clothes.

[86]*Time hath weaned me . . . what love hath done:* These lines, amounting to about half a page, first appeared in the second edition.

[87]*cookmate:* cockmate, or chief friend; the spelling was changed to "cockmate" in the tenth edition of 1593.

against the stream, so wit always striveth against wisdom; and as
the bee is oftentimes hurt with her own honey, so is wit not seldom
plagued with his own conceit.

"Oh, ye gods, have ye ordained for every malady a medicine, for
every sore a salve, for every pain a plaster, leaving only love remediless? Did ye deem no man so mad to be entangled with desire? Or
thought ye them worthy to be tormented that were so misled? Have
ye dealt more favorably with brute beasts than with reasonable
creatures? The filthy sow when she is sick eateth the sea crab and is
immediately recured, the tortoise having tasted the viper sucketh
origanum and is quickly revived, the bear ready to pine licketh up
the ants and is recovered, the dog having surfeited to procure his
vomit eateth grass and findeth remedy, the hart being pierced with
the dart runneth out of hand to the herb dictanum and is healed.
And can men by no herb, by no art, by no way procure a remedy
for the impatient disease of love? Ah, well, I perceive that love is
not unlike the fig tree, whose fruit is sweet, whose root is more
bitter than the claw of a bitter;[88] or like the apple in Persia, whose
blossom savoreth like honey, whose bud is more sour than gall.

"But, oh, impiety! Oh, broad blasphemy against the heavens! Wilt
thou be so impudent, Euphues, to accuse the gods of iniquity? No,
fond fool, no. Neither is it forbidden us by the gods to love, by whose
divine providence we are permitted to live; neither do we want
remedies to recure our maladies, but reason to use the means. But
why go I about to hinder the course of love with the discourse of
law? Hast thou not read, Euphues, that he that loppeth the vine
causeth it to spread fairer? That he that stoppeth the stream forceth
it to swell higher? That he that casteth water on the fire in the
smith's forge maketh it to flame fiercer? Even so, he that seeketh by
counsel to moderate his overlashing affections increaseth his own
misfortune.

"Ah, my Lucilla, would thou wert either less fair or I more
fortunate, either I wiser or thou milder; either I would I were out of
this mad mood, either I would we were both of one mind. But how
should she be persuaded of my loyalty that yet had never one
simple proof of my love? Will she not rather imagine me to be entangled with her beauty than with her virtue, that my fancy being

[88]*claw of a bitter:* bittern (a bird something like a heron, only smaller).
In addition to the sounds of "bitter...bitter(n)," there are the two
different kinds of "bitter"—the sharply bitter taste of the fig tree root and
the sharply painful feeling of a bird's claw.

so lewdly chained[89] at the first will be as lightly changed at the last, that nothing violent can be permanent? Yes, yes, she must needs conjecture so, although it be nothing so; for by how much the more my affection cometh on the sudden, by so much the less will she think it certain. The rattling thunderbolt hath but his clap, the lightning but his flash; and as they both come in a moment, so do they both end in a minute.

"Aye, but Euphues, hath she not heard also that the dry touchwood is kindled with lime, that the greatest mushroom groweth in one night, that the fire quickly burneth the flax, that love easily entereth into the sharp wit without resistance and is harbored there without repentance? If, therefore, the gods have endued her with as much bounty as beauty, if she have no less wit than she hath comeliness, certes she will neither conceive sinisterly of my sudden suit, neither be coy to receive me into her service, neither suspect me of lightness in yielding so lightly, neither reject me disdainfully for loving so hastily.

"Shall I not then hazard my life to obtain my love, and deceive Philautus to receive Lucilla? Yes, Euphues, where love beareth sway, friendship can have no show. As Philautus brought me for his shadow the last supper, so will I use him for my shadow[90] till I have gained his saint. And canst thou, wretch, be false to him that is faithful to thee? Shall his courtesy be cause of thy cruelty? Wilt thou violate the league of faith to inherit the land of folly? Shall affection be of more force than friendship, love than law, lust than loyalty? Knowest thou not that he that loseth his honesty hath nothing else to lose?

"Tush, the case is light where reason taketh place. To love and to live well is not granted to Jupiter. Whoso is blinded with the caul of beauty discerneth no color of honesty. Did not Gyges cut Candaules a coat by his own measure? Did not Paris, though he were a welcome guest to Menelaus, serve his host a slippery prank? If Philautus had loved Lucilla, he would never have suffered Euphues to have seen her. Is it not the prey that enticeth the thief to rifle? Is it not the

---

[89]*chained:* In the second and third editions the word is "changed," but the fourth edition of 1580 returns to the 1578 reading, "chained," which is surely the correct reading: the sounds ("lewdly chained ... lightly changed") are to be similar, but the meanings are to be quite different, as the context makes clear.

[90]*his shadow ... my shadow:* As Bond suggests, the first "shadow" means "close friend"; but the second one means "blind" or "decoy."

pleasant bait that causeth the fleetest fish to bite? Is it not a byword amongst us that gold maketh an honest man an ill man? Did Philautus account Euphues too simple to decipher beauty or superstitious not to desire it? Did he deem him a saint in rejecting fancy, or a sot in not discerning? Thought he him a Stoic that he would not be moved, or a stock that he could not?

"Well, well, seeing the wound that bleedeth inwardly is most dangerous, that the fire kept close burneth most furious, that the oven dammed up baketh soonest, that sores having no vent fester secretly, it is high time to unfold my secret love to my secret friend. Let Philautus behave himself never so craftily, he shall know that it must be a wily mouse that shall breed in the cat's ear; and because I resemble him in wit, I mean a little to dissemble with him in wiles.

"But, oh, my Lucilla, if thy heart be made of that stone which may be mollified only with blood, would I had sipped of that river in Caria which turneth those that drink of it to stones. If thine ears be anointed with the oil of Syria that bereaveth hearing, would mine eyes had been rubbed with the syrup of the cedar tree which taketh away sight. If Lucilla be so proud to disdain poor Euphues, would Euphues were so happy to deny Lucilla; or if Lucilla be so mortified to live without love, would Euphues were so fortunate to live in hate. Aye, but my cold welcome foretelleth my cold suit; aye, but her privy glances signify some good fortune. Fie, fond fool Euphues, why goest thou about to allege those things to cut off thy hope which she perhaps would never have found, or to comfort thyself with those reasons which she never meaneth to propose?

"Tush, it were no love if it were certain, and a small conquest it is to overthrow those that never resisteth. In battles there ought to be a doubtful fight and a desperate end, in pleading a difficult entrance and a diffused determination,[91] in love a life without hope and a death without fear. Fire cometh out of the hardest flint with the steel, oil out of the driest jet by the fire, love out of the stoniest heart by faith, by trust, by time. Had Tarquinius used his love with colors

---

[91]*in pleading ... diffused determination:* A "pleading" was a formal allegation given orally in a court of law. "Diffused" seems to have two senses, one from the parallelism within the sentence and another from the contrast within the clause. The parallelism indicates a derogatory sense: just as a "desperate end" is a reckless, because despairing, end to a battle, so a "diffused determination" is a wordy, verbose ending of an oral statement. But, within the clause, a "difficult entrance" (hesitant beginning) is opposed to a "diffused determination" (fluent ending).

of continuance,[92] Lucretia would either with some pity have answered his desire, or with some persuasion have stayed her death. It was the heat of his lust that made her haste to end her life; wherefore love in neither respect is to be condemned, but he of rashness to attempt a lady furiously, and she of rigor to punish his folly in her own flesh—a fact, in mine opinion, more worthy the name of cruelty than chastity, and fitter for a monster in the deserts than a matron of Rome. Penelope, no less constant than she yet more wise, would be weary to unweave that in the night she spun in the day, if Ulysses had not come home the sooner. There is no woman, Euphues, but she will yield in time; be not therefore dismayed either with high looks or froward words."[93]

Euphues having thus talked with himself, Philautus entered the chamber, and finding him so worn and wasted with continual mourning, neither joying in his meat nor rejoicing in his friend, with watery eyes uttered this speech:

"Friend and fellow, as I am not ignorant of thy present weakness, so I am not privy of the cause; and although I suspect many things, yet can I assure myself of no one thing. Therefore, my good Euphues, for these doubts and dumps of mine, either remove the cause or reveal it. Thou hast hitherto found me a cheerful companion in thy mirth, and now shalt thou find me as careful with thee in thy moan. If altogether thou mayest not be cured, yet mayest thou be comforted. If there be anything that either by my friends may be procured or by my life[94] attained, that may either heal thee in part or help thee in all, I protest to thee by the name of a friend that it shall rather be gotten with the loss of my body, than lost by getting a kingdom.

[92]*colors of continuance:* Literally, the word "continuance" here has a legal connotation with two senses: (1) adjournment until a future date and (2) continuation over a period of time. The implications of these two senses are carefully worked out. One observation is that Tarquin's rape of Lucrece was a mistake, even from his own point of view; Tarquin should have given outward indications (colors) to Lucrece that he was in love with her, but then he should have controlled himself for the moment, pursuing her again at a later time.

[93]*If Lucilla be so proud . . . or froward words:* These lines, amounting to almost a whole page, appeared for the first time in the second edition.

[94]*my friends . . . my life:* In the 1593 edition, followed by the edition of 1597, "life" is changed to "self." Perhaps a better emendation would be to change "friends" to "friendship," thus introducing a friendship–life relationship rather than a friends–self relationship, which does, however, make good sense.

Thou hast tried me; therefore trust me. Thou hast trusted me in many things; therefore try me in this one thing. I never yet failed, and now I will not faint. Be bold to speak and blush not. Thy sore is not so angry but I can salve it, the wound not so deep but I can search it, thy grief not so great but I can ease it. If it be ripe it shall be lanced, if it be broken it shall be tainted,[95] be it never so desperate it shall be cured.

"Rise, therefore, Euphues, and take heart at grass.[96] Younger thou shalt never be; pluck up thy stomach. If love itself have stung thee, it shall not stifle thee. Though thou be enamored of some lady, thou shalt not be enchanted. They that begin to pine of a consumption, without delay preserve themselves with cullises; he that feeleth his stomach enflamed with heat cooleth it eftsoons with conserves.[97] Delays breed dangers; nothing so perilous as procrastination."

Euphues, hearing this comfort and friendly counsel, dissembled his sorrowing heart with a smiling face, answering him forthwith as followeth:

"True it is, Philautus, that he which toucheth the nettle tenderly is soonest stung, that the fly which playeth with the fire is singed in the flame, that he that dallieth with women is drawn to his woe. And as the adamant draweth the heavy iron, the harp the fleet dolphin, so beauty allureth the chaste mind to love and the wisest wit to lust. The example whereof I would it were no less profitable than the experience to me is like to be perilous. The vine watered with wine is soon withered, the blossom in the fattest ground is quickly blasted, the goat the fatter she is the less fertile she is—yea, man the more witty he is the less happy he is. So it is, Philautus—for why should I conceal it from thee of whom I am to take counsel—that since my last and first being with thee at the house of Ferardo, I have felt such a furious battle in mine own body as, if it be not speedily repressed by policy, it will carry my mind, the grand captain in this fight, into endless captivity.

"Ah, Livia, Livia, thy courtly grace without coyness, thy blazing

[95]*broken . . . tainted:* If the wound is already open, without lancing, a tincture or balm will be applied to it.

[96]*take heart at grass:* a variation of two proverbs (Tilley, F359 and G413): "All flesh is grass" and "Grass and hay, we are all mortal." Philautus' meaning (ironic in the circumstances) is given in the sentence following: "Younger thou shalt never be"—and so *carpe diem,* enjoy life while you may.

[97]*cullises . . . conserves:* nourishing broths . . . medicinal preparations (to which sugar is added as a preservative).

beauty without blemish, thy courteous demeanor without curiosity,[98] thy sweet speech savored with wit, thy comely mirth tempered with modesty, thy chaste looks yet lovely, thy sharp taunts yet pleasant, have given me such a check that sure I am at the next view of thy virtues I shall take thee mate.[99] And taking it not of a pawn but of a prince, the loss is to be accounted the less.[100] And though they be commonly in a great choler that receive the mate, yet would I willingly take every minute ten mates to enjoy Livia for my loving mate.

"Doubtless if ever she herself have been scorched with the flames of desire, she will be ready to quench the coals with courtesy in another; if ever she have been attached of[101] love, she will rescue him that is drenched in desire; if ever she have been taken with the fever of fancy, she will help his ague who by a quotidian fit is converted into frenzy. Neither can there be under so delicate a hue lodged deceit, neither in so beautiful a mold a malicious mind. True it is that the disposition of the mind followeth the composition of the body; how, then, can she be in mind any way imperfect who in body is perfect every way?

"I know my success will be good, but I know not how to have access to my goddess; neither do I want courage to discover my love to my friend, but some color to cloak my coming to the house of Ferardo. For if they be in Naples as jealous as they be in the other parts of Italy, then it behooveth me to walk circumspectly and to forge some cause for often coming. If, therefore, Philautus, thou canst set but this feather to mine arrow, thou shalt see me shoot so near that thou wilt account me for a cunning archer.

"And verily if I had not loved thee well, I would have swallowed mine own sorrow in silence, knowing that in love nothing is so dangerous as to participate the means thereof to another, and that two may keep counsel if one be away. I am, therefore, enforced

[98]*curiosity:* fastidiousness (too close attention to details of conduct and behavior).

[99]*take thee mate:* What the reader expects is the usual idiomatic expression, "to take *the* mate" (meaning "to be checkmated"), the opposite of which is "to give the mate" (meaning "to checkmate the other person"). Both senses are included in "take thee mate": in one sense Euphues is captured or defeated by Livia's charms, but in the other sense he captures her for his "loving mate."

[100]*And taking it ... the less:* In chess it is a greater loss to lose the king ("prince") than it is to lose a pawn; but in being checkmated (losing the king) by Livia, Euphues is actually gaining her, and therefore in this particular case the loss of the king is not so great as the loss of a pawn.

[101]*attached of:* seized or attacked by.

perforce to challenge that courtesy at thy hands which erst thou didst promise with thy heart, the performance whereof shall bind me to Philautus and prove thee faithful to Euphues. Now if thy cunning be answerable to thy good will, practice some pleasant conceit upon thy poor patient: one dram of Ovid's art, some of Tibullus' drugs, one of Propertius' pills, which may cause me either to purge my new disease or recover my hoped desire. But I fear me where so strange a sickness is to be recured of so unskillful a physician that either thou wilt be too bold to practice or my body too weak to purge. But seeing a desperate disease is to be committed to a desperate doctor, I will follow thy counsel and become thy cure, desiring thee to be as wise in ministering thy physic as I have been willing to put my life into thy hands."[102]

Philautus, thinking all to be gold that glistered and all to be gospel that Euphues uttered, answered his forged gloze with this friendly close: "In that thou hast made me privy to thy purpose, I will not conceal my practice; in that thou cravest my aid, assure thyself I will be the finger next thy thumb—insomuch as thou shalt never repent thee of the one or the other. For persuade thyself that thou shalt find Philautus during life ready to comfort thee in thy misfortunes and succor thee in thy necessity.[103]

"Concerning Livia, though she be fair yet is she not so amiable as my Lucilla, whose servant I have been the term of three years; but lest comparisons should seem odious, chiefly where both the parties be without comparison, I will omit that. And seeing that we had both rather be talking with them than tattling of them, we will immediately go to them. And truly, Euphues, I am not a little glad that I shall have thee not only a comfort in my life, but also a companion in my love. As thou hast been wise in thy choice, so I hope thou shalt be fortunate in thy chance. Livia is a wench of more wit than beauty, Lucilla of more beauty than wit, both of more honesty than honor, and yet both of such honor as in all Naples there is not one in birth to be compared with any of them both.[104] How much, therefore, have we to rejoice in our choice.

---

[102]*Now if thy cunning ... into thy hands:* These three sentences first appeared in the second edition.

[103]*For persuade ... thy necessity:* This sentence was added in the second edition.

[104]*any of them both:* a typically redundant and emphatic Elizabethan expression; the first three editions let it stand, the next six editions (1580–92) omit "both," and the tenth edition finally emends to the modern "either of them."

"Touching our access, be thou secure. I will flap Ferardo in the mouth with some conceit and fill his old head so full of new fables that thou shalt rather be earnestly entreated to repair to his house than evil entreated to leave it. As old men are very suspicious to mistrust everything, so are they very credulous to believe anything. The blind man doth eat many a fly."

"Yea, but," said Euphues, "take heed, my Philautus, that thou thyself swallow not a gudgeon," which word Philautus did not mark until he had almost digested it.

"But," said Philautus, "let us go devoutly to the shrine of our saints, there to offer our devotion; for my books teach me that such a wound must be healed where it was first hurt, and for this disease we will use a common remedy, but yet comfortable. The eye that blinded thee shall make thee see, the scorpion that stung thee shall heal thee, a sharp sore hath a short cure—let us go."[105]

To the which Euphues consented willingly, smiling to himself to see how he had brought Philautus into a fool's paradise.

Here you may see, gentlemen, the falsehood in fellowship, the fraud in friendship, the painted sheath with the leaden dagger, the fair words that make fools fain. But I will not trouble you with superfluous addition, unto whom I fear me I have been tedious with the bare discourse of this rude history.

Philautus and Euphues repaired to the house of Ferardo, where they found Mistress Lucilla and Livia, accompanied with other gentlewomen, neither being idle nor well employed, but playing at cards. But when Lucilla beheld Euphues she could scarcely contain herself from embracing him, had not womanly shamefastness and Philautus his presence, stayed her wisdom. Euphues, on the other side, was fallen into such a trance that he had not the power either to succor himself or salute the gentlewomen. At the last, Lucilla began, as one that best might be bold, on this manner:

"Gentlemen, although your long absence gave me occasion to think that you disliked your late entertainment, yet your coming at the last hath cut off my former suspicion. And by so much the more you are welcome, by how much the more you were wished for. But you, gentleman," (taking Euphues by the hand) "were the rather wished for, for that your discourse being left unperfect caused us all to long—as women are wont for things that like them—to have an end thereof."

Unto whom Philautus replied as followeth: "Mistress Lucilla,

[105]*for my books teach me . . . let us go:* These lines, amounting to a sentence and a half, were added in the second edition.

though your courtesy made us nothing to doubt of our welcome, yet modesty caused us to pinch courtesy who should first come.[106] As for my friend, I think he was never wished for here so earnestly of any as of himself; whether it might be to renew his talk or to recant his sayings, I cannot tell."

Euphues, taking the tale out of Philautus' mouth, answered, "Mistress Lucilla, to recant verities were heresy, and renew the praises of women, flattery. The only cause I wished myself here was to give thanks for so good entertainment, the which I could no ways deserve, and to breed a greater acquaintance if it might be to make amends."

Lucilla, inflamed with his presence, said, "Nay, Euphues, you shall not escape so, for if my courtesy, as you say, were the cause of your coming, let it also be the occasion of the ending your former discourse. Otherwise I shall think your proof naked, and you shall find my reward nothing."

Euphues, now as willing to obey as she to command, addressed himself to a farther conclusion; who, seeing all the gentlewomen ready to give him the hearing, proceeded as followeth:

"I have not yet forgotten that my last talk with these gentlewomen tended to their praises, and therefore the end must tie up the just proof; otherwise I should set down Venus' shadow without the lively substance.

"As there is no one thing which can be reckoned either concerning love or loyalty wherein women do not excel men, yet in fervency above all others they so far exceed that men are liker to marvel at them than to imitate them, and readier to laugh at their virtues than emulate them. For as they be hard to be won without trial of great faith, so are they hard to be lost without great cause of fickleness. It is long before the cold water seethe, yet being once hot it is long before it be cooled; it is long before salt come to his saltness, but being once seasoned it never loseth his savor.

"I, for mine own part, am brought into a paradise by the only imagination of women's virtues. And were I persuaded that all the devils in hell were women, I would never live devoutly to inherit

---

[106]*pinch courtesy who should first come:* To "pinch courtesy" (or "strain courtesy") had two quite different senses—to insist too much on the observance of courtesy, and to treat with less than due courtesy. In view of the preceding paragraph, the latter meaning seems to be implied; Euphues and Philautus are returning to Lucilla after a "long absence," a bit too long if they are to treat her with the courtesy she deserves. Yet the reason for the delay is not social callousness but modesty: each of them has argued that the other should return first.

heaven; or that they were all saints in heaven, I would live more strictly for fear of hell. What could Adam have done in his paradise before his fall without a woman, or how would he have rise[107] again after his fall with a woman? Artificers are wont in their last works to excel themselves. Yea, God, when he had made all things, at the last made man as most perfect, thinking nothing could be framed more excellent. Yet after him he created a woman, the express image of eternity, the lively picture of nature, the only steel glass[108] for man to behold his infirmities by comparing them with women's perfections. Are they not more gentle, more witty, more beautiful than men? Are not men so bewitched with their qualities that they become mad for love, and women so wise that they detest lust?

"I am entered into so large a field that I shall sooner want time than proof, and so cloy you with variety of praises that I fear me I am like to infect women with pride, which yet they have not, and men with spite, which yet I would not. For as the horse if he knew his own strength were no ways to be bridled, or the unicorn his own virtue were never to be caught, so women, if they knew what excellency were in them, I fear me men should never win them to their wills or wean them from their mind."

Lucilla began to smile, saying, "In faith, Euphues, I would have you stay there. For as the sun when he is at the highest beginneth to go down, so when the praises of women are at the best, if you leave not, they will begin to fail."

But Euphues, being rapt with the sight of his saint, answered, "No, no, Lucilla—"[109]

But whilst he was yet speaking, Ferardo entered, whom they all dutifully welcomed home. Who, rounding[110] Philautus in the ear, desired him to accompany him immediately without farther pausing, protesting it should be as well for his preferment as for his own profit.

Philautus consenting, Ferardo said unto his daughter, "Lucilla, the

---

[107]*rise:* acceptable Elizabethan usage for the modern "risen," which also probably was becoming idiomatic. In this case "rise" probably is to rhyme with "paradise"; it is also to provide a monosyllabic opposite to "fall." (See note 68 in *Rosalind.*)

[108]*steel glass:* a mirror made of polished steel; Gascoigne, in *The Steel Glass,* contends that a crystal mirror is not so "trusty" as a steel mirror in reflecting men as they really are.

[109]*Euphues, taking the tale out of Philautus' mouth . . . "No, no, Lucilla —":* These eight paragraphs, amounting to almost two whole pages, first appeared in the second edition.

[110]*rounding:* whispering.

urgent affairs I have in hand will scarce suffer me to tarry with you one hour. Yet my return, I hope, will be so short that my absence shall not breed thy sorrow. In the mean season I commit all things into thy custody, wishing thee to use thy accustomable courtesy. And seeing I must take Philautus with me, I will be so bold to crave you, gentleman (his friend), to supply his room, desiring you to take this hasty warning for a hearty welcome, and so to spend this time of mine absence in honest mirth. And thus I leave you."

Philautus knew well the cause of this sudden departure, which was to redeem certain lands that were mortgaged in his father's time to the use of Ferardo, who on that condition had beforetime promised him his daughter in marriage. But return we to Euphues.

Euphues was surprised with such incredible joy at this strange event that he had almost sounded;[111] for seeing his corrival to be departed and Ferardo to give him so friendly entertainment, doubted not in time to get the good will of Lucilla. Whom finding in place convenient without company, with a bold courage and comely gesture he began to assay her in this sort:

"Gentlewoman, my acquaintance being so little I am afraid my credit will be less, for that they commonly are soonest believed that are best beloved, and they liked best whom we have known longest. Nevertheless, the noble mind suspecteth no guile without cause, neither condemneth any wight without proof. Having, therefore, notice of your heroical heart, I am the better persuaded of my good hap.

"So it is, Lucilla, that coming to Naples but to fetch fire, as the byword is, not to make my place of abode, I have found such flames that I can neither quench them with the water of free will, neither cool them with wisdom. For as the hop, the pole being never so high, groweth to the end, or as the dry beech, kindled at the root, never leaveth until it come to the top; or as one drop of poison disperseth itself into every vein, so affection having caught hold of my heart and the sparkles of love kindled my liver, will suddenly, though secretly, flame up into my head and spread itself into every sinew. It is your beauty—pardon my abrupt boldness—lady, that hath taken every part of me prisoner and brought me unto this deep distress. But seeing women, when one praiseth them for their deserts, deem that he flattereth them to obtain his desire, I am here present to yield myself to such trial as your courtesy in this behalf shall require.

[111]*sounded:* swooned.

"Yet will you commonly object this to such as serve you and sterve[112] to win your good will that hot love is soon cold, that the bavin[113] though it burn bright is but a blaze, that scalding water if it stand a while turneth almost to ice, that pepper though it be hot in the mouth is cold in the maw, that the faith of men though it fry in their words it freezeth in their works. Which things, Lucilla, albeit they be sufficient to reprove the lightness of someone, yet can they not convince everyone of lewdness; neither ought the constancy of all to be brought in question through the subtlety of a few. For although the worm entereth almost into every wood, yet he eateth not the cedar tree; though the stone cylindrus at every thunderclap roll from the hill, yet the pure sleekstone mounteth at the noise;[114] though the rust fret the hardest steel, yet doth it not eat into the emerald; though polypus change his hue, yet the salamander keepeth his color; though Proteus transform himself into every shape, yet Pygmalion retaineth his old form; though Aeneas were too fickle to Dido, yet Troilus was too faithful to Cressid; though others seem counterfeit in their deeds, yet, Lucilla, persuade yourself that Euphues will be always current in his dealings.

"But as the true gold is tried by the touch, the pure flint by the stroke of the iron, so the loyal heart of the faithful lover is known by the trial of his lady. Of the which trial, Lucilla, if you shall account Euphues worthy, assure yourself he will be as ready to offer himself a sacrifice for your sweet sake as yourself shall be willing to employ him in your service. Neither doth he desire to be trusted any way until he shall be tried every way; neither doth he crave credit at the first, but a good countenance till time his desire[115] shall be made manifest by his deserts. Thus not blinded by light affection, but dazzled with your rare perfection and boldened by your exceeding courtesy, I have unfolded mine entire love, desiring you, having so good leisure, to give so friendly an answer as I may receive comfort and you commendation."

[112]*sterve:* The modern spelling is "starve" but the sense is "die"; the original spelling keeps the rhyme with "serve."

[113]*bavin:* bundle of brushwood; since it burns quickly, "blaze" is thus defined.

[114]*sleekstone mounteth at the noise:* The "sleekstone" was a smooth stone used for smoothing and polishing other surfaces; here apparently it is so smooth that, in contrast with the rough "cylindrus," it defies gravity and rolls up the hill.

[115]*till time his desire:* The sense is either "until time's desire" or "until the time when his [Euphues'] desire"; Croll and Clemons favor the latter sense.

Lucilla, although she were contented to hear this desired discourse, yet did she seem to be somewhat displeased. And truly I know not whether it be peculiar to that sex to dissemble with those whom they most desire, or whether by craft they have learned outwardly to loathe that which inwardly they most love. Yet wisely did she cast this in her head: that if she should yield at the first assault, he would think her a light huswife; if she should reject him scornfully, a very haggard. Minding, therefore, that he should neither take hold of her promise, neither unkindness of her preciseness, she fed him indifferently with hope and despair, reason and affection, life and death. Yet in the end, arguing wittily upon certain questions, they fell to such agreement, as poor Philautus would not have agreed unto if he had been present, yet always keeping the body undefiled. And thus she replied:

"Gentleman, as you may suspect me of idleness in giving ear to your talk, so may you convince me of lightness in answering such toys. Certes, as you have made mine ears glow at the rehearsal of your love, so have you galled my heart with the remembrance of your folly. Though you came to Naples as a stranger, yet were you welcome to my father's house as a friend. And can you then so much transgress the bonds of honor—I will not say of honesty—as to solicit a suit more sharp to me than death? I have hitherto, God be thanked, lived without suspicion of lewdness. And shall I now incur the danger of sensual liberty? What hope can you have to obtain my love, seeing yet I could never afford you a good look? Do you, therefore, think me easily enticed to the bent of your bow because I was easily entreated to listen to your late discourse? Or seeing me, as finely you gloze, to excel all other in beauty, did you deem that I would exceed all other in beastliness?

"But yet I am not angry, Euphues, but in an agony; for who is she that will fret or fume with one that loveth her, if this love to delude me be not dissembled? It is that which causeth me most to fear; not that my beauty is unknown to myself, but that commonly we poor wenches are deluded through light belief, and ye men are naturally inclined craftily to lead your life. When the fox preacheth, the geese perish. The crocodile shroudeth greatest treason under most pitiful tears; in a kissing mouth there lieth a galling mind. You have made so large proffer of your service and so fair promises of fidelity that, were I not over chary of mine honesty, you would inveigle me to shake hands with[116] chastity. But, certes, I will either

---

[116]*shake hands with:* say good-by to.

lead a virgin's life in earth, though I lead apes in hell, or else follow thee rather than thy gifts. Yet am I neither so precise to refuse thy proffer, neither so peevish to disdain thy good will. So excellent always are the gifts which are made acceptable by the virtue of the giver.

"I did at the first entrance discern thy love, but yet dissemble it. Thy wanton glances, thy scalding sighs, thy loving signs caused me to blush for shame and to look wan for fear, lest they should be perceived of any. These subtle shifts, these painted practices, if I were to be won, would soon wean me from the teat of Vesta to the toys of Venus. Besides this, thy comely grace, thy rare qualities, thy exquisite perfection were able to move a mind half mortified to transgress the bonds of maidenly modesty. But God shield, Lucilla, that thou shouldest be so careless of thine honor as to commit the state thereof to a stranger. Learn thou by me, Euphues, to despise things that be amiable, to forgo delightful practices; believe me it is piety to abstain from pleasure.

"Thou art not the first that hath solicited this suit, but the first that goeth about to seduce me; neither discernest thou more than other, but darest more than any; neither hast thou more art to discover thy meaning, but more heart to open thy mind. But thou preferrest me before thy lands, thy livings, thy life; thou offerest thyself a sacrifice for my security, thou profferest me the whole and only sovereignty of thy service. Truly I were very cruel and hardhearted if I should not love thee. Hardhearted albeit I am not, but truly love thee I cannot, whom I doubt to be my lover. Moreover, I have not been used to the court of Cupid, wherein there be more sleights than there be hares in Athon than bees in Hybla than stars in heaven.

"Besides this, the common people here in Naples are not only both very suspicious of other men's matters and manners, but also very jealous over other men's children and maidens. Either, therefore, dissemble thy fancy or desist from thy folly. But why shouldest thou desist from the one, seeing thou canst cunningly dissemble the other? My father is now gone to Venice, and as I am uncertain of his return so am I not privy to the cause of his travel. But yet is he so from hence that he seeth me in his absence. Knowest thou not, Euphues, that kings have long arms and rulers large reaches? Neither let this comfort thee, that at his departure he deputed thee in Philautus' place. Although my face cause him to mistrust my loyalty, yet my faith enforceth him to give me this liberty; though he be suspicious of my fair hue, yet is he secure of my firm honesty.

"But, alas, Euphues, what truth can there be found in a traveler? What stay in a stranger, whose words and bodies[117] both watch but for a wind, whose feet are ever fleeting, whose faith plighted on the shore is turned to perjury when they hoist sail? Who more traitorous to Phyllis than Demophon? Yet he a traveler. Who more perjured to Dido than Aeneas? And he a stranger. Both these queens, both they caitiffs. Who more false to Ariadne than Theseus? Yet he a sailor. Who more fickle to Medea than Jason? Yet he a starter.[118] Both these daughters to great princes, both they unfaithful of their promises. Is it then likely that Euphues will be faithful to Lucilla being in Naples but a sojourner?

"I have not yet forgotten the invective—I can no otherwise term it—which thou madest against beauty, saying it was a deceitful bait with a deadly hook and a sweet poison in a painted pot. Canst thou, then, be so unwise to swallow the bait which will breed thy bane? To swill the drink that will expire thy date? To desire the wight that will work thy death? But it may be that with the scorpion thou canst feed on the earth, or with the quail and roebuck be fat with poison, or with beauty live in all bravery.

"I fear me thou hast the stone continens about thee which is named of the contrary, that though thou pretend faith in thy words, thou devisest fraud in thy heart, that though thou seem to prefer love, thou art inflamed with lust. And what for that? Though thou have eaten the seeds of rocket, which breed incontinency, yet have I chewed the leaf cress which maintaineth modesty. Though thou bear in thy bosom the herb araxa, most noisome to virginity, yet have I the stone that groweth in the Mount Tmolus, the upholder of chastity.

"You may, gentleman, account me for a cold prophet, thus hastily to divine of your disposition. Pardon me, Euphues, if in love I cast beyond the moon, which bringeth us women to endless moan. Although I myself were never burnt, whereby I should dread the fire, yet the scorching of others in the flames of fancy warneth me to beware; though I as yet never tried any faithless, whereby I should be fearful, yet have I read of many that have been perjured, which

---

[117]*stranger . . . bodies:* The lack of agreement here did not bother the Elizabethan, especially if he wanted "bodies" to end with an "s" to match "words." Probably "bodies" here means "gestures" or "actions"; "words" and "bodies" encompass all the outward truth that can be found in a stranger, who cannot yet be known inwardly.

[118]*starter:* wanderer. The "Yet" does not introduce, as we expect it to, a contrast with "fickle"; the previous examples show that "yet" is merely a variation of "and."

causeth me to be careful; though I am able to convince none by proof, yet am I enforced to suspect one upon probabilities. Alas, we silly souls, which have neither wit to decipher the wiles of men nor wisdom to dissemble our affection, neither craft to train in young lovers, neither courage to withstand their encounters, neither discretion to discern their doubling, neither hard hearts to reject their complaints—we, I say, are soon enticed, being by nature simple and easily entangled, being apt to receive the impression of love.

"But, alas, it is both common and lamentable to behold simplicity entrapped by subtlety, and those that have most might to be infected with most malice. The spider weaveth a fine web to hang the fly; the wolf weareth a fair face to devour the lamb; the merlin striketh at the partridge; the eagle often snappeth at the fly; men are always laying baits for women, which are the weaker vessels. But as yet I could never hear man by such snares to entrap man. For true it is that men themselves have by use observed that it must be a hard winter when one wolf eateth another. I have read that the bull being tied to the fig tree loseth his strength, that the whole herd of deer stand at the gaze if they smell a sweet apple, that the dolphin by the sound of music is brought to the shore. And then no marvel it is that if the fierce bull be tamed with the fig tree, if that women, being as weak as sheep, be overcome with a fig; if the wild deer be caught with an apple, that the tame damsel is won with a blossom; if the fleet dolphin be allured with harmony, that women be entangled with the melody of men's speech, fair promises, and solemn protestations.

"But folly it were for me to mark their mischiefs. Since I am neither able, neither they willing, to amend their manners, it becometh me rather to show what our sex should do than to open what yours doth. And seeing I cannot by reason restrain your importunate suit, I will by rigor done on myself cause you to refrain the means. I would to God Ferardo were in this point like to Lysander, which would not suffer his daughters to wear gorgeous apparel, saying it would rather make them common than comely. I would it were in Naples a law, which was a custom in Egypt, that women should always go barefoot, to the intent they might keep themselves always at home, that they should be ever like to the snail which hath ever his house on his head. I mean so to mortify myself that instead of silks I will wear sackcloth; for ouches and bracelets, lear and caddis;[119]

---

[119]*ouches and bracelets, lear and caddis:* Both "lear" and "caddis" mean "tape," such as the kind used to bind the edges of fabric. Although "ouch" can mean "clasp" or "brooch," it also means "bracelet"; the intent may be to give two pairs of synonyms, the first pair being more worldly and prized than the second.

for the lute use the distaff; for the pen, the needle; for lovers' sonnets, David's psalms.

"But yet I am not so senseless altogether to reject your service; which, if I were certainly assured to proceed of a simple mind, it should not receive so simple a reward. And what greater trial can I have of thy simplicity and truth than thine own request which desireth a trial. Aye, but in the coldest flint there is hot fire, the bee that hath honey in her mouth hath a sting in her tail, the tree that beareth the sweetest fruit hath a sour sap—yea, the words of men though they seem smooth as oil yet their hearts are as crooked as the stalk of ivy. I would not, Euphues, that thou shouldest condemn me of rigor in that I seek to assuage thy folly by reason. But take this by the way: that although as yet I am disposed to like of none, yet whensoever I shall love any I will not forget thee. In the mean season account me thy friend, for thy foe I will never be."

Euphues was brought into a great quandary and, as it were, a cold shivering to hear this new kind of kindness—such sweet meat, such sour sauce; such fair words, such faint promises; such hot love, such cold desire; such certain hope, such sudden change; and stood like one that had looked on Medusa's head and so had been turned into a stone.

Lucilla, seeing him in this pitiful plight and fearing he would take stand if the lure were not cast out, took him by the hand and, wringing him softly, with a smiling countenance began thus to comfort him:

"Methinks, Euphues, changing so your color upon the sudden, you will soon change your copy. Is your mind on your meat? A penny for your thought."[120]

"Mistress," quoth he, "if you would buy all my thoughts at that price, I should never be weary of thinking. But seeing it is too dear, read it and take it for nothing."

"It seems to me," said she, "that you are in some brown study, what colors you might best wear for your lady."

"Indeed, Lucilla, you level shrewdly at my thought by the aim of your own imagination. For you have given unto me a true love's knot[121] wrought of changeable silk; and you deem that I am devising how I might have my colors changeable also, that they might agree.

[120]*change your copy . . . your thought:* three proverbs in a row (Tilley, C648, M971, and P203); "change your copy" means "alter your behavior [toward me]."

[121]*true love's knot:* Perhaps the phrase is meant to be ambiguous and convey both "true-love" and "love-knot."

But let this with such toys and devices pass. If it please you to command me any service, I am here ready to attend your leisure."

"No service, Euphues, but that you keep silence until I have uttered my mind, and secrecy when I have unfolded my meaning."

"If I should offend in the one I were too bold, if in the other too beastly."

"Well, then, Euphues," said she, "so it is that for the hope that I conceive of thy loyalty and the happy success that is like to ensue of this our love, I am content to yield thee the place in my heart which thou desirest and deservest above all other; which consent in me if it may any ways breed thy contentation,[122] sure I am that it will every way work my comfort. But as either thou tenderest mine honor or thine own safety, use such secrecy in this matter that my father have no inkling hereof before I have framed his mind fit for our purpose. And though women have small force to overcome men by reason, yet have they good fortune to undermine them by policy. The soft drops of rain pierce the hard marble, many strokes overthrow the tallest oak, a silly woman in time may make such a breach into a man's heart as her tears may enter without resistance. Then doubt not but I will so undermine mine old father, as quickly I will enjoy my new friend.

"Tush, Philautus was liked for fashion sake, but never loved for fancy sake. And this I vow by the faith of a virgin and by the love I bear thee—for greater bands to confirm my vow I have not—that my father shall sooner martyr me in the fire than marry me to Philautus. No, no, Euphues, thou only hast won me by love and shalt only wear me by law. I force not Philautus his fury so I may have Euphues his friendship; neither will I prefer his possessions before thy person, neither esteem better of his lands than of thy love. Ferardo shall sooner disherit me of my patrimony than dishonor me in breaking my promise. It is not his great manors but thy good manners that shall make my marriage. In token of which my sincere affection I give thee my hand in pawn and my heart forever to be thy Lucilla."

Unto whom Euphues answered in this manner: "If my tongue were able to utter the joys that my heart hath conceived, I fear me though I be well beloved yet I should hardly be believed. Ah, my Lucilla, how much am I bound to thee, which preferrest mine unworthiness before thy father's wrath, my happiness before thine

[122]*contentation:* contentment.

own misfortune, my love before thine own life. How might I excel thee in courtesy whom no mortal creature can exceed in constancy? I find it now for a settled truth, which erst I accounted for a vain talk, that the purple dye will never stain, that the pure civet will never lose his savor, that the green laurel will never change his color, that beauty can never be blotted with discourtesy. As touching secrecy in this behalf, assure thyself that I will not so much as tell it to myself. Command Euphues to run, to ride, to undertake any exploit be it never so dangerous, to hazard himself in any enterprise be it never so desperate."

As they were thus pleasantly conferring the one with the other, Livia, whom Euphues made his stale,[123] entered into the parlor. Unto whom Lucilla spake in these terms, "Dost thou not laugh, Livia, to see my ghostly father keep me here so long at shrift?"

"Truly," answered Livia, "methinks that you smile at some pleasant shift. Either he is slow in inquiring of your faults or you slack in answering of his questions."

And thus being suppertime they all sat down, Lucilla well pleased; no man better content than Euphues, who, after his repast, having no opportunity to confer with his lover, had small lust to continue with the gentlewomen any longer. Seeing therefore he could frame no means to work his delight, he coined an excuse to hasten his departure, promising the next morning to trouble them again as a guest more bold than welcome, although indeed he thought himself to be the better welcome in saying that he would come.

But as Ferardo went in post, so he returned in haste, having concluded with Philautus that the marriage should immediately be consummated. Which wrought such a content in Philautus that he was almost in an ecstasy through the extremity of his passions. Such is the fullness and force of pleasure that there is nothing so dangerous as the fruition. Yet knowing that delays bring dangers, although he nothing doubted of Lucilla whom he loved, yet feared he the fickleness of old men, which is always to be mistrusted. He urged therefore Ferardo to break with his daughter. Who, being willing to have the match made, was content incontinently to procure the means; finding, therefore, his daughter at leisure, and having knowledge of her former love, spake to her as followeth:

"Dear daughter, as thou hast long time lived a maiden, so now thou must learn to be a mother; and as I have been careful to bring

---

[123]*stale:* The sense probably is "decoy," "lure," or "bait"; the decoy functions, however, not in the winning of Lucilla but in the deceiving of Philautus, to whom Euphues pretends an interest in Livia.

thee up a virgin, so am I now desirous to make thee a wife. Neither ought I in this matter to use any persuasions, for that maidens commonly nowadays are no sooner born but they begin to bride it; neither to offer any great portions, for that thou knowest thou shalt inherit all my possessions. Mine only care hath been hitherto to match thee with such an one as should be of good wealth, able to maintain thee; of great worship, able to compare with thee in birth; of honest conditions, to deserve thy love; and an Italian born, to enjoy my lands. At the last I have found one answerable to my desire, a gentleman of great revenues, of a noble progeny, of honest behavior, of comely personage, born and brought up in Naples—Philautus. Thy friend, as I guess; thy husband, Lucilla, if thou like it; neither canst thou dislike him, who wanteth nothing that should cause thy liking, neither hath anything that should breed thy loathing. And surely I rejoice the more that thou shalt be linked to him in marriage whom thou hast loved, as I hear, being a maiden; neither can there any jars kindle between them where the minds be so united, neither any jealousy arise where love hath so long been settled.

"Therefore, Lucilla, to the end the desire of either of you may now be accomplished to the delight of you both, I am here come to finish the contract by giving hands, which you have already begun between yourselves by joining of hearts; that as God doth witness the one in your consciences, so the world may testify the other by your conversations. And therefore, Lucilla, make such answer to my request as may like me and satisfy thy friend."

Lucilla, abashed with this sudden speech of her father yet boldened by the love of her friend, with a comely bashfulness answered him in this manner:

"Reverend sir, the sweetness that I have found in the undefiled estate of virginity causeth me to loathe the sour sauce which is mixed with matrimony; and the quiet life which I have tried, being a maiden, maketh me to shun the cares that are always incident to a mother. Neither am I so wedded to the world that I should be moved with great possessions, neither so bewitched with wantonness that I should be enticed with any man's proportion, neither if I were so disposed would I be so proud to desire one of noble progeny or so precise to choose one only in mine own country. For that commonly these things happen always to the contrary. Do we not see the noble to match with the base, the rich with the poor, the Italian oftentimes with the Portingale.[124] As love knoweth no laws, so it regardeth no

---

[124]*Portingale:* person from Portugal.

conditions; as the lover maketh no pause where he liketh, so he maketh no conscience of these idle ceremonies.

"In that Philautus is the man that threateneth such kindness at my hands and such courtesy at yours that he should account me his wife before he woo me, certainly he is like for me to make his reckoning twice, because he reckoneth without his hostess. And in this Philautus would either show himself of great wisdom to persuade, or me of great lightness to be allured. Although the loadstone draw iron, yet it cannot move gold; though the jet gather up the light straw,[125] yet can it not take up the pure steel. Although Philautus think himself of virtue sufficient to win his lover, yet shall he not obtain Lucilla. I cannot but smile to hear that a marriage should be solemnized where never was any mention of assuring, and that the wooing should be a day after the wedding. Certes, if when I looked merrily on Philautus he deemed it in the way of marriage, or if seeing me disposed to jest he took me in good earnest, then sure he might gather some presumption of my love, but no promise. But methinks it is good reason that I should be at mine own bridal, and not given in the church before I know the bridegroom.

"Therefore, dear father, in mine opinion, as there can be no bargain where both be not agreed, neither any indentures sealed where the one will not consent, so can there be no contract where both be not content, no banns asked lawfully where one of the parties forbiddeth them, no marriage made where no match was meant. But I will hereafter frame myself to be coy, seeing I am claimed for a wife because I have been courteous, and give myself to melancholy, seeing I am accounted won in that I have been merry. And if every gentleman be made of the mettle that Philautus is, then I fear I shall be challenged of as many as I have used to company with, and be a common wife to all those that have commonly resorted hither.

"My duty therefore ever reserved, I here on my knees forswear Philautus for my husband, although I accept him for my friend. And seeing I shall hardly be induced ever to match with any, I beseech you if by your fatherly love I shall be compelled, that I may match with such a one as both I may love and you may like."

Ferardo, being a grave and wise gentleman, although he were thoroughly angry, yet he dissembled his fury to the end he might by craft discover her fancy. And whispering Philautus in the ear,

---

[125]*jet . . . straw:* The mineral called "jet" has the power of attracting light objects, such as straw, when it is rubbed slightly and thereby electrified.

who stood as though he had a flea in his ear, desired him to keep silence until he had undermined her by subtlety. Which Philautus having granted, Ferardo began to sift his daughter with this device:

"Lucilla, thy color showeth thee to be in a great choler, and thy hot words bewray thy heavy wrath; but be patient, seeing all my talk was only to try thee. I am neither so unnatural to wrest thee against thine own will, neither so malicious to wed thee to any against thine own liking. For well I know what jars, what jealousy, what strife, what storms ensue, where the match is made rather by the compulsion of the parents than by the consent of the parties. Neither do I like thee the less in that thou likest Philautus so little; neither can Philautus love thee the worse in that thou lovest thyself so well, wishing rather to stand to thy chance than to the choice of any other.

"But this grieveth me most: that thou art almost vowed to the vain order of the vestal virgins, despising, or at the least not desiring, the sacred bands of Juno her bed. If thy mother had been of that mind when she was a maiden, thou hadst not now been born to be of this mind to be a virgin. Weigh with thyself what slender profit they bring to the commonwealth, what slight pleasure to themselves, what great grief to their parents, which joy most in their offspring and desire most to enjoy the noble and blessed name of a grandfather. Thou knowest that the tallest ash is cut down for fuel because it beareth no good fruit, that the cow that gives no milk is brought to the slaughter, that the drone that gathereth no honey is contemned, that the woman that maketh herself barren by not marrying is accounted among the Grecian ladies worse than a carrion, as Homer reporteth. Therefore, Lucilla, if thou have any care to be a comfort to my hoary hairs or a commodity to thy commonweal, frame thyself to that honorable estate of matrimony, which was sanctified in paradise, allowed of the patriarchs, hallowed of the old prophets, and commended of all persons.

"If thou like any be not ashamed to tell it me, which only am to exhort thee, yea, and, as much as in me lieth, to command thee to love one. If he be base, thy blood will make him noble; if beggarly, thy goods shall make him wealthy; if a stranger, thy freedom may enfranchise him; if he be young, he is the more fitter to be thy fere; if he be old, the liker to thine aged father. For I had rather thou shouldest lead a life to thine own liking in earth than, to thy great torments, lead apes in hell. Be bold, therefore, to make me partner of thy desire which will be partaker of thy disease—yea, and a furtherer of thy delights as far as either my friends, or my lands, or my life will stretch."

Lucilla, perceiving the drift of the old fox her father, weighed with herself what was the best to be done. At the last, not weighing her father's ill will but encouraged by love, shaped him an answer which pleased Ferardo but a little and pinched Philautus on the parson's side[126] on this manner:

"Dear father Ferardo, although I see the bait you lay to catch me, yet I am content to swallow the hook. Neither are you more desirous to take me napping, than I willing to confess my meaning. So it is that love hath as well inveigled me as others, which make it as strange as I. Neither do I love him so meanly that I should be ashamed of his name, neither is his personage so mean that I should love him shamefully. It is Euphues, that lately arrived here at Naples, that hath battered the bulwark of my breast and shall shortly enter as conqueror into my bosom. What his wealth is I neither know it nor weigh it; what his wit is all Naples doth know it and wonder at it. Neither have I been curious to inquire of his progenitors, for that I know so noble a mind could take no original but from a noble man. For as no bird can look against the sun but those that be bred of the eagle, neither any hawk soar so high as the brood of the hobby, so no wight can have such excellent qualities except he descend of a noble race, neither be of so high capacity unless he issue of a high progeny. And I hope Philautus will not be my foe, seeing I have chosen his dear friend; neither you, father, be displeased in that Philautus is displaced. You need not muse that I should so suddenly be entangled. Love gives no reason of choice, neither will it suffer any repulse. Myrrha was enamored of her natured father, Byblis of her brother, Phaedra of her son-in-law. If nature can no way resist the fury of affection, how should it be stayed by wisdom?"

Ferardo, interrupting her in the middle of her discourse, although he were moved with inward grudge yet he wisely repressed his anger, knowing that sharp words would but sharpen her froward will, and thus answered her briefly:

[126]*pinched . . . on the parson's side:* Probably, as Bond suggests, the sense is "deprived . . . of a wedding." If so, the expression seems to have been a clever saying invented by Lyly. In the second edition "parson's" is changed to "person's," but in this instance Lyly himself may not be the reviser. One suspects that the compositor, missing the point of the quip, innocently changes the "a" to "e" because to him "parson's" is simply an alternate spelling of "person's." See note 6 in *Master F. J.*

"Lucilla, as I am not presently to grant my good will, so mean I not to reprehend thy choice. Yet wisdom willeth me to pause until I have called what may happen to my remembrance, and warneth thee to be circumspect lest thy rash conceit bring a sharp repentance. As for you, Philautus, I would not have you despair, seeing a woman doth oftentimes change her desire."

Unto whom Philautus in few words made answer: "Certainly, Ferardo, I take the less grief in that I see her so greedy after Euphues. And by so much the more I am content to leave my suit, by how much the more she seemeth to disdain my service. But as for hope, because I would not by any means taste one dram thereof, I will abjure all places of her abode and loathe her company, whose countenance I have so much loved. As for Euphues—"

And there, staying his speech, he flung out of the doors and, repairing to his lodging, uttered these words:

"Ah, most dissembling wretch Euphues! Oh, counterfeit companion! Couldst thou under the show of a steadfast friend cloak the malice of a mortal foe? Under the color of simplicity shroud the image of deceit? Is thy Livia turned to my Lucilla, thy love to my lover, thy devotion to my saint? Is this the courtesy of Athens, the caviling of scholars, the craft of Grecians? Couldst thou not remember, Philautus, that Greece is never without some wily Ulysses, never void of some Sinon, never to seek of some deceitful shifter? Is it not commonly said of Grecians that craft cometh to them by kind, that they learn to deceive in their cradle? Why, then, did his pretended courtesy bewitch thee with such credulity? Shall my good will be the cause of his ill will? Because I was content to be his friend, thought he me meet to be made his fool? I see now that as the fish scolopidus in the flood Araris at the waxing of the moon is as white as the driven snow and at the waning as black as the burnt coal, so Euphues which at the first increasing of our familiarity was very zealous is now at the last cast become most faithless.

"But why rather exclaim I not against Lucilla, whose wanton looks caused Euphues to violate his plighted faith? Ah, wretched wench, canst thou be so light of love as to change with every wind? So unconstant as to prefer a new lover before thine old friend? Ah, well, I wot that a new broom sweepeth clean and a new garment maketh thee leave off the old though it be fitter, and new wine causeth thee to forsake the old though it be better; much like to the men in the island Scyrum which pull up the old tree when they see the young begin to spring, and not unlike unto the widow of Lesbos which changed all her old gold for new glass. Have I served thee three years faithfully and am I served so unkindly? Shall the fruit of my desire be turned to disdain?

"But unless Euphues had inveigled thee, thou hadst yet been constant; yea, but if Euphues had not seen thee willing to be won, he would never have wooed thee. But had not Euphues enticed thee with fair words, thou wouldst never have loved him; but hadst thou not given him fair looks, he would never have liked thee. Aye, but Euphues gave the onset; aye, but Lucilla gave the occasion. Aye, but Euphues first brake his mind; aye, but Lucilla first bewrayed her meaning. Tush, why go I about to excuse any of them, seeing I have just cause to accuse them both? Neither ought I to dispute which of them hath proffered me the greatest villainy, sith that either of them hath committed perjury. Yet although they have found me dull in perceiving their falsehood, they shall not find me slack in revenging their folly. As for Lucilla, seeing I mean altogether to forget her, I mean also to forgive her, lest in seeking means to be revenged, mine old desire be renewed."

Philautus, having thus discoursed with himself, began to write to Euphues as followeth:

Although hitherto, Euphues, I have shrined thee in my heart for a trusty friend, I will shun thee hereafter as a trothless foe; and although I cannot see in thee less wit than I was wont, yet do I find less honesty. I perceive at the last, although (being deceived) it be too late, that musk, though it be sweet in the smell, is sour in the smack; that the leaf of the cedar tree, though it be fair to be seen, yet the syrup depriveth sight; that friendship, though it be plighted by shaking the hand, yet it is shaken off by fraud of the heart.

But thou hast not much to boast of, for as thou hast won a fickle lady, so hast thou lost a faithful friend. How canst thou be secure of her constancy, when thou hast had such trial of her lightness? How canst thou assure thyself that she will be faithful to thee, which hath been faithless to me?

Ah, Euphues, let not my credulity be an occasion hereafter for thee to practice the like cruelty. Remember this: that yet there hath never been any faithless to his friend that hath not also been fruitless to his God. But I weigh the treachery the less in that it cometh from a Grecian in whom is no truth. Though I be too weak to wrestle for a revenge, yet God, who permitteth no guile to be guiltless, will shortly requite this injury; though Philautus have no policy to undermine thee, yet thine own practices will be sufficient to overthrow thee.

Couldst thou, Euphues, for the love of a fruitless pleasure violate the league of faithful friendship? Didst thou weigh more the enticing looks of a lewd wench than the entire love of a loyal friend? If thou didst determine with thyself at the first to be false, why didst thou swear to be true? If to be true, why art thou false? If thou wast minded both falsely and forgedly to deceive me, why didst thou flatter and dissemble with me at the first? If to love me, why dost thou flinch at the last? If the sacred bands of amity did delight thee, why didst thou break them? If dislike thee,[127] why didst thou praise them?

Dost thou not know that a perfect friend should be like the glazeworm[128] which shineth most bright in the dark, or like the pure frankincense which smelleth most sweet when it is in the fire, or at the least not unlike to the damask rose which is sweeter in the still than on the stalk? But thou, Euphues, dost rather resemble the swallow which in the summer creepeth under the eaves of every house and in the winter leaveth nothing but dirt behind her, or the humble bee which having sucked honey out of the fair flower doth leave it and loathe it, or the spider which in the finest web doth hang the fairest fly.

Dost thou think, Euphues, that thy craft in betraying me shall any whit cool my courage in revenging thy villainy? Or that a gentleman of Naples will put up such an injury at the hands of a scholar? And if I do, it is not for want of strength to maintain my just quarrel, but of will which thinketh scorn to get so vain a conquest. I know that Menelaus for his ten years' war endured ten years' woe, that after all his strife he won but a strumpet, that for all his travail he reduced—I cannot say reclaimed—but a straggler;[129] which was as much, in my judgment, as to strive for a broken glass which is good for nothing. I wish thee rather Menelaus' care than myself his conquest, that thou, being deluded by Lucilla, mayest rather know what it is to be deceived, than I, having conquered thee, should prove what it were to bring back a dissembler. Seeing, therefore, there can no greater revenge light

---

[127]*If dislike thee:* if they (the sacred bands of amity) displeased you.

[128]*glazeworm:* glowworm.

[129]*travail . . . straggler:* Though "travail" and "travel" are often spelled the same way by the Elizabethans, it looks as if "travail" is mainly intended here. "Endurance," "woe," "strife," and "strive" tend to indicate that "travail" is what the sentence is all about. Yet "reduced . . . straggler" means "brought back [from Troy] a straggler [Helen]," and therefore some "traveling" is implied. "Straggler" probably is meant to be synonymous with "strumpet" while carrying the additional sense of "tramp," "vagabond," or even "campfollower."

upon thee than that as thou hast reaped where another hath sown, so another may thresh that which thou hast reaped, I will pray that thou mayest be measured unto with the like measure that thou hast meten unto others; that as thou hast thought it no conscience to betray me, so others may deem it no dishonesty to deceive thee; that as Lucilla made it a light matter to forswear her old friend Philautus, so she may make it a mock to forsake her new fere Euphues. Which if it come to pass, as it is like by my compass, then shalt thou see the troubles and feel the torments which thou hast already thrown into the hearts and eyes of others.

Thus hoping shortly to see thee as hopeless as myself is hapless, I wish my wish were as effectually ended as it is heartily looked for. And so I leave thee.

Thine once,
Philautus

Philautus, dispatching a messenger with this letter speedily to Euphues, went into the fields to walk there, either to digest his choler or chew upon his melancholy.

But Euphues, having read the contents, was well content, setting his talk at naught and answering his taunts in these gibing terms:

I remember, Philautus, how valiantly Ajax boasted in the feats of arms, yet Ulysses bare away the armor; and it may be that though thou crake[130] of thine own courage, thou mayest easily lose the conquest. Dost thou think Euphues such a dastard that he is not able to withstand thy courage or such a dullard that he cannot descry thy craft? Alas, good soul. It fareth with thee as with the hen, which, when the puttock[131] hath caught her chicken, beginneth to cackle; and thou, having lost thy lover, beginneth to prattle.

Tush, Philautus, I am in this point of Euripides his mind, who thinks it lawful for the desire of a kingdom to transgress the bonds of honesty and for the love of a lady to violate and break the bonds of amity. The friendship between man and man, as it is common, so is it of course;[132] between man and woman, as it is seldom, so is it sincere: the one proceedeth of the similitude of manners, the other of the sincerity of the heart. If thou hadst learned the first point of hawking, thou wouldst have learned to have held fast; or the first note of descant, thou wouldst have kept thy *sol fa* to thyself.

---

[130]*crake:* crack, brag.
[131]*puttock:* bird of prey; a general term applied to the kite or the common buzzard.
[132]*of course:* a matter of course, customary.

But thou canst blame me no more of folly in leaving thee to love Lucilla than thou mayest reprove him of foolishness that having a sparrow in his hand letteth her go to catch the pheasant, or him of unskillfulness that seeing the heron leaveth to level his shot at the stock dove, or that woman of coyness that having a dead rose in her bosom throweth it away to gather the fresh violet. Love knoweth no laws. Did not Jupiter transform himself into the shape of Amphitrio[133] to embrace Alcmene, into the form of a swan to enjoy Leda, into a bull to beguile Io, into a shower of gold to win Danae? Did not Neptune change himself into a heifer, a ram, a flood, a dolphin, only for the love of those he lusted after? Did not Apollo convert himself into a shepherd, into a bird, into a lion, for the desire he had to heal his disease? If the gods thought no scorn to become beasts to obtain their best beloved, shall Euphues be so nice in changing his copy to gain his lady? No, no, he that cannot dissemble in love is not worthy to live. I am of this mind: that both might and malice, deceit and treachery, all perjury, any impiety, may lawfully be committed in love, which is lawless.

In that thou arguest Lucilla of lightness thy will hangs in the light of thy wit. Dost thou not know that the weak stomach, if it be cloyed with one diet, doth soon surfeit? That the clown's garlic cannot ease the courtier's disease so well as the pure treacle?[134] That far fet[135] and dear bought is good for ladies? That Euphues, being a more dainty morsel than Philautus, ought better to be accepted?

Tush, Philautus, set thy heart at rest, for thy hap willeth thee to give over all hope both of my friendship and her love. As for revenge, thou art not so able to lend a blow as I to ward it, neither more venturous to challenge the combat than I valiant to answer the quarrel. As Lucilla was caught by fraud, so shall she be kept by force; and as thou wast too simple to espy my craft, so I think thou wilt be too weak to withstand my courage. But if thy revenge stand only upon thy wish, thou shalt never live to see my woe or to have thy will. And so farewell.

Euphues

This letter being dispatched, Euphues sent it and Philautus read it; who, disdaining those proud terms, disdained also to answer them, being ready to ride with Ferardo.

[133]*Amphitrio:* a shortening of "Amphitryon"; other examples are "Aethiop," "Machiavel," and "Cressid."

[134]*clown's garlic . . . pure treacle:* The verbal play centers on "pure treacle" (molasses) as opposed to "clown's treacle" (garlic), the latter sometimes called "poor man's treacle" or "churl's treacle."

[135]*far fet:* far fetched (brought from afar).

Euphues, having for a space absented himself from the house of Ferardo because he was at home, longed sore to see Lucilla; which now opportunity offered unto him, Ferardo being gone again to Venice with Philautus.

But in this his absence one Curio, a gentleman of Naples of little wealth and less wit, haunted Lucilla her company, and so enchanted her that Euphues was also cast off with Philautus. Which thing being unknown to Euphues caused him the sooner to make his repair to the presence of his lady. Whom he finding in her muses began pleasantly to salute in this manner:

"Mistress Lucilla, although my long absence might breed your just anger, for that lovers desire nothing so much as often meeting, yet I hope my presence will dissolve your choler, for that lovers are soon pleased when of their wishes they be fully possessed. My absence is the rather to be excused in that your father hath been always at home, whose frowns seemed to threaten my ill fortune; and my presence at this present the better to be accepted in that I have made such speedy repair to your presence."

Unto whom Lucilla answered with this glyeke:[136] "Truly, Euphues, you have missed the cushion, for I was neither angry with your long absence, neither am I well pleased at your presence; the one gave me rather a good hope hereafter never to see you, the other giveth me a greater occasion to abhor you."

Euphues, being nipped on the head, with a pale countenance, as though his soul had forsaken his body, replied as followeth: "If this sudden change, Lucilla, proceed of any desert of mine, I am here not only to answer the fact but also to make amends for my fault; if of any new motion or mind to forsake your new friend, I am rather to lament your inconstancy than revenge it. But I hope that such hot love cannot be so soon cold, neither such sure faith be rewarded with so sudden forgetfulness."

Lucilla, not ashamed to confess her folly, answered him with this frump: "Sir, whether your deserts or my desire have wrought this change it will boot you little to know. Neither do I crave amends, neither fear revenge. As for fervent love, you know there is no fire so hot but it is quenched with water, neither affection so strong but is weakened with reason. Let this suffice thee: that thou know I care not for thee."

"Indeed," said Euphues, "to know the cause of your alteration

[136]*glyeke:* gleek, gibe.

would boot me little, seeing the effect taketh such force. I have heard that women either love entirely or hate deadly, and seeing you have put me out of doubt of the one, I must needs persuade myself of the other. This change will cause Philautus to laugh me to scorn and double thy lightness in turning so often. Such was the hope that I conceived of thy constancy that I spared not in all places to blaze thy loyalty, but now my rash conceit will prove me a liar and thee a light huswife."

"Nay," said Lucilla, "now shalt thou not laugh Philautus to scorn, seeing you have both drunk of one cup. In misery, Euphues, it is great comfort to have a companion. I doubt not but that you will both conspire against me to work some mischief, although I nothing fear your malice. Whosoever accounteth you a liar for praising me may also deem you a lecher for being enamored of me, and whosoever judgeth me light in forsaking of you may think thee as lewd in loving of me. For thou that thoughtest it lawful to deceive thy friend must take no scorn to be deceived of thy foe."

"Then I perceive, Lucilla," said he, "that I was made thy stale and Philautus thy laughingstock; whose friendship, I must confess indeed, I have refused to obtain thy favor. And since another hath won that we both have lost, I am content for my part; neither ought I to be grieved, seeing thou art fickle."

"Certes, Euphues," said Lucilla, "you spend your wind in waste, for your welcome is but small and your cheer is like to be less. Fancy giveth no reason of his change, neither will be controlled for any choice. This is, therefore, to warn you that from henceforth you neither solicit this suit, neither offer any way your service. I have chosen one, I must needs confess, neither to be compared to Philautus in wealth nor to thee in wit, neither in birth to the worst of you both. I think God gave it me for a just plague for renouncing Philautus and choosing thee. And since I am an example to all women of lightness, I am like also to be a mirror to them all of unhappiness. Which ill luck I must take by so much the more patiently, by how much the more I acknowledge myself to have deserved it worthily."

"Well, Lucilla," answered Euphues, "this case breedeth my sorrow the more in that it is so sudden, and by so much the more I lament it by how much the less I looked for it. In that my welcome is so cold and my cheer so simple, it nothing toucheth me—seeing your fury is so hot and my misfortune so great—that I am neither willing to receive it nor you to bestow it. If tract of time or want of trial had caused this metamorphosis, my grief had been more tolerable and your fleeting more excusable. But coming in a moment undeserved, unlooked for, unthought of, it increaseth my sorrow and thy shame."

"Euphues," quoth she, "you make a long harvest for a little corn, and angle for the fish that is already caught. Curio—yea, Curio—is he that hath my love at his pleasure and shall also have my life at his commandment; and although you deem him unworthy to enjoy that which erst you accounted no wight worthy to embrace, yet seeing I esteem him more worth than any, he is to be reputed as chief. The wolf chooseth him for her make that hath or doth endure most travail for her sake.[137] Venus was content to take the blacksmith with his poltfoot. Cornelia here in Naples disdained not to love a rude miller. As for changing, did not Helen, that pearl of Greece, thy country-woman, first take Menelaus, then Theseus, and last of all Paris? If brute beasts give us examples that those are most to be liked of whom we are best beloved, or if the princess of beauty, Venus, and her heirs, Helen and Cornelia, show that our affection standeth on our free will, then am I rather to be excused than accused. Therefore, good Euphues, be as merry as you may be, for time may so turn that once again you may be."

"Nay, Lucilla," said he, "my harvest shall cease, seeing others have reaped my corn; as for angling for the fish that is already caught, that were but mere folly. But in my mind, if you be a fish you are either an eel which as soon as one hath hold on her tail will slip out of his hand, or else a minnow which will be nibbling at every bait but never biting. But what fish soever you be, you have made both me and Philautus to swallow a gudgeon.

"If Curio be the person, I would neither wish thee a greater plague nor him a deadlier poison. I, for my part, think him worthy of thee and thou unworthy of him: for although he be in body deformed, in mind foolish, an innocent born, a beggar by misfortune, yet doth he deserve a better than thyself, whose corrupt manners have stained thy heavenly hue, whose light behavior hath dimmed the lights of thy beauty, whose unconstant mind hath betrayed the innocency of so many a gentleman.

"And in that you bring in the example of a beast to confirm your folly, you show therein your beastly disposition, which is ready to follow such beastliness. But Venus played false. And what for that? Seeing her lightness serveth for an example, I would wish thou

[137]*make ... sake:* The rhyme is important, but there is no sacrifice of sense; "make" meant "mate" or "companion."

mightest try her punishment for a reward, that being openly taken in an iron net all the world might judge whether thou be fish or flesh. And, certes, in my mind no angle will hold thee; it must be a net. Cornelia loved a miller and thou a miser; can her folly excuse thy fault? Helen of Greece, my countrywoman born, but thine by profession, changed and rechanged at her pleasure, I grant. Shall the lewdness of others animate thee in thy lightness? Why, then, dost thou not haunt the stews because Lais frequented them? Why dost thou not love a bull, seeing Pasiphaë loved one? Why art thou not enamored of thy father, knowing Myrrha was so incensed? These are set down that we, viewing their incontinency, should fly the like impudency, not follow the like excess; neither can they excuse thee of any inconstancy.

"Merry I will be as I may. But if I may hereafter as thou meanest, I will not. And therefore farewell, Lucilla, the most inconstant that ever was nursed in Naples. Farewell, Naples, the most cursed town in all Italy. And women all, farewell."

Euphues, having thus given her his last farewell, yet being solitary, began afresh to recount his sorrow on this manner:

"Ah, Euphues, into what misfortune art thou brought! In what sudden misery art thou wrapped! It is like to fare with thee as with the eagle, which dieth neither for age nor with sickness but with famine; for although thy stomach hunger, yet thy heart will not suffer thee to eat. And why shouldst thou torment thyself for one in whom is neither faith nor fervency? Oh, the counterfeit love of women! Oh, inconstant sex! I have lost Philautus, I have lost Lucilla. I have lost that which I shall hardly find again, a faithful friend.

"Ah, foolish Euphues, why didst thou leave Athens, the nurse of wisdom, to inhabit Naples, the nourisher of wantonness? Had it not been better for thee to have eaten salt with the philosophers in Greece than sugar with the courtiers of Italy? But behold the course of youth which always inclineth to pleasure. I forsook mine old companions to search for new friends, I rejected the grave and fatherly counsel of Eubulus to follow the brainsick humor of mine own will. I addicted myself wholly to the service of women to spend my life in the laps of ladies, my lands in maintenance of bravery, my wit in the vanities of idle sonnets. I had thought that women had been as we men—that is, true, faithful, zealous, constant; but I perceive they be rather woe unto men by their falsehood, jealousy, inconstancy. I was half persuaded that they were made of the perfection of men and would be comforters, but now I see they have tasted of the infection of the serpent and will be corrasives.[138] The physician saith it is dangerous to minister physic unto the patient that hath a cold stomach and a hot liver, lest in giving warmth to the one he inflame the other. So verily it is hard to deal with a woman whose words seem fervent, whose heart is congealed into hard ice, lest, trusting their outward talk, he be betrayed with their inward treachery.

"I will to Athens, there to toss my books, no more in Naples to live with fair looks. I will so frame myself as all youth hereafter shall rather rejoice to see mine amendment, than be animated to follow my former life. Philosophy, physic, divinity shall be my study. Oh, the hidden secrets of nature, the express image of moral virtues, the equal balance of justice, the medicines to heal all diseases—how they begin to delight me! The axioms of Aristotle, the maxims of Justinian, the aphorisms of Galen have suddenly made such a breach into my mind that I seem only to desire them, which did only erst detest them.

"If wit be employed in the honest study of learning, what thing so precious as wit? If in the idle trade of love, what thing more pestilent than wit? The proof of late hath been verified in me, whom nature hath endued with a little wit which I have abused with an obstinate will. Most true it is that the thing the better it is the greater is the abuse, and that there is nothing but through the malice of man may be abused. Doth not the fire, an element so necessary that without it man cannot live, as well burn the house as burn in the house if it be abused? Doth not treacle as well poison as help, if it be taken out of time? Doth not wine if it be immoderately taken kill the stomach, inflame the liver, mischief the drunken? Doth not physic destroy if it be not well tempered? Doth not law accuse if it be not rightly interpreted? Doth not divinity condemn if it be not faithfully construed? Is not poison taken out of the honeysuckle by the spider, venom out of the rose by the canker, dung out of the maple tree by the scorpion? Even so the greatest wickedness is drawn out of the greatest wit if it be abused by will, or entangled with the world, or inveigled with women.

"But seeing I see mine own impiety, I will endeavor myself to amend all that is past and to be a mirror of godliness hereafter. The rose, though a little it be eaten with the canker, yet, being distilled, yieldeth sweet water; the iron, though fretted with the rust, yet, being burnt in the fire, shineth brighter; and wit, although it hath been

[138]*corrasives:* corrosives. The vowel sound of "corrasives" runs through this and the following sentence, and therefore it will not do to use the modern spelling, "corrosives."

eaten with the canker of his own conceit and fretted with the rust of vain love, yet, being purified in the still of wisdom and tried in the fire of zeal, will shine bright and smell sweet in the nostrils of all young novices.

"As therefore I gave a farewell to Lucilla, a farewell to Naples, a farewell to women, so now do I give a farewell to the world; meaning rather to macerate myself with melancholy than pine in folly, rather choosing to die in my study amidst my books than to court in Italy in the company of ladies."

Euphues, having thus debated with himself, went to his bed, there either with sleep to deceive his fancy, or with musing to renew his ill fortune or recant his old follies.[139]

But it happened immediately Ferardo to return home. Who, hearing this strange event, was not a little amazed, and was now more ready to exhort Lucilla from the love of Curio than before to the liking of Philautus. Therefore in all haste, with watery eyes and a woeful heart, began on this manner to reason with his daughter:

"Lucilla—daughter I am ashamed to call thee, seeing thou hast neither care of thy father's tender affection nor of thine own credit— what sprite hath enchanted thy spirit that every minute thou alterest thy mind? I had thought that my hoary hairs should have found comfort by thy golden locks and my rotten age great ease by thy ripe years. But, alas, I see in thee neither wit to order thy doings, neither will to frame thyself to discretion, neither the nature of a child, neither the nurture of a maiden, neither—I cannot without tears speak it—any regard of thine honor, neither any care of thine honesty. I am now enforced to remember thy mother's death, who I think was a prophetess in her life: for oftentimes she would say that thou hadst more beauty than was convenient for one that should be honest, and more cockering[140] than was meet for one that should be a matron.

"Would I had never lived to be so old or thou to be so obstinate, either would I had died in my youth in the court or thou in thy cradle. I would to God that either I had never been born or thou never bred. Is this the comfort that the parent reapeth for all his care? Is obstinacy paid for obedience, stubbornness rendered for duty,

---

[139]*Euphues, having ... old follies:* This paragraph was added in the second edition; at the same time "But" was inserted before "It happened" at the start of the next paragraph.

[140]*cockering:* pampering. The implication is that the parents had brought Lucilla up too indulgently for her eventually to become a wife and mother. See an earlier use of the word on p. 130. Below (p. 186), when the father calls Lucilla a "cockney," he means "spoiled child."

malicious desperateness for filial fear? I perceive now that the wise painter saw more than the foolish parent can, who painted love going downward, saying it might well descend but ascend it could never. Danaus, whom they report to be the father of fifty children, had among them all but one that disobeyed him in a thing most dishonest; but I that am father to one more than I would be, although one be all, have that one most disobedient to me in a request lawful and reasonable. If Danaus seeing but one of his daughters without awe became himself without mercy, what shall Ferardo do in this case who hath one and all most unnatural to him in a most just cause?

"Shall Curio enjoy the fruit of my travails, possess the benefit of my labors, inherit the patrimony of mine ancestors, who hath neither wisdom to increase them nor wit to keep them? Wilt thou, Lucilla, bestow thyself on such an one as hath neither comeliness in his body nor knowledge in his mind nor credit in his country? Oh, I would thou hadst either been ever faithful to Philautus or never faithless to Euphues, or would thou wouldst be most fickle to Curio. As thy beauty hath made thee the blaze of Italy, so will thy lightness make thee the byword of the world. Oh, Lucilla, Lucilla! Would thou wert less fair or more fortunate, either of less honor or greater honesty, either better minded or soon buried.

"Shall thine old father live to see thee match with a young fool? Shall my kind heart be rewarded with such unkindness? Ah, Lucilla, thou knowest not the care of a father nor the duty of a child, and as far art thou from piety as I from cruelty. Nature will not permit me to disherit my daughter, and yet it will suffer thee to dishonor thy father. Affection causeth me to wish thy life, and shall it entice thee to procure my death? It is mine only comfort to see thee flourish in thy youth, and is it thine to see me fade in mine age? To conclude, I desire to live to see thee prosper, and thou to see me perish.

"But why cast I the effect of this unnaturalness in thy teeth, seeing I myself was the cause? I made thee a wanton and thou hast made me a fool, I brought thee up like a cockney and thou hast handled me like a cockscomb—I speak it to mine own shame—I made more of thee than became a father and thou less of me than beseemed a child. And shall my loving care be cause of thy wicked cruelty? Yea, yea, I am not the first that hath been too careful nor the last that shall be handled so unkindly: it is common to see fathers too fond and children too froward.

"Well, Lucilla, the tears which thou seest trickle down my cheeks, and my drops of blood, which thou canst not see, that fall from my heart, enforce me to make an end of my talk. And if thou have any duty of a child, or care of a friend, or courtesy of a stranger, or feeling of a Christian, or humanity of a reasonable creature, then release thy father of grief and acquit thyself of ungratefulness. Otherwise thou shalt but hasten my death and increase thine own defame; which if thou do, the gain is mine and the loss thine, and both infinite."

Lucilla, either so bewitched that she could not relent or so wicked that she would not yield to her father's request, answered him on this manner:

"Dear father, as you would have me to show the duty of a child, so ought you to show the care of a parent; for as the one standeth in obedience, so the other is grounded upon reason. You would have me as I owe duty to you to leave Curio, and I desire you as you owe me any love that you suffer me to enjoy him. If you accuse me of unnaturalness in that I yield not to your request, I am also to condemn you of unkindness in that you grant not my petition. You object I know not what to Curio. But it is the eye of the master that fatteth the horse, and the love of the woman that maketh the man. To give reason for fancy were to weigh the fire and measure the wind.

"If, therefore, my delight be the cause of your death, I think my sorrow would be an occasion of your solace. And if you be angry because I am pleased, certes I deem you would be content if I were deceased; which if it be so that my pleasure breed your pain and mine annoy your joy, I may well say that you are an unkind father and I an unfortunate child. But, good father, either content yourself with my choice, or let me stand to the main chance. Otherwise the grief will be mine and the fault yours, and both untolerable."

Ferardo, seeing his daughter to have neither regard of her own honor nor his request, conceived such an inward grief that in short space he died, leaving Lucilla the only heir of his lands and Curio to possess them. But what end came of her,[141] seeing it is nothing incident to the history of Euphues, it were superfluous to insert it, and so incredible that all women would rather wonder at it than believe it. Which event being so strange, I had rather leave them in a muse what it should be than in a maze in telling what it was.

---

[141]*what end came of her:* Lucilla dies shameless and unrepenting; see Euphues' letter to Philautus, Bond, I, 311.

Philautus, having intelligence of Euphues his success and the false-hood of Lucilla, although he began to rejoice at the misery of his fellow, yet, seeing her fickleness, could not but lament her folly and pity his friend's misfortune, thinking that the lightness of Lucilla enticed Euphues to so great liking. Euphues and Philautus having conference between themselves, casting discourtesy in the teeth each of the other, but chiefly noting disloyalty in the demeanor of Lucilla, after much talk renewed their old friendship, both abandoning Lucilla as most abominable. Philautus was earnest to have Euphues tarry in Naples, and Euphues desirous to have Philautus to Athens; but the one was so addicted to the court, the other so wedded to the uni-versity, that each refused the offer of the other. Yet this they agreed between themselves: that though their bodies were by distance of place severed, yet the conjunction of their minds should neither be separated by the length of time nor alienated by change of soil.

"I, for my part," said Euphues, "to confirm this league give thee my hand and my heart."

And so likewise did Philautus. And so, shaking hands, they bid each other farewell.

♣ Of Apolonius and Sila   1

FROM *Farewell to the Military Profession*
(1581)

BARNABY RICH

Unlike Hemingway's *Farewell to Arms,* Barnaby Rich's *Farewell to the Military Profession* (1581) is not about war at all. Captain Rich has put his military life behind him to write eight harmless tales for the ladies. His word for the form of "Apolonius and Silla," the second tale, was "history," by which he apparently meant "story" or "tale." A better word is *"novella."* Rich's favorite source of plot materials was William Painter's *Palace of Pleasure* (1566), a collection of *novelle* translated and adapted largely from Boccaccio and Bandello. Silla, the name of the heroine in "Apolonius and Silla," may have come from Cinthio, whose book of *novelle* called *Gli Hecatommithi* Rich knew firsthand.[1]

Yet *"novella"* is not precise enough to be of much help; and "novel," the word Painter applies to each work in his collection, is not helpful either, since all he means by it is *novella* (short story); in lopping off the last syllable, Painter is doing what the Elizabethans often did to anglicize Italian words. Since the eighteenth century, "novel" in English has meant "long story"; and, to further complicate matters, in the twentieth century *"novella"* and *"nouvelle"* have become more or less synonymous terms in English for "story of intermediate length."

But length, though it has a bearing on the peculiar nature or quality of a work of fiction, is not a criterion on which many readers have been able to agree; to the eighteenth century our novels would have seemed short, and to us theirs are interminable. It is more meaningful, therefore—after we have established "Apolonius" as a

[1]See Cranfill, ed., *Rich's Farewell to Military Profession,* p. 267.

work belonging to the *novella* tradition, dating back to Boccaccio and the fourteenth century—to say that it is basically a "romance," as opposed to "novel," "anatomy," "confession," or any other specific form.[2] Silla is a paragon of beauty and steadfastness; as Apolonius says, she represents "true love most pure and unstained." At the end, bride and groom pass "the residue of their days with such delight as those that have accomplished the perfection of their felicities." The background is both vague and fixed; and in the Christian *vs.* non-Christian world there can be no doubt which is the white and virtuous side and which the black and evil. In a sense, "Apolonius" is an historical romance, and Rich's own word "history" is accidentally appropriate. The action takes place sometime before 1453, when Mohammed II captured Constantinople; Silla's references to the "goddess of love" and to "you sacred gods" seem to be an inconsistent effort to set the time all the way back to a pre-Christian Roman world.

"Apolonius" has one or two elements of realism that we associate with the novel form. In the climactic scene the heroine bares her breasts to show that she is indeed a woman, and the narrator does not hesitate to describe what we are to see.[3] The diction is usually neutral and the vocabulary severely limited, especially in the dialogue; but the narrator—in his general comments on human nature, in his summaries of action, and in his reporting of indirect discourse—occasionally uses a strikingly colloquial and idiomatic phrase ("put rummer before the wind," "ready prest") or a common proverb ("turned Jack out of office").

[2]There may be some advantage in calling "Apolonius" a "tale," by which we could mean the short form of "romance"; "short story" could bear the same relationship with "novel." See Frye, *Anatomy of Criticism*, pp. 304–305.

[3]But although the description is frank, in a typically Elizabethan way, there is no hint of prurience. The Italians evidently enjoyed pornographic stories more than the Elizabethans did, but the Italian *novella* was not nearly so engrossed with sex as many people have supposed. *Playboy*, "the men's entertainment magazine," reprinted in its June, 1966, issue a *novella* by Masuccio, a fifteenth-century follower of Boccaccio. The editor of *Playboy* supplied the title, "The Miller Would a Cobbler Be," as well as the caption, "ribald classic." He should have added that of the 50 stories in Masuccio's *Il Novellino* (1476), only 17 deal with the subject of illicit love, and several of the 17 are not "ribald" so much as frank and outspoken. See two works by D. P. Rotunda, "A Tabulation of Early Italian Tales," *Univ. of California Publications in Modern Philology*, XIV (1930), 331–343; and *Motif-Index of the Italian Novella in Prose*, Indiana Univ. Publications, Folklore Series (Bloomington, Ind., 1942).

In his edition of Shakespeare's songs and poems, Edward Hubler has this to say in a discussion of *Venus and Adonis:*

> [Shakespeare] had begun his career with story for story's sake, and although he never lost his interest in action and never condescended to it, his progress to a large extent lay in his giving the stories values beyond and in addition to their values as action. The ways of doing this are infinite in number, and one of them is to adduce reasons for a proposed action.[4]

Hubler reflects a twentieth-century attitude, that a little action may go a long way; with Virginia Woolf, we expect a scene to have "sudden lightning flashes of significance." It is true that Shakespeare never lost his interest in action; but in the Renaissance view, from Boccaccio to Shakespeare, there was nothing about action that need involve an author's condescension. The expression "story for story's sake" is not of Elizabethan origin; at that time a story by definition tended to have a strong story-line, a definite and full sequence of action. *Master F. J.* and *Euphues* were exceptions. In the fourteenth century it did not occur to any of Boccaccio's ten narrators (the seven young ladies and three young men who tell their stories to each other while a plague rages in Florence) that action is a subservient element in prose fiction; instead, they reveal through action their boundless curiosity about the multiplicity of human events, in which they usually find pleasure, or even inspiration, and hardly ever, as we do, any cause for despair.

What Shakespeare learned was to make every action count, to relate the scenes and let them explain each other; he works mainly *through* action, not beyond and in addition to it. As Kenneth Muir has observed, Rich has Julina and Silvio go off to bed in a way that does not fit the atmosphere of romance.[5] Rejection of such an action for *Twelfth Night* (which Shakespeare based on "Apolonius") shows an awareness of negative implications. The narrator of "Apolonius" announces at the beginning that by "desert" he means "where the party beloved doth requite us with the like." For the disdainful ladies of the Petrarchan tradition, he apparently intends to substitute women who return love. But Julina returns it too easily and warmly. Unlike Lodge and Shakespeare, Rich lacks the tact to create the new English romantic heroines, who may be delightfully bold and yet at the same time absolutely chaste.

[4]*Shakespeare's Songs and Poems* (New York, 1959), p. xxix.
[5]*Shakespeare's Sources* (London, 1957), p. 73.

"Apolonius" is not as interesting as several of the other romances of the period. It lacks the atmosphere of *Rosalind*, the shrewd commentary of *Pandosto*, and the brilliant scenes of *Thomas of Reading*. It represents the *novella* form transplanted into England without much of the original Italian energy and variety, and without a distinctive contribution by Rich himself. Yet Cranfill is right that Rich can tell a story concisely and that occasionally he shows skill (especially in the fifth story of *Farewell*) at delineating characters, to whom he sometimes gives a lively dialogue.[6]

Apparently we are to take literally Rich's comment that the second tale in *Farewell*, along with tales 1, 5, 7, and 8, were "forged only for delight, neither credible to be believed nor hurtful to be perused." Referring to all eight of the *novelle*, Rich has this to say in a short essay at the end called "The Conclusion":

> For mine own excuse herein I answer that in the writing of them I have used the same manner that many of our young gentlemen useth nowadays in the wearing of their apparel—which is rather to follow a fashion that is new, be it never so foolish, than to be tied to a more decent custom that is clean out of use; sometime wearing their hair frizzled so long that makes them look like a water spaniel, sometimes so short like a new-shorn sheep; . . . their jerkins sometimes with high collars buttoned close under their chin; sometimes with no collars at all about their necks, like a wench in a red waistcoat that were washing of a buck; sometimes with long, saucy sleeves that will be in every dish before his master; sometimes without sleeves, like Scogin's man, that used to run of sleeveless errands; their doublets sometime faggot-waisted above the navel, sometimes cowbellied below the flanks, that the gentleman must undo a button when he goes to piss.[7]

Rich is perhaps more accurate than he realizes when he says that he is "merely following a fashion that is new, be it never so foolish"; certainly he appears not to have his heart in the writing of romances. But his style suddenly comes alive when he begins a "character" of the young gentleman of fashion. Gone are the heavy, periodic sentences and the monotonous present participles; the rhythm is flexible, the language vivid and idiomatic. Like Nashe, Rich has many aversions

[6]Cranfill, ed., *Farewell*, pp. xxxvii–xxxviii. One may note also that Rich's narrator is an achievement almost as interesting as Gascoigne's narrator in *Master F. J.* But the difference is significant: the whole of *Master F. J.* filters through a consistent and convincing narrator, but in "Apolonius" the narrator scorns romance elements ("sorrowful signs," "piteous countenances") on one occasion and approves of them on another; his humorously ironic view of courtly love is only sporadic.   [7]Pages 204–205.

to contemporary Elizabethan life; and the character sketch is an ideal form in which to channel his peeves, one at a time. Nashe's characters in *The Unfortunate Traveler* are more powerfully imaginative; and Joseph Hall's, in *Characters of Virtues and Vices* (1608), are more selective and relevant as to details; but Rich's are equally concrete and incisive.[8]

If only Rich could have combined his satiric style, into which he threw himself enthusiastically, with his romance style, which he inherited from the past but in which he could never really believe, he might have put together a vital romance form. *Pandosto* and *Thomas of Reading* are typical of the successful romances of the period in that they are mixtures of style. *Rosalind*, almost "pure" romance, is the exception; but even it involves a "modernizing," a bringing of medieval romance form up to date for an Elizabethan public. One of the truly great romances of the period is *As You Like It*, in which the old medieval romance ideals are not rejected but, on the contrary, are reinforced as they meet squarely the laughter and scorn of astringent Renaissance satire and parody.

⋙⟨§⟩⋘

To the Right Courteous Gentlewomen, both of England and Ireland, Barnaby Rich Wisheth All Things They Should Have Appertaining to Their Honor, Estimation, and All Other Their Honest Delights

Gentlewomen, I am sure there are many (but especially of such as best know me) that will not a little wonder to see such alteration in me that, having spent my younger days in the wars amongst men and vowed myself only unto Mars, should now in my riper years desire to live in peace amongst women and to consecrate myself wholly unto Venus. But yet the wiser sort can very well consider that the older we wax the riper our wit, and the longer we live the better we can conceive of things appertaining to our own profits. Though harebrained youth overhaled[9] me for a time that I knew not bale from bliss, yet wisdom now hath warned me that I well know cheese from

---

[8]See Wolf, ed., *Rich's Faultes Faults, and Nothing Else But Faultes*, pp. 63–76.

[9]*overhaled:* overpowered; overhauled.

chalk: I see now it is less painful to follow a fiddle in a gentlewoman's chamber than to march after a drum in the field, and more sound sleeping under a silken canopy close by a friend than under a bush in the open field within a mile of our foe, and nothing so dangerous to be wounded with the luring look of our beloved mistress as with the cruel shot of our hateful enemy—the one possessed with a pitiful heart to help where she hath hurt, the other with a deadly hate to kill where they might save.

Experience now hath taught me that to be of Mars' crew there is nothing but pain, travail, turmoil, disquiet, cold, hunger, thirst, penury, bad lodging, worse fare, unquiet sleep, with a number of other calamities that haps I know not how. And when a soldier hath thus served in many a bloody broil, a flap with a foxtail[10] shall be his best reward, for I see no better recompense that any of them can get. Now, contrary, to be of Venus' band there is pleasure, sport, joy, solace, mirth, peace, quiet rest, dainty fare, with a thousand other delights such as I cannot rehearse. And a man having served but a reasonable time may sometimes take a taste at his mistress' lips for his better recompense.

But now, gentlewomen, as I have vowed myself to be at your dispositions, so I know not how to frame myself to your contentations.[11] When I consider with how many commendable qualities he ought to be endued that should be welcomed into your blessed companies, I find in myself no one manner of exercise that might give me the least hope to win your good likings.

As first for dancing, although I like the measures very well, yet I could never tread them aright nor to use measure in anything[12] that I went about, although I desired to perform all things by line and by level,[13] whatever I took in hand.

Our galliards are so curious[14] that they are not for my dancing, for they are so full of tricks and turns that he which hath no more

[10]*flap with a foxtail:* a proverb (Tilley, F344), meaning to get very little reward.

[11]*frame myself to your contentations:* conduct myself in such a way as to give you pleasure(s).

[12]*to use measure in anything:* "measure" involves a pun: in the proverb (Tilley, M806) the sense of "measure" is "mean" ("There is a measure in all things"); but "measure" is also to be taken as "a solemn dance step."

[13]*by line and by level:* a proverb (Tilley, L305), meaning to do things well and, as we say, "according to the book" or "in a prescribed manner."

[14]*galliards ... curious:* lively dances in triple time ... intricate.

but the plain cinquepace[15] is no better accounted of than a very bungler; and for my part, they might as soon teach me to make a capricornus as a caper[16] in the right kind that it should be.

For a jig my heels are too heavy, and these brawls are so busy that I love not to beat my brains about them.

A round is too giddy a dance for my diet; for let the dancers run about with as much speed as they may, yet are they never a whit the nigher to the end of their course unless with often turning they hap to catch a fall. And so they end the dance with shame that was begun but in sport.

These hornpipes I have hated from my very youth, and I know there are many other that loves them as evil as I.

Thus you may perceive that there is no dance but either I like not of them or they like not of me so that I can dance neither.

There resteth, then, if I could play of any instrument or that I had any sight in song whereby I might delight your dainty ears, gentlewomen, by sweet playing or feigning[17] some pretty ditties. But to the first, my fingers would never be brought in frame; for the second, my mouth is so unpleasant, either to sing or to feign, as would rather breed your loathing than your liking.

Why yet if I could discourse pleasantly to drive away the time with amorous devices, or that my conceit would serve me either to propone pretty questions or to give ready answers, with a number of other delights too long to be rehearsed, there were some comfort that I might be allowed of amongst you. But my capacity is so gross, my wits be so blunt, and all my other senses are so dull that I am sure you would sooner condemn me for a dunce than confirm me for a disciple fit to whisper a tale in a gentlewoman's ear.

But yet I trust, gentlewomen, when you shall perceive the zeal that I bear to my new profession, although you will not presently admit

[15]*cinquepace:* a lively dance step involving five paces; it is sometimes referred to as identical with the galliard, but Rich thinks of it as a separate step—equally fast, perhaps, but much less complicated than the galliard. (See Raleigh, *Shakespeare's England,* II, 443–444.)

[16]*capricornus . . . caper:* The caper, the jig, the brawl, the round, and the hornpipe are all lively dance steps popular in the sixteenth century. In "capricornus . . . caper," there is, in addition to the alliteration, a play on "caper"; the root of "capricornus" is "caper," meaning "goat" (with "cornu" tacking on the sense of "horn"). In other words, Rich says that he is just as likely to make a horned goat as he is a good caper on the dance floor—and that is not very likely.

[17]*feigning:* a musical term, meaning to sing softly or hum.

me to the pulpit, yet you will not deny me to be one of your parish. Where if it please you but to place me in the body of the church, you shall find my devotion as much as he that kneels next the chancel door.[18]

And here, gentlewomen, the better to manifest the farther regard of my duty, I have presented you with a few rough-hewn histories— yet, I dare undertake, so warely[19] polished that there is nothing let slip that might breed offense to your modest minds.

I have made bold to publish them under your savecundites,[20] and I trust it shall nothing at all offend you. My last request is that at your pleasures you will peruse them and with your favors you will defend them. Which if I may perceive not to be misliked of amongst you, my encouragement will be such that I trust, within a very short space, you shall see me grow from a young puny[21] to a sufficient scholar. And thus, gentlewomen, wishing to you all what yourselves do best like of, I humbly take my leave.

Yours in the way of honesty,
Barnaby Rich

To the Noble Soldiers both of England and Ireland, Barnaby Rich Wisheth as to Himself

There is an old proverb, noble soldiers, and thus it followeth: it is better to be happy than wise. But what it is to be happy how should I discipher, who never in my life could yet attain to any hap at all that was good? And yet I have had soldier's luck and sped as well as the rest of my profession. And with wisdom I will not meddle; I never came where it grew. But this I dare boldly affirm (and the experience of the present time doth make daily proof) that wit stands by in a threadbare coat where folly sometimes sits in a velvet gown. And how often is it seen that vice shall be advanced where virtue is little or naught at all regarded, small desert shall highly be preferred where well doing shall go unrewarded, and flattery shall be wel-

---

[18]*next the chancel door:* at the altar (just inside the chancel door).

[19]*warely:* circumspectly, prudently; apparently the sense here is that although the writing may be rough, the tales have been inspected carefully for anything morally offensive.

[20]*savecundites:* safe-conducts (in a figurative sense—referring to the "protection" that he hopes the ladies will grant *Farewell* in return for his dedicating it to them).

[21]*puny:* a student recently admitted to a school; a freshman.

comed for a guest of great account where plain Tom Tell Troth shall be thrust out of doors by the shoulders. And to speak a plain truth indeed, do ye not see pipers, parasites, fiddlers, dancers, players, jesters, and such others better esteemed and made of, and greater benevolence used toward them, than to any others that endeavor themselves to the most commendable qualities?

Then seeing the abuse of this present age is such that follies are better esteemed than matters of greater weight, I have stepped onto the stage amongst the rest, contented to play a part, and have gathered together this small volume of histories all treating (sir-reverence of you)[22] of love.

I remember that in my last book, entitled the *Alarm to England,* I promised to take in hand some other thing. But believe me, it was not this that I meant, for I pretended then to have followed on; and where I ended with the decay of martial discipline, so I meant to have begun again with the disciplines of war, and withal to have set forth the orders of sundry battles and the manner of skirmishes, with many plats of fortification—but especially those of the low countries, as Delft, Deltshaven, Rotterdam, Leyden, the Brielle (both the head and the town), Gorcum, Gouldsluce, Maaselandesluce, the Krimpen, with divers others worthy the perusing for such as have not seen them.[23]

But I see the time serves not for any such thing to be accounted of. And therefore to fit the time the better, I have put forth these loving histories, the which I did write in Ireland at a vacant time before the coming over of James Fitzmaurice.[24] And it pleased me the better to do it only to keep myself from idleness, and yet they say it were better to be idle than ill occupied. But I trust I shall please gentlewomen, and that is all the gain that I look for. And herein I do but follow the course of the world. For many nowadays go about by as great device as may be how they might become women themselves. How many gentlemen shall you see at this present day that, I dare undertake, in the wearing of their apparel, in the setting of their ruffs,

[22]*sir-reverence of you:* with all respect for you.

[23]*my last book . . . not seen them:* Rich's book had appeared in 1578. The places he names (Delft, etc.) were the scenes of battles fought in the Netherlands in the 1570's between the Spanish on one side and the Dutch and English on the other. (See Cranfill's edition, pp. 234 ff., for a complete account.)

[24]*James Fitzmaurice:* a tireless Irish patriot who tried unsuccessfully to get the British out of Ireland. His "coming over" refers to his coming back to Ireland with foreign help in July, 1579.

and the frizzling of their hair are more newfangled and foolish than any courtesan of Venice?

And I beseech you, gentlemen, give me leave to tell you a tale that comes even now in my mind; the matter is not worth the hearing but yet very strange unto me at the first.

It was my fortune, at my last being at London, to walk through the Strand towards Westminster, where I met one came riding towards me on a footcloth nag,[25] appareled in a French ruff, a French cloak, a French hose,[26] and in his hand a great fan of feathers, bearing them up (very womanly) against the side of his face. And for that I had never seen any man wear them before that day, I began to think it impossible that there might a man be found so foolish as to make himself a scorn to the world to wear so womanish a toy, but rather thought it had been some shameless woman that had disguised herself like a man, in our hose and our cloaks. For our doublets, gowns, caps, and hats they had got long ago.

But by this time he was come something near me, and I might see he had a beard, whereby I was assured that he should have been a man, whereat I began to muse with myself whether his simplicity were more to be pitied or his folly more to be laughed at. For in mine opinion it is as fond a sight to see a man with such a bauble in his hand as to see a woman ride through the street with a lance in hers.

And as he passed by me, I saw three following that were his men; and taking the hindermost by the arm, I asked him what gentlewoman his master was. But the fellow, not understanding my meaning, told me his master's name and so departed.

I began then to muse with myself to what end that fan of feathers served, for it could not be to defend the sun from the burning of his beauty, for it was in the beginning of February when the heat of the sun may be very well endured. Now if it were to defend the wind or the coldness of the air, methinks a French hood had been a great deal better, for that had been both gentlewoman like and, being close

---

[25]*footcloth nag:* The "footcloth" was a large, often gaudily patterned cloth draped over the saddle or the back of the horse and hanging almost to the ground on either side of the horse. Apparently the footcloth was a sign of wealth, of having "arrived"; Cranfill suggests (p. 237) that its practical use was to keep mud off the shoes.

[26]*French ruff . . . French hose:* The word "French" is to suggest affectation—the wearing of an elaborate foreign style as opposed to the plain English cut. A "ruff" was a collar or cuff arranged in horizontal flutings; "hose" were not socks, but tight-fitting breeches.

pinned down about his ears, would have kept his head a great deal warmer. And then a French hood on his head, a French ruff about his neck, a French cloak on his back, and a pair of French hose on his legs had been right—*a la mode de France*. And this had been something suitable to his wit.

But I think he did it rather to please gentlewomen and, the better to show what honor he bare them, would wear one of the greatest vanities that long[27] to their sex. And to this end, gentlemen, I have told you my tale—that you might perceive the sundry means we use and all to please women. I see it is the path that all desire to pace, and sure I would wish my friends to tread the same trace. For what is he that is wise which desires to be a soldier? Mars' court is full of bale. Venus' is full of bliss. And, my good companions and fellow soldiers, if you will follow mine advice, lay aside your weapons, hang up your armors by the walls, and learn another while (for your better advancements) to pipe, to fiddle, to sing, to dance, to lie, to forge, to flatter, to carry tales, to set ruff, or to do anything that your appetites best serves unto and that is better fitting for the time. This is the only mean that is best for a man to bring himself in credit. Otherwise I know not which ways a man might bend himself, either to get gain or good report.

For first the military profession, by means whereof men were advanced to the greatest renown, is now become of so slender estimation that there is no account neither made of it nor any that shall profess it.

To become a courtier, there is as little gain to be gotten. For Liberality, who was wont to be a principal officer, as well in the court as in the country, by whose means welldoing could never go unrewarded, is turned Jack out of office[28] and others appointed to have the custody of him to hold him short, that he range no more abroad, so that no man can speak with him. And they say the poor gentleman is so fleeced from time to time by those that be his keepers that he hath nothing to give that is good but it falls to their shares.

To become a student in the law, there are such a number of them already that methinks it is not possible that one of them should honestly thrive by another. And some will say that one lawyer, and one goshawk, were enough in one shire. But, of my conscience, there are more lawyers in some one shire in England, with attorneys,

---

[27]*long:* belong.
[28]*turned Jack out of office:* a proverb (Tilley, J23); said of anyone dismissed from a job.

solicitors (or, as they are termed, brokers of causes or pettifoggers) than there are goshawks in all Norway.

To become a merchant, traffic is so dead by means of these foreign broils that, unless a man would be a thief to his country to steal out prohibited wares,[29] there were small gains to be gotten.

To become a farmer, lands be so racked at such a rate that a man should but toil all the days of his life to pay his landlord's rent.

But what occupation or handicraft might a man then follow to make himself rich when every science depends upon newfangled fashions? For he that today is accounted for the finest workman, within one month some new found fellow comes out with some new found fashion; and then he bears the prize and the first accounted but a bungler. And within another month after, the second shall be served with the same sauce. And thus there is no artificer that can hold his credit long.

Such is the miserable condition of this our present time; this is the course of the world—but especially here in England, where there is no man thought to be wise but he that is wealthy; where no man is thought to speak a truth but such as can lie, flatter, and dissemble; where there is no advice allowed for good but such as tendeth more for gain than for glory. And what pinching for a penny that should be spent in our country's defense? How prodigal for a pound to be spent upon vanities and idle devices? What small recompense to soldiers that fights with foes for their country's quiet? How liberal to lawyers that sets friends at defiance and disquiets a whole commonwealth? What fawning upon him whom fortune doth advance? What frowning on him whom she hath brought low? What little care of the poor and such as be in want? What feasting of the rich and such as be wealthy? What sumptuous houses built by men of mean estate? What little hospitality kept from high and low degree?

And here I cannot but speak of the bounty of that noble gentleman, Sir Christopher Hatton,[30] my very good master and upholder, who, having builded a house in Northamptonshire called by the name of Holdenby,[31] which house—for the bravery of the buildings,

[29]*steal out prohibited wares:* take certain staples (eggs, butter, hides, etc.) out of the country and sell them abroad, in spite of the government's specific order not to do so.

[30]*Sir Christopher Hatton:* A favorite of Queen Elizabeth's who was made lord chancellor in 1587, Hatton (1540–1591) was a patron of many literary men, including Spenser.

[31]*a house . . . by the name of Holdenby:* James I bought Holdenby in 1605, and Charles I was imprisoned there in 1647.

for the stateliness of the chambers, for the rich furniture of the lodgings, for the conveyance of the offices, and for all other necessaries
appertinent to a palace of pleasure—is thought by those that have
judgment to be incomparable and to have no fellow in England that
is out of her majesty's hands. And although this house is not yet
fully finished and is but a new erection, yet it differeth far from the
works that are used nowadays in many places. I mean where the
houses are built with a great number of chimneys and yet the smoke
comes forth but at one only tunnel. This house is not built on that
manner, for as it hath sundry chimneys so they cast forth several
smokes.

And such worthy port[32] and daily hospitality kept that, although
the owner himself useth not to come there once in two years, yet I
dare undertake there is daily provision to be found convenient to
entertain any nobleman, with his whole train, that should hap to call
in of a sudden. And how many gentlemen and strangers, that comes
but to see the house, are there daily welcomed, feasted, and well
lodged. From whence should he come—be he rich, be he poor—that
should not there be entertained if it please him to call in. To be short,
Holdenby giveth daily relief to such as be in want for the space of
six or seven miles compass.

Peradventure those that be envious will think this tale nothing
appertinent to the matter that I was in hand withal, but I trust my
offense is the less considering I have spoken but a truth and do wish
that every other man were able to say as much for his master and
so an end.

And now where I left off I was telling what pride, what covetousness, what whoredom, what gluttony, what blasphemy, what riot,
what excess, what drunkenness, what swearing, what bribery, what
extortion, what usury, what oppression, what deceit, what forgery,
what vice in general is daily entertained and practiced in England.
And although it hath pleased God by wonderful signs and miracles to
forewarn us of his wrath and call us to repentance, yet you see the
world runneth forwards and keepeth his wonted course without any
remorse of conscience, neither making sign nor proffer to amend.
But like as we see an old sore being once overrun will not be cured
with any moderate medicine but must be eaten with corrosives till it
comes to the quick, and like as we say one poison must be a means
to expel another, so what should we otherwise think of ourselves but

[32]*worthy port:* grand style of living.

if we be grown to such extremity as no gentle admonition will serve to reclaim us? What other thing should we look for but a mischief to be the medicine? God will not suffer that vice shall always flourish; he will surely root it out at the last. And how long hath he already borne with us in our wickedness? And what reformation is there had amongst us unless it be to go from evil to worse?

But if we did duly consider how mercifully he hath still dealt with us, how favorably he hath preserved us, and how wonderfully he hath defended us, I think we should not be altogether so unthankful as we show ourselves to be. For who knoweth not what an eyesore this little isle of England hath been to the whole world? And how long have we lived (as it were) in contempt of such countries as be our next neighbors, who, still inveighing our quiet and happy government, have practiced by as many devices as they could to bring us into their own predicament, had it not been the only providence of God that preserved us? Or what friendship might we yet hope to find at any of their hands if their opportunity would serve them to be revenged of the despite which long ago they had conceived against us?

First the French hath ever been our enemies by nature, the Scots by custom,[33] the Spaniards for religion. The Dutch, although we have stood them in great stead and holp them at many a pinch, yet I could buy as much friendship as they do all owe us for a barrel of English beer. If we should go any further, then we come to the pope, the Turk, and the devil; and what friendship they bear us I think everyone can imagine.

And here we might consider how wonderfully God hath wrought on our behalves and with all humbleness of heart give him daily thanks for his benefits bestowed upon us; but most of all, and especially, for our most gracious and sovereign lady, Queen Elizabeth, who from time to time he hath so mightily preserved to be the very instrument of his mercy and loving kindness towards us and for whose sake, no doubt, he hath forborne us in his displeasure, as many times he did the children of Israel at the request of his servant, Moses.

First, how was she assaulted in her sister's time by those ravening wolves that daily sought her death? For they all stood in doubt that she should be that Judith which should cut off proud Holofernes' head. And it pleased God to bring it even so to pass, not only defending her from their cruelty and rage, but raised her up, indeed, to the utter subversion of those bloody butchers and to the great comfort of us all that were in bondage and subject to tyranny.

[33]*the Scots by custom:* The phrase was omitted in the 1606 edition.

Not only setting us free from those detestable enormities that so corrosived our consciences, but made open way and passage for the word of God freely to be published (I think) to our own destruction that so unworthily receive it. Upon this, how many mighty enemies protested against her, and what harm have any of them been able to do her? And how many treasons and privy conspiracies sith that time hath been practiced by our pelting papists against her? But God hath revealed and brought them to light.

Let us therefore pray unto God that he would so lengthen her days that we might still enjoy so gracious a princess long to govern and reign over us. And that from time to time he would so direct her noble council, in all their meetings and consultations, as may redound to his glory, to the benefit of their country, and to their own immortal fame.

Let us likewise pray that God would root such covetous hearts out of England that, for the sparing of a penny for the present time, care not to let slip such matter as may cost many a pound hereafter this.

Now, lastly, and as mariners use to sing at the sea, God save my mate and me also. And God send all soldiers that hath honestly served their country better consideration than of long time they have had.

And thus, noble soldiers and gentlemen all, I have held you with a long sermon; neither can I tell how my preaching will be allowed of. I crave no more, but wish you all better fortune than I know the present time will afford you, and so will rest at your disposition.

Barnaby Rich

To the Readers in General

I assure thee, gentle reader, when I first took in hand to write these discourses, I meant nothing less than to put them in print, but writ them at the request of some of my dearest friends, sometimes for their disport to serve their private use. And now again by great importunity I am forced to send them all to the printer.

The histories, altogether, are eight in number, whereof the first, the second, the fifth, the seventh, and eighth are tales that are but forged only for delight, neither credible to be believed nor hurtful to be perused. The third, the fourth, and the sixth are Italian histories written likewise for pleasure by Master L. B.[34]

[34]*Master L. B.:* Edmond Malone suggested that "L. B." stands for "Lodowick Bryskett," but no proof is available. See Cranfill's edition, pp. xxii ff.

And here, gentle reader, I must instantly entreat thee that, if thou findest any words or terms seeming more indecent than peradventure thou wilt like of, think that I have set them down as more appropriate to express the matter they entreat of than either for want of judgment or good manners. Trusting that as I have written them in jest, so thou wilt read them but to make thyself merry. I wish they might as well please thee in the reading as they displease me in putting them forth. I bid thee heartily farewell.

Barnaby Rich

W. J.,[35] Gentleman, in Praise
of the Author

Who seeks by Lady Fame to reap renown,
    Must ask consent of worthy virtue's grace:
To her belongs the stallment of the crown;
    She yields all those their just deserved place
As tread her path and run her royal race.
    Such rich rewards to each she yields each where
As might become this worthy Rich to wear.

The painful man that tills his ground reaps fruit;
    Each merit hath his meed, pain hath his hire.
Desert requires that fame should not stand mute,
    Where wisdom doth to virtue's ways aspire.
The hope of gain doth set men's hearts on fire;
    Then yield him thanks that erst hath undertook,
For thy delight, to pen this little book.

Let Momus' mates[36] chat on, in their despite;
    Let wranglers wreak and wrest the worst they may.
The wisest sort will judge and take delight,
    Though jangling jays that know not what they say,
Will oftentimes their witless wit bewray.
    Yet Rich shall reap what he by right hath won,
Deserved praise for that which here is done.
Finis.   W. J., Gentleman

[35]W. J.: The identity of this person is also unknown, though Cranfill (p. 243) makes some intelligent guesses.
[36]Momus' mates: followers of Momus, god of mockery and censure.

Baptist Starr[37] in Praise
of the Author

If due desert should reap reward,
　Or worthy merit guerdon have,
Why should not Rich press forth himself,
　The lovely laurel crown to crave?
Whose life in field that won him praise
　He leads at home in Pallas' ways.

Scorn not then, Zoilus,[38] his good hap,
　That can his will subdue and tame;
But try to tread his path whereby
　Thou mayst thy life with virtue frame.
Allow his pain, and pen to write,
　Who naught pretends but thy delight.

Lo he who wonted was in field,
　To meet his furious foe in face,
Hath scaled Parnassus' hill, where he
　Attends Minerv', her noble grace.
And there his pen doth play his part,
　As did elsewhere his shield and dart.
　　　　　　　Finis.　　B.S.

The Printer to the Reader

The fragrant rose can make no choice,
　Who shall upon him light;
The sprawling spider turns to gall,
　The bee to honey right.

So fares it with this book, whose leaves
　Are open spread to thee;
Make choice, good reader, of the best:
　Suck honey with the bee.

[37]*Baptist Starr:* apparently a citizen and cooper of London, not usually
given to versifying (Cranfill, pp. 244 f.).

[38]*Zoilus:* Greek critic of the fourth century B.C., who was severely critical
of Homer and Plato.

> Misconster not each merry phrase;
> Deem not the worst of it.
> Which is not penned to do thee hurt,
> But recreate[39] thy wit.
>
> And for such faults as scaped have
> The press, whereof there's store,
> Reprove the printer for his haste,
> Blame not the book therefore.
>
> But as by mirth 'tis meant to move
> Thy mind to some delight,
> Reward his pain with praise, which did
> These pleasant stories write.
>
> Finis

Of Apolonius and Silla

The Argument of the Second History: Apolonius, duke, having spent a year's service in the wars against the Turk, returning homeward with his company by sea, was driven by force of weather to the Isle of Cyprus, where he was well received by Pontus, governor of the same isle. With whom Silla, daughter to Pontus, fell so strangely in love that after Apolonius was departed to Constantinople, Silla, with one man, followed; and coming to Constantinople, she served Apolonius in the habit of a man; and after many pretty accidents falling out, she was known to Apolonius who, in requital of her love, married her.

There is no child that is born into this wretched world but, before it doth suck the mother's milk, it taketh first a soope[40] of the cup of error which maketh us, when we come to riper years, not only to enter into actions of injury but many times to stray from that is right and reason. But in all other things, wherein we show ourselves to be most drunken with this poisoned cup, it is in our actions of love. For the lover is so estranged from that is right, and wandereth so wide from the bounds of reason, that he is not able to deem white from black, good from bad, virtue from vice. But only led by the appetite of his own affections, and grounding them on the foolishness of his own

---

[39]*recreate:* refresh, enliven.
[40]*soope:* sope, sup = mouthful, gulp.

fancies, will so settle his liking on such a one as either by desert or unworthiness will merit rather to be loathed than loved.

If a question might be asked, what is the ground, indeed, of reasonable love, whereby the knot is knit of true and perfect friendship? I think those that be wise would answer "Desert"—that is, where the party beloved doth requite us with the like. For otherwise if the bare show of beauty or the comeliness of personage might be sufficient to confirm us in our love, those that be accustomed to go to fairs and markets might sometimes fall into love with twenty in a day. Desert must then be, of force, the ground of reasonable love. For to love them that hate us, to follow them that fly from us, to fawn on them that frown on us, to curry favor with them that disdain us, to be glad to please them that care not how they offend us—who will not confess this to be an erroneous love neither grounded upon wit nor reason?

Wherefore, right courteous gentlewomen, if it please you with patience to peruse this history following, you shall see Dame Error so play her part with a leash of lovers, a male and two females, as shall work a wonder to your wise judgment in noting the effect of their amorous devices and conclusions of their actions. The first, neglecting the love of a noble dame, young, beautiful, and fair (who, only for his good will, played the part of a serving man, contented to abide any manner of pain only to behold him). He again setting his love of a dame that, despising him, being a noble duke, gave herself to a serving man (as she had thought, but it otherwise fell out, as the substance of this tale shall better describe).

And because I have been something tedious in my first discourse, offending your patient ears with the hearing of a circumstance overlong, from henceforth that which I mind to write shall be done with such celerity as the matter that I pretend to pen may in any wise permit me, and thus followeth the history.

During the time that the famous city of Constantinople remained in the hands of the Christians, amongst many other noblemen that kept their abiding in that flourishing city, there was one whose name was Apolonius, a worthy duke, who, being but a very young man and even then new come to his possessions, which were very great, levied a mighty band of men, at his own proper charges, with whom he served against the Turk during the space of one whole year. In which time, although it were very short, this young duke so behaved himself, as well by prowess and valiance showed with his own hands as otherwise by his wisdom and liberality used towards his soldiers, that all the world was filled with the fame of this noble duke.

When he had thus spent one year's service, he caused his trumpet to sound a retreat; and gathering his company together and embarking themselves, he set sail, holding his course towards Constantinople. But being upon the sea, by the extremity of a tempest which suddenly fell, his fleet was dissevered, some one way and some another. But he himself recovered the Isle of Cyprus, where he was worthily received by Pontus, duke and governor of the same isle, with whom he lodged while his ships were new repairing.

This Pontus that was lord and governor of this famous isle was an ancient duke and had two children, a son and a daughter. His son was named Silvio, of whom hereafter we shall have further occasion to speak; but at this instant he was in the parts of Africa, serving in the wars.

The daughter's name was Silla, whose beauty was so peerless that she had the sovereignty amongst all other dames, as well for her beauty as for the nobleness of her birth. This Silla, having heard of the worthiness of Apolonius, this young duke, who, besides his beauty and good graces, had a certain natural allurement, that, being now in his company in her father's court, she was so strangely attached[41] with the love of Apolonius, that there was nothing might content her but his presence and sweet sight, and although she saw no manner of hope to attain to that she most desired, knowing Apolonius to be but a guest and ready to take the benefit of the next wind and to depart into a strange country. Whereby she was bereaved of all possibility ever to see him again, and therefore strived with herself to leave her fondness. But all in vain; it would not be. But like the fowl which is once limed the more she striveth the faster she tieth herself, so Silla was now constrained perforce her will to yield to love. Wherefore from time to time she used so great familiarity with him as her honor might well permit, and fed him with such amorous baits as the modesty of a maid could reasonably afford. Which when she perceived did take but small effect, feeling herself so much outraged with the extremity of her passion, by the only countenance that she bestowed upon Apolonius it might have been well perceived that the very eyes pleaded unto him for pity and remorse.

But Apolonius, coming but lately from out the field, from the chasing of his enemies, and his fury not yet thoroughly dissolved nor purged from his stomach, gave no regard to those amorous enticements which, by reason of his youth, he had not been acquainted

[41]*attached:* seized.

withal. But his mind ran more to hear his pilots bring news of a merry wind to serve his turn to Constantinople, which in the end came very prosperously. And giving Duke Pontus hearty thanks for his great entertainment, taking his leave of himself and the Lady Silla his daughter, departed with his company, and with a happy gale arrived at his desired port.

Gentlewomen, according to my promise, I will here, for brevity's sake, omit to make repetition of the long and dolorous discourse recorded by Silla for this sudden departure of her Apolonius, knowing you to be as tenderly hearted as Silla herself, whereby you may the better conjecture the fury of her fever.

But Silla, the further that she saw herself bereaved of all hope ever any more to see her beloved Apolonius, so much the more contagious were her passions, and made the greater speed to execute that she had premeditated in her mind, which was this: amongst many servants that did attend upon her, there was one whose name was Pedro, who had a long time waited upon her in her chamber, whereby she was well assured of his fidelity and trust. To that Pedro, therefore, she bewrayed first the fervency of her love borne to Apolonius, conjuring him in the name of the goddess of love herself, and binding him by the duty that a servant ought to have that tendereth his mistress' safety and good liking. And desiring him, with tears trickling down her cheeks, that he would give his consent to aid and assist her in that she had determined—which was for that she was fully resolved to go to Constantinople, where she might again take the view of her beloved Apolonius—that he according to the trust she had reposed in him would not refuse to give his consent secretly to convey her from out her father's court according as she should give him direction, and also to make himself partaker of her journey and to wait upon her till she had seen the end of her determination.

Pedro, perceiving with what vehemency his lady and mistress had made request unto him, albeit he saw many perils and doubts, depending in her pretense[42] notwithstanding, gave his consent to be at her disposition, promising her to further her with his best advice and to be ready to obey whatsoever she would please to command him. The match being thus agreed upon and all things prepared in a readiness for their departure, it happened there was a galley of

[42]*depending in her pretense:* The sense seems to be "relying on her claim"; as his mistress, she can request him to do something, and it is his duty to assent.

Constantinople ready to depart. Which, Pedro understanding, came to the captain, desiring him to have passage for himself and for a poor maid that was his sister which were bound to Constantinople upon certain urgent affairs. To which request the captain granted, willing him to prepare aboard with all speed because the wind served him presently to depart.

Pedro now coming to his mistress and telling her how he had handled the matter with the captain, she liking very well of the device, disguising herself into very simple attire, stole away from out her father's court and came with Pedro, whom now she calleth brother, aboard the galley where, all things being in readiness and the wind serving very well, they launched forth with their oars and set sail.

When they were at the sea, the captain of the galley taking the view of Silla, perceiving her singular beauty, he was better pleased in beholding of her face than in taking the height either of the sun or star. And thinking her, by the homeliness of her apparel, to be but some simple maiden, calling her into his cabin, he began to break with her after the sea fashion, desiring her to use his own cabin for her better ease. And during the time that she remained at the sea, she should not want a bed; and then whispering softly in her ear he said that, for want of a bedfellow, he himself would supply that room.

Silla, not being acquainted with any such talk, blushed for shame, but made him no answer at all. My captain, feeling such a bickering within himself, the like whereof he had never endured upon the sea, was like to be taken prisoner aboard his own ship and forced to yield himself a captive without any cannon shot. Wherefore, to salve all sores and thinking it the readiest way to speed, he began to break with Silla in the way of marriage, telling her how happy a voyage she had made to fall into the liking of such a one as himself was, who was able to keep and maintain her like a gentlewoman, and for her sake would likewise take her brother into his fellowship, whom he would by some means prefer in such sort that both of them should have good cause to think themselves thrice happy—she to light of such a husband, and he to light of such a brother.

But Silla, nothing pleased with these preferments, desired him to cease his talk, for that she did think herself, indeed, to be too unworthy such a one as he was. Neither was she minded yet to marry, and therefore desired him to fix his fancy upon some that were better worthy than herself was, and that could better like of his courtesy than she could do.

The captain, seeing himself thus refused, being in a great chafe he said as followeth:

"Then seeing you make so little account of my courtesy, proffered to one that is so far unworthy of it, from henceforth I will use the office of my authority. You shall know that I am the captain of this ship and have power to command and dispose of things at my pleasure. And seeing you have so scornfully rejected me to be your loyal husband, I will now take you by force and use you at my will; and so long as it shall please me, will keep you for mine own store. There shall be no man able to defend you, nor yet to persuade me from that I have determined,

Silla, with these words being struck into a great fear, did think it now too late to rue her rash attempt, determined rather to die with her own hands than to suffer herself to be abused in such sort. Therefore she most humbly desired the captain, so much as he could, to save her credit and, seeing that she must needs be at his will and disposition, that for that present he would depart and suffer her till night, when in the dark he might take his pleasure without any manner of suspicion to the residue of his company. The captain, thinking now the goal to be more than half won, was contented so far to satisfy her request, and departed out leaving her alone in his cabin.

Silla, being alone by herself, drew out her knife ready to strike herself to the heart; and falling upon her knees, desired God to receive her soul as an acceptable sacrifice for her follies, which she had so wilfully committed, craving pardon for her sins, and so forth—continuing a long and pitiful reconciliation to God. In the midst whereof there suddenly fell a wonderful storm, the terror whereof was such that there was no man but did think the seas would presently have swallowed them. The billows so suddenly arose with the rage of the wind that they were all glad to fall to heaving out of water, for otherwise their feeble galley had never been able to have brooked the seas. This storm continued all that day and the next night; and they, being driven to put rummer before the wind[43] to

---

[43]*put rummer before the wind:* The spelling in all the early editions is "romer," an obsolete form of "rummer," which meant "large drinking glass" or "liquor contained in a large drinking glass." But such a meaning does not fit the context. What Rich may have in mind is "rummage," in the nautical sense of arranging, or rearranging, goods in the hold of a ship; perhaps the implication here is that the weight should be on the side toward the wind, to prevent tipping over.

keep the galley ahead the billow, were driven upon the main shore, where the galley brake all to pieces. There was every man providing to save his own life. Some got upon hatches, boards, and casks and were driven with the waves to and fro; but the greatest number were drowned, amongst the which Pedro was one.

But Silla herself, being in the cabin as you have heard, took hold of a chest that was the captain's; the which, by the only providence of God, brought her safe to the shore. The which, when she had recovered, not knowing what was become of Pedro, her man, she deemed that both he and all the rest had been drowned, for that she saw nobody upon the shore but herself. Wherefore, when she had a while made great lamentations, complaining her mishaps, she began in the end to comfort herself with the hope that she had to see her Apolonius and found such means that she brake open the chest that brought her to land, wherein she found good store of coin and sundry suits of apparel that were the captain's.

And now, to prevent a number of injuries that might be proffered to a woman that was left in her case, she determined to leave her own apparel and to sort herself into some of those suits that, being taken for a man, she might pass through the country in the better safety. And as she changed her apparel, she thought it likewise convenient to change her name. Wherefore, not readily happening of any other, she called herself Silvio, by the name of her own brother whom you have heard spoken of before.

In this manner she traveled to Constantinople, where she inquired out the palace of the Duke Apolonius. And thinking herself now to be both fit and able to play the servingman, she presented herself to the duke, craving his service. The duke, very willing to give succor unto strangers, perceiving him to be a proper, smug[44] young man, gave him entertainment. Silla thought herself now more than satisfied for all the casualties that had happened unto her in her journey that she might at her pleasure take but the view of the Duke Apolonius, and above the rest of his servants was very diligent and attendant upon him. The which the duke perceiving, began likewise to grow into good liking with the diligence of his man and therefore made him one of his chamber. Who but Silvio, then, was most neat[45] about him in helping of him to make him ready in a morning in the setting of his ruffs. In the keeping of his chamber Silvio pleased his master so well

[44]smug: trim, neat.
[45]neat: skillful. Cranfill (p. 270) agrees with Collier that "neat" should be emended to "near."

that, above all the rest of his servants about him, he had the greatest credit; and the duke put him most in trust.

At this very instant, there was remaining in the city a noble dame, a widow, whose husband was but lately deceased, one of the noblest men that were in the parts of Grecia,[46] who left his lady and wife large possessions and great livings. This lady's name was called Julina, who, besides the abundance of her wealth and the greatness of her revenues, had likewise the sovereignty of all the dames of Constantinople for her beauty.

To this Lady Julina, Apolonius became an earnest suitor; and according to the manner of wooers, besides fair words, sorrowful sighs, and piteous countenances, there must be sending of loving letters, chains, bracelets, broaches, rings, tablets, gems, jewels, and presents I know not what. So my duke, who in the time that he remained in the Isle of Cyprus had no skill at all in the art of love although it were more than half proffered unto him, was now become a scholar in love's school and had already learned his first lesson— that is, to speak pitifully, to look ruthfully,[47] to promise largely, to serve diligently, and to please carefully. Now he was learning his second lesson—that is, to reward liberally, to give bountifully, to present willingly, and to write lovingly. Thus Apolonius was so busied in his new study that I warrant you there was no man that could challenge him for playing the truant, he followed his profession with so good a will. And who must be the messenger to carry the tokens and love letters to the Lady Julina but Silvio, his man; in him the duke reposed his only confidence, to go between him and his lady.

Now, gentlewomen, do you think there could have been a greater torment devised wherewith to afflict the heart of Silla than herself to be made the instrument to work her own mishap and to play the attorney in a cause that made so much against herself? But Silla, altogether desirous to please her master, cared nothing at all to offend herself, followed his business with so good a will, as if it had been in her own preferment.

Julina, now having many times taken the gaze of this young youth Silvio, perceiving him to be of such excellent perfect grace, was so entangled with the often sight of this sweet temptation that she fell into as great a liking with the man as the master was with herself. And on a time Silvio, being sent from his master with a message to

46*Grecia:* Greece.
47*ruthfully:* compassionately.

the Lady Julina, as he began very earnestly to solicit in his master's behalf, Julina, interrupting him in his tale, said:

"Silvio, it is enough that you have said for your master; from henceforth, either speak for yourself or say nothing at all."

Silla, abashed to hear these words, began in her mind to accuse the blindness of love that Julina, neglecting the good will of so noble a duke, would prefer her love unto such a one as nature itself had denied to recompense her liking.

And now for a time, leaving matters depending as you have heard, it fell out that the right Silvio indeed (whom you have heard spoken of before, the brother of Silla) was come to his father's court into the Isle of Cyprus. Where, understanding that his sister was departed, in manner as you have heard conjectured, that the very occasion did proceed of some liking had between Pedro, her man (that was missing with her), and herself. But Silvio, who loved his sister as dearly as his own life, and the rather for that as she was his natural sister both by father and mother, so the one of them was so like the other in countenance and favor that there was no man able to discern the one from the other by their faces, saving by their apparel the one being a man, the other a woman.

Silvio, therefore, vowed to his father, not only to seek out his sister Silla, but also to revenge the villainy, which he conceived in Pedro, for the carrying away of his sister. And thus departing, having traveled through many cities and towns without hearing any manner of news of those he went to seek for, at the last he arrived at Constantinople where, as he was walking in an evening for his own recreation on a pleasant green yard without the walls of the city, he fortuned to meet with the Lady Julina, who likewise had been abroad to take the air. And as she suddenly cast her eyes upon Silvio, thinking him to be her old acquaintance by reason they were so like one another, as you have heard before, said unto him:

"Sir Silvio, if your haste be not the greater, I pray you let me have a little talk with you, seeing I have so luckily met you in this place."

Silvio, wondering to hear himself so rightly named, being but a stranger not of above two days continuance in the city, very courteously came towards her, desirous to hear what she would say.

Julina, commanding her train something to stand back, said as followeth:

"Seeing my good will and friendly love hath been the only cause to make me so prodigal to offer that I see is so lightly rejected, it maketh me to think that men be of this condition—rather to desire those things which they cannot come by than to esteem or value of that which both largely and liberally is offered unto them. But if the liberality of my proffer hath made to seem less the value of the thing that I meant to present, it is but in your own conceit,[48] considering how many noblemen there hath been here before, and be yet at this present, which hath both served, sued, and most humbly entreated to attain to that which, to you, of myself I have freely offered—and I perceive is despised, or at the least very lightly regarded."

Silvio, wondering at these words, but more amazed that she could so rightly call him by his name, could not tell what to make of her speeches—assuring himself that she was deceived and did mistake him—did think, notwithstanding, it had been a point of great simplicity[49] if he should forsake that which fortune had so favorably proffered unto him—perceiving by her train that she was some lady of great honor, and viewing the perfection of her beauty and the excellency of her grace and countenance—did think it impossible that she should be despised; and therefore answered thus:

"Madam, if before this time, I have seemed to forget myself in neglecting your courtesy, which so liberally you have meant unto me, please it you to pardon what is past; and from this day forwards, Silvio remaineth ready prest[50] to make such reasonable amends as his ability may any ways permit, or as it shall please you to command.

Julina, the gladdest woman that might be to hear these joyful news, said:

"Then, my Silvio, see you fail not tomorrow at night to sup with me at my own house, where I will discourse farther with you what amends you shall make me."

To which request Silvio gave his glad consent, and thus they departed very well pleased.

And as Julina did think the time very long till she had reaped the fruit of her desire, so Silvio he wished for harvest before corn could grow, thinking the time as long till he saw how matters would fall out. But not knowing what lady she might be, he presently (before Julina was out of sight) demanded of one that was walking by what

[48]*conceit:* conception.

[49]*simplicity:* stupidity (on his own part); usually "simplicity" means "ignorance," but here it carries a stronger connotation.

[50]*ready prest:* an idiomatic phrase in which both words mean "ready"; often the expression was "ready and prest" (corresponding to our "ready and willing" or "ready and eager").

she was and how she was called, who satisfied Silvio in every point, and also in what part of the town her house did stand, whereby he might inquire it out.

Silvio, thus departing to his lodging, passed the night with very unquiet sleeps; and the next morning his mind ran so much of his supper that he never cared neither for his breakfast nor dinner. And the day, to his seeming, passed away so slowly that he had thought the stately steeds had been tired that draw the chariot of the sun, or else some other Joshua had commanded them again to stand, and wished that Phaëthon had been there with a whip.[51]

Julina, on the other side, she had thought the clock-setter had played the knave, the day came no faster forwards. But six o'clock, being once strucken, recovered comfort to both parties. And Silvio hastening himself to the palace of Julina where by her he was friendly welcomed and, a sumptuous supper being made ready, furnished with sundry sorts of delicate dishes. They sat them down, passing the supper time with amorous looks, loving countenances, and secret glances conveyed from the one to the other, which did better satisfy them than the feeding of their dainty dishes.

Suppertime being thus spent, Julina did think it very unfitly if she should turn Silvio to go seek his lodging in an evening, desired him, therefore, that he would take a bed in her house for that night. And bringing him up into a fair chamber that was richly furnished, she found such means that, when all the rest of her household servants were abed and quiet, she came herself to bear Silvio company. Where concluding upon conditions that were in question between them, they passed the night with such joy and contentation as might in that convenient time be wished for, but only that Julina, feeding too much of some one dish above the rest, received a surfeit whereof she could not be cured in forty weeks after—a natural inclination in all women which are subject to longing and want the reason[52] to use a moderation in their diet. But the morning approaching, Julina took her leave and conveyed herself into her own chamber.

And when it was fair daylight, Silvio, making himself ready, departed likewise about his affairs in the town, debating with himself

---

[51]*Joshua ... Phaëthon ... whip:* Joshua was the Old Testament leader of the Israelites after the death of Moses; to finish a battle with his enemies, he commanded the sun to stop setting (Joshua, X, 12 ff.). Rich sees Phaëthon, of the Greek myth, in the opposite way: in driving the chariot of the sun fast, he speeds up the passage of time.

[52]*want the reason:* lack the will power.

how things had happened—being well assured that Julina had
mistaken him; and therefore, for fear of further evils, determined
to come to more there, but took his journey towards other places in
the parts of Grecia to see if he could learn any tidings of his
sister Silla.

The Duke Apolonius, having made a long suit and never a whit
the nearer of his purpose, came to Julina to crave her direct answer
either to accept of him, and of such conditions as he proffered unto
her, or else to give him his last farewell.

Julina, as you have heard, had taken an earnest penny of another
whom she had thought had been Silvio, the duke's man, was at a
controversy in herself what she might do. One while she thought,
seeing her occasion served so fit, to crave the duke's good will for
the marrying of his man; then again, she could not tell what displeasure the duke would conceive in that she should seem to prefer
his man before himself, did think it therefore best to conceal the
matter till she might speak with Silvio, to use his opinion how these
matters should be handled. And hereupon resolving herself, desiring
the duke to pardon her speeches, said as followeth:

"Sir duke, for that from this time forwards I am no longer of
myself, having given my full power and authority over to another
whose wife I now remain by faithful vow and promise. And albeit I
know the world will wonder, when they shall understand the fondness
of my choice, yet I trust you yourself will nothing dislike with me
sith I have meant no other thing than the satisfying of mine own
contentation and liking."

The duke, hearing these words, answered: "Madam, I must then
content myself, although against my will, having the law in your
own hands, to like of whom you list and to make choice where it
pleaseth you."

Julina, giving the duke great thanks, that would content himself
with such patience, desired him likewise to give his free consent and
good will to the party whom she had chosen to be her husband.

"Nay, surely, madam," quoth the duke, "I will never give my
consent that any other man shall enjoy you than myself. I have made
too great account of you than so lightly to pass you away with my
good will. But seeing it lieth not in me to let you, having (as you say)
made your own choice, so from hence forwards I leave you to your
own liking, always willing you well, and thus will take my leave."

The duke departed towards his own house very sorrowful that
Julina had thus served him. But in the mean space that the duke had
remained in the house of Julina, some of his servants fell into talk

and conference with the servants of Julina. Where, debating between them of the likelihood of the marriage between the duke and the lady, one of the servants of Julina said that he never saw his lady and mistress use so good countenance to the duke himself as she had done to Silvio, his man; and began to report with what familiarity and courtesy she had received him, feasted him, and lodged him, and that, in his opinion, Silvio was like to speed before the duke, or any other that were suitors.

This tale was quickly brought to the duke himself, who, making better inquiry in the matter, found it to be true that was reported and, better considering of the words which Julina had used towards himself, was very well assured that it could be no other than his own man that had thrust his nose so far out of joint—wherefore, without any further respect, caused him to be thrust into a dungeon, where he was kept prisoner in a very pitiful plight.

Poor Silvio, having got intelligence by some of his fellows what was the cause that the duke his master did bear such displeasure unto him, devised all the means he could, as well by meditation by[53] his fellows as otherwise by petitions and supplications to the duke, that he would suspend his judgment till perfect proof were had in the matter. And then if any manner of thing did fall out against him, whereby the duke had cause to take any grief, he would confess himself worthy not only of imprisonment, but also of most vile and shameful death. With these petitions he daily plied the duke, but all in vain. For the duke thought he had made so good proof that he was thoroughly confirmed in his opinion against his man.

But the Lady Julina, wondering what made Silvio that he was so slack in his visitation, and why he absented himself so long from her presence, began to think that all was not well. But in the end, perceiving no decoction[54] of her former surfeit (received as you have heard) and finding in herself an unwonted swelling in her belly, assuring herself to be with child, fearing to become quite bankrupt of her honor, did think it more than time to seek out a father, and made such secret search and diligent inquiry that she learned the truth how Silvio was kept in prison by the duke his master. And minding to find a present remedy, as well for the love she bore to

---

[53]*meditation by:* All four of the early editions read "meditation by" when "meditation of" would seem to make more sense; but perhaps the idea is that Silvio's friends are trying to devise or think up a plan. Another possibility is that Rich intended "mediation," not "meditation."

[54]*decoction:* reduction, dissolving.

Silvio as for the maintenance of her credit and estimation, she speedily hasted to the palace of the duke to whom she said as followeth:

"Sir duke, it may be that you will think my coming to your house in this sort doth something pass the limits of modesty, the which, I protest before God, proceedeth of this desire—that the world should know how justly I seek means to maintain my honor. But to the end I seem not tedious with prolixity of words, nor to use other than direct circumstances, know, sir, that the love I bear to my only beloved Silvio, whom I do esteem more than all the jewels in the world, whose personage I regard more than my own life, is the only cause of my attempted journey, beseeching you that all the whole displeasure, which I understand you have conceived against him, may be imputed unto my charge, and that it would please you lovingly to deal with him whom of myself I have chosen rather for the satisfaction of mine honest liking than for the vain preeminences or honorable dignities looked after by ambitious minds."

The duke, having heard this discourse, caused Silvio presently to be sent for and to be brought before him, to whom he said:

"Had it not been sufficient for thee, when I had reposed myself in thy fidelity and the trustiness of thy service, that thou shouldst so traitorously deal with me, but since that time hast not spared still to abuse me with so many forgeries and perjured protestations not only hateful unto me, whose simplicity thou thinkest to be such that by the plot of thy pleasant tongue thou wouldst make me believe a manifest untroth, but most abominable be thy doings in the presence and sight of God—that hast not spared to blaspheme his holy name by calling him to be a witness to maintain thy leasings, and so detestably wouldst forswear thyself in a matter that is so openly known?"

Poor Silvio, whose innocency was such that he might lawfully swear, seeing Julina to be there in place, answered thus:

"Most noble duke, well understanding your conceived grief, most humbly I beseech you patiently to hear my excuse—not minding thereby to aggravate or heap up your wrath and displeasure, protesting before God that there is nothing in the world which I regard so much, or do esteem so dear, as your good grace and favor. But desirous that your grace should know my innocency, and to clear myself of such impositions wherewith I know I am wrongfully accused, which as I understand should be in the practicing of the Lady Julina, who standeth here in place, whose acquittance for my better discharge now I most humbly crave, protesting before the almighty God that neither in thought, word, nor deed, I have not otherwise used myself than according to the bond and duty of a servant that is both willing and desirous to further his master's suits. Which if I have otherwise said than that is true, you, Madam Julina, who can very well decide the depths of all this doubt, I most humbly beseech you to certify a troth—if I have in anything missaid, or have otherwise spoken than is right and just."

Julina, having heard this discourse which Silvio had made, perceiving that he stood in great awe of the duke's displeasure, answered thus:

"Think not, my Silvio, that my coming hither is to accuse you of any misdemeanor towards your master; so I do not deny but in all such embassages wherein towards me you have been employed, you have used the office of a faithful and trusty messenger. Neither am I ashamed to confess that the first day that mine eyes did behold the singular behavior, the notable courtesy, and other innumerable gifts wherewith my Silvio is endued, but that beyond all measure my heart was so inflamed that impossible it was for me to quench the fervent love, or extinguish the least part of my conceived torment, before I had bewrayed the same unto him; and of my own motion craved his promised faith and loyalty of marriage.

"And now is the time to manifest the same unto the world which hath been done before God and between ourselves—knowing that it is not needful to keep secret that which is neither evil done nor hurtful to any person. Therefore, as I said before, Silvio is my husband by plighted faith whom I hope to obtain without offense or displeasure of anyone, trusting that there is no man that will so far forget himself as to restrain that which God hath left at liberty for every wight, or that will seek by cruelty to force ladies to marry otherwise than according to their own liking.

"Fear not then, my Silvio, to keep your faith and promise, which you have made unto me; and as for the rest, I doubt not things will so fall out as you shall have no manner of cause to complain."

Silvio, amazed to hear these words for that Julina, by her speech, seemed to confirm that which he most of all desired to be quit of, said:

"Who would have thought that a lady of so great honor and reputation would herself be the ambassador of a thing so prejudicial and uncomely for her estate? What plighted promises be these which be spoken of, altogether ignorant unto me? Which if it be otherwise than I have said, you sacred gods consume me straight with flashing flames of fire! But what words might I use to give credit to the truth and innocency of my cause?

"Ah, Madam Julina, I desire no other testimony than your own honesty and virtue, thinking that you will not so much blemish the brightness of your honor, knowing that a woman is, or should be, the image of courtesy, continency, and shamefacedness. From the which so soon as she stoopeth and leaveth the office of her duty and modesty, besides the degraduation[55] of her honor, she thrusteth herself into the pit of perpetual infamy.

"And as I cannot think you would so far forget yourself, by the refusal of a noble duke, to dim the light of your renown and glory, which hitherto you have maintained amongst the best and noblest ladies, by such a one as I know myself to be, too far unworthy your degree and calling. So most humbly I beseech you to confess a troth—whereto tendeth those vows and promises you speak of, which speeches be so obscure unto me, as I know not for my life how I might understand them."

Julina, something nipped with these speeches, said: "And what is the matter that now you make so little account of your Julina that, being my husband in deed, have the face to deny me, to whom thou art contracted by so many solemn oaths? What, art thou ashamed to have me to thy wife? How much oughtest thou rather to be ashamed to break thy promised faith and to have despised the holy and dreadful name of God!

"But that time constraineth me to lay open that which shame rather willeth I should dissemble and keep secret, behold me then here, Silvio, whom thou hast gotten with child: who, if thou be of such honesty as I trust for all this I shall find, then the thing is done without prejudice or any hurt to my conscience—considering that by the professed faith, thou didst account me for thy wife; and I received thee for my spouse and loyal husband, swearing by the almighty God that no other than you have made the conquest and triumph of my chastity, whereof I crave no other witness than yourself and mine own conscience."

I pray you, gentlewomen, was not this a foul oversight of Julina, that would so precisely swear so great an oath, that she was gotten with child by one that was altogether unfurnished with implements for such a turn? For God's love take heed, and let this be an example to you, when you be with child, how you swear who is the father before you have had good proof and knowledge of the party; for men be so subtle and full of sleight that God knoweth a woman may quickly be deceived.

But now to return to our Silvio who, hearing an oath sworn so

[55]*degraduation:* degradation.

divinely that he had gotten a woman with child, was like to believe that it had been true in very deed; but remembering his own impediment, thought it impossible that he should commit such an act. And therefore, half in a chafe, he said:

"What law is able to restrain the foolish indiscretion of a woman that yieldeth herself to her own desires? What shame is able to bridle or withdraw her from her mind and madness, or with what snaffle is it possible to hold her back from the execution of her filthiness? But what abomination is this that a lady of such a house should so forget the greatness of her estate, the alliance whereof she is descended, the nobility of her deceased husband, and maketh no conscience to shame and slander herself with such a one as I am, being so far unfit and unseemly for her degree? But how horrible is it to hear the name of God so defaced that we make no more account but for the maintenance of our mischiefs; we fear no whit at all to forswear his holy name, as though he were not in all his dealings most righteous, true, and just; and will not only lay open our leasings[56] to the world, but will likewise punish the same with most sharp and bitter scourges."

Julina, not able to endure him to proceed any farther in his sermon, was already surprised with a vehement grief, began bitterly to cry out, uttering these speeches following:

"Alas, is it possible that the sovereign justice of God can abide a mischief so great and cursed? Why may I not now suffer death rather than the infamy which I see to wander before mine eyes? Oh, happy and more than right happy had I been if inconstant fortune had not devised this treason wherein I am surprised and caught. Am I thus become to be entangled with snares and in the hands of him who, enjoying the spoils of my honor, will openly deprive me of my fame by making me a common fable to all posterity in time to come? Ah, traitor and discourteous wretch, is this the recompense of the honest and firm amity which I have borne thee? Wherein have I deserved this discourtesy? By loving thee more than thou art able to deserve? Is it I, arrant thief, is it I upon whom thou thinkest to work thy mischiefs? Dost thou think me no better worth but that thou mayest prodigally waste my honor at thy pleasure? Didst thou dare to adventure upon me, having thy conscience wounded with so deadly a treason? Ah, unhappy and above all other most unhappy, that have so charily preserved mine honor, and now am made a prey to satisfy a young man's lust, that hath coveted nothing but the spoil of my chastity and good name."

[56]*leasings:* lies, falsehoods.

Herewithal the tears so gushed down her cheeks that she was not able to open her mouth to use any farther speech.

The duke, who stood by all this while and heard this whole discourse, was wonderfully moved with compassion towards Julina, knowing that from her infancy she had ever so honorably used herself that there was no man able to detect her of any misdemeanor otherwise than beseemed a lady of her estate. Wherefore, being fully resolved that Silvio his man had committed this villainy against her, in a great fury drawing his rapier, he said unto Silvio:

"How canst thou, arrant thief, show thyself so cruel and careless to such as do thee honor? Hast thou so little regard of such a noble lady as humbleth herself to such a villain as thou art, who, without any respect either of her renown or noble estate, canst be content to seek the wrack and utter ruin of her honor? But frame thyself to make such satisfaction as she requireth—although I know, unworthy wretch, that thou art not able to make her the least part of amends—or I swear by God that thou shalt not escape the death which I will minister to thee with my own hands. And therefore advise thee well what thou doest."

Silvio, having heard this sharp sentence, fell down on his knees before the duke craving for mercy, desiring that he might be suffered to speak with the lady Julina apart, promising to satisfy her according to her own contentation.

"Well," quoth the duke, "I take thy word, and therewithal I advise thee that thou perform thy promise, or otherwise I protest before God I will make thee such an example to the world that all traitors shall tremble for fear, how they do seek the dishonoring of ladies."

But now Julina had conceived so great grief against Silvio that there was much ado to persuade her to talk with him. But remembering her own case, desirous to hear what excuse he could make, in the end she agreed.

And being brought into a place severally by themselves, Silvio began with a piteous voice to say as followeth: "I know not, madam, of whom I might make complaint—whether of you or of myself, or rather of fortune, which hath conducted and brought us both into so great adversity. I see that you receive great wrong, and I am condemned against all right; you in peril to abide the bruit of spiteful tongues, and I in danger to lose the thing that I most desire. And although I could allege many reasons to prove my sayings true, yet I refer myself to the experience and bounty of your mind."

And herewithal, loosing his garments down to his stomach, and

showed Julina his breasts and pretty teats, surmounting far the whiteness of snow itself, saying:

"Lo, madam, behold here the party whom you have challenged to
be the father of your child. See, I am a woman, the daughter of a
noble duke, who, only for the love of him whom you so lightly have
shaken off, have forsaken my father, abandoned my country, and in
manner as you see am become a serving man, satisfying myself but
with the only sight of my Apolonius.

"And now, madam, if my passion were not vehement and my torments without comparison, I would wish that my feigned griefs might
be laughed to scorn and my dissembled pains to be rewarded with
flouts. But my love being pure, my travail continual, and my griefs
endless, I trust, madam, you will not only excuse me of crime, but
also pity my distress, the which I protest I would still have kept
secret if my fortune would so have permitted."

Julina did now think herself to be in a worse case than ever she
was before, for now she knew not whom to challenge to be the
father of her child; wherefore, when she had told the duke the very
certainty of the discourse which Silvio had made unto her, she
departed to her own house with such grief and sorrow that she purposed never to come out of her own doors again alive, to be a wonder
and mocking stock to the world.

But the duke, more amazed to hear this strange discourse of Silvio,
came unto him, whom, when he had viewed with better consideration,
perceived, indeed, that it was Silla, the daughter of duke Pontus, and
embracing her in his arms, he said:

"Oh, the branch of all virtue and the flower of courtesy itself,
pardon me, I beseech you, of all such discourtesies as I have ignorantly committed towards you—desiring you that, without farther
memory of ancient griefs, you will accept of me, who is more joyful
and better contented with your presence than if the whole world
were at my commandment.

"Where hath there ever been found such liberality in a lover which,
having been trained up and nourished amongst the delicacies and
banquets of the court, accompanied with trains of many fair and
noble ladies living in pleasure and in the midst of delights, would
so prodigally adventure yourself, neither fearing mishaps nor misliking
to take such pains as I know you have not been accustomed unto. Oh,
liberality never heard of before! Oh, fact that can never be sufficiently rewarded! Oh, true love most pure and unstained!"

Herewithal sending for the most artificial[57] workmen, he provided for her sundry suits of sumptuous apparel; and the marriage day appointed, which was celebrated with great triumph through the whole city of Constantinople, everyone praising the nobleness of the duke. But so many as did behold the excellent beauty of Silla gave her the praise above all the rest of the ladies in the troop.

The matter seemed so wonderful and strange that the bruit was spread throughout all the parts of Grecia, insomuch that it came to the hearing of Silvio, who, as you have heard, remained in those parts to inquire of his sister. He, being the gladdest man in the world, hasted to Constantinople, where, coming to his sister, he was joyfully received and most lovingly welcomed and entertained of the duke his brother-in-law.

After he had remained there two or three days, the duke revealed unto Silvio the whole discourse how it happened between his sister and the Lady Julina, and how his sister was challenged for getting a woman with child. Silvio, blushing with these words, was stricken with great remorse to make Julina amends—understanding her to be a noble lady and was left defamed to the world through his default. He therefore bewrayed the whole circumstance to the duke; whereof the duke, being very joyful, immediately repaired with Silvio to the house of Julina, whom they found in her chamber in great lamentation and mourning. To whom the duke said:

"Take courage, madam, for behold here a gentleman that will not stick both to father your child and to take you for his wife—no inferior person, but the son and heir of a noble duke, worthy of your estate and dignity."

Julina, seeing Silvio in place,[58] did know very well that he was the father of her child, and was so ravished with joy that she knew not whether she were awake or in some dream. Silvio, embracing her in his arms, craving forgiveness of all that passed,[59] concluded with her the marriage day which was presently accomplished with great joy, and contentation to all parties. And thus Silvio, having attained a noble wife, and Silla his sister her desired husband, they passed the residue of their days with such delight as those that have accomplished the perfection of their felicities.

Finis

---

[57]*artificial:* skillful.
[58]*in place:* on the spot; standing there.
[59]*passed:* had passed.

ॐ Pandosto

The Triumph of Time
(1588)

ROBERT GREENE

Pandosto or *The History of Dorastus and Fawnia* (1588) may best
be described as a romance-anatomy. It reflects Greene's increasing dis-
satisfaction with a pure romance form. The tone throughout is
astringent; the reader is held back from identification with the
characters, whom the narrator analyzes objectively and precisely.
Both *Pandosto* and *The Winter's Tale*, which Shakespeare modeled
on *Pandosto*, are at first disturbing in their combination of dissimilar
elements. On second reading, they seem, like Donne's poems, bold
and exciting.

But Greene is not one to chisel out a perfect little gem. He depends
too much on coincidence, employs a surprisingly limited vocabulary,
and in general gives the impression of being a somewhat careless and
hurried writer. But for all that, he is an artist. One injustice we can
do him is to let our scanty knowledge of his private life affect our
judgment of his works, as Ernest A. Baker has done:

> He was a weak and emotional man, easily influenced, with little
> more depth of character than that with which he endows his
> Philadors, Francescos, and Robertos. His life was squalid rather
> than tragic; and through some tender and idyllic passages in his
> works, as well as from the testimony of his friends, one may discern
> much in it that merits compassion, if not esteem.[1]

[1]Baker, *The History of the English Novel*, II, 92–93. Baker is not the
only offender. Such statements as "Greene's habit of putting the prejudices
of his readers far ahead of his own convictions" (in Esler, "Robert Greene

"Tender and idyllic passages" may not be as extenuating to us as they were to Baker. We may take them or leave them, depending on whether they are appropriate to the narrative. In *Pandosto* they are appropriate to the love scenes between Dorastus and Fawnia, but in the toughminded analysis of Pandosto's jealousy they would have been out of place. Whether or not it is true that Greene was "a weak and emotional man," he does not, as Baker implies, weakly and emotionally draw his characters. What he does, instead, is to analyze effectively a weak and emotional man, Pandosto. If his own weaknesses helped him perform the analysis, they helped him do it with insight and intelligence.

In Lyly, Greene had a fine precedent; and his debt to Lyly goes considerably deeper than a reference to Euphues in two or three of his prose fiction titles. Greene uses a good many of the same sound effects that we have noticed in *Euphues*, often prefers indirect discourse to dialogue, and in monologue constructs a "set piece" that functions as a little oration. He also uses proverbs almost as extensively as Lyly does—sometimes quoting them exactly, more often varying them to fit his own rhythms, and occasionally even inventing a proverb-sounding expression.[2]

But the differences outweigh the similarities. Greene is much more interested in narrative than Lyly is; and although *Pandosto* is not carefully put together as a whole (and ends too abruptly), it is not only full of exciting action, but each segment of the action is under control. Unlike Rich, Greene is fully aware that every incident implies something with regard to the characters' and the narrator's values. *Pandosto* does not move from topic to topic—from Education to Love to Friendship—as does *Euphues*. It moves from action to action; and although education, love, and friendship are involved in the action, they emerge as themes from the narrative structure.

Just as Greene is not content with the pure romance form, he is not content with a clear separation of scene, summary, and commentary. In one sentence we are up fairly close (though never very

---

and the Spanish Armada") are now tossed off without any mention of evidence, as though everyone knows exactly what Elizabethan prejudices and Greene's convictions were and were not.

[2]There is a similar pattern (of quoting, adapting, inventing) in Lyly's and Greene's uses of Pliny (or information that derives ultimately from Pliny). But as Stanley Wells has shown, in "Greene and Pliny," *N&Q*, VIII (1961), 422–424, some of the expressions that formerly seemed to be invented by Greene are actually traceable to Pliny.

close), seeing and hearing firsthand; in the next sentence the narrator moves us back and gives us a brief summary of events from the past. All the while, in a phrase here and a sentence there, he is telling us what the characters are thinking and feeling. Since he is an "omniscient" narrator, his statements are not mere expressions of opinion; they represent absolute and certain knowledge.

The narrator's final objective evidently is to enable the reader to understand the situation as a whole in all its complexity. Accordingly, the narrator does not concentrate entirely on Pandosto's point of view; instead, he shifts to Bellaria, then to Egistus, and back to Pandosto. One effect of the shift back and forth is that the reader fully understands Pandosto's neurotic conduct. But another, contrary, effect is that the reader is in no doubt whatever regarding Bellaria's and Egistus' innocence, as the following passage shows:

> Bellaria (who in her time was the flower of courtesy), willing to show how unfeignedly she loved her husband by his friend's entertainment, used him likewise so familiarly that her countenance bewrayed how her mind was affected towards him, oftentimes coming herself into his bedchamber to see that nothing should be amiss to mislike him.
>
> This honest familiarity increased daily more and more betwixt them, for Bellaria noting in Egistus a princely and bountiful mind adorned with sundry and excellent qualities, and Egistus finding in her a virtuous and courteous disposition, there grew such a secret uniting of their affections that the one could not well be without the company of the other. Insomuch that when Pandosto was busied with such urgent affairs that he could not be present with his friend Egistus, Bellaria would walk with him into the garden, where they two in private and pleasant devices would pass away the time to both their contents (pp. 233–34).

The queen's coming into Egistus' bedroom is omitted in *The Winter's Tale;* it does not occur on or off stage, possibly for the reason that Shakespeare feared it might compromise the queen. But Greene's form, with the narrator's omniscient analysis, allows for a bolder presentation. Shakespeare is better in showing the queen's natural warmth, but Greene is better in showing that from Pandosto's point of view her warmth may be seen in a highly questionable light. Pandosto's inordinate jealousy is prepared for most clearly and convincingly.[3]

[3]For a recent analysis of Shakespeare's uses of *Pandosto,* see Lawlor, "*Pandosto* and the Nature of Dramatic Romance." Lawlor concentrates on differences of characterization and plot; he suggests that Shakespeare found Bellaria's trial scene—a queen on trial—rich with dramatic possibilities.

Pandosto is a transitional work. We may observe that in Gascoigne, Lyly, and Rich there is a strong tendency to write only about aristocratic characters. Greene's main characters are aristocratic, too, and his dedication is addressed only to gentlemen readers. But *Pandosto* is different in that a character of low birth is important to the outcome. Porrus, the shepherd, becomes Sir Porrus; and there is nothing satirical or humorous about his promotion. As a wealthy landowner, he is to be reckoned with; and at the climax of the plot he bravely presents the casket with all the proof of Fawnia's identity, thus saving her life. Before that he had been for sixteen years her loving and responsible foster-father. After creating Porrus, Greene is now almost ready for *A Notable Discovery of Cozenage,* in which he not only addresses himself earnestly to middle- and lower-class readers (as well as to gentlemen), but uses them as characters in the narrative itself.[4]

To The Gentlemen Readers, Health

The paltering poet, Aphranius,[5] being blamed for troubling the Emperor Trajan with so many doting poems, adventured notwithstanding

[4]It would seem possible that much of the alleged dishonesty, insincerity, and opportunism that critics have accused Greene of are in reality a tension between two opposing forces that one may observe in the later works, beginning with *Pandosto*—naturally conservative tastes and attitudes on the one hand *vs.* strong efforts to keep abreast of rapidly changing times on the other hand. *Pandosto* is mostly aristocratic, but in *A Notable Discovery* Greene seems to be making an effort to recognize a social fact—that "plain country men" are rising in the world and becoming very important people. The effort, as we shall see in *A Notable Discovery,* produces an interesting ambiguity: the cozeners are wrong to victimize the unwary country man, but the latter's stupidity (and possibly something worse) makes him unworthy of our sympathy.

Two recent critics have dealt with Greene's conservatism. See Waldo F. McNeir, "Greene's Medievalization of Ariosto," *RLC,* XXIX (1955), 351–360; and Irving Ribner, "Greene's Attack on Marlowe: Some Light on *Alphonsus* and *Selimus,*" *SP,* LII (1955), 162–171. McNeir shows that in the play *Orlando Furioso* (1588) Greene rejects much of Ariosto and returns to "the primal tradition of romance" (p. 351). Similarly, Ribner notes (p. 165) that in *Alphonsus* and *Selimus* Greene replaces Marlowe's irreverence with traditional and orthodox views.

[5]*poet, Aphranius:* The only poet whose name approximates the spelling or sound of "Aphranius" seems to be Lucius Afranius; but the trouble is

still to present him with rude and homely verses, excusing himself with the courtesy of the emperor, which did as friendly accept, as he fondly offered. So, gentlemen, if any condemn my rashness for troubling your ears with so many unlearned pamphlets, I will straight shroud myself under the shadow of your courtesies and, with Aphranius, lay the blame on you as well for friendly reading them as on myself for fondly penning them. Hoping, though fond, curious—or rather currish—backbiters breathe out slanderous speeches, yet the courteous readers (whom I fear to offend) will requite my travail at the least with silence; and in this hope I rest, wishing you health and happiness.

Robert Greene

To The Right Honorable George Clifford, Earl of Cumberland,[6] Robert Greene Wisheth Increase of Honor and Virtue

The Rascians, right honorable, when by long gazing against the sun they become half blind, recover their sights by looking on the black loadstone. Unicorns, being glutted with browsing on roots of liquorice, sharpen their stomachs with crushing bitter grass.

Alexander vouchsafed as well to smile at the crooked picture of Vulcan as to wonder at the curious counterfeit of Venus. The mind is sometimes delighted as much with small trifles as with sumptuous triumphs, and as well pleased with hearing of Pan's homely fancies as of Hercules' renowned labors.

Silly[7] Baucis could not serve Jupiter in a silver plate but in a wooden dish. All that honor Aesculapius deck not his shrine with

---

that Afranius lived around 100 B.C., a good 200 years before the Roman Emperor Trajan. It would seem that here, and elsewhere throughout *Pandosto*, the "learned" reference, in itself, is not important enough to Greene for him to check its historical accuracy. Apparently he uses it only to add weight and concreteness to his central idea, which in this case is the writer's relationship with a select reading public. In the following notes there will be no attempt to explain or assess such allusions; the aim will be only to give, either in the text or in a note, the correct modern spelling—so that the reader, if he so desires, may himself use the appropriate reference books.

[6]*George Clifford, Earl of Cumberland:* Clifford (1558–1605) was commander of the ship "Elizabeth Bonaventure" against the Spanish Armada in 1588; as buccaneer, gambler, and man-about-town, he was well known in the 1580's and 1590's.

[7]*Silly:* innocent, simple (in a good sense).

jewels. Apollo gives oracles as well to the poor man for his mite as to the rich man for his treasure. The stone echites is not so much liked for the color as for virtue, and gifts are not to be measured by the worth but by the will. Myson, that unskillful painter of Greece, adventured to give unto Darius the shield of Pallas so roughly shadowed as he smiled more at the folly of the man than at the imperfection of his art. So I present unto your honor *The Triumph Of Time* so rudely finished as I fear your honor will rather frown at my impudency than laugh at my ignorancy. But I hope my willing mind shall excuse my slender skill, and your honor's courtesy shadow my rashness.

They which fear the biting of vipers do carry in their hands the plumes of a phoenix. Phidias drew Vulcan sitting in a chair of ivory. Caesar's crow durst never cry "Ave," but when she was perched on the Capitol. And I seek to shroud this imperfect pamphlet under your honor's patronage, doubting the dint of such envenomed vipers as seek with their slanderous reproaches to carp at all—being oftentimes most unlearned of all—and assure myself that your honor's renowned valor and virtuous disposition shall be a sufficient defense to protect me from the poisoned tongues of such scorning sycophants; hoping that, as Jupiter vouchsafed to lodge in Philemon's thatched cottage and Philip of Macedon to take a bunch of grapes of a country peasant, so I hope your honor, measuring my work by my will and weighing more the mind than the matter, will—when you have cast a glance at this toy—with Minerva, under your golden target cover a deformed owl. And in this hope I rest, wishing unto you and the virtuous countess, your wife, such happy success as your honors can desire or I imagine.

Your Lordship's most dutifully to command,

Robert Greene

Pandosto

Among all the passions wherewith human minds are perplexed there is none that so galleth with restless despite as the infectious sore of jealousy. For all other griefs are either to be appeased with sensible persuasions, to be cured with wholesome counsel, to be relieved in want, or by tract of time to be worn out—jealousy only excepted, which is so sauced with suspicious doubts and pinching mistrust that whoso seeks by friendly counsel to raze out this hellish passion, it forthwith suspecteth[8] that he giveth this advice to cover his own guiltiness. Yea, whoso is pained with this restless torment doubteth all, distrusteth himself, is always frozen with fear and fired with suspicion; having that wherein consisteth all his joy to be the breeder of his misery. Yea, it is such a heavy enemy to that holy estate of matrimony, sowing between the married couples such deadly seeds of secret hatred as—love being once razed out by spiteful distrust— there oft ensueth bloody revenge, as this ensuing history manifestly proveth. Wherein Pandosto (furiously incensed by causeless jealousy) procured the death of his most loving and loyal wife and his own endless sorrow and misery.

In the country of Bohemia there reigned a king called Pandosto, whose fortunate success in wars against his foes and bountiful courtesy towards his friends in peace made him to be greatly feared and loved of all men. This Pandosto had to wife a lady called Bellaria, by birth royal, learned by education, fair by nature, by virtues famous—so that it was hard to judge whether her beauty, fortune, or virtue won the greatest commendations. These two, linked together in perfect love, led their lives with such fortunate content that their subjects greatly rejoiced to see their quiet disposition. They had not been married long but fortune (willing to increase their happiness) lent them a son so adorned with the gifts of nature as the perfection of the child greatly augmented the love of the parents and the joy of their commons. Insomuch that the Bohemians, to show their inward joys by outward actions, made bonfires and triumphs throughout all the kingdom, appointing jousts and tourneys for the honor of their young prince. Whither resorted not only his nobles but also divers kings and princes which were his neighbors, willing to show their friendship they ought[9] to Pandosto and to win fame and glory by their prowess and valor. Pandosto, whose mind was fraught with princely liberality, entertained the kings, princes, and noblemen with such submiss courtesy and magnifical bounty that they all saw how willing he was to gratify their good wills, making a general feast for his subjects which continued by the space of twenty days. All which time the jousts and tourneys were kept, to the great content both of the lords and ladies there present. This solemn triumph being once ended, the assembly taking their leave of Pandosto and Bellaria, the young son (who was called Garinter) was nursed up in the house, to the great joy and content of the parents. Fortune, envious

[8]*it . . . suspecteth:* it is to be suspected.   [9]*ought:* owed.

of such happy success, willing to show some sign of her inconstancy, turned her wheel and darkened their bright sun of prosperity with the misty clouds of mishap and misery. For it so happened that Egistus, King of Sicily (who in his youth had been brought up with Pandosto) desirous to show that neither tract of time nor distance of place could diminish their former friendship, provided a navy of ships and sailed into Bohemia to visit his old friend and companion who, hearing of his arrival, went himself in person and his wife Bellaria (accompanied with a great train of lords and ladies) to meet Egistus. And spying him, alighted from his horse, embraced him very lovingly, protesting that nothing in the world could have happened more acceptable to him than his coming, wishing his wife to welcome his old friend and acquaintance. Who (to show how she liked him whom her husband loved) entertained him with such familiar courtesy as Egistus perceived himself to be very well welcome.

After they had thus saluted and embraced each other, they mounted again on horseback and rode toward the city (devising and recounting how, being children, they had passed their youth in friendly pastimes) where, by the means of the citizens, Egistus was received with triumphs and shows in such sort that he marveled how on so small a warning they could make such preparation.

Passing the streets thus with such rare sights, they rode on to the palace, where Pandosto entertained Egistus and his Sicilians with such banqueting and sumptuous cheer so royally as they all had cause to commend his princely liberality. Yea, the very basest slave that was known to come from Sicily was used with such courtesy that Egistus might easily perceive how both he and his were honored for his friend's sake. Bellaria (who in her time was the flower of courtesy), willing to show how unfeignedly she loved her husband by his friend's entertainment, used him likewise so familiarly that her countenance bewrayed[9a] how her mind was affected towards him, oftentimes coming herself into his bedchamber to see that nothing should be amiss to mislike him.

This honest familiarity increased daily more and more betwixt them, for Bellaria noting in Egistus a princely and bountiful mind adorned with sundry and excellent qualities, and Egistus finding in her a virtuous and courteous disposition, there grew such a secret uniting of their affections that the one could not well be without the

[9a]*bewrayed:* revealed.

company of the other. Insomuch that when Pandosto was busied with such urgent affairs that he could not be present with his friend Egistus, Bellaria would walk with him into the garden, where they two in private and pleasant devices would pass away the time to both their contents.

This custom still continuing betwixt them, a certain melancholy passion entering the mind of Pandosto drove him into sundry and doubtful thoughts. First he called to mind the beauty of his wife Bellaria, the comeliness and bravery of his friend Egistus (thinking that love was above all laws, and therefore to be stayed with no law, that it was hard to put fire and flax together without burning, that their open pleasures might breed his secret displeasures). He considered with himself that Egistus was a man, and must needs love; that his wife was a woman, and therefore subject unto love; and that where fancy forced, friendship was of no force.

These and such like doubtful thoughts, a long time smothering in his stomach, began at last to kindle in his mind a secret mistrust which, increased by suspicion, grew at last to a flaming jealousy that so tormented him as he could take no rest. He then began to measure all their actions and to misconstrue of their too private familiarity, judging that it was not for honest affection but for disordinate fancy. So that he began to watch them more narrowly to see if he could get any true or certain proof to confirm his doubtful suspicion.

While thus he noted their looks and gestures (and suspected their thoughts and meanings) they two (silly souls who doubted nothing of this, his treacherous intent) frequented daily each other's company, which drove him into such a frantic passion that he began to bear a secret hate to Egistus and a lowering countenance to Bellaria, who, marveling at such unaccustomed frowns, began to cast beyond the moon and to enter into a thousand sundry thoughts which way she should offend[10] her husband; but, finding in herself a clear conscience, ceased to muse until such time as she might find fit opportunity to demand the cause of his dumps.

In the meantime, Pandosto's mind was so far charged with jealousy that he did no longer doubt, but was assured (as he thought) that his friend Egistus had entered a wrong point in his tables[11] and

[10]*should offend:* could be offending.

[11]*Egistus had entered a wrong point in his tables:* a reference to the game of backgammon, with a second meaning of a sexual nature. Egistus has put one of his "men" at the wrong "point" on a backgammon board, which is composed of two tables and 24 alternating black and white points or squares.

so had played him false play. Whereupon, desirous to revenge so great an injury, he thought best to dissemble the grudge with a fair and friendly countenance, and so (under the shape of a friend) to show him the trick of a foe. Devising with himself a long time how he might best put away Egistus without suspicion of treacherous murder, he concluded at last to poison him. Which opinion pleasing his humor, he became resolute in his determination and, the better to bring the matter to pass, he called unto him his cupbearer, with whom in secret he broke the matter (promising to him for the performance thereof to give him a thousand crowns of yearly revenues).

His cupbearer, either being of a good conscience or willing, for fashion sake, to deny such a bloody request, began with great reasons to persuade Pandosto from his determinate mischief—showing him what an offense murder was to the gods, how such unnatural actions did more displease the heavens than men,[12] and that causeless cruelty did seldom or never escape without revenge. He laid before his face that Egistus was his friend, a king, and one that was come into his kingdom to confirm a league of perpetual amity betwixt them; that he had and did show him a most friendly countenance; how Egistus was not only honored of his own people by obedience but also loved of the Bohemians for his courtesy; and that if now he should without any just or manifest cause poison him it would not only be a great dishonor to his majesty and a means to sow perpetual enmity between the Sicilians and the Bohemians, but also his own subjects would repine at such treacherous cruelty.

These and such like persuasions of Franion (for so was his cupbearer called) could no whit prevail to dissuade him from his devilish enterprise. But remaining resolute in his determination, his fury so fired with rage as it could not be appeased with reason, he began with bitter taunts to take up his man and to lay before him two baits—preferment and death—saying that if he would poison Egistus he should advance him to high dignities, if he refused to do it of an obstinate mind no torture should be too great to requite his disobedience.

Franion, seeing that to persuade Pandosto any more was but to strive against the stream, consented (as soon as opportunity would give him leave) to dispatch Egistus, wherewith Pandosto remained

---

[12]*the heavens than men:* With these words, sig. A4ᵛ in the 1588 edition ends; and since all of sig. B is missing in the only extant copy of that first edition, the 1592 (or second) edition must be used as copytext until "devoid of pity," the first words on sig. C of the 1588 edition (as explained in note 19).

somewhat satisfied, hoping that now he should be fully revenged of such mistrusted injuries, intending also (as soon as Egistus was dead) to give his wife a sop of the same sauce and to be rid of those which were the cause of his restless sorrow.

While thus he lived in this hope, Franion, being secret in his chamber, began to meditate with himself in these terms:

"Ah, Franion, treason is loved of many, but the traitor hated of all. Unjust offenses may for a time escape without danger, but never without revenge. Thou art servant to a king and must obey at command; yet, Franion, against law and conscience it is not good to resist a tyrant with arms, nor to please an unjust king with obedience. What shalt thou do? Folly refused gold, and frenzy preferment. Wisdom seeketh after dignity, and counsel looketh for gain. Egistus is a stranger to thee, and Pandosto thy sovereign. Thou hast little cause to respect the one, and oughtest to have great care to obey the other. Think this, Franion: that a pound of gold is worth a ton of lead,[13] great gifts are little gods, and preferment to a mean man is a whetstone to courage. There is nothing sweeter than promotion nor lighter than report. Care not, then, though most count thee a traitor so all call thee rich. Dignity, Franion, advanceth thy posterity and evil report can hurt but thyself. Know this: where eagles build, falcons may prey; where lions haunt, foxes may steal; kings are knowen to command, servants are blameless to consent. Fear not thou, then, to lift at Egistus—Pandosto shall bear the burden. Yea, but, Franion, conscience is a worm that ever biteth but never ceaseth; that which is rubbed with the stone galactites will never be hot; flesh dipped in the Sea Aegeum[14] will never be sweet; the herb tragion, being once bit with an asp, never groweth; and conscience, once stained with innocent blood, is always tied to a guilty remorse. Prefer thy content before riches and a clear mind before dignity: so, being poor, thou shalt have rich peace; or else, rich, thou shalt enjoy disquiet."

Franion, having muttered out these or such like words, seeing either he must die with a clear mind or live with a spotted conscience, he was so cumbered with divers cogitations that he could take no rest until at last he determined to break the matter to Egistus. But, fearing that the king should either suspect or hear of such matters, he

[13]*a pound of gold is worth a ton of lead:* One is surprised to learn that this proverb-sounding statement is not in Tilley's collection. Following the practice of Lyly, Greene not only modifies old proverbs, but he actually creates new ones.

[14]*Sea Aegeum:* the Aegean Sea (*Mare Aegaeum*).

concealed the device till opportunity would permit him to reveal it. Lingering thus in doubtful fear, in an evening he went to Egistus' lodging and, desirous to break with him of certain affairs that touched the king (after all were commanded out of the chamber) Franion made manifest the whole conspiracy which Pandosto had devised against him, desiring Egistus not to account him a traitor for bewraying his master's counsel—but to think that he did it for conscience, hoping that although his master (inflamed with rage or incensed by some sinister reports or slanderous speeches) had imagined such causeless mischief. Yet when time should pacify his anger and try those talebearers but flattering parasites, then he would count him as a faithful servant that with such care had kept his master's credit.

Egistus had not fully heard Franion tell forth his tale but a quaking fear possessed all his limbs, thinking that there was some treason wrought and that Franion did but shadow his craft with these false colors. Wherefore he began to wax in choler and said that he doubted not Pandosto, since he was his friend and there had never as yet been any breach of amity. He had not sought to invade his lands, to conspire with his enemies, to dissuade his subjects from their allegiance, but in word and thought he rested his at all times. He knew not, therefore, any cause that should move Pandosto to seek his death but suspected it to be a compacted knavery of the Bohemians to bring the king and him at odds.

Franion, staying him in the midst of his talk, told him that to dally with princes was with the swans to sing against their death and that if the Bohemians had intended any such secret mischief, it might have been better brought to pass than by revealing the conspiracy. Therefore his majesty did ill to misconstrue of his good meaning since his intent was to hinder treason, not to become a traitor and to confirm his premises.[15] If it please his majesty to flee into Sicily for the safeguard of his life, he would go with him. And if then he found not such a practice to be pretended, let his imagined treachery be repaid with most monstrous torments.

Egistus hearing the solemn protestation of Franion, began to consider that in love and kingdoms neither faith nor law is to be re-

---

[15]*premises:* The fourth edition of 1607 emended "premises" to "promises," and modern editors, beginning with Collier, seem to have agreed with the emendation; but "premises" in the 1592 edition—the 1588 edition, lacking sig. B, must be ignored at this point—may refer to Egistus' suppositions, regarding Pandosto's conduct and motives, in the previous paragraph.

spected, doubting that Pandosto thought by his death to destroy his men and with speedy war to invade Sicily. These and such doubts thoroughly weighed, he gave great thanks to Franion, promising if he might with life return to Syracuse that he would create him a duke in Sicily, craving his counsel how he might escape out of the country.

Franion, who, having some small skill in navigation, was well acquainted with the ports and havens and knew every danger in the sea, joining in counsel with the master of Egistus' navy, rigged all their ships and, setting them afloat, let them lie at anchor, to be in the more readiness when time and wind should serve. Fortune, although blind, yet by chance favoring this just cause, sent them within six days a good gale of wind which Franion seeing fit for their purpose to put Pandosto out of suspicion the night before they should sail he went to him and promised that the next day he would put the device in practice for he had got such a forcible poison as the very smell thereof should procure sudden death.

Pandosto was joyful to hear this good news and thought every hour a day till he might be glutted with bloody revenge. But his suit had but ill success. For Egistus, fearing that delay might breed danger and willing that the grass should not be cut from under his feet, taking bag and baggage with the help of Franion, conveyed himself and his men out of a postern gate of the city so secretly and speedily that without any suspicion they got to the seashore, where, with many a bitter curse, taking their leave of Bohemia, they went aboard. Weighing their anchors and hoisting sail, they passed as fast as wind and sea would permit towards Sicily, Egistus being a joyful man that he had safely passed such treacherous perils.

But as they were quietly floating on the sea, so Pandosto and his citizens were in an uproar. For, seeing that the Sicilians without taking their leave were fled away by night, the Bohemians feared some treason and the king thought that without question his suspicion was true, seeing his cupbearer had bewrayed the sum of his secret pretense. Whereupon he began to imagine that Franion and his wife Bellaria had conspired with Egistus and that the fervent affection she bore him was the only means of his secret departure. Insomuch that, incensed with rage, he commanded that his wife should be carried to straight prison[16] until they heard further of his pleasure.

---

[16]*to straight prison:* In the 1609 edition the word order becomes "straight to prison," which seems more idiomatic to us. Probably, however, Greene wrote "to straight prison." The primary sense seems to be "strait" (narrow, constricted); but we shall do well to leave the original spelling, "straight," because there may be an additional sense of "directly": Bellaria goes directly to prison.

The guard, unwilling to lay their hands on such a virtuous princess, and yet fearing the king's fury, went very sorrowfully to fulfill their charge. Coming to the queen's lodging, they found her playing with her young son Garinter, unto whom, with tears doing the message, Bellaria, astonished at such a hard censure and finding her clear conscience a sure advocate to plead in her case, went to the prison most willingly. Where, with sighs and tears, she passed away the time till she might come to her trial.

But Pandosto, whose reason was suppressed with rage and whose unbridled folly was incensed with fury (seeing Franion had bewrayed his secrets and that Egistus might well be railed on but not revenged) determined to wreak all his wrath on poor Bellaria. He therefore caused a general proclamation to be made through all his realm: that the queen and Egistus had by the help of Franion not only committed most incestuous adultery but also had conspired the king's death, whereupon the traitor Franion was fled away with Egistus and Bellaria was most justly imprisoned. This proclamation being once blazed through the country, although the virtuous disposition of the queen did half discredit the contents, yet the sudden and speedy passage of Egistus and the secret departure of Franion induced them (the circumstances thoroughly considered) to think that both the proclamation was true and the king greatly injured. Yet they pitied her case as sorrowful, that so good a lady should be crossed with such adverse fortune. But the king, whose restless rage would admit no pity, thought that although he might sufficiently requite his wife's falsehood with the bitter plague of pinching penury, yet his mind should never be glutted with revenge till he might have fit time and opportunity to repay the treachery of Egistus with a fatal injury. But a curst cow hath ofttimes short horns and a willing mind but a weak arm.[17] For Pandosto, although he felt that revenge was a spur to war and that envy always proffereth steel, yet he saw that Egistus was not only of great puissance and prowess to withstand him but had also many kings of his alliance to aid him if need should serve (for he married to the emperor's daughter of Russia). These and such like considerations something daunted Pandosto's courage, so that he was content rather to put up a manifest injury with peace than hunt after

[17]*But a curst cow ... weak arms:* The first part of the sentence is a proverb (Tilley, C751): "A curst cow has short horns." The sense of "curst" is "savage"; with short horns the "cow" (evidently not a harmless milk cow) will be able to do little damage ("hath ... a weak arm"). Compare proverb D447: "A curst dog must be tied short." One expects a play on horns and cuckoldry, but it does not seem to be implied.

revenge with dishonor and loss—determining, since Egistus had escaped scot-free, that Bellaria should pay for all at an unreasonable price.

Remaining thus resolute in this determination, Bellaria continuing still in prison and hearing the contents of the proclamation, knowing that her mind was never touched with such affection nor that Egistus had ever offered her such discourtesy, would gladly have come to her answer, that both she might have known her unjust accusers and cleared herself of that guiltless crime.

But Pandosto was so inflamed with rage and infected with jealousy as he would not vouchsafe to hear her nor admit any just excuse, so that she was fain to make a virtue of her need and with patience to bear these heavy injuries. As thus she lay crossed with calamities, a great cause to increase her grief, she found herself quick with child. Which as soon as she felt stir in her body, she burst forth into bitter tears, exclaiming against fortune in these terms:

"Alas, Bellaria, how unfortunate art thou because fortunate. Better hadst thou been born a beggar than a prince: so shouldst thou have bridled fortune with want, where now she sporteth herself with thy plenty. Ah, happy life where poor thoughts and mean desires live in secure content, not fearing fortune because too low for fortune. Thou seest now, Bellaria, that care is a companion to honor, not to poverty; that high cedars are frushed[18] with tempests when low shrubs are not touched with the wind; precious diamonds are cut with the file when despised pebbles lie safe in the sand. Delphi is sought to by princes, not beggars; and fortune's altars smoke with kings' presents, not with poor men's gifts. Happy are such, Bellaria, that curse fortune for contempt, not fear, and may wish they were, not sorrow they have been. Thou art a princess, Bellaria, and yet a prisoner—born to the one by descent, assigned to the other by despite; accused without cause, and therefore oughtest to die without care. For patience is a shield against fortune and a guiltless mind yieldeth not to sorrow.

"Ah, but infamy galleth unto death and liveth after death. Report is plumed with time's feathers and envy oftentimes soundeth fame's trumpet. Thy suspected adultery shall fly in the air and thy known virtues shall lie hid in the earth. One mole staineth a whole face and what is once spotted with infamy can hardly be worn out with time.

---

[18]*frushed:* struck violently (enough to bruise or crush); apparently the word was becoming obsolete by the 1629 edition, which emended to "crushed."

Die then, Bellaria. Bellaria, die; for if the gods should say thou art guiltless, yet envy would hear the gods but never believe the gods. Ah, hapless wretch, cease these terms. Desperate thoughts are fit for them that fear shame, not for such as hope for credit. Pandosto hath darkened thy fame but shall never discredit thy virtues; suspicion may enter a false action but proof shall never put in his plea. Care not, then, for envy, since report hath a blister on her tongue; and let sorrow bite them which offend, not touch thee that are faultless. But, alas, poor soul, how canst thou but sorrow? Thou art with child, and by him that, instead of kind pity, pincheth thee in cold prison."

And with that, such gasping sighs so stopped her breath that she could not utter any more words, but, wringing her hands and gushing forth streams of tears, she passed away the time with bitter complaints.

The jailor, pitying these her heavy passions, thinking that if the king knew she were with child he would somewhat appease his fury and release her from prison, went in all haste and certified Pandosto what the effect of Bellaria's complaint was. Who, no sooner heard the jailor say she was with child but (as one possessed with a frenzy) he rose up in a rage, swearing that she and the bastard brat she was withal should die, if the gods themselves said no—thinking assuredly, by computation of time, that Egistus, and not he, was father to the child. This suspicious thought galled afresh this half-healed sore insomuch as he could take no rest until he might mitigate his choler with a just revenge, which happened presently after. For Bellaria was brought to bed of a fair and beautiful daughter, which no sooner Pandosto heard but he determined that both Bellaria and the young infant should be burnt with fire.

His nobles, hearing of the king's cruel sentence, sought by persuasions to divert him from this bloody determination: laying before his face the innocency of the child and the virtuous disposition of his wife; how she had continually loved and honored him so tenderly that without due proof he could not, nor ought not, to appeach her of that crime; and if she had faulted, yet it were more honorable to pardon with mercy than to punish with extremity, and more kingly to be commended of pity than accused of rigor; and, as for the child, if he should punish it for the mother's offense, it were to strive against nature and justice, and that unnatural actions do more offend the gods than men; how causeless cruelty nor innocent blood never escapes without revenge.

These and such like reasons could not appease his rage, but he rested resolute in this: that Bellaria, being an adulteress, the child was a bastard, and he would not suffer that such an infamous brat should call him father. Yet at last, seeing his noblemen were importunate upon him, he was content to spare the child's life—and yet to put it to a worser death. For he found out this device: that seeing (as he thought) it came by fortune, so he would commit it to the charge of fortune. And therefore he caused a little cockboat to be provided, wherein he meant to put the babe and then send it to the mercy of the seas and the destinies. From this his peers in no wise could persuade him but that he sent presently two of his guard to fetch the child. Who, being come to the prison and with weeping tears recounting their master's message, Bellaria no sooner heard the rigorous resolution of her merciless husband but she fell down in a sound,[18a] so that all thought she had been dead. Yet at last, being come to herself, she cried and screeched out in this wise.

"Alas, sweet, unfortunate babe, scarce born before envied by fortune. Would the day of thy birth had been the term of thy life. Then shouldst thou have made an end to care and prevented thy father's rigor. Thy faults cannot yet deserve such hateful revenge. Thy days are too short for so sharp a doom. But thy untimely death must pay thy mother's debts, and her guiltless crime must be thy ghastly curse. And shalt thou, sweet babe, be committed to fortune? When thou art already spited by fortune, shall the seas be thy harbor and the hard boat thy cradle? Shall thy tender mouth, instead of sweet kisses, be nipped with bitter storms? Shalt thou have the whistling winds for thy lullaby and the salt sea foam instead of sweet milk? Alas, what destinies would assign such hard hap? What father would be so cruel, or what gods will not revenge such rigor? Let me kiss thy lips, sweet infant, and wet thy tender cheeks with my tears and put this chain about thy little neck, that if fortune save thee it may help to succor thee. Thus, since thou must go to surge in the ghastful seas, with a sorrowful kiss I bid thee farewell. And I pray the gods thou mayst fare well."

Such and so great was her grief that, her vital spirits being suppressed with sorrow, she fell again down in a trance, having her senses so sotted with care that after she was revived yet she lost her memory and lay for a great time without moving, as one in a trance. The guard left her in this perplexity and carried the child to the king,

[18a]*sound:* swoon.

who, quite devoid of pity,[19] commanded that without delay it should be put in the boat, having neither sail nor other[20] to guide it, and so to be carried into the midst of the sea and there left to the wind and wave as the destinies please to appoint. The very shipmen, seeing the sweet countenance of the young babe, began to accuse the king of rigor and to pity the child's hard fortune. But fear constrained them to that which their nature did abhor, so that they placed it in one of the ends of the boat and, with a few green boughs, made a homely cabin to shroud it as they could from wind and weather. Having thus trimmed the boat, they tied it to a ship and so haled it into the main sea and then cut in sunder the cord. Which they had no sooner done but there arose a mighty tempest which tossed the little boat so vehemently in the waves that the shipmen thought it could not continue long without sinking. Yea, the storm grew so great that, with much labor and peril, they got to the shore.

But leaving the child to her fortunes, again to Pandosto, who, not yet glutted with sufficient revenge, devised which way he should best increase his wife's calamity. But first assembling his nobles and counselors, he called her for the more reproach into open court, where it was objected against her that she had committed adultery with Egistus and conspired with Franion to poison Pandosto her husband but, their pretense being partly spied, she counseled them to flee away by night for their better safety.

Bellaria, who, standing like a prisoner at the bar, feeling in herself a clear conscience to withstand her false accusers (seeing that no less than death could pacify her husband's wrath) waxed bold and desired that she might have law and justice (for mercy she neither craved nor hoped for) and that those perjured wretches which had falsely accused her to the king might be brought before her face to give in evidence. But Pandosto, whose rage and jealousy was such as no reason nor equity could appease, told her that, for her accusers, they were of such credit as their words were sufficient witness and that the sudden and secret flight of Egistus and Franion confirmed that which they had confessed.[21] And as for her, it was her part to deny such a monstrous crime and to be imprudent in forswearing the fact, since

[19]*devoid of pity:* With these words we return to the 1588 edition, which will remain the copytext to the end. See note 12, above.

[20]*nor other:* nor any other means (probably including a "rudder," which was the emendation for "other" in the 1607 edition).

[21]*they had confessed:* The ambiguous "they" has reference to "her accusers," earlier in the sentence; "confessed" means "certified by oath."

she had passed all shame in committing the fault. But her stale countenance should stand for no coin,[22] for as the bastard which she bore was served, so she should with some cruel death be requited.

Bellaria, no whit dismayed with this rough reply, told her husband Pandosto that he spoke upon choler and not in conscience, for her virtuous life had been ever such as no spot of suspicion could ever stain. And if she had borne a friendly countenance to Egistus, it was in respect he was his friend and not for any lusting affection. Therefore, if she were condemned without any further proof it was rigor and not law.

The noblemen which sat in judgment said that Bellaria spoke reason and entreated the king that the accusers might be openly examined and sworn, and if then the evidence were such as the jury might find her guilty (for seeing she was a princess, she ought to be tried by her peers) then let her have such punishment as the extremity of the law will assign to such malefactors.

The king presently made answer that in this case he might and would dispense with the law and that the jury, being once paneled, they should take his word for sufficient evidence: otherwise he would make the proudest of them repent it.

The noblemen, seeing the king in choler, were all whist. But Bellaria, whose life then hung in the balance, fearing more perpetual infamy than momentary death, told the king if his fury might stand for a law that it were vain to have the jury yield their verdict. And therefore she fell down upon her knees and desired the king that, for the love he bore to his young son Garinter (whom she brought into the world) that he would grant her a request, which was this: that it would please his majesty to send six of his noblemen whom he best trusted to the Isle of Delphi, there to inquire of the Oracle of Apollo whether she had committed adultery with Egistus or conspired to poison him with Franion; and if the god Apollo, who by his divine essence knew all secrets, gave answer that she was guilty, she were content to suffer any torment, were it never so terrible.

The request was so reasonable that Pandosto could not for shame deny it unless he would be counted of all his subjects more willful than wise. He therefore agreed that, with as much speed as might be, there should be certain ambassadors dispatched to the Isle of Delphi. And in the mean season he commanded that his wife should be kept in close prison.

[22]*should stand for no coin:* should not be of any value (in mitigating her punishment).

Bellaria, having obtained this grant, was now more careful[23] for her little babe that floated on the seas than sorrowful for her own mishap. For of that she doubted; of herself she was assured, knowing if Apollo should give oracle according to the thoughts of the heart, yet the sentence should go on her side. Such was the clearness of her mind in this case.

But Pandosto, whose suspicious head still remained in one song, chose out six of his nobility whom he knew were scarce indifferent men in the queen's behalf and, providing all things fit for their journey, sent them to Delphi. They, willing to fulfill the king's command and desirous to see the situation and custom of the island, dispatched their affairs with as much speed as might be and embarked themselves to this voyage, which (the wind and weather serving fit for their purpose) was soon ended.

For within three weeks they arrived at Delphi, where they were no sooner set on land but with great devotion they went to the temple of Apollo, and there offering sacrifice to the god and gifts to the priest (as the custom was) they humbly craved an answer of their demand. They had not long kneeled at the altar but Apollo with a loud voice said, "Bohemians, what you find behind the altar, take and depart."

They, forthwith obeying the oracle, found a scroll of parchment wherein was written these words in letters of gold:

The Oracle

Suspicion is no proof. Jealousy is an unequal judge. Bellaria is chaste, Egistus blameless, Franion a true subject, Pandosto treacherous, his babe an innocent. And the king shall live without an heir if that which is lost be not found.

As soon as they had taken out this scroll, the priest of the god commanded them that they should not presume to read it before they came in the presence of Pandosto, unless they would incur the displeasure of Apollo. The Bohemian lords, carefully obeying his command, taking their leave of the priest, with great reverence departed out of the temple and went to their ships and, as soon as wind would permit them, sailed toward Bohemia. Whither in short time they safely arrived and, with great triumph, issuing out of their ships, went to the king's palace. Whom they found in his chamber accompanied with other noblemen.

[23]*careful*: anxious.

Pandosto no sooner saw them but with a merry countenance he welcomed them home, asking, "What news?"

They told his majesty that they had received an answer of the god written in a scroll but with this charge: that they should not read the contents before they came in the presence of the king. And with that they delivered him the parchment.

But his noblemen entreated him that since therein was contained either the safety of his wife's life and honesty or her death and perpetual infamy, that he would have his nobles and commons assembled in the judgment hall, where the queen, brought in as prisoner, should hear the contents. If she were found guilty by the oracle of the god, then all should have cause to think his rigor proceeded of due desert. If her grace were found faultless, then she should be cleared before all, since she had been accused openly. This pleased the king so that he appointed the day and assembled all his lords and commons and caused the queen to be brought in before the judgment seat, commanding that the indictment should be read wherein she was accused of adultery with Egistus and of conspiracy with Franion.

Bellaria, hearing the contents, was no whit astonished but made this cheerful answer: "If the divine powers be privy to human actions (as no doubt they are), I hope my patience shall make fortune blush and my unspotted life shall stain spitefully discredit. For although lying report hath sought to appeach[24] mine honor, and suspicion hath intended to soil my credit with infamy, yet where virtue keepeth the fort, report and suspicion may assail but never sack. How I have led my life before Egistus' coming, I appeal, Pandosto, to the gods and to thy conscience. What hath passed betwixt him and me the gods only know and I hope will presently reveal. That I loved Egistus I cannot deny, that I honored him I shame not to confess: to the one I was forced by his virtues, to the other for his dignities. But as touching lascivious lust, I say Egistus is honest and hope myself to be found without spot. For Franion, I can neither accuse him nor excuse him, for I was not privy to his departure. And that this is true which I have here rehearsed I refer myself to the divine oracle."

Bellaria had no sooner said but the king commanded that one of his dukes should read the contents of the scroll. Which after the commons had heard, they gave a great shout, rejoicing and clapping their hands that the queen was clear of that false accusation. But the

[24]*appeach:* impeach, accuse.

king, whose conscience was a witness against him of his witless fury
and false suspected jealousy, was so ashamed of his rash folly that
he entreated his nobles to persuade Bellaria to forgive and forget
these injuries, promising not only to show himself a loyal and loving
husband but also to reconcile himself to Egistus and Franion—revealing then, before them all, the cause of their secret flight and how
treacherously he thought to have practiced his death if the good mind
of his cupbearer[25] had not prevented his purpose.

As thus he was relating the whole matter, there was word brought
him that his young son Garinter was suddenly dead. Which news,
so soon as Bellaria heard (surcharged before with extreme joy and
now suppressed with heavy sorrow) her vital spirits were so stopped
that she fell down presently dead, and could be never revived. This
sudden sight so appalled the king's senses that he sank from his seat
in a sound so as he was fain to be carried by his nobles to his palace,
where he lay by the space of three days without speech.

His commons were as men in despair, so diversely distressed;
there was nothing but mourning and lamentation to be heard throughout all Bohemia—their young prince dead, their virtuous queen
bereaved of her life, and their king and sovereign in great hazard.
This tragical discourse of fortune so daunted them as they went like
shadows, not men. Yet somewhat to comfort their heavy hearts, they
heard that Pandosto was come to himself and had recovered his
speech. Who, as in a fury, brayed out these bitter speeches:

"Oh, miserable Pandosto, what surer witness than conscience?
What thoughts more sour than suspicion? What plague more bad than
jealousy? Unnatural actions offend the gods more than men, and
causeless cruelty never escapes without revenge. I have committed
such a bloody fact as, repent I may, but recall I cannot. Ah, jealousy,
a hell to the mind and a horror to the conscience—suppressing reason
and inciting rage, a worse passion than frenzy, a greater plague than
madness. Are the gods just? Then let them revenge such brutish
cruelty: my innocent babe I have drowned in the seas, my loving
wife I have slain with slanderous suspicion, my trusty friend I have
sought to betray. And yet the gods are slack to plague such offenses.
Ah, unjust Apollo, Pandosto is the man that hath committed the
fault. Why should Garinter, silly child, abide the pain? Well, since

---

[25]*he thought . . . his death . . . his cupbearer:* Pandosto thought . . . Egistus'
death . . . Pandosto's cupbearer.

the gods mean to prolong my days to increase my dolor, I will offer my guilty blood a sacrifice to those sackless[26] souls, whose lives are lost by my rigorous folly."

And with that he reached at a rapier to have murdered himself. But his peers, being present, stayed him from such a bloody act, persuading him to think that the commonwealth consisted on his safety and that those sheep could not but perish that wanted a shepherd (wishing that, if he would not live for himself, yet he should have care of his subjects and to put such fancies out of his mind, since in sores past help salves do not heal but hurt, and in things past cure care is a corrasive).[27]

With these and such like persuasions the king was overcome and began somewhat to quiet his mind, so that as soon as he could go abroad he caused his wife to be embalmed and wrapped in lead with her young son Garinter, erecting a rich and famous sepulcher wherein he entombed them both, making such solemn obsequies at her funeral as all Bohemia might perceive he did greatly repent him of his forepassed folly, causing this epitaph to be engraven on her tomb in letters of gold:

The Epitaph

Here lies entombed Bellaria fair,
  Falsely accused to be unchaste;
Cleared by Apollo's sacred doom,
  Yet slain by jealousy at last.

Whate're thou be that passeth by,
Curse him that caused this queen to die.

This epitaph being engraven, Pandosto would once a day repair to the tomb and there with watery plaints bewail his misfortune, coveting no other companion but sorrow nor no other harmony but repentance.

But leaving him to his dolorous passions, at last let us come to show the tragical discourse of the young infant. Who, being tossed with wind and wave, floated two whole days without succor, ready at every puff to be drowned in the sea, till at last the tempest ceased and the little boat was driven with the tide into the coast of Sicily,

---

[26]*sackless:* innocent (from "sac," meaning "crime").

[27]*corrasive:* corrosive (but the assonance in "ca*re*" and "cor*ra*sive" may be important). See footnote 138 in *Euphues.*

where, sticking upon the sands, it rested. Fortune (minding to be wanton, willing to show that as she hath wrinkles on her brows, so she hath dimples in her cheeks) thought after so many sour looks to lend a feigned smile and, after a puffing storm to bring a pretty calm, she began thus to dally.

It fortuned a poor mercenary shepherd that dwelled in Sicily, who got his living by other men's flocks, missed one of his sheep. And thinking it had strayed into the covert that was hard by, sought very diligently to find that which he could not see, fearing either that the wolves or eagles had undone him (for he was so poor as a sheep was half his substance), wandered down toward the sea cliffs to see if perchance the sheep was browsing on the sea ivy whereon they greatly do feed. But not finding her there, as he was ready to return to his flock, he heard a child cry. But knowing there was no house near, he thought he had mistaken the sound and that it was the bleating of his sheep.

Wherefore, looking more narrowly, as he cast his eye to the sea he spied a little boat, from whence, as he attentively listened, he might hear the cry to come. Standing a good while in a maze, at last he went to the shore and, wading to the boat, as he looked in he saw the little babe lying all alone, ready to die for hunger and cold, wrapped in a mantle of scarlet richly embroidered with gold, and having a chain about the neck. The shepherd, who before had never seen so fair a babe nor so rich jewels, thought assuredly that it was some little god, and began with great devotion to knock on his breast. The babe, who writhed with the head to seek for the pap, began again to cry afresh. Whereby the poor man knew that it was a child which by some sinister means was driven thither by distress of weather—marveling how such a silly infant (which, by the mantle and the chain, could not be but born of noble parentage) should be so hardly crossed with deadly mishap.

The poor shepherd, perplexed thus with divers thoughts, took pity of the child and determined with himself to carry it to the king, that there it might be brought up according to the worthiness of birth. For his ability could not afford to foster it, though his good mind was willing to further it. Taking, therefore, the child in his arms, as he folded the mantle together the better to defend it from cold, there fell down at his foot a very fair and rich purse, wherein he found a great sum of gold. Which sight so revived the shepherd's spirits as he was greatly ravished with joy and daunted with fear: joyful to see such a sum in his power and fearful, if it should be

known, that it might breed his further danger. Necessity wished him
at the least to retain the gold, though he would not keep the child.
The simplicity of his conscience feared him from such deceitful
bribery. Thus was the poor man perplexed with a doubtful dilemma
until at last the covetousness of the coin overcame him. For what
will not the greedy desire of gold cause a man to do? So that he was
resolved in himself to foster the child and with the sum to relieve
his want. Resting thus resolute in this point, he left seeking of his
sheep and, as covertly and secretly as he could, went by a byway
to his house, lest any of his neighbors should perceive his carriage.[28]

As soon as he was got home, entering in at the door, the child
began to cry. Which his wife hearing—and seeing her husband with
a young babe in his arms—began to be somewhat jealous, yet marveling that her husband should be so wanton abroad, since he was so
quiet at home. But as women are naturally given to believe the
worst, so his wife, thinking it was some bastard, began to crow
against her goodman and taking up a cudgel (for the most, master
went breechless)[29] swore solemnly that she would make clubs trumps
if he brought any bastard brat within her doors.

The goodman, seeing his wife in her majesty with her mace in
her hand, thought it was time to bow for fear of blows and desired
her to be quiet, for there was none such matter; but if she could hold
her peace, they were made forever. And with that he told her the
whole matter: how he had found the child in a little boat, without
any succor, wrapped in that costly mantle, and having that rich
chain about the neck. But at last when he showed her the purse full
of gold, she began to simper something sweetly, and, taking her
husband about the neck, kissed him after her homely fashion, saying
that she hoped God had seen their want and now meant to relieve
their poverty and (seeing they could get no children) had sent them
this little babe to be their heir.

"Take heed in any case," quoth the shepherd, "that you be secret
and blab it not out when you meet with your gossips, for if you do
we are like not only to lose the gold and jewels but our other goods
and lives."

"Tush," quoth his wife, "profit is a good hatch before the door.

[28]*carriage:* load (what he was carrying).
[29]*for the most, master went breechless:* In the first phrase "part" is
understood ("for the most part"); "master went breechless" means "master
did not wear the breeches in the family."

Fear not. I have other things to talk of than of this. But I pray you let us lay up the money surely and the jewels, lest by any mishap it be spied."

After that they had set all things in order, the shepherd went to his sheep with a merry note; and the goodwife learned to sing lullaby at home with her young babe, wrapping it in a homely blanket instead of a rich mantle, nourishing it so cleanly and carefully as it began to be a jolly girl. Insomuch that they began both of them to be very fond of it, seeing, as it waxed in age, so it increased in beauty. The shepherd, every night at his coming home, would sing and dance it on his knee and prattle, that in a short time it began to speak and call him "Dad" and her "Mom".

At last, when it grew to ripe years, that it was about seven years old, the shepherd left keeping of other men's sheep, and, with the money he found in the purse, he bought him the lease of a pretty farm and got a small flock of sheep. Which when Fawnia (for so they named the child) came to the age of ten years, he set her to keep. And she with such diligence performed her charge as the sheep prospered marvelously under her hand.

Fawnia thought Porrus had been her father and Mopsa her mother (for so was the shepherd and his wife called) honored and obeyed them with such reverence that all the neighbors praised the dutiful obedience of the child. Porrus grew in short time to be a man of some wealth and credit (for fortune favored him in having no charge but Fawnia) that he began to purchase land, intending after his death to give it to his daughter. So that divers rich farmers' sons came as wooers to his house. For Fawnia was something cleanly attired, being of such singular beauty and excellent wit that whoso saw her would have thought she had been some heavenly nymph and not a mortal creature. Insomuch that when she came to the age of sixteen years she so increased with exquisite perfection both of body and mind as her natural disposition did bewray that she was born of some high parentage.

But the people, thinking she was daughter to the shepherd Porrus, rested only amazed at her beauty and wit. Yea, she won such favor and commendations in every man's eye, as her beauty was not only praised in the country but also spoken of in the court. Yet such was her submiss modesty that, although her praise daily increased, her mind was no whit puffed up with pride, but humbled herself as became a country maid and the daughter of a poor shepherd. Every day she went forth with her sheep to the field, keeping them with such care and diligence as all men thought she was very painful, defending her face from the heat of the sun with no other veil but with a garland made of boughs[30] and flowers. Which attire became her so gallantly as she seemed to be the goddess Flora herself for beauty.

Fortune, who all this while had showed a friendly face, began now to turn her back and to show a lowering countenance—intending as she had given Fawnia a slender check, so she would give her a harder mate. To bring which to pass, she laid her train[31] on this wise: Egistus had but one only son called Dorastus about the age of twenty years—a prince so decked and adorned with the gifts of nature, so fraught with beauty and virtuous qualities as not only his father joyed to have so good a son, but all his commons rejoiced that God had lent them such a noble prince to succeed in the kingdom. Egistus, placing all his joy in the perfection of his son, seeing that he was now marriageable, sent ambassadors to the King of Denmark to entreat a marriage between him and his daughter, who, willingly consenting, made answer that the next spring, if it please Egistus with his son to come into Denmark, he doubted not but they should agree upon reasonable conditions. Egistus, resting satisfied with this friendly answer, thought convenient in the meantime to break with his son. Finding, therefore, on a day fit opportunity, he spoke to him in these fatherly terms.

"Dorastus, thy youth warneth me to prevent the worst, and mine age to provide the best. Opportunities neglected are signs of folly; actions measured by time are seldom bitten with repentance. Thou art young and I old. Age hath taught me that which thy youth cannot yet conceive. I therefore will counsel thee as a father, hoping thou wilt obey as a child. Thou seest my white hairs are blossoms for the grave, and thy fresh color fruit for time and fortune. So that it behooveth me to think how to die and for thee to care how to live. My crown I must leave by death and thou enjoy my kingdom by succession. Wherein I hope thy virtue and prowess shall be such as, though my subjects want my person, yet they shall see in thee my perfection. That nothing either may fail to satisfy thy mind or

---

[30]*boughs:* The actual spelling in the 1588 edition is "bowes," which could possibly mean "bows" (bow-knots of ribbon) but probably means "boughs" (in this case very small branches of trees or shrubs).

[31]*train:* stratagem.

increase thy dignities, the only care I have is to see thee well married before I die and thou become old."

Dorastus, who from his infancy delighted rather to die with Mars in the field than to dally with Venus in the chamber, fearing to displease his father and yet not willing to be wed, made him this reverent answer:

"Sir, there is no greater bond than duty nor no straiter law than nature. Disobedience in youth is often galled with despite in age. The command of the father ought to be a constraint to the child; so parents' wills are laws, so they pass not all laws. May it please your grace therefore to appoint whom I shall love, rather than by denial I should be appeached of disobedience. I rest content to love, though it be the only thing I hate."

Egistus, hearing his son to fly far from the mark, began to be somewhat choleric and therefore made him this hasty answer:

"What, Dorastus, canst thou not love? Cometh this cynical passion of prone desires or peevish frowardness? What, dost thou think thyself too good for all, or none good enough for thee? I tell thee, Dorastus, there is nothing sweeter than youth nor swifter decreasing while it is increasing. Time passed with folly may be repented but not recalled. If thou marry in age, thy wife's fresh colors will breed in thee dead thoughts and suspicion and thy white hairs, her loathsomeness and sorrow. For Venus' affections are not fed with kingdoms or treasures but with youthful conceits and sweet amours. Vulcan was allotted to shake the tree but Mars allowed to reap the fruit. Yield, Dorastus, to thy father's persuasions, which may prevent thy perils. I have chosen thee a wife fair by nature, royal by birth, by virtues famous, learned by education, and rich by possessions, so that it is hard to judge whether her bounty or fortune, her beauty or virtue, be of greater force. I mean, Dorastus, Euphania, daughter and heir to the King of Denmark."

Egistus, pausing here awhile, looking when his son should make him answer and seeing that he stood still as one in a trance, he shook him up thus sharply:

"Well, Dorastus, take heed. The tree alpya[32] wasteth not with fire but withereth with the dew. That which love nourisheth not, perisheth with hate. If thou like Euphania thou breedest my content, and in loving her thou shalt have my love. Otherwise—"

---

[32]*tree alpya*: apparently not "alpia" or "aplist," for that is a grass seed. Greene may have invented the term.

And with that he flung from his son in a rage, leaving him a sorrow-ful man in that he had by denial displeased his father, and half angry with himself that he could not yield to that passion whereto both reason and his father persuaded him. But see how fortune is plumed with time's feathers and how she can minister strange causes to breed strange effects.

It happened not long after this that there was a meeting of all the farmers' daughters in Sicily, whither Fawnia was also bidden as the mistress of the feast. Who, having attired herself in her best garments, went among the rest of her companions to the merry meeting, there spending the day in such homely pastimes as shepherds use.

As the evening grew on and their sports ceased, each taking their leave of other, Fawnia, desiring one of her companions to bear her company, went home by the flock to see if they were well folded. And as they returned it fortuned that Dorastus (who all that day had been hawking and killed store of game) encountered by the way these two maids. And casting his eye suddenly on Fawnia, he was half afraid, fearing that with Actaeon he had seen Diana. For he thought such exquisite perfection could not be found in any mortal creature.

As thus he stood in a maze, one of his pages told him that the maid with the garland on her head was Fawnia, the fair shepherd, whose beauty was so much talked of in the court. Dorastus, desirous to see if nature had adorned her mind with any inward qualities as she had decked her body with outward shape, began to question with her whose daughter she was, of what age, and how she had been trained up. Who answered him with such modest reverence and sharpness of wit that Dorastus thought her outward beauty was but a counterfeit to darken her inward qualities, wondering how so courtly behavior could be found in so simple a cottage, and cursing fortune that had shadowed wit and beauty with such hard fortune.

As thus he held her a long while with chat, Beauty, seeing him at discovert,[33] thought not to lose the vantage but struck him so deeply with an envenomed shaft as he wholly lost his liberty and became a slave to Love, which before contemned love (glad now to gaze on a poor shepherd, who before refused the offer of a rich princess). For the perfection of Fawnia had so fixed his fancy as he felt his mind greatly changed and his affections altered. Cursing Love that had

[33]*at discovert:* off his guard (literally, "in an uncovered condition").

wrought such a change and blaming the baseness of his mind that would make such a choice, but thinking these were but passionate toys that might be thrust out at pleasure to avoid the siren that enchanted him, he put spurs to his horse and bade this fair shepherd farewell.

Fawnia, who all this while had marked the princely gesture of Dorastus, seeing his face so well featured and each limb so perfectly framed, began greatly to praise his perfection, commending him so long till she found herself faulty and perceived that if she waded but a little further she might slip over her shoes.[34] She therefore, seeking to quench that fire which never was put out, went home and, feigning herself not well at ease, got her to bed. Where, casting a thousand thoughts in her head, she could take no rest. For if she waked she began to call to mind his beauty and, thinking to beguile such thoughts with sleep, she then dreamed of his perfection. Pestered thus with these unacquainted passions, she passed the night as she could in short slumbers.

Dorastus, who all this while rode with a flea in his ear,[35] could not by any means forget the sweet favor of Fawnia, but rested so bewitched with her wit and beauty as he could take no rest. He felt fancy to give the assault and his wounded mind ready to yield as vanquished. Yet he began with divers considerations to suppress this frantic affection, calling to mind that Fawnia was a shepherd—one not worthy to be looked at of a prince, much less to be loved of such a potentate—thinking what a discredit it were to himself and what a grief it would be to his father, blaming fortune and accusing his own folly, that should be so fond as but once to cast a glance at such a country slut.

As thus he was raging against himself, Love, fearing if she dallied long to lose her champion, stepped more nigh and gave him such a fresh wound as it pierced him at the heart, that he was fain to yield, maugre his face, and to forsake the company and get him to his chamber. Where, being solemnly set, he burst into these passionate terms:

"Ah, Dorastus, art thou alone? No, not alone while thou art tired with these unacquainted passions. Yield to fancy thou canst not, by

[34]*slip over her shoes:* fall in love (literally, "step into water over her shoe tops").

[35]*rode with a flea in his ear:* a slight variation of the proverb (Tilley, F354): "To go away with a flea in his ear"—that is, in great excitement.

thy father's counsel. But in a frenzy thou art, by just destinies. Thy father were content if thou couldst love, and thou therefore discontent because thou dost love. Oh, divine love, feared of men because honored of the gods, not to be suppressed by wisdom because not to be comprehended by reason. Without law and therefore above all law.

"How now, Dorastus, why dost thou blaze that with praises which thou hast cause to blaspheme with curses? Yet why should they curse love that are in love? Blush, Dorastus, at thy fortune, thy choice, thy love. Thy thoughts cannot be uttered without shame nor thy affections without discredit. Ah, Fawnia, sweet Fawnia, thy beauty, Fawnia. Shamest not thou, Dorastus, to name one unfit for thy birth, thy dignities, thy kingdoms? Die, Dorastus. Dorastus, die: better hadst thou perish with high desires than live in base thoughts. Yea, but beauty must be obeyed because it is beauty—yet framed of the gods to feed the eye, not to fetter the heart.

"Ah, but he that striveth against love shooteth with them of Scyrum, against the wind, and with the cockatrice pecketh against the steel. I will therefore obey because I must obey. Fawnia, yea, Fawnia shall be my fortune, in spite of fortune. The gods above disdain not to love women beneath: Phoebus liked Sibylla; Jupiter, Io. And why not I then Fawnia, one something inferior to these in birth, but far superior to them in beauty; born to be a shepherd, but worthy to be a goddess.

"Ah, Dorastus, wilt thou so forget thyself as to suffer affection to suppress wisdom and love to violate thine honor? How sour will thy choice be to thy father, sorrowful to thy subjects, to thy friends a grief, most gladsome to thy foes. Subdue, then, thy affections and cease to love her whom thou couldst not love, unless blinded with too much love. Tush, I talk to the wind and in seeking to prevent the causes, I further the effects. I will yet praise Fawnia, honor (yea, and love) Fawnia and at this day follow content, not counsel. Do, Dorastus; thou canst but repent."

And with that his page came into the chamber, whereupon he ceased from his complaints, hoping that time would wear out that which fortune had wrought.

As thus he was pained, so poor Fawnia was diversely perplexed. For the next morning, getting up very early, she went to her sheep, thinking with hard labors to pass away her new conceived amours. Beginning very busily to drive them to the field and then to shift the folds, at last, wearied with toil, she sat her down where (poor soul) she was more tried[36] with fond affections. For love began to assault her insomuch that, as she sat upon the side of a hill, she began to accuse her own folly in these terms:

"Unfortunate Fawnia, and therefore unfortunate because Fawnia, thy shepherd's hook showeth thy poor state, thy proud desires an aspiring mind: the one declareth thy want, the other thy pride. No bastard hawk must soar so high as the hobby,[37] no fowl gaze against the sun but the eagle. Actions wrought against nature reap despite, and thoughts above fortune, disdain.

"Fawnia, thou art a shepherd, daughter to poor Porrus. If thou rest content with this, thou art like to stand. If thou climb, thou art sure to fall. The herb anita,[38] growing higher than six inches, becometh a weed; Nylus,[39] flowing more than twelve cubits, procureth a dearth. Daring affections that pass measure are cut short by time or fortune. Suppress then, Fawnia, those thoughts which thou mayest shame to express. But, ah, Fawnia, love is a lord who will command by power and constrain by force.

"Dorastus, ah, Dorastus is the man I love. The worse is thy hap and the less cause hast thou to hope. Will eagles catch at flies, will cedars stoop to brambles, or mighty princes look at such homely trulls? No, no, think this: Dorastus' disdain is greater than thy desire. He is a prince respecting his honor, thou a beggar's brat forgetting thy calling. Cease, then, not only to say but to think to love Dorastus. And dissemble thy love, Fawnia, for better it were to die with grief than to live with shame. Yet in despite of love I will sigh, to see if I can sigh out love."

Fawnia, somewhat appeasing her griefs with these pithy persuasions, began, after her wonted manner, to walk about her sheep and to keep them from straying into the corn, suppressing her affection with the due consideration of her base estate and with the impossibilities of her love (thinking it were frenzy, not fancy, to covet that which the very destinies did deny her to obtain).

[36]*tried:* The 1607 edition has no textual authority, but it may have corrected an error (transposed letters) in the 1588–95 editions by emending "tried" to "tired."

[37]*bastard hawk ... hobby:* Fawnia evidently is thinking of the hobby as a pure-bred hawk, as opposed to just any ordinary mongrel kind (never dreaming that she herself is the former and not the latter).

[38]*anita:* anise, which includes both "anisum" and "anethum" (the latter spelled "anete" in Wyclif's Bible).

[39]*Nylus:* the Nile River.

But Dorastus was more impatient in his passions. For love so fiercely assailed him that neither company nor music could mitigate his martyrdom, but did rather far the more increase his malady. Shame would not let him crave counsel in this case, nor fear of his father's displeasure reveal it to any secret friend. But he was fain to make a secretary of himself and to participate his thoughts with his own troubled mind.

Lingering thus awhile in doubtful suspense, at last stealing secretly from the court without either men or page, he went to see if he could espy Fawnia walking abroad in the field. But, as one having a great deal more skill to retrieve the partridge with his spaniels than to hunt after such a strange prey, he sought but was little the better. Which cross luck drove him into a great choler, that he began both to accuse love and fortune. But as he was ready to retire, he saw Fawnia sitting all alone under the side of a hill, making a garland of such homely flowers as the fields did afford. This sight so revived his spirits that he drew nigh, with more judgment to take a view of her singular perfection which he found to be such as in that country attire she stained[40] all the courtly dames of Sicily.

While thus he stood gazing with piercing looks on her surpassing beauty, Fawnia cast her eye aside and spied Dorastus. Which[41] sudden sight made the poor girl to blush and to dye her crystal cheeks with a vermilion red, which gave her such a grace as she seemed far more beautiful. And with that she rose up, saluting the prince with such modest curtsies as he wondered how a country maid could afford such courtly behavior. Dorastus, repaying her curtsy with a smiling countenance, began to parley with her on this manner:

"Fair maid," quoth he, "either your want is great or a shepherd's life very sweet, that your delight is in such country labors. I cannot conceive what pleasure you should take unless you mean to imitate the nymphs, being yourself so like a nymph. To put me out of this doubt, show me what is to be commended in a shepherd's life and what pleasures you have to countervail these drudging labors."

Fawnia, with blushing face, made him this ready answer: "Sir, what richer state than content, or what sweeter life than quiet? We shepherds are not born to honor nor beholding unto beauty. The less care we have to fear fame or fortune. We count our attire brave

---

[40]*stained:* eclipsed, put into the shade.
[41]*Which:* In this case we may definitely accept the emendation of the 1607 edition; "with," the reading of the 1588–95 editions, makes no sense.

enough if warm enough, and our food dainty if to suffice nature. Our greatest enemy is the wolf, our only care in safekeeping our flock. Instead of courtly ditties, we spend the days with country songs. Our amorous conceits are homely thoughts, delighting as much to talk of Pan and his country pranks as ladies to tell of Venus and her wanton toys. Our toil is in shifting the folds and looking to the lambs' easy labors, oft singing and telling tales (homely pleasures). Our greatest wealth, not to covet; our honor, not to climb; our quiet, not to care. Envy looketh not so low as shepherds. Shepherds gaze not so high as ambition. We are rich in that we are poor with content, and proud only in this: that we have no cause to be proud."

This witty answer of Fawnia so inflamed Dorastus' fancy as he commended himself for making so good a choice (thinking: if her birth were answerable to her wit and beauty, that she were a fit mate for the most famous prince in the world). He therefore began to sift her more narrowly on this manner:

"Fawnia, I see thou art content with country labors because thou knowest not courtly pleasures. I commend thy wit and pity thy want. But wilt thou leave thy father's cottage and serve a courtly mistress?"

"Sir," quoth she, "beggars ought not to strive against fortune, nor to gaze after honor, lest either their fall be greater or they become blind. I am born to toil for the court, not in the court—my nature unfit for their nurture. Better live, then, in mean degree than in high disdain."

"Well said, Fawnia," quoth Dorastus, "I guess at thy thoughts; thou art in love with some country shepherd."

"No, sir," quoth she. "Shepherds cannot love that are so simple, and maids may not love that are so young."

"Nay, therefore," quoth Dorastus, "maids must love because they are young, for Cupid is a child and Venus, though old, is painted with fresh colors."

"I grant," quoth she, "age may be painted with new shadows, and youth may have imperfect affections. But what art concealeth in one, ignorance revealeth in the other."

Dorastus, seeing Fawnia held him so hard, thought it was vain so long to beat about the bush. Therefore he thought to have given her a fresh charge. But he was so prevented by certain of his men, who, missing their master, came posting to seek him, seeing that he was gone forth all alone. Yet before they drew so nigh that they might hear their talk, he used these speeches:

"Why, Fawnia, perhaps I love thee; and then thou must needs yield, for thou knowest I can command and constrain."

"Truth, sir," quoth she, "but not to love. For constrained love is force, not love. And know this, sir: mine honesty is such as I had rather die than be a concubine, even to a king. And my birth so base as I am unfit to be a wife to a poor farmer."

"Why, then," quoth he, "thou canst not love Dorastus?"

"Yes," said Fawnia, "when Dorastus becomes a shepherd."

And with that the presence of his men broke off their parley, so that he went with them to the palace and left Fawnia sitting still on the hillside. Who, seeing that the night drew on, shifted her folds and busied herself about other work, to drive away such fond fancies as began to trouble her brain. But all this could not prevail, for the beauty of Dorastus had made such a deep impression in her heart as it could not be worn out without cracking, so that she was forced to blame her own folly in this wise:

"Ah, Fawnia, why dost thou gaze against the sun or catch at the wind? Stars are to be looked at with the eye, not reached at with the hand. Thoughts are to be measured by fortunes, not by desires. Falls come not by sitting low, but by climbing too high. What, then, shall all fear to fall because some hap to fall? No. Luck cometh by lot, and fortune windeth those threads which the destinies spin. Thou art favored, Fawnia, of a prince; and yet thou art so fond to reject desired favors. Thou hast denial at thy tongue's end and desire at thy heart's bottom. A woman's fault—to spurn at that with her foot which she greedily catcheth at with her hand. Thou lovest Dorastus, Fawnia, and yet seemest to lower. Take heed; if he retire, thou wilt repent. For unless he love, thou canst but die. Die, then, Fawnia, for Dorastus doth but jest: the lion never preyeth on the mouse nor falcons stoop not to dead stales.[42] Sit down, then, in sorrow. Cease to love, and content thyself that Dorastus will vouchsafe to flatter Fawnia, though not to fancy Fawnia. Heigh-ho! Ah, fool, it were seemlier for thee to whistle as a shepherd than to sigh as a lover."

And with that she ceased from these perplexed passions, folding her sheep and hying home to her poor cottage.

But such was the incessant sorrow of Dorastus to think on the

___

[42]*dead stales:* The "stale" was a live bird, such as a pigeon, used to entice other birds into a snare or net. If a "stale" is dead, and not flying toward the net, she will not decoy a falcon. Perhaps the sense is that if Fawnia herself were a better catch, she would be able to lure Dorastus into an honorable marriage.

wit and beauty of Fawnia (and to see how fond he was, being a prince, and how froward she was, being a beggar) that he began to lose his wonted appetite, to look pale and wan—instead of mirth, to feed on melancholy; for courtly dances, to use cold dumps. Insomuch that not only his own men but his father and all the court began to marvel at his sudden change, thinking that some lingering sickness had brought him into this state. Wherefore he caused physicians to come. But Dorastus neither would let them minister nor so much as suffer them to see his urine, but remained still so oppressed with these passions as he feared in himself a further inconvenience. His honor wished him to cease from such folly, but love forced him to follow fancy. Yea, and in despite of honor, love won the conquest, so that his hot desires caused him to find new devices. For he presently made himself a shepherd's coat, that he might go unknown and with the less suspicion to prattle with Fawnia, and conveyed it secretly into a thick grove hard joining to the palace. Whither, finding fit time and opportunity, he went all alone. And putting off his princely apparel, got on those shepherd's robes and, taking a great hook in his hand (which he had also gotten), he went very anciently[43] to find out the mistress of his affection. But as he went by the way, seeing himself clad in such unseemly rags, he began to smile at his own folly and to reprove his fondness in these terms:

"Well said, Dorastus, thou keepest a right decorum—base desires and homely attires. Thy thoughts are fit for none but a shepherd, and thy apparel such as only become a shepherd. A strange change from a prince to a peasant. What is it? Thy wretched fortune or thy willful folly? Is it thy cursed destinies or thy crooked desires that appointeth thee this penance? Ah, Dorastus, thou canst but love, and unless thou love thou art like to perish for love. Yet, fond fool, choose flowers, not weeds; diamonds, not pebbles; ladies which may honor thee, not shepherds which may disgrace thee. Venus is painted in silks, not in rags; and Cupid treadeth on disdain when he reacheth at dignity. And yet, Dorastus, shame not at thy shepherd's weed. The heavenly gods have sometime earthly thoughts. Neptune became a ram, Jupiter a bull, Apollo a shepherd—they gods and yet in love, and thou a man, appointed to love."

Devising thus with himself, he drew nigh to the place where

---

[43]*anciently:* as of old (as young men have been doing for centuries). There is another possible sense—in the manner of an ancient bearer (standard bearer), the crook denoting the shepherd just as much as the flag or standard denotes a military man.

Fawnia was keeping her sheep. Who, casting her eye aside and seeing such a mannerly shepherd, perfectly limbed and coming with so good a pace, she began half to forget Dorastus and to favor this pretty shepherd whom she thought she might both love and obtain.

But as she was in these thoughts, she perceived then it was the young prince Dorastus. Wherefore she rose up and reverently saluted him. Dorastus, taking her by the hand, repaid her curtsy with a sweet kiss. And praying her to sit down by him, he began thus to lay the battery:

"If thou marvel, Fawnia, at my strange attire, thou wouldst more muse at my unaccustomed thoughts: the one disgraceth but my outward shape, the other disturbeth my inward senses. I love Fawnia, and therefore what love liketh I cannot mislike. Fawnia, thou hast promised to love, and I hope thou wilt perform no less. I have fulfilled thy request and now thou canst but grant my desire. Thou wert content to love Dorastus when he ceased to be a prince and to become[44] a shepherd. And see: I have made the change and therefore[45] not to miss of my choice."

"Truth," quoth Fawnia, "but all that wear cowls are not monks. Painted eagles are pictures, not eagles. Zeuxis's grapes were like grapes, yet shadows. Rich clothing make not princes, nor homely attire beggars. Shepherds are not called shepherds because they wear hooks and bags, but that they are born poor and live to keep sheep. So this attire hath not made Dorastus a shepherd, but to seem like a shepherd."

"Well, Fawnia," answered Dorastus, "were I a shepherd I could not but like thee, and being a prince I am forced to love thee. Take heed, Fawnia. Be not proud of beauty's painting, for it is a flower that fadeth in the blossom. Those which disdain in youth are despised in age. Beauty's shadows are tricked up with time's colors, which being set to dry in the sun are stained with the sun, scarce pleasing the sight ere they begin not to be worth the sight—not much unlike the herb ephemeron which flourisheth in the morning and is withered before the sun setting. If my desire were against law, thou mightest justly deny me by reason. But I love thee, Fawnia, not to misuse thee as a concubine, but to use thee as my wife. I can promise no more, and mean to perform no less."

[44]*to become:* The sense is "became" (the emendation of the 1609 edition); "ceased" applies to "prince," but not to "shepherd."

[45]*and therefore:* James Winny (*The Descent of Euphues* [Cambridge, 1957], p. 103) inserts "ought"—"and ought therefore."

Fawnia, hearing this solemn protestation of Dorastus, could no longer withstand the assault but yielded up the fort in these friendly terms:

"Ah, Dorastus, I shame to express that thou forcest me with thy sugared speech to confess: my base birth causeth the one, and thy high dignities the other. Beggars' thoughts ought not to reach so far as kings, and yet my desires reach as high as princes. I dare not say, Dorastus, I love thee because I am a shepherd. But the gods know I have honored Dorastus (pardon if I say amiss) yea, and loved Dorastus, with such dutiful affection as Fawnia can perform or Dorastus desire. I yield, not overcome with prayers but with love, resting Dorastus' handmaid, ready to obey his will if no prejudice at all to his honor nor to my credit."

Dorastus, hearing this friendly conclusion of Fawnia, embraced her in his arms, swearing that neither distance, time, nor adverse fortune should diminish his affection, but that in despite of the destinies he would remain loyal unto death.

Having thus plight[46] their troth each to other, seeing they could not have the full fruition of their love in Sicily (for that Egistus' consent would never be granted to so mean a match) Dorastus determined, as soon as time and opportunity would give them leave, to provide a great mass of money (and many rich and costly jewels for the easier carriage) and then to transport themselves and their treasure into Italy, where they should lead a contented life until such time as either he could be reconciled to his father or else, by succession, come to the kingdom.

This device was greatly praised of Fawnia, for she feared if the king his father should but hear of the contract that his fury would be such as no less than death would stand for payment. She therefore told him that delay bred danger, that many mishaps did fall out between the cup and the lip,[47] and that to avoid danger it were best with as much speed as might be to pass out of Sicily, lest fortune might prevent their pretense with some new despite.

Dorastus, whom love pricked forward with desire, promised to dispatch his affairs with as great haste as either time or opportunity would give him leave. And so, resting upon this point, after many embracings and sweet kisses, they departed.

Dorastus, having taken his leave of his best beloved Fawnia, went

[46]*plight:* The "-ed" ending for the past participle of "plight" was not yet current in 1588.

[47]*delay . . . lip:* two proverbs back to back (Tilley, D195 and T191).

to the grove where he had his rich apparel. And there, uncasing himself as secretly as might be, hiding up his shepherd's attire till occasion should serve again to use it, he went to the palace, showing by his merry countenance that either the state of his body was amended or the case of his mind greatly redressed.

Fawnia, poor soul, was no less joyful that, being a shepherd, fortune had favored her so as to reward her with the love of a prince, hoping in time to be advanced from the daughter of a poor farmer to be the wife of a rich king. So that she thought every hour a year, till by their departure they might prevent danger—not ceasing still to go every day to her sheep, not so much for the care of her flock as for the desire she had to see her love and lord, Dorastus. Who oftentimes, when opportunity would serve, repaired thither to feed his fancy with the sweet content of Fawnia's presence. And although he never went to visit her but in his shepherd's rags, yet his oft repair made him not only suspected but known to divers of their neighbors. Who, for the good will they bore to old Porrus, told him secretly of the matter, wishing him to keep his daughter at home, lest she went so oft to the field that she brought him home a young son. For they feared that Fawnia being so beautiful, the young prince would allure her to folly.

Porrus was stricken into a dump at these news, so that, thanking his neighbors for their good will, he hied him home to his wife, and, calling her aside, wringing his hands and shedding forth tears, he broke the matter to her in these terms:

"I am afraid, wife, that my daughter Fawnia hath made herself so fine that she will buy repentance too dear. I hear news which, if they be true, some will wish they had not proved true. It is told me by my neighbors that Dorastus, the king's son, begins to look at our daughter Fawnia. Which, if it be so, I will not give her a halfpenny for her honesty at the year's end. I tell thee, wife, nowadays beauty is a great stale to trap young men, and fair words and sweet promises are two great enemies to a maiden's honesty. And thou knowest where poor men entreat and cannot obtain, there princes may command and will obtain. Though kings' sons dance in nets, they may not be seen.[48] But poor men's faults are spied at a little hole. Well, it is a

48*dance in nets, they may not be seen:* a variation of the proverb (Tilley, N130): "You dance in a net and think nobody sees you." By changing the emphasis, Porrus is able to forge an additional meaning: kings' sons may be seen (however well they may think that they disguise themselves), but the people who see them have to ignore what they see because they are powerless to do anything about it.

hard case where kings' lusts are laws and that they should bind poor men to that which they themselves willfully break."

"Peace, husband," quoth his wife. "Take heed what you say. Speak no more than you should, lest you hear what you would not. Great streams are to be stopped by sleight, not by force; and princes to be persuaded by submission, not by rigor. Do what you can, but no more than you may, lest in saving Fawnia's maidenhead you lose your own head. Take heed, I say, it is ill jesting with edged tools, and bad sporting with kings. The wolf had his skin pulled over his ears for but looking into the lion's den."

"Tush, wife," quoth he. "Thou speakest like a fool. If the king should know that Dorastus had begotten our daughter with child (as I fear it will fall out little better) the king's fury would be such as no doubt we should both lose our goods and lives. Necessity, therefore, hath no law, and I will prevent this mischief with a new device that is come in my head, which shall neither offend the king nor displease Dorastus. I mean to take the chain and the jewels that I found with Fawnia and carry them to the king, letting him then to understand how she is none of my daughter but that I found her beaten up with the water, alone in a little boat, wrapped in a rich mantle wherein was enclosed this treasure. By this means I hope the king will take Fawnia into his service and we, whatsoever chanceth, shall be blameless."

This device pleased the goodwife very well, so that they determined, as soon as they might know the king at leisure, to make him privy to this case.

In the meantime Dorastus was not slack in his affairs, but applied his matters with such diligence that he provided all things fit for their journey. Treasure and jewels he had gotten great store, thinking there was no better friend than money in a strange country. Rich attire he had provided for Fawnia; and because he could not bring the matter to pass without the help and advice of someone, he made an old servant of his called Capnio (who had served him from his childhood) privy to his affairs. Who, seeing no persuasions could prevail to divert him from his settled determination, gave his consent and dealt so secretly in the cause that within short space he had gotten a ship ready for their passage.

The mariners, seeing a fit gale of wind for their purpose, wished Capnio to make no delays, lest if they pretermitted this good weather, they might stay long ere they had such a fair wind. Capnio, fearing that his negligence should hinder the journey, in the night time conveyed the trunks full of treasure into the ship, and by secret means let Fawnia understand that the next morning they meant to depart.

She, upon this news, slept very little that night, but got up very early and went to her sheep, looking every minute when she should see Dorastus, who tarried not long for fear delay might breed danger, but came as fast as he could gallop—and without any great circumstance took Fawnia up behind him and rode to the haven where the ship lay, which was not three quarters of a mile distant from that place.

He no sooner came there but the mariners were ready with their cockboat to set them aboard. Where, being couched together in a cabin, they passed away the time in recounting their old loves till their man Capnio should come.

Porrus, who had heard that this morning the king would go abroad to take the air, called in haste to his wife to bring him his holiday hose and his best jacket, that he might go like an honest, substantial man to tell his tale. His wife, a good, cleanly wench, brought him all things fit and sponged him up very handsomely, giving him the chains and jewels in a little box which Porrus, for the more safety, put in his bosom. Having thus all his trinkets in a readiness, taking his staff in his hand, he bade his wife kiss him for good luck and so he went towards the palace.

But as he was going, fortune (who meant to show him a little false play) prevented his purpose in this wise: he met by chance in his way Capnio, who, trudging as fast as he could with a little coffer under his arm to the ship and, spying Porrus (whom he knew to be Fawnia's father, going towards the palace) being a wily fellow, began to doubt the worst and therefore crossed him the way and asked him whither he was going so early this morning.

Porrus (who knew by his face that he was one of the court), meaning simply,[49] told him that the king's son Dorastus dealt hardly with him, for he had but one daughter who was a little beautiful, and that his neighbors told him the young prince had allured her to folly; he went, therefore, now to complain to the king how greatly he was abused.

Capnio (who straightway smelt the whole matter) began to soothe

---

[49]*meaning simply:* "simply" probably is to be understood two ways: Porrus is honest and without guile himself, but his ignorance of the world makes him easily fooled by someone more sophisticated.

him in his talk and said that Dorastus dealt not like a prince to spoil any poor man's daughter in that sort; he therefore would do the best for him he could because he knew he was an honest man.

"But," quoth Capnio, "you lose your labor in going to the palace, for the king means this day to take the air of the sea and to go aboard of a ship that lies in the haven. I am going before, you see, to provide all things in a readiness. And if you will follow my counsel, turn back with me to the haven, where I will set you in such a fit place as you may speak to the king at your pleasure."

Porrus, giving credit to Capnio's smooth tale, gave him a thousand thanks for his friendly advice and went with him to the haven, making all the way his complaints of Dorastus, yet concealing secretly the chain and the jewels. As soon as they were come to the seaside, the mariners, seeing Capnio, came aland with their cockboat. Who, still dissembling the matter, demanded of Porrus if he would go see the ship. Who, unwillingly, and fearing the worst (because he was not well acquainted with Capnio) made his excuse that he could not brook the sea, therefore would not trouble him.

Capnio, seeing that by fair means he could not get him aboard, commanded the mariners that by violence they should carry him into the ship. Who, like sturdy knaves, hoisted the poor shepherd on their backs and, bearing him to the boat, launched from the land.

Porrus, seeing himself so cunningly betrayed, durst not cry out, for he saw it would not prevail, but began to entreat Capnio and the mariners to be good to him and to pity his estate; he was but a poor man that lived by his labor. They, laughing to see the shepherd so afraid, made as much haste as they could and set him aboard. Porrus was no sooner in the ship but he saw Dorastus walking with Fawnia. Yet he scarce knew her, for she had attired herself in rich apparel which so increased her beauty that she resembled rather an angel than a mortal creature.

Dorastus and Fawnia were half astonished to see the old shepherd, marveling greatly what wind had brought him thither, till Capnio told them all the whole discourse—how Porrus was going to make his complaint to the king, if by policy he had not prevented him; and therefore now, since he was aboard for the avoiding of further danger, it were best to carry him into Italy.

Dorastus praised greatly his man's device and allowed of his counsel. But Fawnia (who still feared Porrus, as her father) began to blush for shame, that by her means he should either incur danger or displeasure.

The old shepherd, hearing this hard sentence—that he should on such a sudden be carried from his wife, his country, and kinfolk into a foreign land amongst strangers—began with bitter tears to make his complaint, and on his knees to entreat Dorastus that pardoning his unadvised folly, he would give him leave to go home, swearing that he would keep all things as secret as they could wish. But these protestations could not prevail, although Fawnia entreated Dorastus very earnestly. But the mariners, hoisting their main sails, weighed anchors and haled[50] into the deep, where we leave them to the favor of the wind and seas, and return to Egistus.

Who, having appointed this day to hunt in one of his forests, called for his son Dorastus to go sport himself because he saw that of late he began to lower. But his men made answer that he was gone abroad, none knew whither—except he were gone to the grove to walk all alone, as his custom was to do every day. The king, willing to waken him out of his dumps, sent one of his men to go seek him. But in vain, for at last he returned, but find him he could not. So that the king went himself to go see the sport. Where, passing away the day, returning at night from hunting, he asked for his son, but he could not be heard of. Which drove the king into a great choler. Whereupon most of his noblemen and other courtiers posted abroad to seek him, but they could not hear of him through all Sicily. Only they missed Capnio, his man, which again made the king suspect that he was not gone far.

Two or three days being passed and no news heard of Dorastus, Egistus began to fear that he was devoured with some wild beasts, and upon that made out a great troop of men to go seek him. Who coasted through all the country and searched in every dangerous and secret place until at last they met with a fisherman that was sitting in a little covert hard by the seaside, mending his nets, when Dorastus and Fawnia took shipping. Who, being examined if he either knew or heard where the king's son was, without any secrecy at all revealed the whole matter—how he was sailed two days past and had in his company his man Capnio, Porrus, and his fair daughter Fawnia. This heavy news was presently carried to the king, who, half dead for sorrow, commanded Porrus' wife to be sent for. She, being come to the palace, after due examination confessed that her neighbors had oft told her that the king's son was too familiar with Fawnia, her daughter; whereupon her husband, fearing the worst, about two days

[50]*haled:* set sail.

past (hearing the king should go an hunting) rose early in the morning and went to make his complaint; but since she neither heard of him nor saw him.

Egistus, perceiving the woman's unfeigned simplicity, let her depart without incurring further displeasure, concealing such secret grief for his son's reckless folly (that he had so forgotten his honor and parentage, by so base a choice to dishonor his father and discredit himself) that with very care and thought he fell into a quartan fever which was so unfit for his aged years and complexion that he became so weak as the physicians would grant him no life.

But his son Dorastus little regarded either father, country, or kingdom in respect of his Lady Fawnia, for fortune smiling on this young novice, lent him so lucky a gale of wind for the space of a day and a night that the mariners lay and slept upon the hatches. But on the next morning, about the break of the day, the air began to overcast, the winds to rise, the seas to swell—yea, presently there arose such a fearful tempest as the ship was in danger to be swallowed up with every sea.[51] The main mast, with the violence of the wind, was thrown overboard, the sails were torn, the tacklings went in sunder,[52] the storm raging still so furiously that poor Fawnia was almost dead for fear, but that she was greatly comforted with the presence of Dorastus. The tempest continued three days, all which time the mariners every minute looked for death, and the air was so darkened with clouds that the master could not tell by his compass in what coast they were. But upon the fourth day, about ten of the clock, the wind began to cease, the sea to wax calm, and the sky to be clear. And the mariners descried the coast of Bohemia, shooting off their ordnance for joy that they had escaped such a fearful tempest.

Dorastus, hearing that they were arrived at some harbor, sweetly kissed Fawnia and bade her be of good cheer. When they told him that the port belonged unto the chief city of Bohemia, where Pandosto kept his court, Dorastus began to be sad, knowing that his father hated no man so much as Pandosto and that the king himself had sought secretly to betray Egistus. This considered, he was half afraid

[51]*sea:* not just "wave" (the emendation of the 1614 edition), but a heavy swell, coming periodically.

[52]*tacklings went in sunder:* The 1592 edition, in omitting the final "s" in "tacklings," probably was a little more idiomatic. A sensible emendation occurred in the 1614 edition— "rent" for "went." But Greene may have intended "went" as the past tense of "go" or the past tense of "wend" (which at that time could mean "twist").

to go on land, but that Capnio counseled him to change his name and his country until such time as they could get some other bark to transport them into Italy. Dorastus, liking this device, made his case privy to the mariners, rewarding them bountifully for their pains and charging them to say that he was a gentleman of Trapalonia[53] called Meleagrus.

The shipmen, willing to show what friendship they could to Dorastus, promised to be as secret as they could or he might wish, and upon this they landed in a little village a mile distant from the city. Where, after they had rested a day, thinking to make provision for their marriage, the fame of Fawnia's beauty was spread throughout all the city, so that it came to the ears of Pandosto.

Who then being about the age of fifty had, notwithstanding, young and fresh affections, so that he desired greatly to see Fawnia. And to bring this matter the better to pass, hearing they had but one man and how they rested at a very homely house, he caused them to be apprehended as spies and sent a dozen of his guard to take them. Who, being come to their lodging, told them the king's message. Dorastus, no whit dismayed, accompanied with Fawnia and Capnio, went to the court (for they left Porrus to keep the stuff)[54] who, being admitted to the king's presence, Dorastus and Fawnia with humble obeisance saluted his majesty.

Pandosto, amazed at the singular perfection of Fawnia, stood half astonished, viewing her beauty. So that he had almost forgot himself what he had to do. At last, with stern countenance, he demanded their names and of what country they were and what caused them to land in Bohemia.

"Sir," quoth Dorastus, "know that my name Meleagrus is—a knight born and brought up in Trapalonia; and this gentlewoman, whom I mean to take to my wife, is an Italian born in Padua, from whence I have now brought her. The cause I have so small a train with me is for that her friends, unwilling to consent, I intended secretly to convey her into Trapalonia. Whither, as I was sailing, by distress of weather I was driven into these coasts. Thus have you heard my name, my country, and the cause of my voyage."

Pandosto, starting from his seat as one in choler, made this rough reply:

---

[53]*Trapalonia:* evidently a fictitious place name; if Pandosto so regards it, that may be one reason why Dorastus arouses his suspicions so quickly.

[54]*the stuff:* the money and jewels that Dorastus had brought along from Sicily.

"Meleagrus, I fear this smooth tale hath but small truth and that thou coverest a foul skin with fair paintings. No doubt this lady, by her grace and beauty, is of her degree more meet for a mighty prince than for a simple knight. And thou, like a perjured traitor, hast bereft her of her parents, to their present grief and her ensuing sorrow. Till, therefore, I hear more of her parentage and of thy calling I will stay you both here in Bohemia."

Dorastus, in whom rested nothing but kingly valor, was not able to suffer the reproaches of Pandosto but that he made him this answer:

"It is not meet for a king, without due proof, to appeach any man of ill behavior, nor upon suspicion to infer belief. Strangers ought to be entertained with courtesy, not to be entreated with cruelty, lest being forced by want to put up injuries the gods revenge their cause with rigor."

Pandosto, hearing Dorastus utter these words, commanded that he should straight be committed to prison until such time as they heard further of his pleasure. But as for Fawnia, he charged that she should be entertained in the court with such courtesy as belonged to a stranger and her calling. The rest of the shipmen he put into the dungeon.

Having thus hardly handled the supposed Trapalonians, Pandosto, contrary to his aged years, began to be somewhat tickled with the beauty of Fawnia. Insomuch that he could take no rest, but cast in his old head a thousand new devices. At last he fell into these thoughts:

"How art thou pestered, Pandosto, with fresh affections and unfit fancies, wishing to possess with an unwilling mind and a hot desire troubled with a cold disdain? Shall thy mind yield in age to that thou hast resisted in youth? Peace, Pandosto, blab not out that which thou mayest be ashamed to reveal to thyself. Ah, Fawnia is beautiful; and it is not for thine honor, fond fool, to name her that is thy captive and another man's concubine. Alas, I reach at that with my hand which my heart would fain refuse—playing like the bird ibis in Egypt, which hateth serpents yet feedeth on their eggs.

"Tush, hot desires turn oftentimes to cold disdain. Love is brittle where appetite, not reason, bears the sway. Kings' thoughts ought not to climb so high as the heavens, but to look no lower than honor. Better it is to peck at the stars with the young eagles than to prey on dead carcasses with the vulture. 'Tis more honorable for Pandosto to die by concealing love than to enjoy such unfit love. Doth Pandosto then love? Yea, whom? A maid unknown, yea, and perhaps immodest, straggled out of her own country. Beautiful but not therefore chaste.

Comely in body but perhaps crooked in mind. Cease, then, Pandosto, to look at Fawnia, much less to love her. Be not overtaken with a woman's beauty, whose eyes are framed by art to enamor, whose heart is framed by nature to enchant, whose false tears know their true times, and whose sweet words pierce deeper than sharp swords."

Here Pandosto ceased from his talk, but not from his love. For although he sought by reason and wisdom to suppress this frantic affection, yet he could take no rest, the beauty of Fawnia had made such a deep impression in his heart. But on a day walking abroad into a park which was hard adjoining to his house, he sent by one of his servants for Fawnia, unto whom he uttered these words:

"Fawnia, I commend thy beauty and wit and now pity thy distress and want. But if thou wilt forsake Sir Meleagrus (whose poverty, though a knight, is not able to maintain an estate answerable to thy beauty) and yield thy consent to Pandosto, I will both increase thee with dignities and riches."

"No, sir," answered Fawnia, "Meleagrus is a knight that hath won me by love, and none but he shall wear me. His sinister mischance shall not diminish my affection, but rather increase my good will. Think not, though your grace hath imprisoned him without cause, that fear shall make me yield my consent. I had rather be Meleagrus' wife and a beggar than live in plenty and be Pandosto's concubine."

Pandosto, hearing the assured answer of Fawnia, would, notwithstanding, prosecute his suit to the uttermost, seeking with fair words and great promises to scale the fort of her chastity, swearing that if she would grant to his desire Meleagrus should not only be set at liberty but honored in his court amongst his nobles. But these alluring baits could not entice her mind from the love of her new-betrothed mate, Meleagrus. Which Pandosto seeing, he left her alone for that time to consider more of the demand.

Fawnia, being alone by herself, began to enter into these solitary meditations:

"Ah, unfortunate Fawnia, thou seest to desire above fortune is to strive against the gods and fortune. Who gazeth at the sun weakeneth his sight. They which stare at the sky fall oft into deep pits. Hadst thou rested content to have been a shepherd, thou needst not to have feared mischance. Better had it been for thee, by sitting low, to have had quiet than, by climbing high, to have fallen into misery. But, alas, I fear not mine own danger but Dorastus' displeasure. Ah, sweet Dorastus, thou art a prince but now a prisoner by too much love procuring thine own loss. Hadst thou not loved Fawnia, thou hadst been fortunate. Shall I then be false to him that hath forsaken kingdoms for my cause? No. Would my death might deliver him, so mine honor might be preserved."

With that, fetching a deep sigh, she ceased from her complaints and went again to the palace, enjoying a liberty without content and proffered pleasure with small joy.

But poor Dorastus lay all this while in close prison, being pinched with a hard restraint and pained with the burden of cold and heavy irons; sorrowing sometimes that his fond affection had procured him this mishap, that by the disobedience of his parents he had wrought his own despite; another while cursing the gods and fortune, that they should cross him with such sinister chance; uttering at last his passions in these words:

"Ah, unfortunate wretch, born to mishap, now thy folly hath his desert. Art thou not worthy for thy base mind to have bad fortune? Could the destinies favor thee, which hast forgot thine honor and dignities? Will not the gods plague him with despite that paineth his father with disobedience? Oh, gods, if any favor or justice be left, plague me, but favor poor Fawnia and shroud her from the tyrannies of wretched Pandosto. But let my death free her from mishap and then, welcome, death."

Dorastus, pained with these heavy passions, sorrowed and sighed, but in vain, for which he used the more patience.

But again to Pandosto, who, broiling at the heat of unlawful lust, could take no rest but still felt his mind disquieted with his new love. So that his nobles and subjects marveled greatly at this sudden alteration, not being able to conjecture the cause of this his continued care. Pandosto, thinking every hour a year till he had talked once again with Fawnia, sent for her secretly into his chamber, whither, though Fawnia unwillingly coming, Pandosto entertained her very courteously, using these familiar speeches, which Fawnia answered as shortly in this wise:

Pandosto

Fawnia, are you become less willful and more wise, to prefer the love of a king before the liking of a poor knight? I think ere this you think it is better to be favored of a king than of a subject.

Fawnia

Pandosto, the body is subject to victories, but the mind not to be subdued by conquest. Honesty[55] is to be preferred before honor, and

---

[55]*Honesty:* chastity (which, as a matter of fact, is the emendation of the sixth edition of 1614, when "honesty" in the sense of "chastity" probably was becoming less used).

a dram of faith weigheth down a ton of gold. I have promised Meleagrus to love and will perform no less.

Pandosto

Fawnia, I know thou art not so unwise in thy choice as to refuse the
offer of a king, nor so ungrateful as to despise a good turn. Thou art
now in that place where I may command, and yet thou seest I entreat.
My power is such as I may compel by force, and yet I sue by prayers.
Yield, Fawnia, thy love to him which burneth in thy love. Meleagrus
shall be set free, thy countrymen discharged, and thou both loved and
honored.

Fawnia

I see, Pandosto, where lust ruleth it is a miserable thing to be a
virgin. But know this, that I will always prefer fame[56] before life and
rather choose death than dishonor.

Pandosto, seeing that there was in Fawnia a determinate courage
to love Meleagrus, and a resolution without fear to hate him, flung
away from her in a rage, swearing if in short time she would not be
won with reason, he would forget all courtesy and compel her to
grant by rigor. But these threatening words no whit dismayed Fawnia,
but that she still both despited and despised Pandosto.

While thus these two lovers strove—the one to win love, the other
to live in hate—Egistus heard certain news by merchants of Bohemia
that his son Dorastus was imprisoned by Pandosto, which made him
fear greatly that his son should be but hardly entreated. Yet considering that Bellaria and he was cleared by the oracle of Apollo, from
that crime wherewith Pandosto had unjustly charged them, he thought
best to send with all speed to Pandosto, that he should set free his
son Dorastus and put to death Fawnia and her father Porrus. Finding
this by the advice of counsel the speediest remedy to release his son,
he caused presently two of his ships to be rigged and thoroughly
furnished with provision of men and victuals and sent divers of his
nobles ambassadors into Bohemia. Who, willing to obey their king and
receive their young prince, made no delays for fear of danger, but,
with as much speed as might be, sailed towards Bohemia.

The wind and seas favored them greatly, which made them hope
of some good hap, for within three days they were landed. Which
Pandosto no sooner heard of their arrival, but he in person went to
meet them, entreating them with such sumptuous and familiar cour-

[56]*fame:* reputation, good name.

tesy that they might well perceive how sorry he was for the former injuries he had offered to their king, and how willing (if it might be) to make amends.

As Pandosto made report to them how one Meleagrus, a knight of Trapalonia, was lately arrived with a lady called Fawnia in his land, coming very suspiciously, accompanied only with one servant and an old shepherd, the ambassadors perceived by the half what the whole tale meant and began to conjecture that it was Dorastus, who, for fear to be known, had changed his name. But dissembling the matter, they shortly arrived at the court, where, after they had been very solemnly and sumptuously feasted, the noblemen of Sicily being gathered together, they made report of their embassage: where they certified Pandosto that Meleagrus was son and heir to the King Egistus, and that his name was Dorastus; how, contrary to the king's mind, he had privily conveyed away that Fawnia, intending to marry her, being but daughter to that poor shepherd Porrus; whereupon the king's request was that Capnio, Fawnia, and Porrus might be murdered and put to death, and that his son Dorastus might be sent home in safety.

Pandosto, having attentively and with great marvel heard their embassage, willing to reconcile himself to Egistus and to show him how greatly he esteemed his labor—although love and fancy forbade him to hurt Fawnia—yet, in despite of love, he determined to execute Egistus' will without mercy. And therefore he presently sent for Dorastus out of prison; who, marveling at this unlooked-for courtesy, found at his coming to the king's presence that which he least doubted of[57]—his father's ambassadors. Who no sooner saw him but, with great reverence, they honored him. And Pandosto, embracing Dorastus, set him by him very lovingly in a chair of state. Dorastus, ashamed that his folly was bewrayed, sat a long time as one in a muse till Pandosto told him the sum of his father's embassage. Which he had no sooner heard but he was touched at the quick for the cruel sentence that was pronounced against Fawnia. But neither could his sorrow nor persuasions prevail, for Pandosto commanded that Fawnia, Porrus, and Capnio should be brought to his presence. Who were no sooner come but Pandosto, having his former love turned to a disdainful hate, began to rage against Fawnia in these terms:

"Thou disdainful vassal, thou currish kite, assigned by the destinies to base fortune, and yet with an aspiring mind gazing after honor,

[57]*doubted of:* expected.

how durst thou presume, being a beggar, to match with a prince? By thy alluring looks to enchant the son of a king to leave his own country to fulfill thy disordinate lusts? Oh, despiteful mind, a proud heart in a beggar is not unlike to a great fire in a small cottage, which warmeth not the house but burneth it. Assure thyself, thou shalt die.

"And thou, old doting fool, whose folly hath been such as to suffer thy daughter to reach above thy fortune, look for no other meed but the like punishment.

"But, Capnio, thou which hast betrayed the king and hast consented to the unlawful lust of thy lord and master, I know not how justly I may plague thee. Death is too easy a punishment for thy falsehood; and to live, if not in extreme misery, were not to show thee equity. I therefore award that thou shall have thine eyes put out and continually, while thou diest, grind in a mill like a brute beast."

The fear of death brought a sorrowful silence upon Fawnia and Capnio. But Porrus, seeing no hope of life, burst forth into these speeches:

"Pandosto, and ye noble ambassadors of Sicily, seeing without cause I am condemned to die, I am yet glad I have opportunity to disburden my conscience before my death. I will tell you as much as I know, and yet no more than is true. Whereas I am accused that I have been a supporter of Fawnia's pride and she disdained as a vile beggar, so it is that I am neither father unto her nor she daughter unto me. For so it happened that I, being a poor shepherd in Sicily, living by keeping other men's flocks, one of my sheep straying down to the seaside as I went to seek her, I saw a little boat driven upon the shore. Wherein I found a babe of six days old, wrapped in a mantle of scarlet, having about the neck this chain. I, pitying the child and desirous of the treasure, carried it home to my wife, who with great care nursed it up and set it to keep sheep. Here is the chain and the jewels, and this Fawnia is the child whom I found in the boat. What she is, or of what parentage, I know not. But this I am assured: that she is none of mine."

Pandosto would scarce suffer him to tell out his tale but that he inquired the time of the year, the manner of the boat, and other circumstances. Which, when he found agreeing to his count, he suddenly leaped from his seat and kissed Fawnia, wetting her tender cheeks with his tears and crying, "My daughter, Fawnia, ah, sweet Fawnia! I am thy father, Fawnia!"

This sudden passion of the king drove them all into a maze, especially Fawnia and Dorastus. But when the king had breathed himself awhile in this new joy, he rehearsed before the ambassadors the whole matter—how he had entreated his wife Bellaria for jealousy, and that this was the child whom he sent to float in the seas.

Fawnia was not more joyful that she had found such a father than Dorastus was glad he should get such a wife. The ambassadors rejoiced that their young prince had made such a choice; that those kingdoms which, through enmity, had long time been dissevered, should now, through perpetual amity, be united and reconciled. The citizens and subjects of Bohemia, hearing that the king had found again his daughter which was supposed dead, joyful that there was an heir apparent to his kingdom, made bonfires and shows throughout the city. The courtiers and knights appointed jousts and tourneys to signify their willing minds in gratifying the king's hap.

Eighteen days being passed in these princely sports, Pandosto, willing to recompense old Porrus, of a shepherd made him a knight. Which done, providing a sufficient navy to receive him and his retinue, accompanied with Dorastus, Fawnia, and the Sicilian ambassadors, he sailed towards Sicily, where he was most princely entertained by Egistus. Who, hearing this comical event, rejoiced greatly at his son's good hap and, without delay (to the perpetual joy of the two young lovers), celebrated the marriage.

Which was no sooner ended but Pandosto, calling to mind how first he betrayed his friend Egistus; how his jealousy was the cause of Bellaria's death; that, contrary to the law of nature, he had lusted after his own daughter—moved with these desperate thoughts, he fell in a melancholy fit and, to close up the comedy with a tragical stratagem, he slew himself. Whose death, being many days bewailed of Fawnia, Dorastus, and his dear friend Egistus, Dorastus, taking his leave of his father, went with his wife and the dead corpse into Bohemia. Where, after they were[58] sumptuously entombed, Dorastus ended his days in contented quiet.

Finis

---

[58]*they were:* The 1609 edition emends to "it was"; but Greene may have thought of "corpse" as involving a plural sense (like "remains").

ॐ Rosalind

*Euphues' Golden Legacy Found After
His Death in His Cell at Silexedra*
(1590)

THOMAS LODGE

In the last paragraph of *Rosalind* (1590) Thomas Lodge addresses the reader directly: "If you gather any fruits by this legacy, speak well of Euphues for writing it and me for fetching it." We should take this statement as something more than an attempt to bear out the subtitle, *"Euphues' Golden Legacy Found After His Death in His Cell at Silexedra."*[1] It is an acknowledgment of Lodge's debt to Lyly. Indeed, there are some rather striking similarities, among which we may note the use of alliteration and assonance, the tendency to build isocolons and antitheses, the copious use of proverbs, the formal diction spiced with an occasional slang or colloquial expression. *Rosalind* is like *Euphues* also in that the main characters are all of high rank. Even much of the imagery, and particularly the frequent references to blemishes, is similar.

Yet Lodge's style has a different tone, which conveys a warmth and sympathy toward lovers. Unlike Lyly, Lodge is not primarily analytical. Style is not an end; it is a vehicle to carry narrative romance and a convincing medium in which noble heroes and heroines speak to each other in elevated language. Lodge creates an appropriate elevation, neither too high nor too low. Although a sentence here and there exactly in Lyly's manner is not difficult to find, usually Lodge chooses to make Lyly's clauses less self-consciously witty and

[1]*Silexedra:* a place mentioned in the last paragraph of Lyly's *Euphues and His England* (1580): "Gentlemen, Euphues is musing in the bottom of the mountain Silixsedra; Philautus married in the isle of England. . . ."

more evenly flowing in rhythm, as in Saladyne's declaration of love
to Aliena:

"Fair mistress, if I be blunt in discovering my affections and use
little eloquence in leveling out my loves, I appeal for pardon to
your own principles that say shepherds use few ceremonies, for
that they acquaint themselves with few subtleties. To frame myself,
therefore, to your country fashion with much faith and little
flattery, know, beautiful shepherdess, that whilst I lived in the
court I knew not love's cumber, but I held affection as a toy, not
as a malady, using fancy as the Hiperboreido do their flowers
which they wear in their bosom all day and cast them in the fire
for fuel at night. I liked all because I loved none, and who was
most fair, on her I fed mine eye, but as charily as the bee that as
soon as she hath sucked honey from the rose flies straight to the
next marigold. Living thus at mine own list I wondered at such
as were in love, and when I read their passions I took them only
for poems that flowed from the quickness of the wit, not the
sorrows of the heart. But now, fair nymph, since I became a
forester, love hath taught me such a lesson that I must confess
his deity and dignity, and say as there is nothing so precious as
beauty so there is nothing more piercing than fancy. For since first
I arrived in this place and mine eye took a curious survey of your
excellence, I have been so fettered with your beauty and virtue as,
sweet Aliena, Saladyne without further circumstance loves Aliena"
(pp. 370–71).

Ordinarily we would not think of Saladyne's speech, or Lodge's style,
as "blunt" and using "little eloquence." Saladyne of course is being
modest regarding his eloquence; but to some extent we are to take
what he says literally: his speech, when compared to Euphues' speech
(and Lyly's style), is much less elaborately worked out. The balancing
of clauses, when it exists at all, is less precise; and the amount of
alliteration, internal rhyme, and assonance is cut down severely. We
are to note that "dignity" and "beauty" are important values in the
forest, and therefore Lodge's rhythm and sound effects are not *mere*
eloquence; they are to communicate dignity and beauty. For our
taste the flow is more than a little too smooth; we keep expecting to
find clues that the narrator is exaggerating, that the sweetness is
ironic. (Possibly Shakespeare, when he came to study *Rosalind* closely
for use in *As You Like It* toward the end of the century, had the same
reaction, for he introduces a great deal of mockery and laughter.)
But the sweetness is not uncritical and sentimental; it fits Lodge's
considered idea of the pastoral, which for him requires a middle
style, flexible and yet dignified Lodge's style avoids the "subtleties"

that Saladyne dislikes in the courtly lover—avoids the frills of a superficial, if not immoral, life in which affection becomes a mere toy—and yet it is not so plain either as to allow the high ranking pastoral lovers to appear in any sense ordinary.

There are three pairs of lovers—Rosader–Rosalind, Saladyne–Alinda, and Montanus–Phoebe. Since the last pair is of low birth, Phoebe is right in one sense when she finds Ganymede (Rosalind in disguise) a worthier object than Montanus; but she is also right in another sense when she allows herself to be persuaded to love the shepherd Montanus, a member of her own class. Love is not a social leveler in *Rosalind*. Although it is a strong and worthy emotion in all hearts, its quality varies in proportion to the nobility of the individual; and each individual should love his own kind.

Just as Lodge molds his own style after careful study of Lyly's euphuism, he builds, with similar independence of mind, a romance form out of various medieval and Renaissance narrative materials. Probably his only direct source was "Gamelyn" (*c.* 1350), a 902-line poetic romance, in which he appears to have found a number of plot details: a knight has three sons, the youngest of whom is Gamelyn, the hero; a franklin has two sons, both of whom are killed by a champion wrestler; Gamelyn defeats the wrestler; Gamelyn and old Adam the spencer (steward) escape from the clutches of Gamelyn's oldest brother, John, and set out for the "wild wood."[2] Lodge changes all the names—Gamelyn to Rosader, John to Saladyne, and Adam the spencer to Adam Spencer. But that is only the beginning. He adds the rightful king and the usurping king, with their daughters Rosalind and Alinda. Above all, he introduces the three love stories and invests the two noble love attachments with what we now call "romantic love." The wild wood becomes an idyllic pastoral setting named Arden.[3]

[2]See Donald B. Sands, ed., *Middle English Verse Romances* (New York, 1966), pp. 154–181. Sands places "Gamelyn" in the Matter of England, along with "King Horn," "Havelok the Dane," and "Athelston." "Gamelyn" had not been published by 1590, but it was available to Lodge in a number of manuscript copies. One interesting fact is that in all the manuscripts except one Gamelyn's father is "Sir John of Boundis," but in the one manuscript he is "Sir John of Burdeuxs." See the note for line 3 in Sands, p. 157.

[3]W. W. Greg probably went too far when he said that the "entire pastoral element, as well as the courtly scenes of the earlier portion of the novel, are Lodge's own invention" (*Pastoral Poetry and Pastoral Drama* [London, 1906], p. 146.) Edwin Greenlaw suggested that Sidney's *Arcadia* was a source ("Shakespeare's Pastorals," *SP*, XIII [1916], 13). But even if Greenlaw's evidence is correct in every detail, Lodge's debt to Sidney was not extensive. About all we can say is that Lodge probably read widely

Lodge takes the romantic love and the idyllic setting seriously, but not too seriously; the style and narrative structure contribute a leisurely charm, a lightness of touch, with here and there a stroke of humor, mostly of a fairly subtle nature. The description of Corydon's "holiday suit" is a good example of the humor. Corydon is the old "clown," the "poor peasant" who is Montanus' wise friend and fellow shepherd. After seeing that Aliena and Ganymede are well settled in Arden, Corydon remains in touch with them on almost equal terms. When Aliena accepts Saladyne, Cordyon is invited to the wedding, to which he appears

> in his holiday suit, marvelous seemly in a russet jacket welted with the same and faced with red worsted, having a pair of blue camlet sleeves bound at the wrists with four yellow laces, closed afore very richly with a dozen of pewter buttons. His hose was of gray kersey, with a large slop, barred overthwart the pocket holes with three fair guards stitched of either side with red thread; his stock was of the own, sewed close to his breech, and for to beautify his hose he had trussed himself round with a dozen of new threaden points of medley color; his bonnet was green whereon stood a copper brooch with the picture of St. Denis; and, to want nothing that might make him amorous in his old days, he had a fair shirt band of fine lockram, whipped over with Coventry blue of no small cost. Thus attired, Corydon bestirred himself as chief stickler in these actions and had strowed all the house with flowers, that it seemed rather some of Flora's choice bowers than any country cottage (pp. 383–84).

As Hallett Smith has observed, the humor springs from the incongruity of various items in Corydon's costume. The jacket is of russet but the sleeves are of camlet, an expensive material made partly of silk; the camlet and the number of buttons seem to indicate the attire of a nobleman, while the "three fair guards" probably suggest the dress of a servant.[4] To say the least, Corydon has decked himself out

---

and borrowed eclectically; the Arden he creates owes little to any one of his predecessors. See, however, footnote 82 in *Master F. J.*; Lodge may have taken a hint from Gascoigne or Ariosto.

[4]See Hallett Smith, *Elizabethan Poetry* (Cambridge, Mass., 1952), p. 17n., and Roy Lamson and Hallett Smith, eds., *The Golden Hind* (New York, 1942), pp. 665–666. The first chapter of *Elizabethan Poetry* is an analysis of the pastoral, including the prose as well as the poetry, in the Elizabethan period. One of several comments relevant to Lodge's *Rosalind* is the following: "The general tendency of English pastoral literature was to subdue the sexual element and make the love scenes romantic and innocent" (p. 16).

wondrously; and we are to laugh at his combinations of materials and colors that would not be acceptable at court. On the other hand, we are to admire his aplomb, his sense of freedom to dress as he wishes. Arden is an unusually free and beautiful place; flamboyant and unorthodox attire is appropriate there. Anyway, Corydon is not flouting court fashion; he is blissfully ignorant of it.

Much of the humor in *Rosalind* is confined to the love of Montanus for Phoebe. Again, a kind of incongruity is involved: although Montanus and Phoebe are peasants, it is they who practice courtly love and not the two noble pairs of lovers. Phoebe is the disdainful lady *par excellence,* and Montanus is the despairing lover. Yet their love is not held up to scorn for the reason that it is merely one extreme of true love; all that is wrong with it is Phoebe's inability to realize, until she is taught a lesson, that we must all seize the day. The ideal lady should be like Rosalind, chaste but at the same time emancipated from medieval mores and willing to meet her lover half way in courtship.

The narrator of *Rosalind* has the respect for the emotions so necessary in the writing of romance. "Fancy" is not only the state of being in love (fancying the beloved), but also a highly valued faculty involved in the discriminating process of falling in love. In this latter sense "fancy" has peculiar powers: the eye and heart of the beholder are instantly and powerfully affected by a worthy object, a member of the opposite sex who is physically attractive and morally virtuous. The eye and heart have, in a sense, a mind of their own, for love occurs before there is time for analysis and reflection; having occurred, it is permanent and irrevocable.

The main theme of *Rosalind* is the great power of love for good, and the emphasis in the present of the story is on love's power to make whole and complete. Yet love is not merely a comfortable feeling, and there is much to go awry with it, which perhaps accounts for the narrator's gentle handling of Phoebe. Both Rosalind and Rosader experience the restlessness and the pangs that in medieval romance tend to be felt only by the male lover. The language tells us constantly that love is complex and unpredictable. The conventional figure, oxymoron ("bitter pleasure," "amorous anguish"), is especially functional. "Although," "but," and "wherefore" introduce a number of clauses, and on the subject of love the sentence structure becomes unusually parenthetical. For analogy the narrator occasionally refers to the characters of classical literature—Adonis and Leander, as well as Troilus and Paris. Although the range of classical reference is not especially wide, a few names, like Ixion, seem to have a special significance and are repeated several times. In presuming to love Rosalind, Rosader thinks of himself as another Ixion, who dared to woo no less than Juno herself. The analogy apparently is to suggest, from Rosader's point of view, Rosalind's unattainability. The rest of the myth—Ixion's murder of his father-in-law and his ingratitude to Jupiter for purifying him of the murder-guilt—does not seem to be suggested by the narrator's allusion (though it is true that Saladyne's future father-in-law, Torismond, dies in battle at the end and that Saladyne undergoes a reformation). But Rosalind's unattainability is only Rosader's illusion; the narrator acquaints us with her point of view, too, and we know that she is attainable—and anything but the disdainful lady of the Petrarchan sonnet tradition. Rosalind is young, beautiful, chaste—and ripe for the marriage toward which everything points as soon as she and Rosader meet and fall in love.

Rosalind is thus conservative, if not puritanical, in its love idealism. "Rosader's Third Sonnet" is something more than a conventional "eternizing" sonnet. The reference in it to Petrarch and Laura, like the references to Ixion, is highly selective. The analogy between Rosader and Petrarch is in the "faith confirmed at all essays"; the analogy between Rosalind and Laura is that each is highly esteemed by her lover. Nothing is said of Laura's marriage to another man or of her consequent disdain and Petrarch's hopeless passion; the historical details are not to be thought of: it is simply that Petrarch and Laura represent a perfect love of a former age, and now Rosader and Rosalind represent a perfect love of the present age.

Part of the interest that *Rosalind* still has for us after almost four centuries is the extent to which it constantly makes use of basic—one might almost say "archetypal"—situations. Sir John of Bordeaux's relationship with his three sons is especially suggestive of fundamental patterns of conduct relating to a family in which the wife is dead and the children have been motherless for some years. Sir John's sons are very different from each other, and we can see from the beginning (as in Dostoevsky's *Brothers Karamazov*) that one of them is going to cause trouble. Sir John (like Lear) has never concealed the fact that his youngest child is his favorite, and the advice that he leaves with his sons is good enough if you take it out of context and treat it as a set piece; but (like Polonius' advice to Laertes) it is somewhat longwinded and self-indulgent, and it has no effect in preventing the violence that takes place almost immediately after his death. The unloved oldest son, whose soliloquies make us sympathetic to his plight and prepare us for his later reformation, compels Rosader to be his servant (and one is reminded of a similarly basic situation in Emily Bronte's *Wuthering Heights,* in which the unloved Hindley makes a servant of the loved Heathcliff after the death of Hindley's father).

But the essential genius of *Rosalind* is its oneness, the degree to which all contributing forms and elements have been assimilated. "Gamelyn" is there, along with many another medieval and Renaissance romance; euphuism is the basis of the style; and a new Renaissance attitude toward women and married love informs the whole. Lodge's fusion is so thorough that nothing dangles or jars. A few critics have found fault with the slow pace of the action once Rosalind has entered Arden; but action in the forest is supposed to be in slow motion, to emphasize that it is an idyllic place, with different physical laws from the court. There are just the right amounts of major expectancy and minor surprise (such as Aliena's snatching the sonnet from Saladyne's "bosom," p. 369). For a single moment Rosalind *is* Ganymede (p. 312), the woman and the role becoming one; and we are reminded that Lodge is a thoughtful storyteller who knows how to let the action suggest meanings that enrich the storyline. To anyone in any age who likes romance, *Rosalind* is very satisfactory indeed.

⌘

To the Right Honorable and His Most Esteemed Lord, the Lord of Hunsdon, Lord Chamberlain of Her Majesty's Household, and Governor of Her Town of Berwick: T. L. G.[5] Wisheth Increase of All Honorable Virtues

Such Romans, right honorable, as delighted in martial exploits attempted their actions in the honor of Augustus, because he was a patron of soldiers; and Virgil dignified him with his poems as a Maecenas of scholars—both jointly advancing his royalty as a prince warlike and learned. Such as sacrifice to Pallas present her with bays as she is wise and with armor as she is valiant, observing herein that excellent τὸ πρέπον which dedicateth honors according to the perfection of the person.

[5]*T. L. G.:* Thomas Lodge, Gentleman ("T. L. Gent." on the title page).

When I entered, right honorable, with a deep insight into the consideration of these premises, seeing your lordship to be a patron of all martial men and a Maecenas of such as apply themselves to study, wearing with Pallas both the lance and the bay, and aiming with Augustus at the favor of all by the honorable virtues of your mind, being myself first a student, and after falling from books to arms even vowed in all my thoughts dutifully to affect your lordship. Having with Captain Clarke made a voyage to the islands of Terceras[6] and the Canaries, to beguile the time with labor I writ this book, rough (as hatched in the storms of the ocean) and feathered in the surges of many perilous seas. But as it is the work of a soldier and a scholar, I presumed to shroud it under your honor's patronage as one that is the fautor[7] and favorer of all virtuous actions, and whose honorable loves, grown from the general applause of the whole commonwealth for your higher deserts, may keep it from the malice of every bitter tongue.

Other reasons more particular, right honorable, challenge in me a special affection to your lordship as being a scholar with your two noble sons, Master Edmond Carew and Master Robert Carew, two scions worthy of so honorable a tree, and a tree glorious in such honorable fruit, as also being scholar in the university under that learned and virtuous knight, Sir Edward Hobbie[8] when he was bachelor in arts, a man as well lettered as well born and, after the etymology of his name, soaring as high as the wings of knowledge can mount him, happy every way, and the more fortunate as blessed in the honor of so virtuous a lady. Thus, right honorable, the duty that I owe to the sons chargeth me that all my affection be placed on the father; for where the branches are so precious the tree of force must be most excellent.

Commanded and emboldened thus with the consideration of these forepassed reasons to present my book to your lordship, I humbly entreat your honor will vouch of my labors, and favor a soldier's and a scholar's pen with your gracious acceptance, who answers in

[6]*Terceras:* By "Terceras" Lodge apparently means the Azores; actually, Terceira was only one of the nine islands comprising the Azores, "Terceira" literally meaning "third" (the third of these islands to be discovered by the Portuguese). N. Burton Paradise, in *Thomas Lodge* (New Haven, Conn., 1931), p. 37, suggests that the voyage took place in the spring of 1585.

[7]*fautor:* patron, protector.

[8]*Hobbie:* Sir Edward Hoby (1560–1617) was a close friend of Sir John Harington, the translator of Ariosto; he was also the son of Sir Thomas Hoby, the translator of Castiglione.

affection what he wants in eloquence; so devoted to your honor, as his only desire is, to end his life under the favor of so martial and learned a patron.

Resting thus in hope of your lordship's courtesy in deigning the patronage of my work, I cease, wishing you as many honorable fortunes as your lordship can desire or I imagine.

Your honor's soldier,
humbly affectionate,
Thomas Lodge

To the Gentlemen Readers

Gentlemen, look not here to find any sprigs of Pallas' bay tree, nor to hear the humor of any amorous laureate, nor the pleasing vein of any eloquent orator: *nolo altum sapere,* they be matters above my capacity. The cobbler's check shall never light on my head, *ne sutor ultra crepidam;*[9] I will go no further than the latchet, and then all is well. Here you may perhaps find some leaves of Venus' myrtle, but hewn down by a soldier with his curtal ax, not bought with the allurement of a filed tongue. To be brief, gentlemen, room for a soldier and a sailor that gives you the fruits of his labors that he wrought in the ocean, when every line was wet with a surge and every humorous passion counterchecked with a storm. If you like it, so; and yet I will be yours in duty, if you be mine in favor. But if Momus or any squint-eyed ass that hath mighty ears to conceive with Midas, and yet little reason to judge—if he come aboard our bark to find fault with the tackling when he knows not the shrouds, I'll down into the hold and fetch out a rusty poleax that saw no sun this seven year, and either well bebast[10] him or heave the coxcomb overboard to feed cods. But courteous gentlemen that favor most, backbite none, and pardon what is overslipped; let such come and welcome—I'll into the steward's room and fetch them a can of our best beverage. Well, gentlemen, you have *Euphues' Legacy.* I fetched it as far as the islands of Terceras, and therefore read it. Censure with favor, and farewell.

Yours,
T. L.

---

[9]*ne sutor ultra crepidam:* "Let not the shoemaker go beyond his last." Pliny, in *Natural History,* Book XXXV, Chapter 36, claims that the Greek painter Apelles (fourth century B.C.) made the remark to rebuff a cobbler, who dared to criticize one of Apelles' paintings.

[10]*bebast:* thrash (baste, lambaste).

The Schedule Annexed to Euphues' Testament,
the Tenor of His Legacy, the Token of His Love[11]

The vehemency of my sickness, Philautus, hath made me doubtful of life; yet must I die in counseling thee like Socrates, because I love thee. Thou hast sons by Camilla, as I hear, who, being young in years, have green thoughts, and, nobly born, have great minds. Bend them in their youth like the willow, lest thou bewail them in their age for their wilfulness. I have bequeathed them a golden legacy, because I greatly love thee. Let them read it as Archelaus did Cassander— to profit by it; and in reading let them meditate, for I have approved it the best method. They shall find Love anatomized by Euphues with as lively colors as in Apelles' table—roses to whip him when he is wanton, reasons to withstand him when he is wily.

Here may they read that virtue is the king of labors, opinion the mistress of fools; that unity is the pride of nature, and contention the overthrow of families: here is elleborus bitter in taste, but beneficial in trial. I have nothing to send thee and Camilla but this counsel: that instead of worldly goods you leave your sons virtue and glory, for better were they to be partakers of your honors than lords of your manors. I feel death that summoneth me to my grave, and my soul desirous of his God. Farewell, Philautus, and let the tenor of my counsel be applied to thy children's comfort.

Euphues dying to live.

If any man find this scroll, send it to Philautus in England.

---

[11]*The Schedule ... Love:* "The Schedule" appears for the first time in the second edition of 1592, not in the first edition of 1590. But as W. W. Greg suggests in his edition (p. 167), neither the title page nor the final paragraph is entirely clear without it. "The Schedule" would seem, therefore, not to be an insertion of new material written for the second edition, but a vital element mistakenly omitted from the first edition. Euphues and Philautus are principal characters in Lyly's *Euphues: The Anatomy of Wit* (1578); Camilla is the heroine of Lyly's *Euphues and His England* (1580).

Rosalind

There dwelled adjoining to the city of Bordeaux a knight of most honorable parentage, whom fortune had graced with many favors and nature honored with sundry exquisite qualities, so beautified with the excellence of both as it was a question whether fortune or nature were more prodigal in deciphering the riches of their bounties. Wise he was, as holding in his head a supreme conceit of policy, reaching with Nestor into the depth of all civil government; and to make his wisdom more gracious he had that *salem ingenii* and pleasant eloquence that was so highly commended in Ulysses. His valor was no less than his wit, nor the stroke of his lance no less forcible than the sweetness of his tongue was persuasive; for he was for his courage chosen the principal of all the knights of Malta.[12]

This hardy knight, thus enriched with virtue and honor, surnamed Sir John of Bordeaux, having passed the prime of his youth in sundry battles against the Turks, at last (as the date of time hath his course) grew aged. His hairs were silver-hued, and the map of age was figured on his forehead; honor sat in the furrows of his face, and many years were portrayed in his wrinkled lineaments, that all men might perceive his glass was run and that nature of necessity challenged her due. Sir John (that with the phoenix knew the term of his life was now expired, and could, with the swan, discover his end by her songs) having three sons by his wife Lynida, the very pride of all his forepassed years, thought now (seeing death by constraint would compel him to leave them) to bestow upon them such a legacy as might bewray his love and increase their ensuing amity. Calling, therefore, these young gentlemen before him, in the presence of all his fellow knights of Malta, he resolved to leave them a memorial of his fatherly care in setting down a method of their brotherly duties. Having, therefore, death in his looks to move them to pity, and tears in his eyes to paint out the depth of his passions, taking his eldest son by the hand he began thus:

[12]*the knights of Malta:* Lodge is not clear about when *Rosalind* takes place; on the whole, it seems rather timeless. But in 1565 the island of Malta was besieged by 40,000 Turks, and a small band of men who called themselves Knights of St. John of Jerusalem, a kind of foreign legion or militant order of Christians, successfully defended the island. Lodge would seem to be exploiting a contemporary knowledge of these events without actually tying Sir John specifically to them.

Sir John of Bordeaux' Legacy He Gave to His Sons

"Oh, my sons, you see that fate hath set a period of my years, and destinies have determined the final end of my days. The palm tree waxeth away-ward, for he stoopeth in his height, and my plumes are full of sick feathers touched with age. I must to my grave that dischargeth all cares, and leave you to the world that increaseth many sorrows; my silver hairs containeth great experience, and in the number of my years are penned down the subtleties of fortune. Therefore, as I leave you some fading pelf to countercheck poverty, so I will bequeath you infallible precepts that shall lead you unto virtue.

"First, therefore, unto thee Saladyne, the eldest, and therefore the chiefest pillar of my house, wherein should be engraven as well the excellence of thy father's qualities as the essential form of his proportion, to thee I give fourteen plowlands with all my manor houses and richest plate. Next unto Fernandyne I bequeath twelve plowlands. But unto Rosader, the youngest, I give my horse, my armor, and my lance with sixteen plowlands; for if the inward thoughts be discovered by outward shadows, Rosader will exceed you all in bounty and honor. Thus, my sons, have I parted in your portions the substance of my wealth, wherein if you be as prodigal to spend as I have been careful to get, your friends will grieve to see you more wasteful than I was bountiful, and your foes smile that my fall did begin in your excess.

"Let mine honor be the glass of your actions, and the fame of my virtues the lodestar to direct the course of your pilgrimage. Aim your deeds by my honorable endeavors, and show yourselves scions worthy of so flourishing a tree, lest, as the birds *halcyones*, which exceed in whiteness, I hatch young ones that surpass in blackness.[13]

"Climb not, my sons; aspiring pride is a vapor that ascendeth high, but soon turneth to a smoke. They which stare at the stars stumble upon stones, and such as gaze at the sun (unless they be eagle-eyed) fall blind. Soar not with the hobby, lest you fall with the lark; nor attempt not with Phaëthon, lest you drown with Icarus. Fortune,

[13]*the birds halcyones, which exceed in whiteness ... blackness:* Pliny (X, 49) and others refer (correctly) to the halcyon or kingfisher bird as predominantly blue, not white. But like Lyly and Greene (see note 2 in *Pandosto*), Lodge feels free to take liberties with encyclopedia-type information. Mainly we are to follow Sir John's discussion of honor; the sounds ("scions ... *halcyones*") and the antithesis ("whiteness ... blackness") are to amplify that discussion.

when she wills you to fly, tempers your plumes with wax; and therefore either sit still and make no wing, or else beware the sun and hold Daedalus' axiom authentical: *medium tenere tutissimum*. Low shrubs have deep roots, and poor cottages great patience. Fortune looks ever upward, and envy aspireth to nestle with dignity. Take heed, my sons; the mean is sweetest melody, where strings high stretched either soon crack or quickly grow out of tune.

"Let your country's care be your heart's content, and think that you are not born for yourselves but to level your thoughts to be loyal to your prince, careful for the commonweal, and faithful to your friends. So shall France say, 'These men are as excellent in virtues as they be exquisite in features.'

"Oh, my sons, a friend is a precious jewel within whose bosom you may unload your sorrows and unfold your secrets, and he either will relieve with counsel or persuade with reason. But take heed in the choice: the outward show makes not the inward man, nor are the dimples in the face the calendars of truth. When the licorice leaf looketh most dry, then it is most wet. When the shores of Lepanthus[14] are most quiet, then they forepoint a storm. The baaran leaf the more fair it looks, the more infectious it is, and in the sweetest words is oft hid the most treachery. Therefore, my sons, choose a friend as the Hiperborei do the metals:[15] sever them from the ore with fire and let them not bide the stamp before they be current. So try and then trust; let time be touchstone of friendship, and then friends faithful lay them up for jewels.

"Be valiant, my sons, for cowardice is the enemy to honor; but not too rash, for that is an extreme. Fortitude is the mean, and that is limited within bonds and prescribed with circumstance.

"But above all," and with that he fetched a deep sigh, "beware

---

[14]*Lepanthus:* The Elizabethans refer frequently to "Lepanto" as the scene of a naval battle (1571) in which Don John of Austria defeated the Turks. But, once again, as in the case of the Knights of Malta, the reference is merely oblique and suggestive. The "baaran" leaf (the "b" is capitalized in the 1590 edition) probably is an invention or a misspelling; there seems to be no other Elizabethan reference to it.

[15]*the Hiperborei do the metals:* usually spelled "Hyperboreans," but the spelling in the 1590 edition is either "Hiperborei" or "Hiperboreido." Later (p. 371) Lodge seems to make a rather vague use of the Greek legend, according to which the Hyperboreans lived beyond the north wind in eternal sunshine and great abundance. Their alleged smelting probably is Lodge's own invention, to lend (in the manner of Lyly) emphasis and the ring of authenticity to the point about friendship.

of love, for it is far more perilous than pleasant, and yet I tell you it allureth as ill as the sirens. Oh, my sons, fancy is a fickle thing, and beauty's paintings are tricked up with time's colors, which, being set to dry in the sun, perish with the same. Venus is a wanton, and though her laws pretend liberty yet there is nothing but loss and glistering misery. Cupid's wings are plumed with the feathers of vanity, and his arrows, where they pierce, enforce nothing but deadly desires. A woman's eye, as it is precious to behold so it is prejudicial to gaze upon, for as it affordeth delight so it snareth unto death. Trust not their fawning favors, for their loves are like the breath of a man upon steel, which no sooner lighteth on but it leapeth off; and their passions are as momentary as the colors of a polyp[16] which changeth at the sight of every object. My breath waxeth short, and mine eyes dim; the hour is come, and I must away. Therefore let this suffice: women are wantons, and yet men cannot want[17] one; and, therefore, if you love, choose her that hath her eyes of adamant that will turn only to one point, her heart of a diamond that will receive but one form, her tongue of a sethin leaf that never wags but with a southeast wind. And yet, my sons, if she have all these qualities—to be chaste, obedient, and silent—yet for that she is a woman, shalt thou find in her sufficient vanities to countervail her virtues.

"Oh, now, my sons, even now take these my last words as my latest legacy, for my thread is spun, and my foot is in the grave. Keep my precepts as memorials of your father's counsels, and let them be lodged in the secret of your hearts; for wisdom is better than wealth, and a golden sentence worth a world of treasure. In my fall see and mark, my sons, the folly of man, that, being dust, climbeth with Biares[18] to reach at the heavens and ready every minute to die, yet hopeth for an age of pleasures. Oh, man's life is like lightning that is but a flash, and the longest date of his years but as a bavin's blaze![19] Seeing, then, man is so mortal, be careful that thy life be virtuous, that thy death may be full of admirable honors. So shalt thou challenge fame to be thy fautor, and put oblivion to exile with thine

[16]*polyp:* Pliny has a long description of the various species of polyp or polypus (spelled "Polipe" in the 1590 edition); in IX, 42, Pliny describes the chameleon-like changes of color.

[17]*want:* lack, do without.

[18]*Biares:* probably a mistake for "Briareus," the emendation in the 1609 edition; Briareus (or Aegaeon) in one legend was a giant who attacked Olympus.

[19]*bavin's blaze:* the short burst of fire from a bundle of dry brushwood or firewood.

honorable actions. But, my sons, lest you should forget your father's axioms, take this scroll, wherein read what your father, dying, wills you to execute living."

At this he shrunk down in his bed and gave up the ghost.

John of Bordeaux being thus dead was greatly lamented of his sons and bewailed of his friends, especially of his fellow knights of Malta, who attended on his funerals, which were performed with great solemnity. His obsequies done, Saladyne caused next his epitaph the contents of the scroll to be portrayed out, which were to this effect:

The Contents of the Schedule Which
Sir John of Bordeaux Gave to His Sons

My sons, behold what portion I do give:
I leave you goods, but they are quickly lost;
I leave advice to school you how to live;
I leave you wit, but won with little cost.
But keep it well, for counsel still is one
When father, friends, and worldly goods are gone.

In choice of thrift let honor be thy gain;
Win it by virtue and by manly might.
In doing good esteem thy toil no pain;
Protect the fatherless and widow's right.
Fight for thy faith, thy country, and thy king,
For why? This thrift will prove a blessed thing.

In choice of wife prefer the modest chaste;
Lilies are fair in show but foul in smell;
The sweetest looks by age are soon defaced;
Then choose thy wife by wit and living well.
Who brings thee wealth, and many faults withal,
Presents thee honey mixed with bitter gall.

In choice of friends beware of light belief;
A painted tongue may shroud a subtle heart;
The sirens' tears do threaten mickle grief;
Foresee, my sons, for fear of sudden smart.
Choose in thy wants, and he that friends thee then,
When richer grown, befriend him thou again.

Learn of the ant in summer to provide;
Drive with the bee the drone from out thy hive;
Build like the swallow in the summer tide;
Spare not too much, my sons, but, sparing, thrive;
Be poor in folly, rich in all but sin;
So by thy death thy glory shall begin.

Saladyne, having thus set up the schedule and hanged about his father's hearse many passionate poems, that France might suppose him to be passing sorrowful, he clad himself and his brothers all in black and, in such sable suits, discoursed his grief. But as the hyena when she mourns is then most guileful, so Saladyne under this show of grief shadowed a heart full of contented thoughts. The tiger, though he hide his claws, will at last discover his rapine; the lion's looks are not the maps of his meaning, nor a man's physiognomy[20] is not the display of his secrets. Fire cannot be hid in the straw nor the nature of man so concealed but at last it will have his course; nurture and art may do much, but that *natura naturans*, which by propagation is ingrafted in the heart, will be at last perforce predominant according to the old verse, *Naturam expellas furca licet, tamen usque recurret*.[21] So fared it with Saladyne, for after a month's mourning was passed, he fell to consideration of his father's testament—how he had bequeathed more to his younger brothers than himself; that Rosader was his father's darling but now under his tuition; that as yet they were not come to years, and he, being their guardian, might, if not defraud them of their due, yet make such havoc of their legacies and lands as they should be a great deal the lighter. Whereupon he began thus to meditate with himself:

Saladyne's Meditation with Himself

"Saladyne, how art thou disquieted in thy thoughts and perplexed with a world of restless passions, having thy mind troubled with the tenor of thy father's testament and thy heart fired with the hope of present preferment. By the one thou art counseled to content thee with thy fortunes, by the other persuaded to aspire to higher wealth. Riches, Saladyne, is a great royalty, and there is no sweeter physic than store. Avicen,[22] like a fool, forgot in his aphorisms to say that

---

[20]*physiognomy:* In the 1590 edition "iog" is omitted from the middle of "physiognomy"; but since the word "physiognomer" appears on sig. N1ᵛ (p. 361 in this edition), we may take the liberty of inserting the "iog" here and on pp. 348 and 352.

[21]*Naturam . . . recurret:* "Drive out nature with a fork, and she will nevertheless return." As Greg points out (p. 168), this line, without *"licet,"* is from Horace's *Epistles*, I, x, 24.

[22]*Avicen:* that is, Avicenna (980–1037), the Persian philosopher. The Elizabethans make no bones about shortening (anglicizing) foreign nouns; they often omit the last syllable of "Machiavelli" and "novella" (and that is how the word "novel" came into our language).

gold was the most precious restorative and that treasure was the most excellent medicine of the mind.

"Oh, Saladyne, what, were thy father's precepts breathed into the wind? Hast thou so soon forgotten his principles? Did he not warn thee from coveting without honor and climbing without virtue? Did he not forbid thee to aim at any action that should not be honorable? And what will be more prejudicial to thy credit than the careless ruin of thy brothers' welfare? Why, shouldst not thou be the pillar of thy brothers' prosperity? And wilt thou become the subversion of their fortunes? Is there any sweeter thing than concord, or a more precious jewel than amity? Are you not sons of one father, scions of one tree, birds of one nest? And wilt thou become so unnatural as to rob them whom thou shouldst relieve? No, Saladyne, entreat them with favors and entertain them with love; so shalt thou have thy conscience clear and thy renown excellent.

"Tush, what words are these, base fool? Far unfit, if thou be wise, for thy humor.[23] What though thy father at his death talked of many frivolous matters, as one that doted for age and raved in his sickness—shall his words be axioms and his talk be so authentical that thou wilt, to observe them, prejudice thyself? No, no, Saladyne, sick men's wills that are parole[24] and have neither hand nor seal are like the laws of a city written in dust, which are broken with the blast of every wind. What, man, thy father is dead, and he can neither help thy fortunes nor measure thy actions. Therefore, bury his words with his carcass and be wise for thyself. What, 'tis not so old as true, *non sapit, qui sibi non sapit*.

"Thy brother is young, keep him now in awe, make him not checkmate with thyself, for *nimia familiaritas contemptum parit*. Let him know little, so shall he not be able to execute much. Suppress his wits with a base estate, and though he be a gentleman by nature, yet form him anew and make him a peasant by nurture; so shalt thou keep him as a slave and reign thyself sole lord over all thy father's possessions. As for Fernandyne, thy middle brother, he is a scholar and hath no mind but on Aristotle; let him read on Galen while thou riflest with gold, and pore on his book till thou dost purchase lands. Wit is great wealth; if he have learning it is enough, and so let all rest."

In this humor was Saladyne making his brother Rosader his footboy

[23]*humor:* In the 1604 edition "humor" is emended to "honor."
[24]*wills that are parole:* wills that exist only by word of mouth (a legal term).

for the space of two or three years, keeping him in such servile subjection as if he had been the son of any country vassal. The young gentleman bore all with patience till on a day, walking in the garden by himself, he began to consider how he was the son of John of Bordeaux, a knight renowned for many victories and a gentleman famosed[25] for his virtues; how, contrary to the testament of his father, he was not only kept from his land and entreated as a servant, but smothered in such secret slavery as he might not attain to any honorable actions.

"Ah," quoth he to himself (nature working these effectual passions) "why should I, that am a gentleman born, pass my time in such unnatural drudgery? Were it not better either in Paris to become a scholar, or in the court a courtier, or in the field a soldier, than to live a footboy to my own brother? Nature hath lent me wit to conceive, but my brother denied me art to contemplate. I have strength to perform any honorable exploit, but no liberty to accomplish my virtuous endeavors. Those good parts that God hath bestowed upon me, the envy of my brother doth smother in obscurity. The harder is my fortune, and the more his frowardness."

With that, casting up his hand he felt hair on his face; and perceiving his beard to bud, for choler he began to blush and swore to himself he would be no more subject to such slavery. As thus he was ruminating of his melancholy passions, in came Saladyne with his men and, seeing his brother in a brown study and to forget his wonted reverence, thought to shake him out of his dumps thus:

"Sirrah," quoth he, "what, is your heart on your halfpenny,[26] or are you saying a dirge for your father's soul? What, is my dinner ready?"

At this question, Rosader, turning his head askance and bending his brows as if anger there had plowed the furrows of her wrath, with his eyes full of fire he made this reply:

"Dost thou ask me, Saladyne, for thy cates? Ask some of thy churls who are fit for such an office. I am thine equal by nature though not by birth, and though thou hast more cards in the bunch,[27] I have as many trumps in my hands as thyself. Let me question with thee: why hast thou felled my woods, spoiled my manor houses, and made havoc of such utensils as my father bequeathed unto me? I tell thee, Saladyne, either answer me as a brother or I will trouble thee as an enemy."

[25]*famosed:* made famous.
[26]*is your heart on your halfpenny:* a proverb (Tilley, H315); the sense here is "are you feeling sorry for yourself?"   [27]*bunch:* pack.

At this reply of Rosader's, Saladyne smiled as laughing at his presumption and frowned as checking his folly; he therefore took him up thus shortly:

"What, sirrah! Well, I see early pricks the tree that will prove a thorn.[28] Hath my familiar conversing with you made you coy, or my good looks drawn you to be thus contemptuous? I can quickly remedy such a fault, and I will bend the tree while it is a wand. In faith, sir boy, I have a snaffle for such a headstrong colt. You, sirs, lay hold on him and bind him, and then I will give him a cooling card[29] for his choler."

This made Rosader half mad, that, stepping to a great rake that stood in the garden, he laid such load upon his brother's men that he hurt some of them and made the rest of them run away. Saladyne, seeing Rosader so resolute and with his resolution so valiant, thought his heels his best safety and took him to a loft adjoining to the garden, whither Rosader pursued him hotly. Saladyne, afraid of his brother's fury, cried out to him thus:

"Rosader, be not so rash. I am thy brother and thine elder, and if I have done thee wrong I'll make thee amends. Revenge not anger in blood, for so shalt thou stain the virtue of old Sir John of Bordeaux. Say wherein thou art discontent and thou shalt be satisfied. Brothers' frowns ought not to be periods of wrath. What, man, look not so sourly; I know we shall be friends and better friends than we have been, for *amantium ira amoris redintegratio est.*"

These words appeased the choler of Rosader (for he was of a mild and courteous nature) so that he laid down his weapons and, upon the faith of a gentleman, assured his brother he would offer him no prejudice. Whereupon Saladyne came down, and after a little parley they embraced each other and became friends; and Saladyne promising Rosader the restitution of all his lands, "and what favor else," quoth he, "any ways my ability or the nature of a brother may perform." Upon these sugared reconciliations they went into the house, arm in arm together, to the great content of all the old servants of Sir John of Bordeaux.

Thus continued the pad hidden in the straw till it chanced that Torismond, king of France, had appointed for his pleasure a day of

---

[28]*early pricks ... thorn:* a proverb (Tilley, T232); Shakespeare's version in 3 *Henry VI,* V, 13, carries exactly the same meaning: "What? Can so young a thorn begin to prick?"

[29]*cooling card:* The sense is "damper"—something that will decrease choler (thus reinforcing "snaffle" in the previous sentence); what "cooling card" referred to exactly in card playing is obscure, but presumably it was a card that ruined an otherwise promising hand.

wrestling[30] and of tournament to busy his commons' heads, lest being idle their thoughts should run upon more serious matters and call to remembrance their old banished king. A champion there was to stand against all comers—a Norman, a man of tall stature and of great strength, so valiant that in many such conflicts he always bore away the victory, not only overthrowing them which he encountered, but often with the weight of his body killing them outright. Saladyne, hearing of this, thinking now not to let the ball fall to the ground but to take opportunity by the forehead, first by secret means convented with the Norman and procured him with rich rewards to swear that if Rosader came within his claws he should never more return to quarrel with Saladyne for his possessions. The Norman, desirous of pelf—as *quis nisi mentis inops oblatum respuit aurum?*—taking great gifts for little gods, took the crowns of Saladyne to perform the stratagem.

Having thus the champion tied to his villainous determination by oath, he prosecuted the intent of his purpose thus. He went to young Rosader, who in all his thoughts reached at honor and gazed no lower than virtue commanded him, and began to tell him of this tournament and wrestling—how the king should be there and all the chief peers of France, with all the beautiful damsels of the country.

"Now, brother," quoth he, "for the honor of Sir John of Bordeaux, our renowned father, to famous that house that never hath been found without men approved in chivalry, show thy resolution to be peremptory. For myself thou knowest though I am eldest by birth, yet never having attempted any deeds of arms, I am youngest to perform any martial exploits, knowing better how to survey my lands than to charge my lance. My brother Fernandyne he is at Paris poring on a few papers, having more insight into sophistry and principles of philosophy than any warlike endeavors; but thou, Rosader, the youngest in years but the eldest in valor, art a man of strength and darest do what honor allows thee. Take thou my father's lance, his sword, and his horse and hie thee to the tournament; and either there valiantly crack a spear or try with the Norman for the palm of activity."

The words of Saladyne were but spurs to a free horse, for he had scarce uttered them ere Rosader took him in his arms, taking his proffer so kindly that he promised in what he might to requite his courtesy.

[30]*wrestling:* spelled "wrastling" in the 1590 edition (and still so pronounced by descendants of the Elizabethans now living in the southeastern and central parts of the United States).

The next morrow was the day of the tournament, and Rosader was so desirous to show his heroical thoughts that he passed the night with little sleep. But as soon as Phoebus had vailed the curtain of the night and made Aurora blush with giving her the *bezo les labres* in her silver couch, he got him up and, taking his leave of his brother, mounted himself towards the place appointed, thinking every mile ten leagues till he came there.

But leaving him, so desirous of the journey, to Torismond, the king of France, who having by force banished Gerismond (their lawful king, that lived as an outlaw in the forest of Arden) sought now by all means to keep the French busied with all sports that might breed their content. Amongst the rest he had appointed this solemn tournament, whereunto he in most solemn manner resorted, accompanied with the twelve peers of France,[31] who, rather for fear than love, graced him with the show of their dutiful favors. To feed their eyes and to make the beholders pleased with the sight of most rare and glistering objects, he had appointed his own daughter, Alinda, to be there and the fair Rosalind, daughter unto Gerismond, with all the beautiful damsels that were famous for their features in all France. Thus in that place did love and war triumph in a sympathy; for such as were martial might use their lance to be renowned for the excellence of their chivalry, and such as were amorous might glut themselves with gazing on the beauties of most heavenly creatures.

As every man's eye had his several survey, and fancy was partial in their looks, yet all in general applauded the admirable riches that nature bestowed on the face of Rosalind; for upon her cheeks there seemed a battle between the Graces who should bestow most favors to make her excellent. The blush that gloried Luna when she kissed the shepherd on the hills of Latmos was not tainted with such a pleasant dye as the vermilion flourished on the silver hue of Rosalind's countenance. Her eyes were like those lamps that make the wealthy covert of the heavens more gorgeous, sparkling favor and disdain, courteous and yet coy, as if in them Venus had placed all her amorets[32] and Diana all her chastity. The trammels of her hair, folded in a caul[33] of gold, so far surpassed the burnished glister of the metal as the sun doth the meanest star in brightness. The tresses that folds in the

[31]*the twelve peers of France:* still another vaguely evocative reference, this time to the twelve principal knights (Roland, Oliver, and ten others) who were to Charlemagne what the knights of the Round Table were to Arthur.

[32]*amorets:* love glances.

[33]*caul:* net.

brows of Apollo were not half so rich to the sight, for in her hairs it seemed love had laid herself in ambush to entrap the proudest eye that durst gaze upon their excellence. What should I need to decipher her particular beauties, when by the censure of all she was the paragon of all earthly perfection? This Rosalind sat, I say, with Alinda as a beholder of these sports and made the cavaliers crack their lances with more courage. Many deeds of knighthood that day were performed, and many prizes were given according to their several deserts.

At last, when the tournament ceased, the wrestling began; and the Norman presented himself as challenger against all comers. But he looked like Hercules when he advanced himself against Achelous, so that the fury of his countenance amazed all that durst attempt to encounter with him in any deed of activity, till at last a lusty franklin of the country came with two tall men, that were his sons, of good lineaments and comely personage. The eldest of these, doing his obeisance to the king, entered the list, and presented himself to the Norman, who straight coped with him, and as a man that would triumph in the glory of his strength, roused himself with such fury that not only he gave him the fall but killed him with the weight of his corpulent personage. Which the younger brother seeing, leaped presently into the place and, thirsty after the revenge, assailed the Norman with such valor that at the first encounter he brought him to his knees; which repulsed so the Norman that, recovering himself, fear of disgrace doubling his strength, he stepped so sternly to the young franklin that taking him up in his arms he threw him against the ground so violently that he broke his neck and so ended his days with his brother. At this unlooked for massacre, the people murmured and were all in a deep passion of pity; but the franklin, father unto these, never changed his countenance but, as a man of a courageous resolution, took up the bodies of his sons without any show of outward discontent.

All this while stood Rosader and saw this tragedy. Who, noting the undoubted virtue of the franklin's mind, alighted off from his horse and presently sat down on the grass and commanded his boy to pull off his boots, making him ready to try the strength of this champion. Being furnished as he would, he clapped the franklin on the shoulder and said thus:

"Bold yeoman, whose sons have ended the term of their years with honor, for that I see thou scornest fortune with patience and thwartest the injury of fate with content in brooking the death of thy sons, stand awhile, and either see me make a third in their tragedy or else revenge their fall with an honorable triumph."

The franklin, seeing so goodly a gentleman to give him such courteous comfort, gave him hearty thanks with promise to pray for his happy success. With that Rosader vailed bonnet to the king and lightly leaped within the lists, where, noting more the company than the combatant, he cast his eye upon the troop of ladies that glistered there like the stars of heaven. But at last Love, willing to make him as amorous as he was valiant, presented him with the sight of Rosalind, whose admirable beauty so inveigled the eye of Rosader that, forgetting himself, he stood and fed his looks on the favor of Rosalind's face; which she perceiving blushed, which was such a doubling of her beauteous excellence that the bashful red of Aurora at the sight of unacquainted Phaëthon was not half so glorious.

The Norman, seeing this young gentleman fettered in the looks of the ladies, drove him out of his memento[34] with a shake by the shoulder. Rosader, looking back with an angry frown, as if he had been wakened from some pleasant dream, discovered to all by the fury of his countenance that he was a man of some high thoughts. But when they all noted his youth and the sweetness of his visage, with a general applause of favors, they grieved that so goodly a young man should venture in so base an action. But seeing it were to his dishonor to hinder him from his enterprise, they wished him to be graced with the palm of victory. After Rosader was thus called out of his memento by the Norman, he roughly clapped to him[35] with so fierce an encounter that they both fell to the ground, and with the violence of the fall were forced to breathe; in which space the Norman called to mind by all tokens that this was he whom Saladyne had appointed him to kill. Which conjecture made him stretch every limb and try every sinew that, working his death, he might recover the gold which so bountifully was promised him.

On the contrary part, Rosader while he breathed was not idle, but still cast his eye upon Rosalind, who, to encourage him with a favor, lent him such an amorous look as might have made the most coward desperate; which glance of Rosalind so fired the passionate desires of Rosader that, turning to the Norman, he ran upon him and braved

[34]*memento:* The sense is "reverie," possibly deriving from an early meaning of "memento" as "prayer" (which is also absorbing).

[35]*he roughly clapped to him:* an expression not recorded in the *OED* and made all the more difficult in that we are not sure to whom the pronouns refer; "he" should refer to Rosader (though we cannot be sure that it does). Probably the sense is that Rosader laid hold of the Norman.

him with a strong encounter. The Norman received him as valiantly, that there was a sore combat, hard to judge on whose side fortune would be prodigal. At last Rosader, calling to mind the beauty of his new mistress, the fame of his father's honors, and the disgrace that should fall to his house by his misfortune, roused himself and threw the Norman against the ground, falling upon his chest with so willing a weight that the Norman yielded nature her due and Rosader the victory.

The death of this champion, as it highly contented the franklin as a man satisfied with revenge, so it drew the king and all the peers into a great admiration, that so young years and so beautiful a personage should contain such martial excellence. But when they knew him to be the youngest son of Sir John of Bordeaux, the king rose from his seat and embraced him, and the peers entreated him with all favorable courtesy, commending both his valor and his virtues, wishing him to go forward in such haughty deeds that he might attain to the glory of his father's honorable fortunes.

As the king and lords graced him with embracing, so the ladies favored him with their looks, especially Rosalind, whom the beauty and valor of Rosader had already touched. But she accounted love a toy, and fancy a momentary passion, that as it was taken in with a gaze might be shaken off with a wink, and therefore feared not to dally in the flame; and to make Rosader know she affected him, took from her neck a jewel and sent it by a page to the young gentleman. The prize that Venus gave to Paris was not half so pleasing to the Trojan as this gem was to Rosader, for if fortune had sworn to make him sole monarch of the world, he would rather have refused such dignity than have lost the jewel sent him by Rosalind. To return her with the like he was unfurnished, and yet that he might more than in his looks discover his affection, he stepped into a tent and, taking pen and paper, writ this fancy:

Two suns at once from one fair heaven there shined,
Ten branches from two boughs tipped all with roses,
Pure locks more golden than is gold refined,
Two pearled rows that nature's pride encloses;

Two mounts fair marble white, down-soft and dainty,
A snow-dyed orb, where love increased by pleasure
Full woeful makes my heart and body fainty,
Her fair, my woe, exceeds all thought and measure.

In lines confused my luckless harm appeareth,
Whom sorrow clouds, whom pleasant smiling cleareth.

This sonnet he sent to Rosalind, which when she read she blushed, but with a sweet content in that she perceived love had allotted her so amorous a servant.

Leaving her to her new entertained fancies, again to Rosader. Who, triumphing in the glory of this conquest, accompanied with a troop of young gentlemen that were desirous to be his familiars, went home to his brother Saladyne's, who was walking before the gates to hear what success his brother Rosader should have, assuring himself of his death and devising how, with dissimuled sorrow, to celebrate his funerals. As he was in this thought, he cast up his eye and saw where Rosader returned with the garland on his head, as having won the prize, accompanied with a crew of boon companions. Grieved at this, he stepped in and shut the gate. Rosader, seeing this and not looking for such unkind entertainment, blushed at the disgrace and yet smothering his grief with a smile, he turned to the gentlemen and desired them to hold his brother excused, for he did not this upon any malicious intent or niggardise[36] but, being brought up in the country, he absented himself as not finding his nature fit for such youthful company. Thus he sought to shadow abuses proffered him by his brother; but in vain, for he could by no means be suffered to enter. Whereupon he ran his foot against the door and broke it open, drawing his sword and entering boldly into the hall, where he found none (for all were fled) but one Adam Spencer, an Englishman, who had been an old and trusty servant to Sir John of Bordeaux. He for the love he bore to his deceased master, favored the part of Rosader and gave him and his such entertainment as he could. Rosader gave him thanks and, looking about, seeing the hall empty, said:

"Gentlemen, you are welcome; frolic and be merry. You shall be sure to have wine enough, whatsoever your fare be. I tell you, cavaliers, my brother hath in his house five tun of wine, and as long as that lasteth I beshrew him that spares his liquor."

With that he burst open the buttery door, and with the help of Adam Spencer covered the tables and set down whatsoever he could find in the house; but what they wanted in meat Rosader supplied with drink. Yet had they royal cheer and withal such a hearty welcome as would have made the coarsest meats seem delicates. After they had feasted and frolicked it twice or thrice with an upsy freeze,[37] they all took their leaves of Rosader and departed. As soon

---

[36]*he did not ... niggardise:* Saladyne did not ... niggardliness.

[37]*with an upsy freeze:* "freeze" may be a mistake for, or variation of, "Friese." The expression "with an upsy Friese" meant "bottoms up in the Frisian manner."

as they were gone, Rosader, growing impatient of the abuse, drew his sword and swore to be revenged on the discourteous Saladyne. Yet by the means of Adam Spencer, who sought to continue friendship and amity betwixt the brethren, and through the flattering submission of Saladyne, they were once again reconciled, and put up all forepassed injuries with a peaceable agreement, living together for a good space in such brotherly love as did not only rejoice the servants but made all the gentlemen and bordering neighbors glad of such friendly concord. Saladyne, hiding fire in the straw and concealing a poisoned hate in a peaceable countenance (yet deferring the intent of his wrath till fitter opportunity), he showed himself a great favorer of his brother's virtuous endeavors. Where, leaving them in this happy league, let us return to Rosalind.

Rosalind, returning home from the triumph, after she waxed solitary, love presented her with the idea of Rosader's perfection, and, taking her at discovert, struck her so deep as she felt herself grow passing passionate. She began to call to mind the comeliness of his person, the honor of his parents and the virtues that, excelling both, made him so gracious in the eyes of everyone. Sucking in thus the honey of love by imprinting in her thoughts his rare qualities, she began to surfeit with the contemplation of his virtuous conditions; but when she called to remembrance her present estate and the hardness of her fortunes, desire began to shrink and fancy to vail bonnet,[38] that between a chaos of confused thoughts she began to debate with herself in this manner:

Rosalind's Passion

"Unfortunate Rosalind, whose misfortunes are more than thy years and whose passions are greater than thy patience. The blossoms of thy youth are mixed with the frosts of envy, and the hope of thy ensuing fruits perish in the bud. Thy father is by Torismond banished from the crown, and thou, the unhappy daughter of a king, detained captive, living as disquieted in thy thoughts as thy father discontented in his exile. Ah, Rosalind, what cares wait upon a crown, what griefs are incident to dignity, what sorrows haunt royal palaces! The greatest seas have the sorest storms, the highest birth subject to the most bale, and of all trees the cedars soonest shake with the wind. Small currents are ever calm, low valleys not scorched in any

---

[38]*vail bonnet:* take off and lower her hat (as a sign of submission).

lightnings, nor base men tied to any baleful prejudice. Fortune flies, and if she touch poverty it is with her heel, rather disdaining their want with a frown than envying their wealth with disparagement. Oh, Rosalind, hadst thou been born low thou hadst not fallen so high, and yet being great of blood thine honor is more if thou brookest misfortune with patience.

"Suppose I contrary fortune with content; yet fates, unwilling to have me any way happy, have forced love to set my thoughts on fire with fancy. Love, Rosalind? Becometh it women in distress to think of love? Tush, desire hath no respect of persons: Cupid is blind and shooteth at random, as soon hitting a rag as a robe and piercing as soon the bosom of a captive as the breast of a libertine. Thou speakest it, poor Rosalind, by experience; for being every way distressed, surcharged with cares and overgrown with sorrows, yet amidst the heap of all these mishaps love hath lodged in thy heart the perfection of young Rosader, a man every way absolute as well for his inward life as for his outward lineaments, able to content the eye with beauty and the ear with the report of his virtue.

"But consider, Rosalind, his fortunes and thy present estate: thou art poor and without patrimony, and yet the daughter of a prince; he a younger brother and void of such possessions as either might maintain thy dignities or revenge thy father's injuries. And hast thou not learned this of other ladies, that lovers cannot live by looks, that women's ears are sooner content with a dram of give me than a pound of hear me, that gold is sweeter than eloquence, that love is a fire and wealth is the fuel, that Venus' coffers should be ever full? Then, Rosalind, seeing Rosader is poor, think him less beautiful because he is in want and account his virtues but qualities of course for that he is not endued with wealth. Doth not Horace tell thee what method is to be used in love? *Querenda pecunia primum, post nummos virtus.* Tush, Rosalind, be not over rash, leap not before thou look; either love such a one as may with his lands purchase thy liberty or else love not at all. Choose not a fair face with an empty purse, but say as most women use to say, *Si nihil attuleris, ibis Homere foras.*

"Why, Rosalind, can such base thoughts harbor in such high beauties? Can the degree of a princess, the daughter of Gerismond, harbor such servile conceits as to prize gold more than honor, or to measure a gentleman by his wealth, not by his virtues? No, Rosalind, blush at thy base resolution and say if thou lovest either Rosader or none. And why? Because Rosader is both beautiful and virtuous."

Smiling to herself to think of her new entertained passions, taking up her lute that lay by her, she warbled out this ditty:

Rosalind's Madrigal

Love in my bosom like a bee
    Doth suck his sweet;
Now with his wings he plays with me,
    Now with his feet.
Within mine eyes he makes his nest,
His bed amidst my tender breast;
My kisses are his daily feast,
And yet he robs me of my rest.
    Ah, wanton, will ye?

And if I sleep, then percheth he
    With pretty flight,
And makes his pillow of my knee
    The livelong night.
Strike I my lute, he tunes the string,
He music plays if so I sing;
He lends me every lovely thing,
Yet cruel he my heart doth sting.
    Whist, wanton, still ye?

Else I with roses every day
    Will whip you hence,
And bind you when you long to play,
    For your offense;
I'll shut mine eyes to keep you in,
I'll make you fast it for your sin,
I'll count your power not worth a pin.
Alas, what hereby shall I win,
    If he gainsay me?

What if I beat the wanton boy
    With many a rod?
He will repay me with annoy,
    Because a god.
Then sit thou safely on my knee,
And let thy bower my bosom be;
Lurk in mine eyes, I like of thee.
Oh, Cupid, so thou pity me,
    Spare not, but play thee.

Scarce had Rosalind ended her madrigal before Torismond came in with his daughter Alinda and many of the peers of France who were enamored of her beauty. Which Torismond perceiving, fearing lest her perfection might be the beginning of his prejudice and the hope of his fruit end in the beginning of her blossoms, he thought to banish her from the court.

"For," quoth he to himself, "her face is so full of favor that it pleads pity in the eye of every man; her beauty is so heavenly and divine that she will prove to me as Helen did to Priam: some one of the peers will aim at her love, end[39] the marriage, and then in his wife's right attempt the kingdom. To prevent, therefore, had I wist in[40] all these actions, she tarries not about the court, but shall, as an exile, either wander to her father or else seek other fortunes."

In this humor, with a stern countenance full of wrath, he breathed out this censure unto her before the peers, that charged her that that night she were not seen about the court.

"For," quoth he, "I have heard of thy aspiring speeches and intended treasons."

This doom was strange unto Rosalind; and presently, covered with the shield of her innocence, she boldly broke out in reverend terms to have cleared herself. But Torismond would admit of no reason, nor durst his lords plead for Rosalind (although her beauty had made some of them passionate) seeing the figure of wrath portrayed in his brow. Standing thus all mute, and Rosalind amazed, Alinda, who loved her more than herself, with grief in her heart and tears in her eyes, falling down on her knees began to entreat her father thus:

Alinda's Oration to Her Father in Defense of Fair Rosalind

"If, mighty Torismond, I offend in pleading for my friend, let the law of amity crave pardon for my boldness; for where there is depth of affection there friendship alloweth a privilege. Rosalind and I have been fostered up from our infancies, and nursed under the harbor of our conversing together with such private familiarities, that custom had wrought an union of our nature, and the sympathy of our affections such a secret love that we have two bodies and one soul. Then marvel not, great Torismond, if, seeing my friend distressed, I find myself perplexed with a thousand sorrows; for her virtuous and honorable thoughts, which are the glories that maketh women excellent, they be such as may challenge love and raze out suspicion. Her

[39]*end:* bring about.
[40]*had I wist in:* I had knowledge of; "since" is perhaps implied before "had."

obedience to your majesty I refer to the censure of your own eye that, since her father's exile, hath smothered all griefs with patience and, in the absence of nature, hath honored you with all duty as her own father by nurture, not in word uttering any discontent, nor in thought (as far as conjecture may reach) hammering on revenge; only in all her actions seeking to please you and to win my favor. Her wisdom, silence, chastity, and other such rich qualities I need not decipher; only it rests for me to conclude in one word that she is innocent. If, then, fortune, who triumphs in variety of miseries, hath presented some envious person as minister of her intended stratagem to taint Rosalind with any surmise of treason, let him be brought to her face and confirm his accusation by witnesses; which proved, let her die, and Alinda will execute the massacre. If none can avouch any confirmed relation of her intent, use justice, my lord— it is the glory of a king—and let her live in your wonted favor; for if you banish her, myself, as copartner of her hard fortunes, will participate in exile some part of her extremities."

Torismond, at this speech of Alinda, covered his face with such a frown as tyranny seemed to fit triumphant in his forehead, and checked her up with such taunts as made the lords (that only were hearers) to tremble.

"Proud girl," quoth he, "hath my looks made thee so light of tongue or my favors encouraged thee to be so forward that thou darest presume to preach after thy father? Hath not my years more experience than thy youth and the winter of mine age deeper insight into civil policy than the prime of thy flourishing days? The old lion avoids the toils where the young one leaps into the net, the care of age is provident and foresees much, suspicion is a virtue where a man holds his enemy in his bosom. Thou, fond girl, measurest all by present affection, and as thy heart loves, thy thoughts censure; but if thou knewest that in liking Rosalind thou hatchest up a bird to peck out thine own eyes, thou wouldst entreat as much for her absence as now thou delightest in her presence. But why do I allege policy to thee? Sit you down, huswife,[41] and fall to your needle. If idleness make you so wanton or liberty so malapert, I can quickly tie you to a sharper task. And you, maid, this night be packing either into Arden to your father or whither best it shall content your humor; but in the court you shall not abide."

[41]*huswife:* Our term "hussy" or "minx" is close to the meaning here, which is "saucy girl." But see p. 335, where the sense is "housewife," which in the 1590 edition is also spelled "huswife." See also note 29 in *Euphues.*

This rigorous reply of Torismond nothing amazed Alinda, for still she prosecuted her plea in the defense of Rosalind, wishing her father (if his censure might not be reversed) that he would appoint her partner of her exile; which, if he refused to do, either she would by some secret means steal out and follow her or else end her days with some desperate kind of death. When Torismond heard his daughter so resolute, his heart was so hardened against her that he set down a definitive and peremptory sentence that they should both be banished. Which presently was done, the tyrant rather choosing to hazard the loss of his only child than any ways to put in question the state of his kingdom. So suspicious and fearful is the conscience of an usurper. Well, although his lords persuaded him to retain his own daughter yet his resolution might not be reversed, but both of them must away from the court without either more company or delay. In he went with great melancholy and left these two ladies alone. Rosalind waxed very sad and sat down and wept. Alinda she smiled and, sitting by her friend, began thus to comfort her:

Alinda's Comfort to Perplexed Rosalind

"Why, how now, Rosalind, dismayed with a frown of contrary fortune? Have I not oft heard thee say that high minds were discovered in fortune's contempt and heroical seen in the depth of extremities? Thou wert wont to tell others that complained of distress that the sweetest salve for misery was patience and the only medicine for want that precious emplaster[42] of content. Being such a good physician to others, wilt thou not minister receipts to thyself? But perchance thou wilt say, *Consulenti nunquam caput doluit.*

"Why, then, if the patients that are sick of this disease can find in themselves neither reason to persuade nor art to cure, yet, Rosalind, admit of the counsel of a friend and apply the salves that may appease thy passions. If thou grievest that being the daughter of a prince and envy thwarteth thee with such hard exigents, think that royalty is a fair mark, that crowns have crosses when mirth is in cottages, that the fairer the rose is the sooner it is bitten with caterpillars, the more orient the pearl is the more apt to take a blemish; and the greatest birth, as it hath most honor, so it hath much envy. If, then, fortune aimeth at the fairest, be patient, Rosalind, for first by thine exile thou goest to thy father. Nature is higher prized than wealth, and the love of one's parents ought to be more precious than all dignities. Why,

---

[42]*emplaster:* plaster (a medicinal balm or salve).

then, doth my Rosalind grieve at the frown of Torismond, who, by offering her a prejudice, proffers her a great pleasure? And more, mad lass, to be melancholy when thou hast with thee Alinda, a friend who will be a faithful copartner of all thy misfortunes, who hath left her father to follow thee and chooseth rather to brook all extremities than to forsake thy presence. What, Rosalind, *solamen miseris socios habuisse doloris.* Cheerily, woman, as we have been bedfellows in royalty we will be fellow mates in poverty. I will ever be thy Alinda, and thou shalt ever rest to me Rosalind; so shall the world canonize our friendship and speak of Rosalind and Alinda as they did of Pylades and Orestes. And if ever fortune smile, and we return to our former honor, then folding ourselves in the sweet of our friendship, we shall merrily say, calling to mind our forepassed miseries: *olim haec meminisse juvabit.*"

At this, Rosalind began to comfort her; and after she had wept a few kind tears in the bosom of her Alinda, she gave her hearty thanks, and then they sat them down to consult how they should travel. Alinda grieved at nothing but that they might have no man in their company, saying it would be their greatest prejudice in that two women went wandering without either guide or attendant.

"Tush," quoth Rosalind, "art thou a woman and hast not a sudden shift to prevent a misfortune? I, thou seest, am of a tall stature and would very well become the person and apparel of a page. Thou shalt be my mistress, and I will play the man so properly, that, trust me, in what company soever I come I will not be discovered. I will buy me a suit and have my rapier very handsomely at my side; and if any knave offer wrong, your page will show him the point of his weapon."

At this Alinda smiled, and upon this they agreed and presently gathered up all their jewels, which they trussed up in a casket; and Rosalind in all haste provided her of robes, and Alinda (from her royal weeds) put herself in more homely attire. Thus fitted to the purpose, away go these two friends, having now changed their names, Alinda being called Aliena and Rosalind Ganymede. They traveled along the vineyards, and by many byways at last got to the forest side, where they traveled by the space of two or three days without seeing any creature, being often in danger of wild beasts and pained with many passionate sorrows. Now the black ox began to tread on their feet,[43] and Alinda thought of her wonted royalty; but when she

---

[43]*black ox . . . their feet:* a slight variation of a proverb (Tilley, O103): "The black ox never trod on his foot" (he has not yet felt the burden of married life).

cast her eyes on her Rosalind, she thought every danger a step to honor.

Passing thus on along, about midday they came to a fountain compassed with a groove of cypress trees so cunningly and curiously planted, as if some goddess had entreated nature in that place to make her an arbor. By this fountain sat Aliena and her Ganymede, and forth they pulled such victuals as they had and fed as merrily as if they had been in Paris with all the king's delicates—Aliena only grieving that they could not so much as meet with a shepherd to discourse them the way to some place where they might make their abode. At last Ganymede, casting up his eye, espied where on a tree was engraven certain verses, which as soon as he espied he cried out, "Be of good cheer, mistress; I spy the figures of men, for here in these trees be engraven certain verses of shepherds or some other swains that inhabit hereabout."

With that Aliena start up joyful to hear these news, and looked, where they found carved in the bark of a pine tree this passion:

Montanus' Passion

Hadst thou been born whereas perpetual cold
Makes Tanais hard and mountains silver old;
Had I complained unto a marble stone,
Or to the floods bewrayed my bitter moan,
   I then could bear the burden of my grief.
But even the pride of countries at thy birth,
Whilst heavens did smile, did new array the earth
            With flowers chief;
Yet thou the flower of beauty blessed born,
Hast pretty looks but all attired in scorn.
Had I the power to weep sweet Myrrha's tears,
Or by my plaints to pierce repining ears;
Hadst thou the heart to smile at my complaint,
To scorn the woes that doth my heart attaint,
   I then could bear the burden of my grief.
But not my tears, but truth with thee prevails,
And seeming sour my sorrows thee assails,
            Yet small relief;
For if thou wilt thou art of marble hard,
And if thou please my suit shall soon be heard.

"No doubt," quoth Aliena, "this poesy is the passion of some perplexed shepherd that, being enamored of some fair and beautiful shepherdess, suffered some sharp repulse, and therefore complained of the cruelty of his mistress."

"You may see," quoth Ganymede, "what mad cattle you women be, whose hearts sometimes are made of adamant that will touch with no impression and sometime of wax that is fit for every form. They delight to be courted, and then they glory to seem coy; and when they are most desired, then they freeze with disdain. And this fault is so common to the sex, that you see it painted out in the shepherd's passions, who found his mistress as froward as he was enamored."

"And I pray you," quoth Aliena, "if your robes were off, what mettle are you made of that you are so satirical against women? Is it not a foul bird defiles the own nest? Beware, Ganymede, that Rosader hear you not; if he do, perchance you will make him leap so far from love that he will anger every vein in your heart."

"Thus," quoth Ganymede, "I keep decorum: I speak now as I am Aliena's page, not as I am Gerismond's daughter; for put me but into a petticoat, and I will stand in defiance to the uttermost that women are courteous, constant, virtuous, and what not."

"Stay there," quoth Aliena, "and no more words, for yonder be characters graven upon the bark of the tall beech tree."

"Let us see," quoth Ganymede; and with that they read a fancy written to this effect:

> First shall the heavens want starry light,
> The seas be robbed of their waves,
> The day want sun, and sun want bright,
> The night want shade, the dead men graves,
> The April flowers and leaf and tree,
> Before I false my faith to thee.
>
> First shall the tops of highest hills
> By humble plains be overpried,[44]
> And poets scorn the Muses' quills,
> And fish forsake the water glide,
> And Iris lose her colored weed,[45]
> Before I fail thee at thy need.

[44]*overpried:* The sense seems to be "pried over" (raised over by force of leverage); if so, this example is more than 200 years earlier than any given in the *OED*. Other possible senses are "overprize" (overrate) and "overpry" (examine inquisitively), but they do not seem to fit well.

[45]*lose her colored weed:* Elizabethan spelling made no distinction between "loose" (the spelling in the early editions) and "lose," which seems to be the meaning here; contrast the sense of "loose" (free of bonds) on p. 322. "Weed" literally means "garment," but here it means "petals."

First direful hate shall turn to peace,
  And love relent in deep disdain,
And death his fatal stroke shall cease,
  And envy pity every pain,
And pleasure mourn and sorrow smile,
Before I talk of any guile.

First time shall stay his stayless race,
  And winter bless his brows with corn,
And snow bemoisten July's face,
  And winter spring, and summer mourn,
Before my pen, by help of fame,
Cease to recite thy sacred name.
                              Montanus

"No doubt," quoth Ganymede, "this protestation grew from one full of passions."

"I am of that mind, too," quoth Aliena, "but see, I pray, when poor women seek to keep themselves chaste, how men woo them with many feigned promises, alluring with sweet words as the Sirens, and after proving as trothless as Aeneas. Thus promised Demophon to his Phyllis, but who at last grew more false?"

"The reason was," quoth Ganymede, "that they were women's sons and took that fault of their mother, for if man had grown from man, as Adam did from the earth, men had never been troubled with inconstancy."

"Leave off," quoth Aliena, "to taunt thus bitterly, or else I'll pull off your page's apparel and whip you, as Venus doth her wantons, with nettles."

"So you will," quoth Ganymede, "persuade me to flattery, and that needs not. But come, seeing we have found here by this fount the tract of shepherds by their madrigals and roundelays, let us forward; for either we shall find some folds, sheepcotes, or else some cottages wherein for a day or two to rest."

"Content," quoth Aliena, and with that they rose up and marched forward till towards the even; and then, coming into a fair valley (compassed with mountains whereon grew many pleasant shrubs) they might descry where two flocks of sheep did feed. Then, looking about, they might perceive where an old shepherd sat, and with him a young swain, under a covert most pleasantly situated. The ground where they sat was diapered with Flora's riches, as if she meant to wrap Tellus in the glory of her vestments. Round about in the form of an amphitheater were most curiously planted pine trees interseamed with lemons and citrons, which with the thickness of their boughs so shadowed the place that Phoebus could not pry into the secret of that arbor; so united were the tops with so thick a closure that Venus might there in her jollity have dallied unseen with her dearest paramour. Fast by, to make the place more gorgeous, was there a fount so crystalline and clear that it seemed Diana with her Dryads and Hamadryads had that spring as the secret of all their bathings. In this glorious arbor sat these two shepherds, seeing their sheep feed, playing on their pipes many pleasant tunes, and from music and melody falling into much amorous chat. Drawing more nigh we might descry the countenance of the one to be full of sorrow, his face to be the very portraiture of discontent, and his eyes full of woes that, living, he seemed to die. We, to hear what these were, stole privily behind the thicket, where we overheard this discourse:

A *Pleasant Eclogue Between Montanus and Corydon*

Corydon

Say, shepherd's boy, what makes thee greet[46] so sore?
Why leaves thy pipe his pleasure and delight?
Young are thy years, thy cheeks with roses dight;
Then sing for joy, sweet swain, and sigh no more.

This milk-white poppy and this climbing pine
Both promise shade; then sit thee down and sing,
And make these woods with pleasant notes to ring,
Till Phoebus deign all westward to decline.

Montanus

Ah, Corydon, unmeet is melody
To him whom proud contempt hath overborn;
Slain are my joys by Phoebe's bitter scorn;
Far hence my weal and near my jeopardy.

Love's burning brand is couched in my breast,
Making a phoenix of my faintful heart;
And though his fury do enforce my smart,
Aye blithe am I to honor his behest.

Prepared to woes since so my Phoebe wills,
My looks dismayed, since Phoebe will disdain;
I banish bliss and welcome home my pain,
So stream my tears as showers from Alpine hills.

[46]*greet:* weep.

In error's mask I blindfold judgment's eye,
I fetter reason in the snares of lust,
I seem secure, yet know not how to trust;
I live by that which makes me, living, die.

Devoid of rest, companion of distress,
Plague to myself, consumed by my thought,
How may my voice or pipe in tune be brought,
Since I am reft of solace and delight?

Corydon

Ah, lorel[47] lad, what makes thee hery[48] love?
A sugared harm, a poison full of pleasure,
A painted shrine full-filled with rotten treasure,
A heaven in show, a hell to them that prove.

A gain in seeming, shadowed still with want,
A broken staff which folly doth uphold,
A flower that fades with every frosty cold,
An orient rose sprung from a withered plant.

A minute's joy to gain a world of grief,
A subtle net to snare the idle mind,
A seeing scorpion, yet in seeming blind,
A poor rejoice, a plague without relief.

For-thy, Montanus, follow mine aread,[49]
Whom age hath taught the trains[50] that fancy useth,
Leave foolish love, for beauty wit abuseth,
And drowns by folly virtue's springing seed.

Montanus

So blames the child the flame because it burns,
And bird the snare because it doth entrap,
And fools true love because of sorry hap,
And sailors curse the ship that overturns.

But would the child forbear to play with flame,
And birds beware to trust the fowler's gin,
And fools foresee before they fall and sin,
And masters guide their ships in better frame,

47*lorel:* worthless.
48*hery:* praise.
49*For-thy . . . aread:* Therefore . . . counsel.
50*trains:* snares.

The child would praise the fire because it warms,
And birds rejoice to see the fowler fail,
And fools prevent before their plagues prevail,
And sailors bless the bark that saves from harms.

Ah, Corydon, though many be thy years,
And crooked eld[51] hath some experience left,
Yet is thy mind of judgment quite bereft,
In view of love whose power in me appears.

The plowman little wots to turn the pen,
Or bookman skills to guide the plowman's cart,
Nor can the cobbler count the terms of art,
Nor base men judge the thoughts of mighty men,

Nor withered age (unmeet for beauty's guide,
Uncapable of love's impression)
Discourse of that whose choice possession
May never to so base a man be tied.

But I whom nature makes of tender mold,
And youth most pliant yields to fancy's fire,
Do build my haven and heaven on sweet desire,
On sweet desire more dear to me than gold.

Think I of love, oh, how my lines aspire!
How haste the Muses to embrace my brows,
And hem my temples in with laurel boughs,
And fill my brains with chaste and holy fire!

Then leave my lines their homely equipage,
Mounted beyond the circle of the sun;
Amazed I read the style when I have done,
And hery love that sent that heavenly rage.

Of Phoebe then, of Phoebe then I sing,
Drawing the purity of all the spheres,
The pride of earth, or what in heaven appears,
Her honored face and fame to light to bring.

In fluent numbers and in pleasant veins,
I rob both sea and earth of all their state,
To praise her parts I charm both time and fate,
To bless the nymph that yields me lovesick pains.

My sheep are turned to thoughts whom froward will
Guides in the restless labyrinth of love;
Fear lends them pasture wheresoe'er they move,
And by their death their life reneweth still.

[51]*eld:* (old) age.

My sheephook is my pen, mine oaten reed
My paper, where my many woes are written;
Thus, silly swain, with love and fancy bitten,
I trace the plains[52] of pain in woeful weed.

Yet are my cares, my broken sleeps, my tears,
My dreams, my doubts, for Phoebe sweet to me,
Who waiteth heaven in sorrow's vale must be,
And glory shines where danger most appears.

Then, Corydon, although I blithe me not,
Blame me not, man, since sorrow is my sweet,
So willeth love, and Phoebe thinks it meet,
And kind Montanus liketh well his lot.

Corydon

Oh, stayless youth, by error so misguided,
Where will prescribeth laws to perfect wits,
Where reason mourns and blame in triumph sits,
And folly poisoneth all that time provided.

With willful blindness bleared, prepared to shame,
Prone to neglect occasion when she smiles;
Alas that love, by fond and froward guiles,
Should make thee tract[53] the path to endless blame.

Ah, my Montanus, cursed is the charm
That hath bewitched so thy youthful eyes;
Leave off in time to like these vanities,
Be forward to thy good and fly thy harm.

As many bees as Hybla daily shields
As many fry as fleet[54] on ocean's face,
As many herds as on the earth do trace,
As many flowers as deck the fragrant fields,

As many stars as glorious heaven contains,
As many storms as wayward winter weeps,
As many plagues as hell enclosed keeps—
So many griefs in love, so many pains.

Suspicions, thoughts, desires, opinions, prayers,
Mislikes, misdeeds, fond joys, and feigned peace;
Illusions, dreams, great pains, and small increase;
Vows, hopes, acceptance, scorns, and deep despairs;

---

[52]*I trace the plains:* One possible sense is "I made my way over the expanse" ("plains" in the sense of "open country"). Greg preferred to take "plains" as "complaints" or "lamentations," and the 1609 edition actually emended to "plaints" (adding the "t").

[53]*tract:* trace.

[54]*fry ... fleet:* (small) fish ... float.

Truce, war, and woe do wait at beauty's gate;
Time lost, lament, reports, and privy grudge;
And, last, fierce love is but a partial judge,
Who yields for service shame, for friendship hate.

Montanus

All adder-like I stop mine ears, fond swain,
So charm no more, for I will never change.
Call home thy flocks in time that straggling range,
For, lo, the sun declineth hence amain.

Terentius

In amore haec omnia insunt vitia—induciae, inimicitiae, bellum, pax rursum. Incerta haec si tu postules ratione certa fieri, nihilo plus agas, quam si des operam, ut cum ratione insanias.[55]

The shepherds having thus ended their eclogue, Aliena stepped with Ganymede from behind the thicket; at whose sudden sight the shepherds arose, and Aliena saluted them thus:

"Shepherds, all hail (for such we deem you by your flocks) and lovers, good luck (for such you seem by your passions)—our eyes being witness of the one and our ears of the other. Although not by love, yet by fortune I am a distressed gentlewoman, as sorrowful as you are passionate and as full of woes as you are of perplexed thoughts. Wandering this way in a forest unknown, only I and my page, wearied with travel, would fain have some place of rest. May you appoint us any place of quiet harbor, be it never so mean, I shall be thankful to you, contented in myself, and grateful to whosoever shall be mine host."

Corydon, hearing the gentlewoman speak so courteously, returned her mildly and reverently this answer:

"Fair mistress, we return you as hearty a welcome as you gave us a courteous salute. A shepherd I am, and this a lover, as watchful to please his wench as to feed his sheep, full of fancies—and therefore, say I, full of follies. Exhort him I may but persuade him I cannot, for love admits neither of counsel nor reason. But leaving him to his passions, if you be distressed, I am sorrowful such a fair creature is crossed with calamity. Pray for you I may, but relieve you I cannot.

---

[55]*In amore ... insanias:* "In love all offenses are included—truces, war, peace once again. If you subject all these uncertainties to the rule of reason, you will do no more than if you tried to rave with reason." The passage is quoted, with several changes, from five lines of poetry in Terence's *The Eunuch*, I, i, 14–18.

Marry, if you want lodging, if you vouch to shroud yourselves in a shepherd's cottage, my house for this night shall be your harbor."

Aliena thanked Corydon greatly and presently sat her down and Ganymede by her. Corydon—looking earnestly upon her, and with a curious survey viewing all her perfections, applauded in his thought her excellence and, pitying her distress, was desirous to hear the cause of her misfortunes—began to question with her thus:

"If I should not, fair damsel, occasionate offense or renew your griefs by rubbing the scar, I would fain crave so much favor as to know the cause of your misfortune, and why and whither you wander with your page in so dangerous a forest."

Aliena (that was as courteous as she was fair) made this reply:

"Shepherd, a friendly demand ought never to be offensive, and questions of courtesy carry privileged pardons in their foreheads. Know, therefore, to discover my fortunes were to renew my sorrows, and I should by discoursing my mishaps but rake fire out of the cinders. Therefore, let this suffice, gentle shepherd: my distress is as great as my travel is dangerous, and I wander in this forest to light on some cottage where I and my page may dwell. For I mean to buy some farm and a flock of sheep and so become a shepherdess, meaning to live low and content me with a country life; for I have heard the swains say that they drunk without suspicion and slept without care."

"Marry, mistress," quoth Corydon, "if you mean so you came in a good time, for my landslord intends to sell both the farm I till and the flock I keep, and cheap you may have them for ready money. And for a shepherd's life, oh, mistress, did you but live awhile in their content you would say the court were rather a place of sorrow than of solace. Here, mistress, shall not fortune thwart you but in mean misfortunes, as the loss of a few sheep, which, as it breeds no beggary, so it can be no extreme prejudice. The next year may mend all with a fresh increase. Envy stirs not us, we covet not to climb, our desires mount not above our degrees, nor our thoughts above our fortunes. Care cannot harbor in our cottages, nor do our homely couches know broken slumbers. As we exceed not in diet, so we have enough to satisfy; and, mistress, I have so much Latin, *satis est quod sufficit.*"

"By my troth, shepherd," quoth Aliena, "thou makest me in love with your country life; and therefore send for thy landslord, and I will buy thy farm and thy flocks, and thou shalt still, under me, be overseer of them both. Only for pleasure sake I and my page will serve you, lead the flocks to the field, and fold them. Thus will I live quiet, unknown, and contented."

This news so gladded the heart of Corydon, that he should not be put out of his farm, that (putting off his shepherd's bonnet) he did her all the reverence that he might. But all this while sat Montanus in a muse thinking of the cruelty of his Phoebe, whom he wooed long but was in no hope to win. Ganymede, who still had the remembrance of Rosader in his thoughts, took delight to see the poor shepherd passionate, laughing at love that in all his actions was so imperious. At last, when she had noted his tears that stole down his cheeks and his sighs that broke from the center of his heart, pitying his lament, she demanded of Corydon why the young shepherd looked so sorrowful.

"Oh, sir," quoth he, "the boy is in love."

"Why," quoth Ganymede, "can shepherds love?"

"Aye," quoth Montanus, "and overlove, else shouldst not thou see me so pensive. Love, I tell thee, is as precious in a shepherd's eye as in the looks of a king; and we country swains entertain fancy with as great delight as the proudest courtier doth affection. Opportunity (that is the sweetest friend to Venus) harboreth in our cottages, and loyalty (the chiefest fealty that Cupid requires) is found more among shepherds than higher degrees. Then ask not if such silly swains can love."

"What is the cause, then," quoth Ganymede, "that love being so sweet to thee, thou lookest so sorrowful?"

"Because," quoth Montanus, "the party beloved is froward and, having courtesy in her looks, holdeth disdain in her tongue's end."

"What hath she, then," quoth Aliena, "in her heart?"

"Desire, I hope, madam," quoth he, "or else, my hope lost, despair in love were death."

As thus they chatted, the sun being ready to set and they not having folded their sheep, Corydon requested she would sit there with her page till Montanus and he lodged their sheep for that night.

"You shall go," quoth Aliena, "but first I will entreat Montanus to sing some amorous sonnet that he made when he hath been deeply passionate."

"That I will," quoth Montanus, and with that he began thus:

Montanus' Sonnet

Phoebe sat,[56]
Sweet she sat,
    Sweet sat Phoebe when I saw her;
White her brow,
Coy her eye,
    Brow and eye, how much you please me!
Words I spent,
Sighs I sent,
    Sighs and words could never draw her.
Oh, my love,
Thou art lost,
    Since no sight could ever ease thee.

Phoebe sat
By a fount,
    Sitting by a fount I spied her.
Sweet her touch,
Rare her voice,
    Touch and voice, what may distain[57] you?
As she sung
I did sigh,
    And by sighs whilst that I tried her,
Oh, mine eyes,
You did lose
    Her first sight whose want did pain you.
Phoebe's flocks,
White as wool;
    Yet were Phoebe's locks more whiter.
Phoebe's eyes,
Dovelike mild,
    Dovelike eyes both mild and cruel.
Montan swears,
In your lamps
    He will die for to delight her.
Phoebe, yield,
Or I die;
    Shall true hearts be fancy's fuel?

[56]*sat:* The spelling in the 1590 edition for the verb in each of the first
three lines of this stanza is "sate," though in the first line of the second
stanza it is "sat." Greg and Baldwin, though they are modernizing, leave the
spelling differences; but to do so is misleading, for "sate" suggests "satisfy"
and is no longer an alternate spelling of "sat," the meaning in all four uses.
(Edward Chauncey Baldwin's edition of *Rosalind* appeared in 1910, published in Boston by Ginn.)

[57]*distain:* outshine, be superior to.

Montanus had no sooner ended his sonnet but Corydon, with a low courtesy, rose up and went with his fellow and shut their sheep in the folds and, after returning to Aliena and Ganymede, conducted them home weary to his poor cottage. By the way there was much good chat with Montanus about his loves, he resolving Aliena that Phoebe was the fairest shepherdess in all France and that in his eye her beauty was equal with the nymphs.

"But," quoth he, "as of all stones the diamond is most clearest and yet most hard for the lapidary to cut, as of all flowers the rose is the fairest and yet guarded with the sharpest prickles, so of all our country lasses Phoebe is the brightest but the most coy of all to stoop unto desire. But let her take heed," quoth he, "I have heard of Narcissus, who, for his high disdain against love, perished in the folly of his own love."

With this they were at Corydon's cottage, where Montanus parted from them and they went in to rest. Alinda[58] and Ganymede, glad of so contented a shelter, made merry with the poor swain; and though they had but country fare and coarse lodging, yet their welcome was so great and their cares so little that they counted their diet delicate and slept as soundly as if they had been in the court of Torismond. The next morn they lay long in bed, as wearied with the toil of unaccustomed travel; but as soon as they got up, Aliena resolved there to set up her rest, and by the help of Corydon swapt a bargain[59] with his landslord and so became mistress of the farm and the flock, herself putting on the attire of a shepherdess and Ganymede of a young swain, every day leading forth her flocks with such delight that she held her exile happy and thought no content[60] to the bliss of a country cottage.

Leaving her thus famous amongst the shepherds of Arden, again to Saladyne.

When Saladyne had a long while concealed a secret resolution of revenge and could no longer hide fire in the flax nor oil in the flame— for envy is like lightning that will appear in the darkest fog—it chanced on a morning very early he called up certain of his servants and went with them to the chamber of Rosader; which, being open, he entered with his crew and surprised his brother, being asleep, and bound him in fetters, and in the midst of his hall chained him to a

[58]*Alinda:* Aliena; it is possible, though not likely, that the narrator intends to remind us that Aliena is Alinda in disguise.

[59]*swapt a bargain:* struck a bargain.

[60]*thought no content:* Understood after this phrase, or possibly omitted by the typesetter, is "could compare."

post. Rosader, amazed at this strange chance, began to reason with his brother about the cause of this sudden extremity, wherein he had wronged and what fault he had committed worthy so sharp a penance. Saladyne answered him only with a look of disdain and went his way, leaving poor Rosader in a deep perplexity. Who, thus abused, fell into sundry passions, but no means of relief could be had; whereupon, for anger, he grew into a discontented melancholy. In which humor he continued two or three days without meat; insomuch that seeing his brother would give him no food, he fell into despair of his life. Which Adam Spencer, the old servant of Sir John of Bordeaux, seeing, touched with the duty and love he ought[61] to his old master, felt a remorse in his conscience of his son's mishap; and, therefore, although Saladyne had given a general charge to his servants that none of them, upon pain of death, should give either meat or drink to Rosader, yet Adam Spencer in the night arose secretly and brought him such victuals as he could provide and unlocked him and set him at liberty. After Rosader had well feasted himself and felt he was loose, straight his thoughts aimed at revenge; and now, all being asleep, he would have quit[62] Saladyne with the method of his own mischief. But Adam Spencer persuaded him to the contrary with these reasons:

"Sir," quoth he, "be content, for this night go again into your old fetters; so shall you try the faith of friends and save the life of an old servant. Tomorrow hath your brother invited all your kindred and allies to a solemn breakfast only to see you, telling them all that you are mad and fain to be tied to a post. As soon as they come, make complaint to them of the abuse proffered you by Saladyne. If they redress you, why so; but if they pass over your plaints *sicco pede,* and hold with the violence of your brother before your innocence, then thus: I will leave you unlocked that you may break out at your pleasure, and at the end of the hall shall you see stand a couple of good poleaxes, one for you and another for me. When I give you a wink, shake off your chains and let us play the men and make havoc amongst them—drive them out of the house and maintain possession by force of arms, till the king hath made a redress of your abuses."

These words of Adam Spencer so persuaded Rosader that he went to the place of his punishment and stood there while[63] the next morning. About the time appointed, came all the guests bidden by Sala-

[61]*ought:* owed.
[62]*quit:* requited.
[63]*while:* until.

dyne, whom he entreated with courteous and curious entertainment, as they all perceived their welcome to be great. The tables in the hall where Rosader was tied were covered; and Saladyne, bringing in his guests together, showed them where his brother was bound and was enchained as a man lunatic. Rosader made reply and, with some invectives, made complaints of the wrongs proffered him by Saladyne, desiring they would in pity seek some means for his relief. But in vain; they had stopped their ears, with Ulysses, that, were his words never so forceable, he breathed only his passions into the wind. They, careless, sat down with Saladyne to dinner, being very frolic and pleasant, washing their heads well with wine. At last, when the fume of the grape had entered pell-mell into their brains, they began in satirical speeches to rail against Rosader. Which, Adam Spencer no longer brooking, gave the sign; and Rosader, shaking off his chains, got a poleax in his hand and flew amongst them with such violence and fury that he hurt many, slew some, and drove his brother and all the rest quite out of the house. Seeing the coast clear, he shut the doors and, being sore an-hungered and seeing such good victuals, he sat him down with Adam Spencer and such good fellows as he knew were honest men, and there feasted themselves with such provision as Saladyne had prepared for his friends.

After they had taken their repast, Rosader rampired[64] up the house, lest upon a sudden his brother should raise some crew of his tenants and surprise them unawares. But Saladyne took a contrary course and went to the sheriff of the shire and made complaint of Rosader. Who, giving credit to Saladyne, in a determined resolution to revenge the gentleman's wrongs, took with him five and twenty tall men and made a vow either to break into the house and take Rosader or else to coop him in till he made him yield by famine. In this determination, gathering a crew together, he went forward to set Saladyne in his former estate. News of this was brought unto Rosader, who, smiling at the cowardice of his brother, brooked all the injuries of fortune with patience, expecting the coming of the sheriff. As he walked upon the battlements of the house, he descried where Saladyne and he drew near with a troop of lusty gallants. At this he smiled and called up Adam Spencer and showed him the envious treachery of his brother and the folly of the sheriff to be so credulous.

"Now, Adam," quoth he, "what shall I do? It rests for me either to yield up the house to my brother and seek a reconcilement or else

---

[64]*rampired:* barricaded (made "ramparts" or "rampires").

issue out and break through the company with courage; for cooped in like a coward I will not be. If I submit, ah, Adam, I dishonor myself, and that is worse than death; for by such open disgraces the fame of men grows odious. If I issue out amongst them, fortune may favor me and I may escape with life. But suppose the worst: if I be slain, then my death shall be honorable to me and so inequal a revenge infamous to Saladyne."

"Why, then, master, forward and fear not. Out amongst them. They be but fainthearted losels; and for Adam Spencer, if he die not at your foot, say he is a dastard."

These words cheered up so the heart of young Rosader that he thought himself sufficient for them all, and therefore prepared weapons for him and Adam Spencer, and were ready to entertain the sheriff. For no sooner came Saladyne and he to the gates, but Rosader, unlooked for, leaped out and assailed them, wounded many of them and caused the rest to give back, so that Adam and he broke through the prease[65] in despite of them all and took their way towards the forest of Arden. This repulse so set the sheriff's heart on fire to revenge that he straight raised all the country and made hue and cry after them. But Rosader and Adam, knowing full well the secret ways that led through the vineyards, stole away privily through the province of Bordeaux and escaped safe to the forest of Arden.

Being come thither, they were glad they had so good a harbor; but fortune, who is like the chameleon—variable with every object and constant in nothing but inconstancy—thought to make them mirrors of her mutability, and therefore still crossed them thus contrarily. Thinking still to pass on by the byways to get to Lyons, they chanced on a path that led into the thick of the forest, where they wandered five or six days without meat, that they were almost famished, finding neither shepherd nor cottage to relieve them. And hunger growing on so extreme, Adam Spencer, being old, began first to faint, and sitting him down on a hill and looking about him, espied where Rosader lay as feeble and as ill perplexed. Which sight made him shed tears and to fall into these bitter terms:

Adam Spencer's Speech

"Oh, how the life of man may well be compared to the state of the ocean seas, that for every calm hath a thousand storms: resembling the rose tree, that for a few fair flowers hath a multitude of sharp

[65]*prease:* press (of a crowd).

prickles. All our pleasures end in pain, and our highest delights are crossed with deepest discontents. The joys of man, as they are few so are they momentary, scarce ripe before they are rotten and withering in the blossom, either parched with the heat of envy or fortune. Fortune—oh, inconstant friend—that in all thy deeds art froward and fickle, delighting, in the poverty of the lowest and the overthrow of the highest, to decipher[66] thy inconstancy. Thou standest upon a globe, and thy wings are plumed with time's feathers, that thou mayest ever be restless. Thou art double-faced like Janus, carrying frowns in the one to threaten and smiles in the other to betray. Thou profferest an eel and performest a scorpion; and where thy greatest favors be, there is the fear of the extremest misfortunes, so variable are all thy actions.

"But why, Adam, dost thou exclaim against fortune? She laughs at the plaints of the distressed, and there is nothing more pleasing unto her than to hear fools boast in her fading allurements or sorrowful men to discover the sower[67] of their passions. Glut her not, Adam, then, with content, but thwart her with brooking all mishaps with patience. For there is no greater check to the pride of fortune than with a resolute courage to pass over her crosses without care. Thou art old, Adam, and thy hairs wax white; the palm tree is already full of blooms, and in the furrows of thy face appears the calendars of death. Wert thou blessed by fortune, thy years could not be many nor the date of thy life long; then sith nature must have her due, what is it for thee to resign her debt a little before the day.

"Ah, it is not this which grieveth me, nor do I care what mishaps fortune can wage against me. But the sight of Rosader—that galleth unto the quick. When I remember the worships of his house, the honor of his fathers, and the virtues of himself, then do I say that fortune and the fates are most injurious to censure so hard extremes against a youth of so great hope. Oh, Rosader, thou art in the flower of thine age and in the pride of thy years, buxom and full of May. Nature hath prodigally enriched thee with her favors, and virtue made thee the mirror of her excellence; and now, through the decree of the unjust stars, to have all these good parts nipped in the blade and blemished by the inconstancy of fortune. Ah, Rosader, could I

[66]*delighting . . . to decipher:* delighting . . . to reveal (make known); Fortune is thus perverse in openly showing her inconstancy and inconsistency of character.

[67]*discover the sower:* reveal that she, Fortune, is the sower of the seeds of their passion.

help thee my grief were the less, and happy should my death be if it might be the beginning of thy relief. But seeing we perish both in one extreme, it is a double sorrow. What shall I do? Prevent the sight of his further misfortune with a present dispatch of mine own life? Ah, despair is a merciless sin."

As he was ready to go forward in his passion, he looked earnestly on Rosader and, seeing him change color, he rose[68] up and went to him and, holding his temples, said, "What cheer, master? Though all fail, let not the heart faint. The courage of a man is showed in the resolution of his death."

At these words Rosader lifted up his eye and, looking on Adam Spencer, began to weep.

"Ah, Adam," quoth he, "I sorrow not to die, but I grieve at the manner of my death. Might I with my lance encounter the enemy and so die in the field, it were honor and content. Might I, Adam, combat with some wild beast and perish as his prey, I were satisfied. But to die with hunger, oh, Adam, it is the extremest of all extremes."

"Master," quoth he, "you see we are both in one predicament, and long I cannot live without meat. Seeing, therefore, we can find no food, let the death of the one preserve the life of the other. I am old and overworn with age; you are young and are the hope of many honors. Let me then die. I will presently cut my veins, and, master, with the warm blood relieve your fainting spirits. Suck on that till I end, and you be comforted."

With that Adam Spencer was ready to pull out his knife, when Rosader, full of courage, though very faint, rose up and wished Adam Spencer to sit there till his return.

"For my mind gives me," quoth he, "I shall bring thee meat."

With that, like a madman, he rose up and ranged up and down the woods, seeking to encounter some wild beast with his rapier, that either he might carry his friend Adam food or else pledge his life in pawn of his loyalty.

It chanced that day that Gerismond, the lawful king of France banished by Torismond, who with a lusty crew of outlaws lived in

---

[68]*rose:* The spelling in the first edition is "rise,"which in 1590 is still acceptable usage for the past tense (rose) and the past participle (risen). But since "rose" is actually used for the past tense on sig. L1 of the 1590 edition (p. 346 in the present edition), the editor has taken the liberty of "normalizing" (here and also on p. 359). Unlike Lyly, as explained in note 107 of *Euphues,* Lodge does not seem to be using "rise" for a sound effect.

that forest, that day in honor of his birth made a feast to all his bold yeomen and frolicked it with store of wine and venison, sitting all at a long table under the shadow of lemon trees. To that place by chance fortune conducted Rosader, who, seeing such a crew of brave men having store of that for want of which he and Adam perished, he stepped boldly to the board's end and saluted the company thus:

"Whatsoever thou be that art master of these lusty squires, I salute thee as graciously as a man in extreme distress may. Know that I and a fellow friend of mine are here famished in the forest for want of food. Perish we must unless relieved by thy favors. Therefore, if thou be a gentleman, give meat to men and to such men as are every way worthy of life. Let the proudest squire that sits at thy table rise and encounter with me in any honorable point of activity whatsoever; and if he and thou prove me not a man, send me away comfortless. If thou refuse this, as a niggard of thy cates, I will have amongst you with my sword; for rather will I die valiantly than perish with so cowardly an extreme."

Gerismond, looking him earnestly in the face and seeing so proper a gentleman in so bitter a passion, was moved with so great pity that, rising from the table, he took him by the hand and bade him welcome, willing him to sit down in his place, and in his room not only to eat his fill but be lord of the feast.

"Gramercy, sir," quoth Rosader, "but I have a feeble friend that lies hereby famished almost for food, aged, and therefore less able to abide the extremity of hunger than myself; and dishonor it were for me to taste one crumb before I made him partner of my fortunes. Therefore, I will run and fetch him, and then I will gratefully accept of your proffer."

Away hies Rosader to Adam Spencer and tells him the news; who was glad of so happy fortune, but so feeble he was that he could not go. Whereupon, Rosader got him up on his back and brought him to the place. Which, when Gerismond and his men saw, they greatly applauded their league of friendship; and Rosader, having Gerismond's place assigned him, would not sit there himself, but set down Adam Spencer. Well, to be short, those hungry squires fell to their victuals and feasted themselves with good delicates and great store of wine.

As soon as they had taken their repast, Gerismond, desirous to hear what hard fortune drove them into those bitter extremes, requested Rosader to discourse, if it were not any way prejudicial unto him, the cause of his travel. Rosader, desirous any way to satisfy the courtesy of his favorable host, first beginning his exordium with a volley of sighs and a few lukewarm tears, prosecuted his discourse and told him from point to point all his fortunes: how he was the youngest son of Sir John of Bordeaux, his name Rosader; how his brother sundry times had wronged him; and, lastly, how for beating the sheriff and hurting his men, he fled.

"And this old man," quoth he, "whom I so much love and honor, is surnamed Adam Spencer, an old servant of my father's and one that for his love never failed me in all my misfortunes."

When Gerismond heard this, he fell on the neck of Rosader; and next discoursing unto him how he was Gerismond, their lawful king exiled by Torismond, what familiarity had ever been betwixt his father Sir John of Bordeaux and him, how faithful a subject he lived and how honorably he died, promising for his sake to give both him and his friend such courteous entertainment as his present estate could minister, and upon this made him one of his foresters. Rosader, seeing it was the king, craved pardon for his boldness in that he did not do him due reverence, and humbly gave him thanks for his favorable courtesy. Gerismond, not satisfied yet with news, began to inquire if he had been lately in the court of Torismond and whether he had seen his daughter Rosalind or no. At this, Rosader fetched a deep sigh and, shedding many tears, could not answer. Yet at last, gathering his spirits together, he revealed unto the king how Rosalind was banished, and how there was such a sympathy of affections between Alinda and her that she chose rather to be partaker of her exile than to part fellowship, whereupon the unnatural king banished them both. And now they are wandered none knows whither; neither could any learn since their departure the place of their abode.

This news drove the king into a great melancholy, that presently he arose from all the company and went into his privy chamber, so secret as the harbor of the woods would allow him. The company was all dashed at these tidings; and Rosader and Adam Spencer, having such opportunity went to take their rest. Where we leave them and return again to Torismond.

The flight of Rosader came to the ears of Torismond, who, hearing that Saladyne was sole heir of the lands of Sir John of Bordeaux, desirous to possess such fair revenues, found just occasion to quarrel with Saladyne about the wrongs he proffered to his brother; and, therefore, dispatching a herehault,[69] he sent for Saladyne in all posthaste. Who, marveling what the matter should be, began to examine

---

[69]*herehault:* herald, messenger.

his own conscience, wherein he had offended his highness; but, emboldened with his innocence, he boldly went with the herehault unto the court. Where, as soon as he came, he was not admitted into the presence of the king, but presently sent to prison. This greatly amazed Saladyne, chiefly in that the jailer had a straight charge over him to see that he should be close prisoner. Many passionate thoughts came in his head, till at last he began to fall into consideration of his former follies and to meditate with himself. Leaning his head on his hand and his elbow on his knee, full of sorrow, grief, and disquieted passions, he resolved into these terms:

Saladyne's Complaint

"Unhappy Saladyne, whom folly hath led to these misfortunes and wanton desires wrapped within the labyrinth of these calamities, are not the heavens doomers of men's deeds? And holds not God a balance in his fist to reward with favor and revenge with justice? Oh, Saladyne, the faults of thy youth, as they were fond so were they foul, and not only discovering little nurture but blemishing the excellence of nature. Whelps of one litter are ever most loving, and brothers that are sons of one father should live in friendship without jar. Oh, Saladyne, so it should be; but thou hast with the deer fed against the wind, with the crab strove against the stream and sought to pervert nature by unkindness. Rosader's wrongs—the wrongs of Rosader, Saladyne—cries for revenge, his youth pleads to God to inflict some penance upon thee, his virtues are pleas that enforce writs of displeasure to cross thee. Thou hast highly abused thy kind and natural brother, and the heavens cannot spare to quite[70] thee with punishment. There is no sting to the worm of conscience, no hell to a mind touched with guilt. Every wrong I offered him, called now to remembrance, wringeth a drop of blood from my heart; every bad look, every frown pincheth me at the quick and says, 'Saladyne, thou hast sinned against Rosader.' Be penitent and assign thyself some penance to discover thy sorrow and pacify his wrath."

In the depth of his passion, he was sent for to the king, who, with a look that threatened death, entertained him and demanded of him where his brother was. Saladyne made answer that upon some riot made against the sheriff of the shire he was fled from Bordeaux, but he knew not whither.

"Nay, villain," quoth he, "I have heard of the wrongs thou hast proffered thy brother since the death of thy father, and by thy means

[70]*quite:* requite.

have I lost a most brave and resolute chevalier. Therefore, in justice to punish thee, I spare thy life for thy father's sake, but banish thee forever from the court and country of France. And see thy departure be within ten days, else trust me thou shalt lose thy head."

And with that the king flew away in a rage and left poor Saladyne greatly perplexed; who, grieving at his exile yet determined to bear it with patience and, in penance of his former follies, to travel abroad in every coast till he had found out his brother Rosader. With whom now I begin.

Rosader, being thus preferred to the place of a forester by Gerismond, rooted out the remembrance of his brother's unkindness by continual exercise, traversing the groves and wild forests, partly to hear the melody of the sweet birds which recorded[71] and partly to show his diligent endeavor in his master's behalf. Yet whatsoever he did or howsoever he walked, the lively image of Rosalind remained in memory; on her sweet perfections he fed his thoughts, proving himself like the eagle a trueborn bird, since as the one is known by beholding the sun, so was he by regarding excellent beauty.

One day among the rest, finding a fit opportunity and place convenient, desirous to discover his woes to the woods, he engraved with his knife on the bark of a myrtle tree this pretty estimate of his mistress' perfection:

Sonetto

Of all chaste birds the phoenix doth excel,
Of all strong beasts the lion bears the bell,
Of all sweet flowers the rose doth sweetest smell,
Of all fair maids my Rosalind is fairest.

Of all pure metals gold is only purest,
Of all high trees the pine hath highest crest,
Of all soft sweets I like my mistress' breast,
Of all chaste thoughts my mistress' thoughts are rarest.

Of all proud birds the eagle pleaseth Jove,
Of pretty fowls kind Venus likes the dove,
Of trees Minerva doth the olive love,
Of all sweet nymphs I honor Rosalind.

Of all her gifts her wisdom pleaseth most,
Of all her graces virtue she doth boast;
For all these gifts my life and joy is lost
If Rosalind prove cruel and unkind.

[71]*recorded:* sang, warbled.

In these and such like passions Rosader did every day eternize the name of his Rosalind; and this day, especially when Aliena and Ganymede, enforced by the heat of the sun to seek for shelter, by good fortune arrived in that place where this amorous forester registered his melancholy passions. They saw the sudden change of his looks, his folded arms, his passionate sighs. They heard him often abruptly call on Rosalind, who, poor soul, was as hotly burned as himself, but that she shrouded her pains in the cinders of honorable modesty. Whereupon, guessing him to be in love and, according to the nature of their sex, being pitiful in that behalf, they suddenly broke off his melancholy by their approach; and Ganymede shook him out of his dumps thus:

"What news, forester? Hast thou wounded some deer and lost him in the fall? Care not, man, for so small a loss; thy fees was but the skin, the shoulder, and the horns. 'Tis hunter's luck to aim fair and miss, and a woodman's fortune to strike and yet go without the game."

"Thou art beyond the mark, Ganymede," quoth Aliena; "his passions are greater and his sighs discovers more loss. Perhaps in traversing these thickets he hath seen some beautiful nymph and is grown amorous."

"It may be so," quoth Ganymede, "for here he hath newly engraven some sonnet. Come and see the discourse of the forester's poems."

Reading the sonnet over and hearing him name Rosalind, Aliena looked on Ganymede and laughed; and Ganymede, looking back on the forester and seeing it was Rosader, blushed. Yet thinking to shroud all under her page's apparel, she boldly returned to Rosader and began thus:

"I pray thee tell me, forester, what is this Rosalind for whom thou pinest away in such passions? Is she some nymph that waits upon Diana's train, whose chastity thou hast deciphered in such epithets? Or is she some shepherdess that haunts these plains whose beauty hath so bewitched thy fancy, whose name thou shadowest in covert under the figure of Rosalind as Ovid did Julia under the name of Corinna? Or, say me forsooth, is it that Rosalind of whom we shepherds have heard talk—she, forester, that is the daughter of Gerismond, that once was king and now an outlaw in this forest of Arden?"

At this Rosader fetched a deep sigh and said, "It is she, oh gentle swain, it is she. That saint it is whom I serve, that goddess at whose shrine I do bend all my devotions, the most fairest of all fairs, the phoenix of all that sex and the purity of all earthly perfection."

"And why, gentle forester, if she be so beautiful and thou so amorous, is there such a disagreement in thy thoughts? Happily she resembleth the rose that is sweet but full of prickles, or the serpent regius that hath scales as glorious as the sun and a breath as infectious as the aconitum is deadly? So thy Rosalind may be most amiable and yet unkind, full of favor and yet froward, coy without wit, and disdainful without reason."

"Oh, shepherd," quoth Rosader, "knewest thou her personage, graced with the excellence of all perfection, being a harbor wherein the Graces shroud their virtues, thou wouldst not breathe out such blasphemy against the beauteous Rosalind. She is a diamond, bright but not hard, yet of most chaste operation, a pearl so orient that it can be stained with no blemish, a rose without prickles, and a princess absolute as well in beauty as in virtue. But I, unhappy I, have let mine eye soar with the eagle against so bright a sun, that I am quite blind; I have with Apollo enamored myself of a Daphne, not, as she, disdainful, but far more chaste than Daphne; I have with Ixion laid my love on Juno and shall, I fear, embrace nought but a cloud. Ah, shepherd, I have reached at a star, my desires have mounted above my degree, and my thoughts above my fortunes. I, being a peasant, have ventured to gaze on a princess, whose honors are too high to vouchsafe such base loves."

"Why, forester," quoth Ganymede, "comfort thyself; be blithe and frolic, man. Love souseth[72] as low as she soareth high; Cupid shoots at a rag as soon as at a robe, and Venus' eye that was so curious sparkled favor on poltfooted Vulcan. Fear not, man; women's looks are not tied to dignity's feathers, nor make they curious esteem where the stone is found but what is the virtue.[73] Fear not, forester; faint heart never won fair lady. But where lives Rosalind now—at the court?"

"Oh, no," quoth Rosader, "she lives I know not where, and that is my sorrow; banished by Torismond, and that is my hell. For might I but find her sacred personage and plead before the bar of her pity the plaint of my passions, hope tells me she would grace me with some favor; and that would suffice as a recompense of all my former miseries."

"Much have I heard of thy mistress' excellence; and I know, forester, thou canst describe her at the full, as one that hast surveyed all her parts with a curious eye. Then do me that favor, to tell me what her perfections be."

"That I will," quoth Rosader, "for I glory to make all ears wonder at my mistress' excellence."

---

[72]*souseth:* plunges.

[73]*what is the virtue:* what is the worth or value (of the precious stone, regardless of where it may be found).

And with that he pulled a paper forth his bosom, wherein he read this:

Rosalind's Description

Like to the clear in highest sphere,
Where all imperial glory shines,
Of selfsame color is her hair,
Whether unfolded or in twines.
   Heigh ho, fair Rosalind.
Her eyes are sapphires set in snow,
Refining heaven by every wink;
The gods do fear whenas they glow,
And I do tremble when I think.
   Heigh ho, would she were mine.

Her cheeks are like the blushing cloud
That beautifies Aurora's face,
Or like the silver crimson shroud
That Phoebus' smiling looks doth grace.
   Heigh ho, fair Rosalind.
Her lips are like two budded roses,
Whom ranks of lilies neighbor nigh,
Within which bounds she balm encloses,
Apt to entice a deity.
   Heigh ho, would she were mine.

Her neck like to a stately tower,
Where Love himself imprisoned lies,
To watch for glances every hour
From her divine and sacred eyes.
   Heigh ho, fair Rosalind.
Her paps are centers of delight,
Her paps are orbs of heavenly frame,
Where nature molds the dew of light,
To feed perfection with the same.
   Heigh ho, would she were mine.

With orient pearl, with ruby red,
With marble white, sapphire blue,
Her body every way is fed,
Yet soft in touch and sweet in view.
   Heigh ho, fair Rosalind.
Nature herself her shape admires,
The gods are wounded in her sight,
And Love forsakes his heavenly fires,
And at her eyes his brand doth light.
   Heigh ho, would she were mine.

Then muse not, nymphs, though I bemoan
The absence of fair Rosalind,
Since for her fair there is fairer none,
Nor for her virtues so divine.
　　Heigh ho, fair Rosalind.
　　Heigh ho, my heart, would God that she were mine.
　　　　　　　　　　　　Periit, quia deperibat.

"Believe me," quoth Ganymede, "either the forester is an exquisite painter or Rosalind fair above wonder; so it makes me blush to hear how women should be so excellent and pages so unperfect."

Rosader, beholding her earnestly, answered thus:

"Truly, gentle page, thou hast cause to complain thee, wert thou the substance; but, resembling the shadow, content thyself. For it is excellence enough to be like the excellence of nature."

"He hath answered you, Ganymede," quoth Aliena. "It is enough for pages to wait on beautiful ladies and not to be beautiful themselves."

"Oh, mistress," quoth Ganymede, "hold you your peace, for you are partial. Who knows not but that all women have desire to tie sovereignty to their petticoats and ascribe beauty to themselves, where if boys might put on their garments perhaps they would prove as comely—if not as comely, it may be more courteous. But tell me, forester," and with that she turned to Rosader, "under whom maintainest thou thy walk?"

"Gentle swain, under the king of outlaws," said he, "the unfortunate Gerismond, who, having lost his kingdom, crowneth his thoughts with content, accounting it better to govern among poor men in peace than great men in danger."

"But hast thou not," said she, "having so melancholy opportunities as this forest affordeth thee, written more sonnets in commendations of thy mistress?"

"I have, gentle swain," quoth he, "but they be not about me. Tomorrow by dawn of day, if your flocks feed in these pastures, I will bring them you; wherein you shall read my passions whilst I feel them; judge my patience when you read it. Till when, I bid farewell."

So giving both Ganymede and Aliena a gentle good night, he resorted to his lodge, leaving Aliena and Ganymede to their prittle-prattle.

"So, Ganymede," said Aliena, the forester being gone, "you are mightily beloved; men make ditties in your praise, spend sighs for your sake, make an idol of your beauty. Believe me, it grieves me not a little to see the poor man so pensive and you so pitiless."

"Ah, Aliena," quoth she, "be not peremptory in your judgments. I hear Rosalind praised as I am Ganymede, but were I Rosalind I could answer the forester. If he mourn for love, there are medicines for love. Rosalind cannot be fair and unkind. And so, madam, you see it is time to fold our flocks, or else Corydon will frown and say you will never prove good housewife."

With that they put their sheep into the cotes and went home to her friend Corydon's cottage, Aliena as merry as might be that she was thus in the company of her Rosalind; but she, poor soul, that had love her lodestar, and her thoughts set on fire with the flame of fancy, could take no rest, but, being alone, began to consider what passionate penance poor Rosader was enjoined to by love and fortune, that at last she fell into this humor with herself:

Rosalind Passionate Alone

"Ah, Rosalind, how the fates have set down in their synod to make thee unhappy: for when fortune hath done her worst, then love comes in to begin a new tragedy; she seeks to lodge her son in thine eyes and to kindle her fires in thy bosom. Beware, fond girl, he is an unruly guest to harbor; for, entering in by entreats, he will not be thrust out by force, and her fires are fed with such fuel as no water is able to quench. Seest thou not how Venus seeks to wrap thee in her labyrinth, wherein is pleasure at the entrance but, within, sorrows, cares, and discontent? She is a siren: stop thine ears at her melody; and a basilisk: shut thine eyes and gaze not at her lest thou perish. Thou art now placed in the country content, where are heavenly thoughts and mean desires. In those lawns where thy flocks feed, Diana haunts. Be as her nymphs, chaste and enemy to love; for there is no greater honor to a maid than to account of fancy as a mortal foe to their sex.

"Daphne, that bonny wench, was not turned into a bay tree as the poets feign, but for her chastity her fame was immortal, resembling the laurel that is ever green. Follow thou her steps, Rosalind, and the rather for that thou art an exile and banished from the court; whose distress, as it is appeased with patience so it would be renewed with amorous passions. Have mind on thy forepassed fortunes, fear the worst, and entangle not thyself with present fancies, lest loving in haste thou repent thee at leisure.

"Ah, but yet, Rosalind, it is Rosader that courts thee, one who, as he is beautiful so he is virtuous, and harboreth in his mind as many good qualities as his face is shadowed with gracious favors; and therefore, Rosalind, stoop to love, lest being either too coy or too cruel, Venus wax wroth and plague thee with the reward of disdain."

Rosalind, thus passionate, was wakened from her dumps by Aliena, who said it was time to go to bed. Corydon swore that was true, for Charles' Wain[74] was risen in the north. Whereupon, each taking leave of other, went to their rest—all but the poor Rosalind, who was so full of passions that she could not possess any content.

Well, leaving her to her broken slumbers, expect what was performed by them the next morning.

The sun was no sooner stepped from the bed of Aurora but Aliena was wakened by Ganymede; who, restless all night, had tossed in her passions, saying it was then time to go to the field to unfold their sheep. Aliena, that spied where the hare was by the hounds and could see day at a little hole, thought to be pleasant with her Ganymede, and therefore replied thus:

"What, wanton, the sun is but new up, and as yet Iris' riches lies folded in the bosom of Flora. Phoebus hath not dried up the pearled dew, and so long Corydon hath taught me it is not fit to lead the sheep abroad, lest the dew being unwholesome, they get the rot. But now see I the old proverb true: he is in haste whom the devil drives, and where love pricks forward there is no worse death than delay. Ah, my good page, is there fancy in thine eye and passions in thy heart? What, hast thou wrapt love in thy looks and set all thy thoughts on fire by affection? I tell thee it is a flame as hard to be quenched as that of Aetna. But nature must have her course. Women's eyes have faculty attractive like the jet and retentive like the diamond; they dally in the delight of fair objects till, gazing on the panther's beautiful skin, repenting experience tell them he hath a devouring paunch."

"Come on," quoth Ganymede, "this sermon of yours is but a subtlety to lie still abed, because either you think the morning cold or else I being gone, you would steal a nap; this shift carries no palm, and therefore up and away. And for love, let me alone. I'll whip him away with nettles and set disdain as a charm to withstand his forces; and, therefore, look you to yourself. Be not too bold, for Venus can make you bend; nor too coy, for Cupid hath a piercing dart that will make you cry *Peccavi*."

[74]*Charles' Wain:* the seven bright stars forming the Big Dipper; literally, the wagon of Charles the Great (Charlemagne).

"And that is it," quoth Aliena, "that hath raised you so early this morning."

And with that she slipped on her petticoat and start up; and as soon as she had made her ready and taken her breakfast, away go these two with their bag and bottles to the field, in more pleasant content of mind than ever they were in the court of Torismond.

They came no sooner nigh the folds, but they might see where their discontented forester was walking in his melancholy. As soon as Aliena saw him, she smiled and said to Ganymede:

"Wipe your eyes, sweeting, for yonder is your sweetheart this morning in deep prayers, no doubt to Venus, that she may make you as pitiful as he is passionate. Come on, Ganymede, I pray thee let's have a little sport with him."

"Content," quoth Ganymede, and with that, to waken him out of his deep memento, he began thus: "Forester, good fortune to thy thoughts and ease to thy passions. What makes you so early abroad this morn? In contemplation, no doubt, of your Rosalind. Take heed, forester, step not too far; the ford may be deep and you slip over the shoes. I tell thee, flies have their spleen, the ants choler, the least hairs shadows, and the smallest loves great desires. 'Tis good, forester, to love but not to overlove, lest in loving her that likes not thee, thou fold thyself in an endless labyrinth."

Rosader, seeing the fair shepherdess and her pretty swain in whose company he felt the greatest ease of his care, he returned them a salute on this manner:

"Gentle shepherds, all hail, and as healthful be your flocks as you happy in content. Love is restless, and my bed is but the cell of my bane, in that there I find busy thoughts and broken slumbers; here, although everywhere passionate, yet I brook love with more patience in that every object feeds mine eye with variety of fancies. When I look on Flora's beauteous tapestry, checkered with the pride of all her treasure, I call to mind that fair face of Rosalind, whose heavenly hue exceeds the rose and the lily in their highest excellence. The brightness of Phoebus' shine puts me in mind to think of the sparkling flames that flew from her eyes and set my heart first on fire; the sweet harmony of the birds puts me in remembrance of the rare melody of her voice, which, like the siren, enchanteth the ears of the hearer. Thus in contemplation I salve my sorrows with applying the perfection of every object to the excellence of her qualities."

"She is much beholding unto you," quoth Aliena, "and so much that I have oft wished with myself that if I should ever prove as amorous as Oenone, I might find as faithful a Paris as yourself."

"How say you by this item, forester?" quoth Ganymede. "The fair shepherdess favors you who is mistress of so many flocks. Leave off, man, the supposition of Rosalind's love—whenas, watching at her,[75] you rove beyond the moon—and cast your looks upon my mistress, who no doubt is as fair though not so royal. One bird in· the hand is worth two in the wood; better possess the love of Aliena than catch frivolously at the shadow of Rosalind."

"I'll tell thee, boy," quoth Rosader,[76] "so is my fancy fixed on my Rosalind that were thy mistress as fair as Leda or Danae, whom Jove courted in transformed shapes, mine eyes would not vouch to entertain their beauties; and so hath love locked me in her perfections that I had rather only contemplate in her beauties than absolutely possess the excellence of any other."

"Venus is to blame, forester, if having so true a servant of you, she reward you not with Rosalind, if Rosalind were more fairer than herself. But leaving this prattle, now I'll put you in mind of your promise about those sonnets which you said were at home in your lodge."

"I have them about me," quoth Rosader. "Let us sit down, and then you shall hear what a poetical fury love will infuse into a man."

With that they sat down upon a green bank shadowed with fig trees, and Rosader, fetching a deep sigh, read them this sonnet:

Rosader's Sonnet

In sorrow's cell I laid me down to sleep,
But waking woes were jealous of mine eyes;
They made them watch and bend themselves to weep,
But weeping tears their want could not suffice.
    Yet since for her they wept who guides my heart,
    They weeping smile and triumph in their smart.

Of these my tears a fountain fiercely springs,
Where Venus bains[77] herself, incensed with love,
Where Cupid bouseth[78] his fair feathered wings,
But I behold what pains I must approve.
    Care drinks it dry, but when on her I think,
    Love makes me weep it full unto the brink.

[75]*watching at her:* perhaps a typographical mistake for "catching at her," as in "catch . . . at the shadow of Rosalind," below. In the 1609 edition "watching" was emended to "snatching."

[76]*Rosader:* The first four editions read "Ganymede," but the 1604 edition correctly emended to "Rosader."

[77]*bains:* bathes.

[78]*bouseth:* wets (though usually "bouse" or "bowse" meant "to drink heavily").

Meanwhile, my sighs yield truce unto my tears;
By them the winds increased and fiercely blow;
Yet when I sigh the flame more plain appears,
And by their force with greater power doth glow.
    Amidst these pains, all phoenix-like I thrive
    Since love, that yields me death, may life revive.
                       Rosader en esperance

"Now, surely, forester," quoth Aliena, "when thou madest this sonnet thou wert in some amorous quandary, neither too fearful as despairing of thy mistress' favors, nor too gleesome as hoping in thy fortunes."

"I can smile," quoth Ganymede, "at the sonettos, canzones, madrigals, rounds, and roundelays that these pensive patients pour out when their eyes are more full of wantonness than their hearts of passions. Then, as the fishers put the sweetest bait to the fairest fish, so these Ovidians (holding *amo* in their tongues when their thoughts come at haphazard) write that they be wrapt[79] in an endless labyrinth of sorrow, when walking in the large leas[80] of liberty, they only have their humors in their inkpot. If they find women so fond that they will with such painted lures come to their lust, then they triumph till they be full gorged with pleasures—and then fly they away like ramage[81] kites to their own content, leaving the tame fool, their mistress, full of fancy yet without ever a feather. If they miss, as dealing with some wary wanton that wants not such a one as themselves but spies their subtlety, they end their amours with a few feigned sighs; and so their excuse is, their mistress is cruel and they smother passions with patience.

"Such, gentle forester, we may deem you to be, that rather pass away the time here in these woods with writing amorets than to be deeply enamored, as you say, of your Rosalind. If you be such a one, then I pray God, when you think your fortunes at the highest and your desires to be most excellent, then that you may with Ixion embrace Juno in a cloud and have nothing but a marble mistress to release your martyrdom; but if you be true and trusty, eye-pained and heart-sick, then accursed be Rosalind if she prove cruel: for, forester, I flatter not—thou art worthy of as fair as she."

[79]*wrapt:* The sense of this favorite word of Lodge's, spelled as it was in the 1590 edition, may be "rapt," as Greg thought; but it probably is what it seems to be—"wrapt," the past tense of "wrap." (See pp. 349 and 386, where the sense definitely is "wrap" or "envelop.")

[80]*leas:* tracts of open ground (such as meadows or pastures).

[81]*ramage:* wild.

Aliena, spying the storm by the wind, smiled to see how Ganymede flew to the fist without any call. But Rosader, who took him flat for a shepherd's swain, made him this answer:

"Trust me, swain," quoth Rosader, "but my canzon[82] was written in no such humor; for mine eye and my heart are relatives, the one drawing fancy by sight, the other entertaining her by sorrow. If thou sawest my Rosalind—with what beauties nature hath favored her, with what perfection the heavens hath graced her, with what qualities the gods have endued her—then wouldst thou say there is none so fickle that could be fleeting unto her. If she had been Aeneas' Dido, had Venus and Juno both scolded him from Carthage, yet her excellence, despite of them, would have detained him at Tyre. If Phyllis had been as beauteous or Ariadne as virtuous, or both as honorable and excellent as she, neither had the filbert tree sorrowed in the death of despairing Phyllis nor the stars have been graced with Ariadne, but Demophon and Theseus had been trusty to their paragons. I will tell thee, swain, if with a deep insight thou couldst pierce into the secrets of my loves and see what deep impressions of her idea affection hath made in my heart, then wouldst thou confess I were passing passionate and no less endued with admirable patience."

"Why," quoth Aliena, "needs there patience in love?"

"Or else in nothing," quoth Rosader, "for it is a restless soare[83] that hath no ease, a canker that still frets, a disease that taketh away all hope of sleep. If, then, so many sorrows, sudden joys, momentary pleasures, continual fears, daily griefs, and nightly woes be found in love, then is not he to be accounted patient that smothers all these passions with silence?"

"Thou speakest by experience," quoth Ganymede, "and therefore we hold all thy words for axioms. But is love such a lingering malady?"

"It is," quoth he, "either extreme or mean, according to the mind of the party that entertains it; for as the weeds grow longer untouched than the pretty flowers, and the flint lies safe in the quarry when the emerald is suffering the lapidary's tool, so mean men are freed from Venus' injuries when kings are environed with a labyrinth of her cares. The whiter the lawn is, the deeper is the mole;[84] the more purer the chrysolite, the sooner stained; and such as have their hearts full of honor, have their loves full of the greatest sorrows. But in

---

[82]*canzon: canzone;* see note 22.

[83]*soare:* The original spelling, "soare," is perhaps to suggest both "soar" and "sore."

[84]*lawn . . . mole:* white linen cloth . . . stain, blemish.

whomsoever," quoth Rosader, "he fixeth his dart, he never leaveth
to assault him till either he hath won him to folly or fancy; for as the
moon never goes without the star Lunisequa, so a lover never goeth
without the unrest of his thoughts. For proof you shall hear another
fancy of my making."

"Now do, gentle forester," quoth Ganymede.
And with that he read over this sonetto:

Rosader's Second Sonetto

Turn I my looks unto the skies,
Love with his arrows wounds mine eyes;
If so I gaze upon the ground,
Love then in every flower is found.
Search I the shade to fly my pain,
He meets me in the shade again;
Wend I to walk in secret grove,
Even there I meet with sacred love.
If so I bain me in the spring,
Even on the brink I hear him sing;
If so I meditate alone,
He will be partner of my moan.
If so I mourn he weeps with me,
And where I am there will he be.
Whenas I talk of Rosalind,
The god from coyness waxeth kind,
And seems in selfsame flames to fry
Because he loves as well as I.
Sweet Rosalind, for pity rue,
Forwhy than love I am more true:
He if he speed will quickly fly
But in thy love I live and die.

"How like you this sonnet?" quoth Rosader.
"Marry," quoth Ganymede, "for the pen well, for the passion ill;
for as I praise the one I pity the other, in that thou shouldst hunt
after a cloud and love either without reward or regard."
" 'Tis not her frowardness," quoth Rosader, "but my hard fortunes
whose destinies have crossed me with her absence; for did she feel
my loves she would not let me linger in these sorrows. Women, as
they are fair, so they respect faith; and estimate more, if they be
honorable, the will than the wealth, having loyalty the object whereat
they aim their fancies. But leaving off these interparleys, you shall

hear my last sonetto, and then you have heard all my poetry."
    And with that he sighed out this:

Rosader's Third Sonnet

Of virtuous love myself may boast alone,
Since no suspect my service may attaint;
For perfect fair she is the only one
Whom I esteem for my beloved saint.
    Thus for my faith I only bear the bell,
    And for her fair she only doth excel.

Then let fond Petrarch shroud his Laura's praise,
And Tasso cease to publish his affect,
Since mine the faith confirmed at all assays,
And hers the fair which all men do respect.
    My lines her fair, her fair my faith assures;
    Thus I by love and love by me endures.

"Thus," quoth Rosader, "here is an end of my poems, but for all this no release of my passions; so that I resemble him that in the depth of his distress hath none but the echo to answer him."

Ganymede, pitying her Rosader, thinking to drive him out of this amorous melancholy, said that now the sun was in his meridional heat and that it was high noon, "therefore we shepherds say 'tis time to go to dinner, for the sun and our stomachs are shepherds' dials. Therefore, forester, if thou wilt take such fare as comes out of our homely scrips, welcome shall answer whatsoever thou wantest in delicates."

Aliena took the entertainment by the end and told Rosader he should be her guest. He thanked them heartily and sat with them down to dinner, where they had such cates as country state did allow them, sauced with such content and such sweet prattle as it seemed far more sweet than all their courtly junkets.

As soon as they had taken their repast, Rosader, giving them thanks for his good cheer, would have been gone; but Ganymede, that was loath to let him pass out of her presence, began thus:

"Nay, forester," quoth he, "if thy business be not the greater, seeing thou sayest thou art so deeply in love, let me see how thou canst woo. I will represent Rosalind and thou shalt be as thou art—Rosader. See in some amorous eclogue how if Rosalind were present, how thou couldst court her; and while we sing of love, Aliena shall tune her pipe and play us melody."

"Content," quoth Rosader.

And Aliena, she to show her willingness, drew forth a recorder and began to wind it.[85] Then the loving forester began thus:

The Wooing Eclogue Betwixt Rosalind and Rosader

Rosader

I pray thee, nymph, by all the working words,
By all the tears and sighs that lovers know,
Or what or thoughts or falt'ring[86] tongue affords,
I crave for mine in ripping up my woe.
Sweet Rosalind, my love—would God, my love—
My life—would God, my life—aye, pity me.
Thy lips are kind and humble like the dove,
And but with beauty pity will not be.
Look on mine eyes made red with rueful tears,
From whence the rain of true remorse descendeth,
All pale in looks am I, though young in years,
And nought but love or death my days befriendeth.
Oh, let no stormy rigor knit thy brows,
Which love appointed for his mercy seat.
The tallest tree by Boreas' breath it bows,
The iron yields with hammer and to heat.
  Oh, Rosalind, then be thou pitiful,
  For Rosalind is only beautiful.

Rosalind

Love's wantons arm their trait'rous suits with tears,
With vows, with oaths, with looks, with showers of gold;
But when the fruit of their affects appears,
The simple heart by subtle sleights is sold.
Thus sucks the yielding ear the poisoned bait,
Thus feeds the heart upon his endless harms,
Thus glut the thoughts themselves on self-deceit,
Thus blind the eyes their sight by subtle charms.
The lovely looks, the sighs that storm so sore,
The dew of deep dissembled doubleness:
These may attempt but are of power no more,
Where beauty leans to wit and soothfastness.
  Oh, Rosader, then be thou wittiful,
  For Rosalind scorns foolish pitiful.

[85]*wind it:* blow (wind) into it.
[86]*or thoughts or falt'ring:* that is, "either thoughts or falt'ring"; it was idiomatic then to write "or . . . or," "either . . . either" (a construction Lyly was fond of), and "either . . . or." The emendation of "or thoughts" to "our thoughts" in the 1592 edition is, however, worth considering.

Rosader

I pray thee, Rosalind, by those sweet eyes
That stain[87] the sun in shine, the morn in clear,
By those sweet cheeks where love encamped lies
To kiss the roses of the springing year.
I tempt thee, Rosalind, by ruthful plaints,
Not seasoned with deceit or fraudful guile,
But firm in pain far more than tongue depaints;
Sweet nymph, be kind and grace me with a smile.
So may the heavens preserve from hurtful food
Thy harmless flocks; so may the summer yield
The pride of all her riches and her good,
To fat thy sheep, the citizens of field.
Oh, leave to arm thy lovely brows with scorn;
The birds their beak, the lion hath his tail,
And lovers nought but sighs and bitter mourn,
The spotless fort of fancy to assail.
Oh, Rosalind, then be thou pitiful,
For Rosalind is only beautiful.

Rosalind

The hardened steel by fire is brought in frame.

Rosader

And Rosalind, my love, than any wool more softer,
And shall not sighs her tender heart inflame?

Rosalind

Were lovers true, maids would believe them ofter.

Rosader

Truth and regard and honor guide my love.

Rosalind

Fain would I trust, but yet I dare not try.

Rosader

Oh, pity me, sweet nymph, and do but prove.

Rosalind

I would resist, but yet I know not why.

[87]*stain:* excel.

Rosader

Oh, Rosalind, be kind, for times will change,
Thy looks aye nill[88] be fair as now they be;
Thine age from beauty may thy looks estrange,
Ah, yield in time, sweet nymph, and pity me.

Rosalind

Oh, Rosalind, thou must be pitiful,
For Rosader is young and beautiful.

Rosader

Oh, gain more great than kingdoms or a crown.

Rosalind

Oh, trust betrayed if Rosader abuse me.

Rosader

First let the heavens conspire to pull me down,
And heaven and earth as abject quite refuse me.
Let sorrows stream about my hateful bower,
And restless horror hatch within my breast.
Let beauty's eye afflict me with a lower,
Let deep despair pursue me without rest,
Ere Rosalind my loyalty disprove,
Ere Rosalind accuse me for unkind.

Rosalind

Then Rosalind will grace thee with her love,
Then Rosalind will have thee still in mind.

Rosader

Then let me triumph more than Tithon's dear,
Since Rosalind will Rosader respect.
Then let my face exile his sorry cheer,
And frolic in the comfort of affect;
And say that Rosalind is only pitiful,
Since Rosalind is only beautiful.

When thus they had finished their courting eclogue in such a familiar clause, Ganymede, as augur of some good fortunes to light upon their affections, began to be thus pleasant:

"How now, forester, have I not fitted your turn? Have I not played the woman handsomely and showed myself as coy in grants as cour-

[88]*aye nill:* will not always.

teous in desires, and been as full of suspicion as men of flattery? And yet to salve all, jumped I not all up with the sweet union of love? Did not Rosalind content her Rosader?"

The forester, at this smiling, shook his head and, folding his arms, made this merry reply:

"Truth, gentle swain, Rosader hath his Rosalind; but as Ixion had Juno, who thinking to possess a goddess, only embraced a cloud. In these imaginary fruitions of fancy, I resemble the birds that fed themselves with Zeuxis' painted grapes, but they grew so lean with pecking at shadows that they were glad with Aesop's cock to scrape for a barley cornel.[89] So fareth it with me, who, to feed myself with the hope of my mistress' favors, soothe myself in thy suits and only in conceit reap a wished for content. But if my food be no better than such amorous dreams, Venus at the year's end shall find me but a lean lover. Yet do I take these follies for high fortunes and hope these feigned affections do divine some unfeigned end of ensuing fancies."

"And thereupon," quoth Aliena, "I'll play the priest: from this day forth Ganymede shall call thee husband and thou shalt call Ganymede wife, and so we'll have a marriage."

"Content," quoth Rosader, and laughed.

"Content," quoth Ganymede, and changed as red as a rose.

And so with a smile and a blush they made up this jesting match that after proved to a marriage in earnest, Rosader full little thinking he had wooed and won his Rosalind.

But all was well. Hope is a sweet string to harp on, and therefore let the forester awhile shape himself to his shadow and tarry fortune's leisure, till she may make a metamorphosis fit for his purpose.

I digress, and therefore to Aliena: who said the wedding was not worth a pin unless there were some cheer, nor that bargain well made that was not stricken up with a cup of wine. And therefore she willed Ganymede to set out such cates as they had and to draw out her bottle, charging the forester, as he had imagined his loves so to conceit these cates to be a most sumptuous banquet, and to take a mazer of wine and to drink to his Rosalind; which Rosader did, and so they passed away the day in many pleasant devices. Till at last Aliena perceived time would tarry no man and that the sun waxed very low, ready to set; which made her shorten their amorous prattle and end the banquet with a fresh carouse. Which done, they all three rose and Aliena broke off thus:

[89]*cornel:* kernel (a little grain or granule).

"Now, forester, Phoebus, that all this while hath been partaker of our sports, seeing every woodman more fortunate in his loves than he is his fancies, seeing thou hast won Rosalind when he could not woo Daphne, hides his head for shame and bids us adieu in a cloud. Our sheep, they, poor wantons, wander towards their folds, as taught by nature their due times of rest; which tells us, forester, we must depart. Marry, though there were a marriage, yet I must carry this night the bride with me, and tomorrow morning if you meet us here, I'll promise to deliver her as good a maid as I find her."

"Content," quoth Rosader, "'tis enough for me in the night to dream on love, that in the day am so fond to dote on love; and so till tomorrow, you to your folds and I will to my lodge."

And thus the forester and they parted. He was no sooner gone, but Aliena and Ganymede went and folded their flocks and, taking up their hooks, their bags, and their bottles, hied homeward. By the way, Aliena, to make the time seem short, began to prattle with Ganymede thus:

"I have heard them say that what the fates forepoint that fortune pricketh down with a period, that the stars are sticklers in Venus' court and desire hangs at the heel of destiny. If it be so, then by all probable conjectures, this match will be a marriage; for if augurism be authentical or the divines' dooms principles, it cannot be but such a shadow portends the issue of a substance; for to that end did the gods force the conceit of this eclogue, that they might discover the ensuing consent of your affections. So that ere it be long, I hope in earnest to dance at your wedding."

"Tush," quoth Ganymede, "all is not malt that is cast on the kiln. There goes more words to a bargain than one. Love feels no footing in the air, and fancy holds it slippery harbor to nestle in the tongue. The match is not yet so surely made but he may miss of his market;[90] but if fortune be his friend, I will not be his foe; and so I pray you, gentle mistress Aliena, take it."

"I take all things well," quoth she, "that is your content, and am glad Rosader is yours; for now I hope your thoughts will be at quiet. Your eye that ever looked at love will now lend a glance on your lambs, and then they will prove more buxom and you more blithe; for the eyes of the master feeds the cattle."

---

[90]*miss of his market:* probably a play on "miss his mark," a proverb (Tilley, M669); more literally, "market" is to recall "bargain" in a previous sentence.

As thus they were in chat, they spied old Corydon where he came plodding to meet them; who told them supper was ready, which news made them speed them home. Where we leave them to the next morrow and return to Saladyne.

All this while did poor Saladyne, banished from Bordeaux and the court of France by Torismond, wander up and down in the forest of Arden, thinking to get to Lyons and so travel through Germany into Italy. But the forest being full of bypaths, and he unskillful of the country coast,[91] slipped out of the way and chanced up into the desert, not far from the place where Gerismond was and his brother Rosader.

Saladyne, weary with wandering up and down and hungry with long fasting, finding a little cave by the side of a thicket, eating such fruit as the forest did afford and contenting himself with such drink as nature had provided and thirst made delicate, after his repast he fell in a dead sleep. As thus he lay, a hungry lion came hunting down the edge of the grove for prey and, espying Saladyne, began to seize upon him; but seeing he lay still without any motion, he left to touch him—for that lions hate to prey on dead carcasses—and yet desirous to have some food, the lion lay down and watched to see if he would stir.

While thus Saladyne slept secure, fortune, that was careful over her champion, began to smile and brought it so to pass that Rosader—having stricken a deer that, but lightly hurt, fled through the thicket—came pacing down by the grove with a boar spear in his hand in great haste. He spied where a man lay asleep and a lion fast by him. Amazed at this sight, as he stood gazing his nose on the sudden bled, which made him conjecture it was some friend of his. Whereupon, drawing more nigh, he might easily discern his visage and perceived by his physiognomy that it was his brother Saladyne; which drove Rosader into a deep passion, as a man perplexed at the sight of so unexpected a chance, marveling what should drive his brother to traverse those secret deserts without any company in such distress and forlorn sort. But the present time craved no such doubting ambages, for either he must resolve to hazard his life for his relief or else steal away and leave him to the cruelty of the lion. In which doubt he thus briefly debated with himself:

[91]*coast:* area, region; he is not on a body of water.

Rosader's Meditation

"Now, Rosader, fortune that long hath whipped thee with nettles means to salve thee with roses and, having crossed thee with many frowns, now she presents thee with the brightness of her favors. Thou that didst count thyself the most distressed of all men mayest account thyself now the most fortunate amongst men, if fortune can make men happy or sweet revenge be wrapt in a pleasing content. Thou seest Saladyne, thine enemy, the worker of thy mis fortunes and the efficient cause of thine exile, subject to the cruelty of a merciless lion, brought into this misery by the gods that they might seem just in revenging his rigor and thy injuries. Seest thou not how the stars are in a favorable aspect, the planets in some pleasing conjunction, the fates agreeable to thy thoughts, and the destinies performers of thy desires in that Saladyne shall die and thou be free of his blood? He receive meed for his amiss, and thou erect his tomb with innocent hands. Now, Rosader, shalt thou return to Bordeaux and enjoy thy possessions by birth and his revenues by inheritance. Now mayest thou triumph in love and hang fortune's altars with garlands. For when Rosalind hears of thy wealth, it will make her love thee more willingly: for women's eyes are made of chrysocoll[92] that is ever unperfect unless tempered with gold, and Jupiter soonest enjoyed Danae because he came to her in so rich a shower. Thus shall this lion, Rosader, end the life of a miserable man, and from distress raise thee to be most fortunate."

And with that, casting his boar spear on his neck, away he began to trudge. But he had not stepped back two or three paces, but a new motion stroke him to the very heart, that, resting his boar spear against his breast, he fell into this passionate humor:

"Ah, Rosader, wert thou the son of Sir John of Bordeaux, whose virtues exceeded his valor and yet the most hardiest knight in all Europe? Should the honor of the father shine in the actions of the son? And wilt thou dishonor thy parentage in forgetting the nature of a gentleman? Did not thy father at his last gasp breathe out this golden principle: brothers' amity is like the drops of balsamum that salveth the most dangerous sores? Did he make a large exhort unto concord, and wilt thou show thyself careless? Oh, Rosader, what though Saladyne hath wronged thee and made thee live an exile in

---

[92]*chrysocoll:* Chrysocolla ("gold-solder") was a name given several minerals, one of which may have been borax.

the forest? Shall thy nature be so cruel, or thy nurture so crooked, or thy thoughts so savage, as to suffer so dismal a revenge? What, to let him be devoured by wild beasts? *Non sapit qui non sibi sapit* is fondly spoken in such bitter extremes. Lose not his life, Rosader, to win a world of treasure; for in having him thou hast a brother, and by hazarding for his life thou gettest a friend and reconcilest an enemy; and more honor shalt thou purchase by pleasuring a foe than revenging a thousand injuries."

With that his brother began to stir and the lion to rouse himself; whereupon Rosader suddenly charged him with the boar spear and wounded the lion very sore at the first stroke. The beast, feeling himself to have a mortal hurt, leapt at Rosader and with his paws gave him a sore pinch on the breast that he had almost fallen; yet as a man most valiant, in whom the sparks of Sir John of Bordeaux remained, he recovered himself and in short combat slew the lion, who at his death roared so loud that Saladyne awakened and, starting up, was amazed at the sudden sight of so monstrous a beast lying slain by him and so sweet a gentleman wounded. He presently, as he was of a ripe conceit, began to conjecture that the gentleman had slain him in his defense. Whereupon, as a man in a trance, he stood staring on them both a good while, not knowing his brother, being in that disguise. At last he burst into these terms:

"Sir, whatsoever thou be, as full of honor thou must needs be by the view of thy present valure,[93] I perceive thou hast redressed my fortunes by thy courage and saved my life with thine own loss, which ties me to be thine in all humble service. Thanks thou shalt have as thy due and more thou canst not have, for my ability denies to perform a deeper debt. But if any ways it please thee to command me, use me as far as the power of a poor gentleman may stretch."

Rosader, seeing he was unknown to his brother, wondered to hear such courteous words come from his crabbed nature; but glad of such reformed nurture, he made this answer:

"I am, sir, whatsoever thou art, a forester and ranger of these walks, who, following my deer to the fall, was conducted hither by some assenting fate, that I might save thee and disparage myself. For coming into this place I saw thee asleep and the lion watching thy awake,[94] that at thy rising he might prey upon thy carcass. At the

---

[93]*valure:* includes "valor," but means also a general "worthiness" or "value."

[94]*thy awake:* Apparently the sense is either "thee awake" or "thy awakening"; all the early editions through 1609 read "thy awake."

first sight I conjectured thee a gentleman, for all men's thoughts ought to be favorable in imagination, and I counted it the part of a resolute man to purchase a stranger's relief, though with the loss of his own blood; which I have performed, thou seest, to mine own prejudice. If, therefore, thou be a man of such worth as I value thee by thy exterior lineaments, make discourse unto me what is the cause of thy present fortunes; for by the furrows in thy face thou seemest to be crossed with her frowns. But whatsoever or howsoever, let me crave that favor, to hear the tragic cause of thy estate."

Saladyne, sitting down and fetching a deep sigh, began thus:

Saladyne's Discourse to Rosader (Unknown)

"Although the discourse of my fortunes be the renewing of my sorrows, and the rubbing of the scar will open a fresh wound, yet that I may not prove ingrateful to so courteous a gentleman, I will rather sit down and sigh out my estate than give any offense by smothering my grief with silence. Know therefore, sir, that I am of Bordeaux and the son and heir of Sir John of Bordeaux, a man for his virtues and valor so famous that I cannot think but the fame of his honors hath reached farther than the knowledge of his personage. The infortunate son of so fortunate a knight am I, my name Saladyne; who, succeeding my father in possessions but not in qualities, having two brethren committed by my father at his death to my charge, with such golden principles of brotherly concord as might have pierced like the sirens' melody into any human ear. But I, with Ulysses, became deaf against his philosophical harmony and made more value of profit than of virtue, esteeming gold sufficient honor and wealth the fittest title for a gentleman's dignity. I set my middle brother to the university to be a scholar, counting it enough if he might pore on a book while I fed upon his revenues; and for the youngest, which was my father's joy, young Rosader—"

And with that naming of Rosader, Saladyne sat him down and wept.

"Nay, forward, man," quoth the forester; "tears are the unfittest salve that any man can apply for to cure sorrows, and therefore cease from such feminine follies, as should drop out of a woman's eye to deceive, not out of a gentleman's look to discover his thoughts, and forward with thy discourse."

"Oh, sir," quoth Saladyne, "this Rosader that wrings tears from mine eyes and blood from my heart was like my father in exterior personage and in inward qualities; for in the prime of his years he aimed all his acts at honor and coveted rather to die than to brook any injury unworthy a gentleman's credit. I, whom envy had made blind and covetousness masked with the veil of self-love, seeing the palm tree grow straight, thought to suppress it, being a twig; but nature will have her course, the cedar will be tall, the diamond bright, the carbuncle glistering, and virtue will shine though it be never so much obscured. For I kept Rosader as a slave and used him as one of my servile hinds until age grew on and a secret insight of my abuse entered into his mind; insomuch that he could not brook it but coveted to have what his father left him and to live of himself. To be short, sir, I repined at his fortunes and he counterchecked me not with ability but valor,[95] until at last, by my friends and aid of such as followed gold more than right or virtue, I banished him from Bordeaux; and he, poor gentleman, lives no man knows where in some distressed discontent. The gods, not able to suffer such impiety unrevenged, so wrought that the king picked a causeless quarrel against me in hope to have my lands, and so hath exiled me out of France forever.

"Thus, thus, sir, am I the most miserable of all men, as having a blemish in my thoughts for the wrongs I proffered Rosader and a touch in my estate[96] to be thrown from my proper possessions by injustice. Passionate thus with many griefs, in penance of my former follies, I go thus pilgrim-like to seek out my brother, that I may reconcile myself to him in all submission and afterward wend to the Holy Land to end my years in as many virtues as I have spent my youth in wicked vanities."

Rosader, hearing the resolution of his brother Saladyne, began to compassionate his sorrows and, not able to smother the sparks of nature with feigned secrecy, he burst into these loving speeches:

"Then know, Saladyne," quoth he, "that thou hast met with Rosader, who grieves as much to see thy distress as thyself to feel the burden of thy misery."

Saladyne, casting up his eye and noting well the physiognomy of the forester, knew that it was his brother Rosader; which made him so bash and blush at the first meeting that Rosader was fain to recomfort him, which he did in such sort that he showed how highly

[95]*ability . . . valor:* The sense of "ability" here may carry a legal sense. Rosader did not use the power legally his, by his father's will, to take action against Saladyne's injustice; he used his own individual courage.

[96]*touch in my estate:* The phrase parallels and complements "blemish in my thoughts." The sense probably is "blemish in my legal right or title to possession," though "estate" may imply also something more general like "status in the world."

he held revenge in scorn. Much ado there was between these two brethren, Saladyne in craving pardon and Rosader in forgiving and forgetting all former injuries—the one submiss, the other courteous; Saladyne penitent and passionate, Rosader kind and loving—that at length nature working an union of their thoughts, they earnestly embraced and fell from matters of unkindness to talk of the country life, which Rosader so highly commended that his brother began to have a desire to taste of that homely content.

In this humor Rosader conducted him to Gerismond's lodge and presented his brother to the king, discoursing the whole matter how all had happened betwixt them. The king looking upon Saladyne, found him a man of a most beautiful personage and saw in his face sufficient sparks of ensuing honors, gave him great entertainment and, glad of their friendly reconcilement, promised such favor as the poverty of his estate might afford; which Saladyne gratefully accepted. And so Gerismond fell to question of Torismond's life. Saladyne briefly discoursed unto him his injustice and tyrannies with such modesty, although he had wronged him, that Gerismond greatly praised the sparing speech of the young gentleman.

Many questions passed, but at last Gerismond began with a deep sigh to inquire if there were any news of the welfare of Alinda or his daughter Rosalind.

"None, sir," quoth Saladyne, "for since their departure they were never heard of."

"Injurious fortune," quoth the king, "that to double the father's misery wrongest the daughter with misfortunes."

And with that, surcharged with sorrows, he went into his cell and left Saladyne and Rosader, whom Rosader straight conducted to the sight of Adam Spencer. Who, seeing Saladyne in that estate, was in a brown study; but when he heard the whole matter, although he grieved for the exile of his master, yet he joyed that banishment had so reformed him that from a lascivious youth he was proved a virtuous gentleman. Looking a longer while and seeing what familiarity passed between them and what favors were interchanged with brotherly affection, he said thus:

"Aye, marry, thus should it be; this was the concord that old Sir John of Bordeaux wished betwixt you. Now fulfill you those precepts he breathed out at his death and, in observing them, look to live fortunate and die honorable."

"Well said, Adam Spencer," quoth Rosader, "but hast any victuals in store for us?"

"A piece of a red deer," quoth he, "and a bottle of wine."

" 'Tis foresters' fare, brother," quoth Rosader, and so they sat down and fell to their cates.

As soon as they had taken their repast and had well dined, Rosader took his brother Saladyne by the hand and showed him the pleasures of the forest and what content they enjoyed in that mean estate. Thus for two or three days he walked up and down with his brother to show him all the commodities that belonged to his walk.

In which time he was missed of his Ganymede, who mused greatly with Aliena what should become of their forester. Somewhile they thought he had taken some word unkindly and had taken the pet;[97] then they imagined some new love had withdrawn his fancy, or haply that he was sick, or detained by some great business of Gerismond's, or that he had made a reconcilement with his brother and so returned to Bordeaux.

These conjectures did they cast in their heads, but especially Ganymede, who having love in her heart proved restless and half without patience, that Rosader wronged her with so long absence. For love measures every minute and thinks hours to be days and days to be months, till they feed their eyes with the sight of their desired object. Thus perplexed lived poor Ganymede. While on a day sitting with Aliena in a great dump, she cast up her eye and saw where Rosader came pacing toward them with his forest bill[98] on his neck. At that sight her color changed, and she said to Aliena:

"See, mistress, where our jolly forester comes."

"And you are not a little glad thereof," quoth Aliena, "your nose bewrays[99] what porridge you love. The wind cannot be tied within his quarter, the sun shadowed with a vail,[100] oil hidden in water, nor love kept out of a woman's looks—but no more of that, *lupus est in fabula.*"

As soon as Rosader was come within the reach of her tongue's end,

[97]*taken the pet:* taken offense (as a "pet" or spoiled child does easily).
[98]*forest bill:* woodman's billhook; a heavy, thick knife with a hooked end for pruning and cutting brushwood; Saladyne carries one, too, as we see on p. 356.
[99]*bewrays: Rosalind,* like *Pandosto,* distinguishes "bewray" (reveal) from "betray" (be a traitor to). There are similar distinctions between "forward" (onward; bold) and "froward" (stubbornly willful) and between "sith" (because) and "since" (from then until now).
[100]*vail:* Greg and Baldwin may be right that the sense is "veil" (cover, clouds). The 1604 edition surely was wrong in emending to "within a vale" (valley). But perhaps the sense of "vail" is "setting" or "going down" (of the sun), as in *Troilus and Cressida,* V, viii, 9: "Even with the vail and darking of the sun."

Aliena began thus: "Why, how now, gentle forester, what wind hath kept you from hence, that being so newly married you have no more care of your Rosalind but to absent yourself so many days? Are these the passions you painted out so in your sonnets and roundelays? I see well hot love is soon cold and that the fancy of men is like to a loose feather that wandereth in the air with the blast of every wind."

"You are deceived, mistress," quoth Rosader. " 'Twas a copy[101] of unkindness that kept me hence in that I being married you carried away the bride. But if I have given any occasion of offense by absenting myself these three days, I humbly sue for pardon—which you must grant, of course, in that the fault is so friendly confessed with penance. But to tell you the truth, fair mistress and my good Rosalind, my eldest brother, by the injury of Torismond, is banished from Bordeaux, and by chance he and I met in the forest."

And here Rosader discoursed unto them what had happened betwixt them; which reconcilement made them glad, especially Ganymede. But Aliena, hearing of the tyranny of her father, grieved inwardly, and yet smothered all things with such secrecy that the concealing was more sorrow than the conceit; yet that her estate might be hid still, she made fair weather of it and so let all pass.

Fortune, that saw how these parties valued not her deity but held her power in scorn, thought to have about with them[102] and brought the matter to pass thus. Certain rascals, that lived by prowling in the forest—who for fear of the provost marshal had caves in the groves and thickets to shroud themselves from his trains—hearing of the beauty of this fair shepherdess, Aliena, thought to steal her away and to give her to the king for a present, hoping, because the king was a great lecher, by such a gift to purchase all their pardons; and therefore came to take her and her page away. Thus resolved, while Aliena and Ganymede were in this sad talk, they came rushing in and laid violent hands upon Aliena and her page, which made them cry out to Rosader; who, having the valor of his father stamped in his heart, thought rather to die in defense of his friends than any way be touched with the least blemish of dishonor, and therefore dealt such blows amongst them with his weapon as he did witness

[101]*copy:* abundance, copious quantity.

[102]*have about with them:* an idiom not recorded in the *OED;* possibly the sense is something like "have at them," which meant "make an attempt at them," "have a stroke [of a weapon] at them," or "have a go at them." The emendation of the 1598 edition is, however, worth considering: "have a bout with them" (have a round of fighting with them). Cf. "have about for a blow at" in *A Notable Discovery* (p. 404).

well upon their carcasses that he was no coward. But as *ne Hercules quidem contra duos,* so Rosader could not resist a multitude, having none to back him, so that he was not only rebated[103] but sore wounded. And Aliena and Gaynmede had been quite carried away by these rascals had not fortune, that meant to turn her frown into a favor, brought Saladyne that way by chance; who, wandering to find out his brother's walk, encountered this crew. And seeing not only a shepherdess and her boy forced, but his brother wounded, he heaved up a forest bill he had on his neck, and the first he stroke had never after more need of the physician, redoubling his blows with such courage that the slaves were amazed at his valor.

Rosader, espying his brother so fortunately arrived and seeing how valiantly he behaved himself, though sore wounded rushed amongst them and laid on such load that some of the crew were slain and the rest fled, leaving Aliena and Ganymede in the possession of Rosader and Saladyne.

Aliena, after she had breathed awhile and was come to herself from this fear, looked about her and saw where Ganymede was busy dressing up the wounds of the forester; but she cast her eye upon this courteous champion that had made so hot a rescue, and that with such affection, that she began to measure every part of him with favor, and in herself to commend his personage and his virtue, holding him for a resolute man that durst assail such a troop of unbridled villains. At last, gathering her spirits together, she returned him these thanks:

"Gentle sir, whatsoever you be that have adventured your flesh to relieve our fortunes, as we hold you valiant so we esteem you courteous and to have as many hidden virtues as you have manifest resolutions. We poor shepherds have no wealth but our flocks, and therefore can we not make requital with any great treasures; but our recompense is thanks and our rewards to our friends without feigning. For ransom, therefore, of this our rescue, you must content yourself to take such a kind gramercy as a poor shepherdess and her page may give—with promise, in what we may, never to prove ingrateful. For this gentleman that is hurt, young Rosader, he is our good neighbor and familiar acquaintance; we'll pay him with smiles and feed him with love looks, and though he be never the fatter at the year's end yet we'll so hamper him that he shall hold himself satisfied."

Saladyne, hearing this shepherdess speak so wisely, began more narrowly to pry into her perfection and to survey all her lineaments

[103]*rebated:* driven back.

with a curious insight, so long dallying in the flame of her beauty that to his cost he found her to be most excellent. For Love, that lurked in all these broils to have a blow or two, seeing the parties at the gaze, encountered them both with such a veny[104] that the stroke pierced to the heart so deep as it could never after be raced[105] out. At last, after he had looked so long till Aliena waxed red, he returned her this answer:

"Fair shepherdess, if fortune graced me with such good hap as to do you any favor, I hold myself as contented as if I had gotten a great conquest; for the relief of distressed women is the special point that gentlemen are tied unto by honor. Seeing then my hazard to rescue your harms was rather duty than courtesy, thanks is more than belongs to the requital of such a favor. But lest I might seem either too coy or too careless of a gentlewoman's proffer, I will take your kind gramercy for a recompense."

All this while that he spoke, Ganymede looked earnestly upon him and said, "Truly, Rosader, this gentleman favors you much in the feature of your face."

"No marvel," quoth he, "gentle swain, for 'tis my eldest brother Saladyne."

"Your brother?" quoth Aliena, and with that she blushed. "He is the more welcome, and I hold myself the more his debtor; and for that he hath in my behalf done such a piece of service, if it please him to do me that honor, I will call him servant and he shall call me mistress."

"Content, sweet mistress," quoth Saladyne, "and when I forget to call you so, I will be unmindful of mine own self."

"Away with these quirks and quiddities of love," quoth Rosader, "and give me some drink, for I am passing thirsty, and then will I home; for my wounds bleed sore, and I will have them dressed."

Ganymede had tears in her eyes and passions in her heart to see her Rosader so pained, and therefore stepped hastily to the bottle and, filling out some wine in a mazer, she spiced it with such comfortable drugs as she had about her and gave it him, which did comfort Rosader, that, rising with the help of his brother, he took his leave of them and went to his lodge.

Ganymede, as soon as they were out of sight, led his flocks down to a vale and there under the shadow of a beech tree sat down and began to mourn the misfortunes of her sweetheart.

---

[104]*veny:* thrust (as in fencing).
[105]*raced:* erased ("it" referring to "stroke").

And Aliena, as a woman passing discontent, severing herself from her Ganymede, sitting under a lemon tree, began to sigh out the passions of her new love and to meditate with herself on this manner:

Aliena's Meditation

"Aye me, now I see and, sorrowing, sigh to see that Diana's laurels are harbors for Venus' doves; that there trace as well through the lawns wantons as chaste ones; that Callisto, be she never so chary, will cast one amorous eye at courting Jove; that Diana herself will change her shape, but she will honor love in a shadow; that maidens' eyes, be they as hard as diamonds, yet Cupid hath drugs to make them more pliable than wax. See, Alinda, how fortune and love have interleagued themselves to be thy foes, and, to make thee their subject or else an abject, have inveigled thy sight with a most beautiful object. A-late thou didst hold Venus for a giglot,[106] not a goddess; and now thou shalt be forced to sue suppliant to her deity. Cupid was a boy and blind, but alas his eye had aim enough to pierce thee to the heart. While I lived in the court I held love in contempt, and in high seats I had small desires. I knew not affection while I lived in dignity, nor could Venus countercheck me as long as my fortune was majesty and my thoughts honor. And shall I now be high in desires when I am made low by destiny? I have heard them say that love looks not at low cottages, that Venus jets in robes not in rags, that Cupid flies so high that he scorns to touch poverty with his heel. Tush, Alinda, these are but old wives' tales and neither authentical precepts nor infallible principles; for experience tells thee that peasants have their passions as well as princes, that swains as they have their labors so they have their amours, and love lurks as soon about a sheepcote as a palace.

"Ah, Alinda, this day in avoiding a prejudice thou art fallen into a deeper mischief: being rescued from the robbers thou art become captive to Saladyne. And what then? Women must love or they must cease to live, and therefore did nature frame them fair that they might be subjects to fancy. But perhaps Saladyne's eye is leveled upon a more seemlier saint. If it be so, bear they passions with patience; say love hath wronged thee that hath not wroong[107] him; and if he be proud in contempt, be thou rich in content and rather die than dis-

---

[106]*giglot:* wanton woman.

[107]*wroong:* wrung (past participle of "wring," to vex or distress); but the original spelling, "wroong," calls attention to the play on "wronged," which is similar both in sound and sense.

cover any desire. For there is nothing more precious in a woman than to conceal love and to die modest. He is the son and heir of Sir John of Bordeaux, a youth comely enough. Oh, Alinda, too comely, else hadst not thou been thus discontent; valiant, and that fettered thine eye; wise, else hadst thou not been now won; but, for all these virtues, banished by thy father; and therefore if he know thy parentage, he will hate the fruit for the tree and condemn the young scion for the old stock. Well, howsoever, I must love, and, whomsoever, I will; and whatsoever betide, Aliena will think well of Saladyne, suppose he of me as he please."

And with that, fetching a deep sigh, she rose up and went to Ganymede, who all this while sat in a great dump, fearing the imminent danger of her friend Rosader; but now Aliena began to comfort her, herself being overgrown with sorrows, and to recall her from her melancholy with many pleasant persuasions. Ganymede took all in the best part, and so they went home together after they had folded their flocks, supping with old Corydon, who had provided their cates. He after supper, to pass away the night while bedtime, began a long discourse how Montanus, the young shepherd that was in love with Phoebe, could by no means obtain any favor at her hands but, still pained in restless passions, remained a hapless[108] and perplexed lover.

"I would I might," quoth Aliena, "once see that Phoebe. Is she so fair that she thinks no shepherd worthy of her beauty, or so froward that no love nor loyalty will content her, or so coy that she requires a long time to be wooed, or so foolish that she forgets that, like a fop, she must have a large harvest for a little corn?"

"I cannot distinguish," quoth Corydon, "of these nice qualities, but one of these days I'll bring Montanus and her down, that you may both see their persons and note their passions; and then where the blame is, there let it rest. But this I am sure," quoth Corydon, "if all maidens were of her mind, the world would grow to a mad pass; for there would be great store of wooing and little wedding, many words and little worship, much folly and no faith."

At this sad sentence of Corydon so solemnly brought forth, Aliena smiled. And because it waxed late, she and her page went to bed, both of them having fleas in their ears to keep them awake: Ganymede for the hurt of her Rosader, and Aliena for the affection she bore to Saladyne. In this discontented humor they passed away the

---

[108]*hapeless:* The spelling in the 1590 edition suggests both "hapless" and "hopeless"; cf. "soare" in note 83. The 1592 edition emended to "hopeless."

time till, falling on sleep, their senses at rest, love left them to their quiet slumbers; which were not long. For as soon as Phoebus rose from his Aurora and began to mount him in the sky, summoning the plow-swains to their handy labor, Aliena arose and, going to the couch where Ganymede lay, awakened her page and said the morning was far spent, the dew small, and time called them away to their folds.

"Ah, ah," quoth Ganymede, "is the wind in that door? Then in faith I perceive that there is no diamond so hard but will yield to the file, no cedar so strong but the wind will shake, nor any mind so chaste but love will change. Well, Aliena, must Saladyne be the man and will it be a match? Trust me, he is fair and valiant, the son of a worthy knight, whom, if he imitate in perfection as he represents him in proportion, he is worthy of no less than Aliena. But he is an exile. What then? I hope my mistress respects the virtues, not the wealth, and measures the qualities, not the substance. Those dames that are like Danae, that like love in no shape but in a shower of gold, I wish them husbands with much wealth and little wit, that the want of the one may blemish the abundance of the other. It should, my Aliena, stain the honor of a shepherd's life to set the end of passions upon pelf. Love's eyes looks not so low as gold; there is no fees to be paid in Cupid's courts, and in elder time (as Corydon hath told me) the shepherd's love-gifts were apples and chestnuts—and then their desires were loyal and their thoughts constant. But now, *Quarenda pecunia primum, post nummos virtus*. And the time is grown to that which Horace in his satires wrote on:

> *omnis enim res—*
> *Virtus, fama, decus, divina humanaque—pulchris*
> *Divitiis parent; quas qui constrinxerit ille*
> *Clarus erit, fortis, justus, sapiens, etiam et rex*
> *Et quicquid volet.*[109]

But, Aliena, let it not be so with thee in thy fancies, but respect his faith and there an end."

Aliena, hearing Ganymede thus forward to further Saladyne in his affections, thought she kissed the child for the nurse's sake and wooed for him that she might please Rosader, made this reply:

"Why, Ganymede, whereof grows this persuasion? Hast thou seen

[109]*omnis . . . volet:* "For all things—virtue, fame, honor, divine and human affairs—submit to riches; whoever has amassed them shall be illustrious, brave, just, wise, a king even, and whatever else he wishes." Horace, *Satires,* II, iii, 94–98 (with a few changes that appear to be intentional).

love in my looks? Or are mine eyes grown so amorous that they discover some new entertained fancies? If thou measurest my thoughts by my countenance, thou mayest prove as ill a physiognomer as the lapidary, that aims at the secret virtues of the topaz by the exterior shadow of the stone. The operation of the agate is not known by the strakes,[110] nor the diamond prized by his brightness but by his hardness. The carbuncle that shineth most is not ever the most precious, and the apothecaries choose not flowers for their colors but for their virtues. Women's faces are not always calendars of fancy, nor do their thoughts and their looks ever agree. For when their eyes are fullest of favors, then they are oft most empty of desire; and when they seem to frown and disdain,[111] then are they most forward to affection. If I be melancholy, then, Ganymede, 'tis not a consequence that I am entangled with the perfection of Saladyne. But seeing fire cannot be hid in the straw nor love kept so covert but it will be spied, what should friends conceal fancies? Know, my Ganymede, the beauty and valor, the wit and prowess, of Saladyne hath fettered Aliena so far, as there is no object pleasing to her eyes but the sight of Saladyne; and if love have done me justice to wrap his thoughts in the folds of my face, and that he be as deeply enamored as I am passionate, I tell thee, Ganymede, there shall be much wooing, for she is already won and what needs a longer battery."

"I am glad," quoth Ganymede, "that it shall be thus proportioned, you to match with Saladyne and I with Rosader; thus have the Destinies favored us with some pleasing aspect, that have made us as private in our loves as familiar in our fortunes."

With this Ganymede start up, made her ready, and went into the fields with Aliena; where, unfolding their flocks, they sat them down under an olive tree, both of them amorous and yet diversely affected—Aliena joying in the excellence of Saladyne and Ganymede sorrowing for the wounds of her Rosader, not quiet in thought till she might hear of his health. As thus both of them sat in their dumps, they might espy where Corydon came running towards them, almost out of breath with his haste.

"What news with you," quoth Aliena, "that you come in such post?"

"Oh, mistress," quoth Corydon, "you have a long time desired to see Phoebe, the fair shepherdess whom Montanus loves; so now, if

---

[110]*strakes:* streaks.

[111]*frown and disdain:* The "and" is an emendation by the 1596 edition, for "at" in the 1590–92 editions.

it please you and Ganymede but to walk with me to yonder thicket, there shall you see Montanus and her sitting by a fountain, he courting with his country ditties and she as coy as if she held love in disdain."

The news were so welcome to the two lovers that up they rose and went with Corydon. As soon as they drew nigh the thicket, they might espy where Phoebe sat, the fairest shepherdess in all Arden, and he the frolickest swain in the whole forest; she in a petticoat of scarlet covered with a green mantle and, to shroud her from the sun, a chaplet of roses, from under which appeared a face full of nature's excellence and two such eyes as might have amated[112] a greater man than Montanus. At gaze upon this gorgeous nymph sat the shepherd, feeding his eyes with her favors, wooing with such piteous looks and courting with such deep-strained sighs as would have made Diana herself to have been compassionate. At last, fixing his looks on the riches of her face, his head on his hand and his elbow on his knee, he sung this mournful ditty:

Montanus' Sonnet

A turtle sat upon a leaveless tree,
　　Mourning her absent fere
　　With sad and sorry cheer.
　　About her wond'ring stood
　　The citizens of wood,
　　And whilst her plumes she rents
　　And for her love laments,
　　The stately trees complain them,
　　The birds with sorrow pain them.
　　Each one that doth her view
　　Her pain and sorrow rue,
　　But were the sorrows known
　　That me hath overthrown,
　　Oh, how would Phoebe sigh if she did look on me!

The lovesick Polypheme that could not see,
　　Who on the barren shore
　　His fortunes doth deplore,
　　And melteth all in moan
　　For Galatea gone,
　　And with his piteous cries
　　Afflicts both earth and skies,
　　And to his woe betook

[112]*amated:* overwhelmed.

Doth break both pipe and hook,
For whom complains the morn,
For whom the sea nymphs mourn,
Alas his pain is nought;
For where my woe but thought,
Oh, how would Phoebe sigh if she did look on me!

Beyond compare my pain,
 Yet glad am I,
If gentle Phoebe deign
 To see her Montan die.

After this, Montanus felt his passions so extreme that he fell into
this exclamation against the injustice of love:

Hélas, tyran, plein de rigueur,
Modère un peu ta violence;
Que te sert si grande despense?[113]
C'est trop de flammes pour un coeur.
Espargnez en une estincelle,[114]
Puis fais ton effort d'esmouvoir,[115]
La fière qui ne veut point voir,
En quel fu je brusle[116] pour elle.
Exécute, Amour, ce dessein,
Et rabaisse un peu son audace,
Son cuer ne doit estre[117] de glace,
Bien que elle ait de neige le sein.

Montanus ended his sonnet with such a volley of sighs and such a
stream of tears as might have moved any but Phoebe to have granted
him favor. But she, measuring all his passions with a coy disdain and
triumphing in the poor shepherd's pathetical humors, smiling at his
martyrdom as though love had been no malady, scornfully warbled
out this sonnet:

Phoebe's Sonnet, a Reply to Montanus' Passion

Down a down,
Thus Phyllis sung,
 By fancy once distressed;

[113]*despense:* Perhaps the sense is "dépense," the emendation suggested
by Greg, who deserves credit for all the modern French equivalents in the
next several notes.
 [114]*estincelle:* étincelle.
 [115]*esmouvoir:* émouvoir.
 [116]*fu je brusle:* feu je brûle.
 [117]*cuer . . . estre:* coeur . . . être.

Whoso by foolish love are stung
    Are worthily oppressed.
And so sing I. With a down, down, etc.

When love was first begot,
And by the mover's will
Did fall to human lot
His solace to fulfill.
Devoid of all deceit,
A chaste and holy fire
Did quicken man's conceit,
And women's breast inspire.
The gods that saw the good
That mortals did approve,
With kind and holy mood
Began to talk of love.

Down a down,
Thus Phyllis sung
By fancy once distressed, etc.

But during this accord,
A wonder strange to hear,
Whilest love in deed and word
Most faithful did appear.
False semblance came in place,
By jealousy attended,
And with a double face
Both love and fancy blended.
Which made the gods forsake,
And men from fancy fly,
And maidens scorn a make,[118]
Forsooth and so will I.

Down a down,
Thus Phyllis sung,
    By fancy once distressed;
Whoso by foolish love are stung
    Are worthily oppressed.
And so sing I.
With down a down, a down down, a down a.

Montanus, hearing the cruel resolution of Phoebe, was so overgrown with passions that from amorous ditties he fell flat into these
terms:

[118]*make:* mate.

"Ah, Phoebe," quoth he, "whereof art thou made that thou regardest not my malady? Am I so hateful an object that thine eyes condemn me for an abject? Or so base that thy desires cannot stoop so low as to lend me a gracious look? My passions are many, my loves more, my thoughts loyalty, and my fancy faith—all devoted in humble devoir to the service of Phoebe. And shall I reap no reward for such fealties? The swain's daily labors is quit with the evening's hire, the plowman's toil is eased with the hope of corn, what the ox sweats out at the plow he fatteneth at the crib; but infortunate Montanus hath no salve for his sorrows nor any hope of recompense for the hazard of his perplexed passions.

"If, Phoebe, time may plead the proof of my truth, twice seven winters have I loved fair Phoebe. If constancy be a cause to farther my suit, Montanus' thoughts have been sealed in the sweet of Phoebe's excellence, as far from change as she from love. If outward passions may discover inward affections, the furrows in my face may decipher the sorrows of my heart, and the map of my looks the griefs of my mind. Thou seest, Phoebe, the tears of despair have made my cheeks full of wrinkles, and my scalding sighs have made the air echo her pity conceived in my plaints. Philomele, hearing my passions, hath left her mournful tunes to listen to the discourse of my miseries. I have portrayed in every tree the beauty of my mistress and the despair of my loves. What is it in the woods cannot witness my woes? And who is it would not pity my plaints? Only Phoebe. And why? Because I am Montanus, and she Phoebe; I a worthless swain, and she the most excellent of all fairs.[119] Beautiful Phoebe! Oh, might I say pitiful, then happy were I though I tasted but one minute of that good hap. Measure Montanus not by his fortunes but by his loves, and balance not his wealth but his desires, and lend but one gracious look to cure a heap of disquieted cares. If not—ah, if Phoebe cannot love—let a storm of frowns end the discontent of my thoughts, and so let me perish in my desires, because they are above my deserts. Only at my death this favor cannot be denied me: that all shall say Montanus died for love of hardhearted Phoebe."

At these words she filled her face full of frowns and made him this short and sharp reply:

"Importunate shepherd, whose loves are lawless because restless, are thy passions so extreme that thou canst not conceal them with patience? Or art thou so folly-sick that thou must needs be fancy-

[119]*fairs:* Greg emended "faires" in the 1590 edition to "fairies," but the sense is "fair ones" (the adjective serving as a noun).

sick? And in thy affection tied to such an exigent as none serves but Phoebe? Well, sir, if your market may be made nowhere else, home again, for your mart is at the fairest. Phoebe is no lettuce for your lips, and her grapes hang so high that gaze at them you may but touch them you cannot. Yet, Montanus, I speak not this in pride but in disdain, not that I scorn thee but that I hate love; for I count it as great honor to triumph over fancy as over fortune. Rest thee content, therefore, Montanus; cease from thy loves and bridle thy looks. Quench the sparkles before they grow to a further flame; for in loving me thou shalt live by loss, and what thou utterest in words are all written in the wind. Wert thou, Montanus, as fair as Paris, as hardy as Hector, as constant as Troilus, as loving as Leander, Phoebe could not love because she cannot love at all; and therefore if thou pursue me with Phoebus, I must fly with Daphne."

Ganymede, overhearing all these passions of Montanus, could not brook the cruelty of Phoebe but, starting from behind the bush, said:

"And if, damsel, you fled from me, I would transform you as Daphne to a bay and then in contempt trample your branches under my feet."

Phoebe at this sudden reply was amazed, especially when she saw so fair a swain as Ganymede; blushing, therefore, she would have been gone, but that he held her by the hand and prosecuted his reply thus:

"What, shepherdess, so fair and so cruel? Disdain beseems not cottages, nor coyness maids; for either they be condemned to be too proud or too froward. Take heed, fair nymph, that in despising love you be not overreached with love and, in shaking off all, shape yourself to your own shadow, and so with Narcissus prove passionate and yet unpitied. Oft have I heard, and sometimes have I seen, high disdain turned to hot desires. Because thou art beautiful be not so coy: as there is nothing more fair, so there is nothing more fading, as momentary, as the shadows which grows from a cloudy sun. Such, my fair shepherdess, as disdain in youth desire in age, and then are they hated in the winter that might have been loved in the prime. A wrinkled maid is like to a parched rose that is cast up in coffers to please the smell, not worn in the hand to content the eye. There is no folly in love to "had I wist,"[120] and therefore be ruled by me. Love while thou art young, lest thou be disdained when thou art old. Beauty nor time cannot be recalled; and if thou love, like of Montanus, for as his desires are many so his deserts are great."

[120]*to "had I wist"*: compared to "if I had but known."

Phoebe all this while gazed on the perfection of Ganymede, as deeply enamored on his perfection as Montanus inveigled with hers; for her eye made survey of his excellent feature, which she found so rare that she thought the ghost of Adonis had been leaped from Elysium in the shape of a swain. When she blushed at her own folly to look so long on a stranger, she mildly made answer to Ganymede thus:

"I cannot deny, sir, but I have heard of love though I never felt love, and have read of such a goddess as Venus though I never saw any but her picture; and perhaps—"

And with that she waxed red and bashful and withal silent. Which, Ganymede perceiving, commended in herself the bashfulness of the maid and desired her to go forward.

"And perhaps, sir," quoth she, "mine eye hath been more prodigal today than ever before—"

And with that she stayed again, as one greatly passionate and perplexed.

Aliena, seeing the hare through the maze, bade her forward with her prattle, but in vain; for at this abrupt period she broke off, and with her eyes full of tears and her face covered with a vermilion dye, she sat down and sighed. Whereupon Aliena and Ganymede, seeing the shepherdess in such a strange plight, left Phoebe with her Montanus, wishing her friendly that she would be more pliant to love, lest in penance Venus joined her to some sharp repentance. Phoebe made no reply but fetched such a sigh that Echo made relation of her plaint, giving Ganymede such an adieu with a piercing glance that the amorous girl-boy perceived Phoebe was pinched by the heel.

But leaving Phoebe to the follies of her new fancy and Montanus to attend upon her, to Saladyne, who all this last night could not rest for the remembrance of Aliena; insomuch that he framed a sweet conceited sonnet to content his humor which he put in his bosom, being requested by his brother Rosader to go to Aliena and Gaynmede to signify unto them that his wounds were not dangerous. A more happy message could not happen to Saladyne, that, taking his forest bill on his neck, he trudgeth in all haste towards the plains where Aliena's flocks did feed, coming just to the place when they returned from Montanus and Phoebe. Fortune so conducted this jolly forester that he encountered them and Corydon, whom he presently saluted in this manner:

"Fair shepherdess, and too fair, unless your beauty be tempered with courtesy and the lineaments of the face graced with the lowliness of mind; as many good fortunes to you and your page as yourselves can desire or I imagine.[121] My brother Rosader, in the grief of his green wounds still mindful of his friends, hath sent me to you with a kind salute to show that he brooks his pains with the more patience in that he holds the parties precious in whose defense he received the prejudice. The report of your welfare will be a great comfort to his distempered body and distressed thoughts, and therefore he sent me with a strict charge to visit you."

"And you," quoth Aliena, "are the more welcome in that you are messenger from so kind a gentleman, whose pains we compassionate with as great sorrow as he brooks them with grief; and his wounds breeds in us as many passions as in him extremities, so that what disquiet he feels in body we partake in heart, wishing, if we might, that our mishap might salve his malady. But seeing our wills yields him little ease, our orisons are never idle to the gods for his recovery."

"I pray you," quoth[122] Ganymede with tears in his eyes, "when the surgeon searched him, held he his wounds dangerous?"

"Dangerous," quoth Saladyne, "but not mortal, and the sooner to be cured in that his patient is not impatient of any pains; whereupon my brother hopes within these ten days to walk abroad and visit you himself."

"In the mean time," quoth Ganymede, "say his Rosalind commends her to him and bids him be of good cheer."

"I know not," quoth Saladyne, "who that Rosalind is, but whatsoever she is, her name is never out of his mouth, but amidst the deepest of his passions he useth Rosalind as a charm to appease all sorrows with patience; insomuch that I conjecture my brother is in love and she some paragon that holds his heart perplexed, whose name he oft records with sighs, sometimes with tears, straight with joy, then with smiles, as if in one person love had lodged a chaos of confused passions. Wherein I have noted the variable disposition of fancy, that like the polyp in colors so it changeth into sundry humors, being, as it should seem, a combat mixed with disquiet and a

---

[121]*or I imagine:* In omitting "I" the 1592 edition makes a possible "improvement," but there is no reason to think that Lodge had anything to do with it.

[122]*"I pray you," quoth:* The first two editions read "I pray youth (quoth"; a comma before "youth" will make sense of the passage, but the 1596 edition probably is correct in emending "youth" to "you." Saladyne is not usually addressed as "youth."

bitter pleasure wrapt in a sweet prejudice, like to the sinople tree, whose blossoms delight the smell and whose fruit infects the taste."

"By my faith," quoth Aliena, "sir, you are deep read in love. Or grows your insight into affection by experience? Howsoever you are a great philosopher in Venus' principles, else could you not discover her secret aphorisms. But sir, our country amours are not like your courtly fancies, nor is our wooing like your suing; for poor shepherds never plain them till love pain them, where the courtier's eyes is full of passions when his heart is most free from affection. They court to discover their eloquence, we woo to ease our sorrows; every fair face with them must have a new fancy sealed with a forefinger kiss and a far-fetched sigh. We here love one and live to that one so long as life can maintain love, using few ceremonies because we know few subtleties and little eloquence for that we lightly account of flattery. Only faith and troth—that's shepherds' wooing—and, sir, how like you of this?"

"So," quoth Saladyne, "as I could tie myself to such love."

"What, and look so low as a shepherdess, being the son of Sir John of Bordeaux? Such desires were a disgrace to your honors."

And with that, surveying exquisitely every part of him, as uttering all these words in a deep passion, she espied the paper in his bosom; whereupon growing jealous that it was some amorous sonnet, she suddenly snatched it out of his bosom and asked if it were any secret. She was bashful and Saladyne blushed, which, she perceiving, said:

"Nay, then, sir, if you wax red, my life for yours 'tis some love matter. I will see your mistress' name, her praises, and your passions."

And with that she looked on it, which was written to this effect:

Saladyne's Sonnet

If it be true that heaven's eternal course
With restless sway and ceaseless turning glides;
If air inconstant be, and swelling source
Turn and returns with many fluent tides;
　　If earth in winter, summer's pride estrange,
　　And nature seemeth only fair in change;

If it be true that our immortal spright,[123]
Derived from heavenly pure, in wand'ring still,
In novelty and strangeness doth delight,
And by discoverent[124] power discerneth ill;

---

[123]*spright:* spirit.
[124]*discoverent:* apparently the adjective form of the verb "discover" (reveal).

And if the body for to work his best
Doth with the seasons change his place of rest;

Whence comes it that, enforced by furious skies,
I change both place and soil but not my heart,
Yet salve not in this change my maladies?
Whence grows it that each object works my smart?
Alas, I see my faith procures my miss,
And change in love against my nature is.

Et florida pungunt.

Aliena, having read over his sonnet, began thus pleasantly to descant upon it:

"I see, Saladyne," quoth she, "that as the sun is no sun without his brightness, nor the diamond accounted for precious unless it be hard, so men are not men unless they be in love; and their honors are measured by their amours, not their labors—counting it more commendable for a gentleman to be full of fancy than full of virtue. I had thought,

Otia si tollas, periere Cupidinis arcus,
Contemptaeque jacent et sine luce faces.[125]

But I see Ovid's axiom is not authentical, for even labor hath her loves and extremity is no pumice stone to raze out fancy. Yourself exiled from your wealth, friends, and country by Torismond, sorrows enough to suppress affections, yet amidst the depth of these extremities love will be lord and show his power to be more predominant than fortune. But I pray you, sir, if without offense I may crave it, are they some new thoughts or some old desires?"

Saladyne, that now saw opportunity pleasant, thought to strike while the iron was hot and, therefore, taking Aliena by the hand, sat down by her; and Ganymede, to give them leave to their loves, found herself busy about the folds whilst Saladyne fell into this prattle with Aliena:

"Fair mistress, if I be blunt in discovering my affections and use little eloquence in leveling out my loves, I appeal for pardon to your own principles that say shepherds use few ceremonies, for that they acquaint themselves with few subtleties. To frame myself, therefore, to your country fashion with much faith and little flattery, know, beautiful shepherdess, that whilst I lived in the court I knew not

[125]Otia . . . faces: "If you take away leisure, Cupid's bow is lost and his torches lie despised and without light." Quoted exactly from Ovid, The Remedies of Love, lines 139–140.

love's cumber, but I held affection as a toy, not as a malady, using fancy as the Hiperboreido[126] do their flowers which they wear in their bosom all day and cast them in the fire for fuel at night. I liked all because I loved none, and who was most fair, on her I fed mine eye, but as charily as the bee that as soon as she hath sucked honey from the rose flies straight to the next marigold. Living thus at mine own list I wondered at such as were in love, and when I read their passions I took them only for poems that flowed from the quickness of the wit, not the sorrows of the heart. But now, fair nymph, since I became a forester, love hath taught me such a lesson that I must confess his deity and dignity, and say as there is nothing so precious as beauty so there is nothing more piercing than fancy. For since first I arrived in this place and mine eye took a curious survey of your excellence, I have been so fettered with your beauty and virtue as, sweet Aliena, Saladyne without further circumstance loves Aliena. I could paint out my desires with long ambages, but, seeing in many words lies mistrust and that truth is ever naked, let this suffice for a country wooing: Saladyne loves Aliena and none but Aliena."

Although these words were most heavenly harmony in the ears of the shepherdess, yet to seem coy at the first courting and to disdain love, howsoever she desired love, she made this reply:

"Ah, Saladyne, though I seem simple, yet I am more subtle than to swallow the hook because it hath a painted bait. As men are wily so women are wary, especially if they have that wit by others' harms to beware. Do we not know, Saladyne, that men's tongues are like Mercury's pipe (that can enchant Argus with an hundred eyes), and their words as prejudicial as the charms of Circe (that transform men into monsters)? If such Sirens sing, we poor women had need stop our ears, lest in hearing we prove so foolish hardy as to believe them, and so perish in trusting much and suspecting little. Saladyne, *piscator ictus sapit;* he that hath been once poisoned, and afterwards fears not to bowse of every potion, is worthy to suffer double penance. Give me leave then to mistrust, though I do not condemn. Saladyne is now in love with Aliena—he a gentleman of great parentage, she a shepherdess of mean parents, he honorable and she poor. Can love consist of contrarieties? Will the falcon perch with the kistress,[127] the lion harbor with the wolf? Will Venus join robes and

---

[126]*Hiperboreido:* the Hyperboreans; see note 15.

[127]*kistress:* kestrel (a small hawk); possibly the ending is to specify the female. No similar spelling is recorded in the *OED;* the misspelling, if such it is, persisted in all the early editions until 1609, when it became "kistrell."

rags together? Or can there be a sympathy between a king and a beggar? Then, Saladyne, how can I believe thee that love should unite our thoughts when fortune hath set such a difference between our degrees? But suppose thou likest of Aliena's beauty. Men in their fancy resemble the wasp, which scorns that flower from which she hath fetched her wax, playing like the inhabitants of the island Tenerifa[128] who when they have gathered the sweet spices, use the trees for fuel; so men, when they have glutted themselves with the fair of women's faces, hold them for necessary evils and, wearied with that which they seemed so much to love, cast away fancy as children do their rattles and loathing that which so deeply before they liked; especially such as take love in a minute and have their eyes attractive, like jet, apt to entertain any object, are as ready to let it slip again."[129]

Saladyne, hearing how Aliena harped still upon one string, which was the doubt of men's constancy, he broke off her sharp invective thus:

"I grant, Aliena," quoth he, "many men have done amiss in proving soon ripe and soon rotten, but particular instances infer no general conclusions; and therefore I hope what others have faulted in shall not prejudice my favors. I will not use sophistry to confirm my love (for that is subtlety), nor long discourses (lest my words might be thought more than my faith). But if this will suffice: that by the honor of a gentleman I love Aliena, and woo Aliena not to crop the blossoms and reject the tree but to consummate my faithful desires in the honorable end of marriage."

At this word "marriage" Aliena stood in a maze what to answer—fearing that if she were too coy, to drive him away with her disdain, and if she were too courteous, to discover the heat of her desires. In a dilemma thus what to do, at last this she said:

"Saladyne, ever since I saw thee I favored thee. I cannot dissemble my desires because I see thou dost faithfully manifest thy thoughts, and in liking thee I love thee so far as mine honor holds fancy still in suspense; but if I knew thee as virtuous as thy father or as well qualified as thy brother Rosader, the doubt should be quickly decided. But for this time, to give thee an answer, assure thyself this: I will either marry with Saladyne or still live a virgin."

---

[128]*Tenerifa:* usually spelled "Tenerife" or "Teneriffe" (but now also "Teyde" or "Teide"); one of the Canary Islands.

[129]*attractive, like jet ... slip again:* The hard, black mineral called "jet" has only a slight magnetic power.

And with this they strained one another's hand, which Ganymede espying, thinking he had had his mistress long enough at shrift, said: "What, a match or no?"

"A match," quoth Aliena, "or else it were an ill market."

"I am glad," quoth Ganymede. "I would Rosader were well here to make up a mess."[130]

"Well remembered," quoth Saladyne. "I forgot I left my brother Rosader alone; and therefore lest, being solitary, he should increase his sorrows, I will haste me to him. May it please you then to command me any service to him, I am ready to be a dutiful messenger."

"Only at this time commend me to him," quoth Aliena, "and tell him though we cannot pleasure him, we pray for him."

"And forget not," quoth Ganymede, "my commendations. But say to him that Rosalind sheds as many tears from her heart as he drops of blood from his wounds; for the sorrow of his misfortunes, feathering all her thoughts with disquiet till his welfare procure her content. Say thus, good Saladyne, and so farewell."

He, having his message, gave a courteous adieu to them both, especially to Aliena; and so, playing loath to depart, went to his brother. But Aliena, she perplexed and yet joyful, passed away the day pleasantly, still praising the perfection of Saladyne, not ceasing to chat of her new love till evening drew on; and then they, folding their sheep, went home to bed. Where we leave them and return to Phoebe.

Phoebe, fired with the uncouth flame of love, returned to her father's house so galled with restless passions as now she began to acknowledge that, as there was no flower so fresh but might be parched with the sun, no tree so strong but might be shaken with a storm, so there was no thought so chaste but time, armed with love, could make amorous. For she that held Diana for the goddess of her devotion was now fain to fly to the altar of Venus, as suppliant now with prayers as she was froward afore with disdain. As she lay in her bed she called to mind the several beauties of young Ganymede; first his locks which, being amber-hued, passeth the wreath that Phoebus puts on to make his front glorious; his brow of ivory was like the seat where love and majesty sits enthroned to enchain fancy; his eyes as bright as the burnishing of the heaven,

---

[130]*make up a mess:* The closest modern equivalent to "mess" is "foursome." The implication is that with Rosader they would have the proper number of four, to sit at a table and eat together from the same dishes.

darting forth frowns with disdain and smiles with favor, lightning[131] such looks as would inflame desire were she wrapt in the circle of the frozen zone; in his cheeks the vermilion teinture[132] of the rose flourished upon natural alabaster, the blush of the morn and Luna's silver show were so lively portrayed that the Trojan that fills out wine to Jupiter was not half so beautiful; his face was full of pleasance and all the rest of his lineaments proportioned with such excellence as Phoebe was fettered in the sweetness of his feature. The idea of these perfections tumbling in her mind made the poor shepherdess so perplexed, as feeling a pleasure tempered with intolerable pains and yet a disquiet mixed with a content, she rather wished to die than to live in this amorous anguish. But wishing is little worth in such extremes, and therefore was she forced to pine in her malady without any salve for her sorrows. Reveal it she durst not (as daring in such matters to make none her secretary),[133] and to conceal it (why, it doubled her grief); for as fire suppressed grows to the greater flame and the current stopped to the more violent stream, so love smothered wrings the heart with the deeper passions.

Perplexed thus with sundry agonies, her food began to fail and the disquiet of her mind began to work a distemperature of her body, that, to be short, Phoebe fell extreme sick and so sick as there was almost left no recovery of health. Her father, seeing his fair Phoebe thus distressed, sent for his friends, who sought by medicine to cure and by counsel to pacify, but all in vain; for although her body was feeble through long fasting, yet she did *magis aegrotare animo quam corpore*. Which her friends perceived and sorrowed at, but salve it they could not.

The news of her sickness was bruited abroad through all the forest; which no sooner came to Montanus' ear but he like a madman came to visit Phoebe. Where, sitting by her bedside, he began his exordium with so many tears and sighs that she, perceiving the extremity of his sorrows, began now, as a lover, to pity them, although Ganymede held her from redressing them. Montanus craved to know the cause of her sickness, tempered with secret plaints; but she

---

[131]*lightning:* A meaning given in the *OED* under "lighten" seems to fit: "to cause (the countenance or looks) to light up with a lively expression." But the first example given is dated 1795.

[132]*teinture:* tint, or tincture (and related to "tainting" on p. 380).

[133]*secretary:* confidant(e). The professional sense (of a person employed to take care of correspondence) is current from the mid-fifteenth century on. The secretary in *Master F. J.* seems to combine these two senses.

answered him (as the rest) with silence, having still the form of Ganymede in her mind and conjecturing how she might reveal her loves. To utter it in words she found herself too bashful; to discourse by any friend she would not trust any in her amours; to remain thus perplexed still and conceal all it was a double death. Whereupon, for her last refuge she resolved to write unto Ganymede, and therefore desired Montanus to absent himself a while but not to depart, for she would see if she could steal a nap. He was no sooner gone out of the chamber, but, reaching to her standish,[134] she took pen and paper and wrote a letter to this effect:

Phoebe to Ganymede Wisheth What She Wants Herself

Fair shepherd—and therefore is Phoebe infortunate because thou art so fair—although hitherto mine eyes were adamants to resist love, yet I no sooner saw thy face but they became amorous to entertain love; more devoted to fancy than before they were repugnant to affection, addicted to the one by nature and drawn to the other by beauty, which, being rare and made the more excellent by many virtues, hath so snared the freedom of Phoebe, as she rests at thy mercy, either to be made the most fortunate of all maidens or the most miserable of all women. Measure not, Ganymede, my loves by my wealth nor my desires by my degrees, but think my thoughts are as full of faith as thy face of amiable favors. Then as thou knowest thyself most beautiful, suppose me most constant. If thou deemest me hardhearted because I hated Montanus, think I was forced to it by fate; if thou sayest I am kindhearted because so lightly I loved thee at the first look, think I was driven to it by destiny, whose influence as it is mighty so it is not to be resisted. If my fortunes were anything but infortunate love, I would strive with fortune. But he that wrests against the will of Venus seeks to quench fire with oil and to thrust out one thorn by putting in another. If then, Ganymede, love enters at the eye, harbors in the heart, and will neither be driven out with physic nor reason, pity me as one whose malady hath no salve but from thy sweet self; whose grief hath no ease but through thy grant; and think I am a virgin who is deeply wronged when I am forced to woo, and conjecture love to be strong that is more forcible than nature. Thus distressed unless by thee eased, I expect either to live fortunate by thy favor or die miserable by thy denial. Living in hope. Farewell.

> She that must be thine or not be at all,
> Phoebe

[134]*standish:* a stand or table especially for writing materials (possibly "stand" plus "dish").

To this letter she annexed this sonnet:

Sonetto

My boat doth pass the straits
Of seas incensed with fire,
Filled with forgetfulness;
Amidst the winter's night,
A blind and careless boy,
Brought up by fond desire,
Doth guide me in the sea
Of sorrow and despite.

For every oar he sets
A rank of foolish thoughts,
And cuts, instead of wave,
A hope without distress;
The winds of my deep sighs,
That thunder still for noughts,
Have split my sails with fear,
With care, with heaviness.

A mighty storm of tears,
A black and hideous cloud,
A thousand fierce disdains
Do slack the halyards oft;
Till ignorance do pull,
And error hale the shrouds,
No star for safety shines,
No Phoebe from aloft.

Time hath subdued art,
And joy is slave to woe,
Alas, Love's guide, be kind;
What, shall I perish so?

This letter and the sonnet being ended, she could find no fit messenger to send it by; and therefore she called in Montanus and entreated him to carry it to Ganymede. Although poor Montanus saw day at a little hole and did perceive what passion pinched her, yet that he might seem dutiful to his mistress in all service he dissembled the matter and became a willing messenger of his own martyrdom. And so, taking the letter, went next morn very early to the plains where Aliena fed her flocks, and there he found Ganymede sitting under a pomegranate tree, sorrowing for the hard fortunes of her

Rosader. Montanus saluted him and, according to his charge, delivered Ganymede the letters, which, he said, came from Phoebe.

At this the wanton blushed, as being abashed to think what news should come from an unknown shepherdess but, taking the letters, unripped the seals and read over the discourse of Phoebe's fancies. When she had read and overread them, Ganymede began to smile and, looking on Montanus, fell into a great laughter, and with that called Aliena to whom she showed the writings. Who, having perused them, conceited them very pleasantly, and smiled to see how love had yoked her who, before, disdained to stoop to the lure. Aliena, whispering Ganymede in the ear and saying, "Knew Phoebe what want there were in thee to perform her will and how unfit thy kind is to be kind to her, she would be more wise and less enamored; but leaving that, I pray thee let us sport with this swain."

At that word, Ganymede turning to Montanus, began to glance at him thus:

"I pray thee tell me, shepherd, by those sweet thoughts and pleasing sighs that grow from my mistress' favors, art thou in love with Phoebe?"

"Oh, my youth," quoth Montanus, "were Phoebe so far in love with me, my flocks would be more fat and their master more quiet; for through the sorrows of my discontent grows the leanness of my sheep."

"Alas, poor swain," quoth Ganymede, "are thy passions so extreme or thy fancy so resolute that no reason will blemish the pride of thy affection and raze out that which thou strivest for without hope?"

"Nothing can make me forget Phoebe while[135] Montanus forget himself, for those characters which true love hath stamped, neither the envy of time nor fortune can wipe away."

"Why, but, Montanus," quoth Ganymede, "enter with a deep insight into the despair of thy fancies and thou shalt see the depth of thine own follies; for, poor man, thy progress in love is a regress to loss, swimming against the stream with the crab and flying with Apis Indica against wind and weather. Thou seekest with Phoebus to win Daphne, and she flies faster than thou canst follow; thy desires soar with the hobby, but her disdain reacheth higher than thou canst make wing. I tell thee, Montanus, in courting Phoebe thou barkest with the wolves of Syria against the moon, and rovest[136] at such a

[135]*while:* until.
[136]*rovest:* shoot(an arrow) at random.

mark with thy thoughts as is beyond the pitch of thy bow, praying to love when love is pitiless and thy malady remediless. For proof, Montanus, read these letters, wherein thou shalt see thy great follies and little hope."

With that Montanus took them and perused them, but with such sorrow in his looks as they bewrayed a source of confused passions in his heart. At every line his color changed and every sentence was ended with a period of sighs. At last, noting Phoebe's extreme desire toward Ganymede and her disdain towards him, giving Ganymede the letter, the shepherd stood as though he had neither won nor lost. Which Ganymede perceiving, wakened him out his dream thus:

"Now, Montanus, dost thou see thou vowest great service and obtainest but little reward? But in lieu of thy loyalty she maketh thee, as Bellerophon, carry thine own bane. Then drink not willingly of that potion wherein thou knowest is poison; creep not to her that cares not for thee. What, Montanus, there are many as fair as Phoebe, but most of all more courteous than Phoebe. I tell thee, shepherd, favor is love's fuel; then since thou canst not get that, let the flame vanish into smoke and rather sorrow for a while than repent thee forever."

"I tell thee, Ganymede," quoth Montanus, "as they which are stung with the scorpion cannot be recovered but by the scorpion, nor he that was wounded with Achilles' lance be cured but with the same truncheon, so Apollo was fain to cry out that love was only eased with love and fancy healed by no medicine but favor. Phoebus had herbs to heal all hurts but this passion, Circe had charms for all chances but for affection and Mercury subtle reasons to refel[137] all griefs but love. Persuasions are bootless, reason lends no remedy, counsel no comfort to such whom fancy hath made resolute; and, therefore, though Phoebe loves Ganymede, yet Montanus must honor none but Phoebe."

"Then," quoth Ganymede, "may I rightly term thee a despairing lover that livest without joy and lovest without hope. But what shall I do, Montanus, to pleasure thee? Shall I despise Phoebe as she disdains thee?"

"Oh," quoth Montanus, "that were to renew my griefs and double my sorrows, for the sight of her discontent were the censure of my death. Alas, Ganymede, though I perish in my thoughts, let not her die in her desires. Of all passions, love is most impatient; then let not

---

[137]*refel:* reject.

so fair a creature as Phoebe sink under the burden of so deep a distress. Being love-sick, she is proved heart-sick—and all for the beauty of Ganymede. Thy proportion hath entangled her affection, and she is snared in the beauty of thy excellence. Then sith she loves thee so dear, mislike not her deadly. Be thou paramour to such a paragon; she hath beauty to content thine eye and flocks to enrich thy store. Thou canst not wish for more than thou shalt win by her; for she is beautiful, virtuous, and wealthy—three deep persuasions to make love frolic."

Aliena, seeing Montanus cut it against the hair and plead that Ganymede ought to love Phoebe, when his only life was the love of Phoebe, answered him thus:

"Why, Montanus, dost thou further this motion, seeing if Ganymede marry Phoebe thy market is clean marred?"

"Ah, mistress," quoth he, "so hath love taught me to honor Phoebe, that I would prejudice my life to pleasure her, and die in despair rather than she should perish for want. It shall suffice me to see her contented and to feed mine eye on her favor. If she marry, though it be my martyrdom, yet if she be pleased I will brook it with patience and triumph in mine own stars to see her desires satisfied. Therefore, if Ganymede be as courteous as he is beautiful, let him show his virtues in redressing Phoebe's miseries."

And this Montanus pronounced with such an assured countenance that it amazed both Aliena and Ganymede to see the resolution of his loves; so that they pitied his passions and commended his patience, devising how they might by any subtlety get Montanus the favor of Phoebe. Straight, as women's heads are full of wiles, Ganymede had a fetch[138] to force Phoebe to fancy the shepherd malgrado[139] the resolution of her mind. He prosecuted his policy thus:

"Montanus," quoth he, "seeing Phoebe is so forlorn, lest I might be counted unkind in not salving so fair a creature, I will go with thee to Phoebe, and there hear herself in word utter that which she hath discoursed with her pen; and then, as love wills me, I will set down my censure.[140] I will home by our house and send Corydon to accompany Aliena."

Montanus seemed glad of this determination, and away they go towards the house of Phoebe. When they drew nigh to the cottage,

---

[138]*fetch:* stratagem.
[139]*malgrado:* an Italian preposition meaning "in spite of."
[140]*censure:* judgment, decision (not necessarily hostile).

Montanus ran afore and went in and told Phoebe that Ganymede was at the door. This word "Ganymede," sounding in the ears of Phoebe, drove her into such an ecstasy for joy that, rising up in her bed, she was half revived, and her wan color began to wax red. And with that came Ganymede in, who saluted Phoebe with such a courteous look that it was half a salve to her sorrows. Sitting him down by her bedside, he questioned about her disease and where the pain chiefly held her. Phoebe looking as lovely as Venus in her night-gear, tainting her face with as ruddy a blush as Clitia[141] did when she bewrayed her loves to Phoebus, taking Ganymede by the hand began thus:

"Fair shepherd, if love were not more strong than nature or fancy the sharpest extreme, my immodesty were the more and my virtues the less; for nature hath framed women's eyes bashful, their hearts full of fear, and their tongues full of silence. But love, that imperious love, where his power is predominant, then he perverts all and wresteth the wealth of nature to his own will. An instance in myself, fair Ganymede; for such a fire hath he kindled in my thoughts that to find ease for the flame, I was forced to pass the bounds of modesty and seek a salve at thy hands for my secret harms. Blame me not if I be overbold, for it is thy beauty; and if I be too forward, it is fancy, and the deep insight into thy virtues, that makes me thus fond. For let me say in a word what may be contained in a volume: Phoebe loves Ganymede."

At this she held down her head and wept, and Ganymede rose, as one that would suffer no fish to hang on his fingers, made this reply:

"Water not thy plants, Phoebe, for I do pity thy plaints; nor seek not to discover thy loves in tears, for I conjecture thy truth by thy passions. Sorrow is no salve for loves, nor sighs no remedy for affection. Therefore frolic, Phoebe, for if Ganymede can cure thee, doubt not of recovery. Yet this let me say without offense, that it grieves me to thwart Montanus in his fancies, seeing his desires have been so resolute and his thoughts so loyal. But thou allegest thou art forced from him by fate; so I tell thee, Phoebe, either some star or else some destiny fits my mind rather, with Adonis, to die in chase than be counted a wanton on Venus' knee. Although I pity thy martyrdom, yet I can grant no marriage; for though I held thee fair yet mine eye is not fettered. Love grows not, like the herb spattanna[142] to his perfection in one night, but creeps with the snail and yet at last

---

[141]*Clitia:* Clytië, the water-nymph in love with Phoebus.
[142]*the herb spattanna:* possibly a name invented by Lodge; not included in the index of the Bohn edition of Pliny.

attains to the top. *Festina lente*, especially in love, for momentary fancies are ofttimes the fruits of follies. If, Phoebe, I should like thee as the Hiperborei do their dates (which banquet with them in the morning and throw them away at night), my folly should be great and thy repentance more. Therefore, I will have time to turn my thoughts, and my loves shall grow up as the water cresses—slowly, but with a deep root. Thus, Phoebe, thou mayest see I disdain not though I desire not, remaining indifferent till time and love makes me resolute. Therefore, Phoebe, seek not to suppress affection, and with the love of Montanus quench the remembrance of Ganymede. Strive thou to hate me as I seek to like of thee, and ever have the duties of Montanus in thy mind; for I promise thee thou mayest have one more wealthy but not more loyal."

These words were corrosives to the perplexed Phoebe, that, sobbing out sighs and straining out tears, she blubbered out these words:

"And shall I, then, have no salve of Ganymede but suspense? No hope but a doubtful hazard? No comfort but be posted off to the will of time? Justly have the gods balanced my fortunes; who, being cruel to Montanus, found Ganymede as unkind to myself; so, in forcing him perish for love, I shall die myself with overmuch love."

"I am glad," quoth Ganymede, "you look into your own faults and see where your shoe wrings you, measuring now the pains of Montanus by your own passions."

"Truth," quoth Phoebe, "and so deeply I repent me of my frowardness toward the shepherd that could I cease to love Ganymede, I would resolve to like Montanus."

"What if I can with reason persuade Phoebe to mislike of Ganymede? Will she then favor Montanus?"

"When reason," quoth she, "doth quench that love that I owe to thee, then will I fancy him; conditionally, that if my love can be suppressed with no reason, as being without reason, Ganymede will only wed himself to Phoebe."

"I grant it, fair shepherdess," quoth he, "and to feed thee with the sweetness of hope, this resolve on: I will never marry myself to woman but unto thyself."

And with that Ganymede gave Phoebe a fruitless kiss and such words of comfort that, before Ganymede departed, she arose out of her bed and made him and Montanus such cheer as could be found in such a country cottage; Ganymede in the midst of their banquet rehearsing the promises of either in Montanus' favor, which highly pleased the shepherd. Thus all three content, and soothed up in hope,

Ganymede took his leave of his Phoebe and departed, leaving her a contented woman and Montanus highly pleased.

But poor Ganymede, who had her thoughts on her Rosader, when she called to remembrance his wounds, filled her eyes full of tears and her heart full of sorrows, plodded to find Aliena at the folds, thinking with her presence to drive away her passions. As she came on the plains she might espy where Rosader and Saladyne sat with Aliena under the shade; which sight was a salve to her grief and such a cordial unto her heart that she tripped alongst the lawns full of joy.

At last Corydon, who was with them, spied Ganymede; and with that the clown rose and, running to meet him, cried:

"Oh, sirrah, a match, a match. Our mistress shall be married on Sunday."

Thus the poor peasant frolicked it before Ganymede, who, coming to the crew, saluted them all and especially Rosader, saying that he was glad to see him so well recovered of his wounds.

"I had not gone abroad so soon," quoth Rosader, "but that I am bidden to a marriage, which on Sunday next must be solemnized, between my brother and Aliena. I see well where love leads, delay is loathsome; and that small wooing serves, where both the parties are willing."

"Truth," quoth Ganymede, "but a happy day should it be if Rosader that day might be married to Rosalind."

"Ah, good Ganymede," quoth he, "by naming Rosalind renew not my sorrows, for the thought of her perfections is the thrall of my miseries."

"Tush, be of good cheer, man," quoth Ganymede, "I have a friend that is deeply experienced in necromancy and magic; what art can do shall be acted for thine advantage. I will cause him to bring in Rosalind if either France or any bordering nation harbor her, and upon that take the faith of a young shepherd."

Aliena smiled to see how Rosader frowned, thinking that Ganymede had jested with him. But breaking off from those matters, the page, somewhat pleasant, began to discourse unto them what had passed between him and Phoebe; which, as they laughed, so they wondered at, all confessing that there is none so chaste but love will change. Thus they passed away the day in chat; and when the sun began to set, they took their leaves and departed, Aliena providing for their marriage day such solemn cheer and handsome robes as fitted their country estate, and yet somewhat the better in that Rosader had promised to bring Gerismond thither as a guest. Ganymede, who then meant to discover herself before her father, had made her a gown of green and a kirtle of the finest sendal, in such sort that she seemed some heavenly nymph harbored in country attire.

Saladyne was not behind in care to set out the nuptials, nor Rosader unmindful to bid guests; who invited Gerismond and all his followers to the feast; who willingly granted, so that there was nothing but the day wanting to this marriage.

In the meanwhile, Phoebe, being a bidden guest, made herself as gorgeous as might be to please the eye of Ganymede; and Montanus suited himself with the cost of many of his flocks to be gallant against that day—for then was Ganymede to give Phoebe an answer of her loves, and Montanus either to hear the doom of his misery or the censure of his happiness. But while this gear[143] was a-brewing, Phoebe passed not one day without visiting her Ganymede, so far was she wrapt in the beauties of this lovely swain. Much prattle they had and the discourse of many passions, Phoebe wishing for the day, as she thought, of her welfare and Ganymede smiling to think what unexpected events would fall out at the wedding. In these humors the week went away, that at last Sunday came.

No sooner did Phoebus' henchman appear in the sky to give warning that his master's horses should be trapped[144] in his glorious couch,[145] but Corydon in his holiday suit, marvelous seemly in a russet jacket welted with the same and faced with red worsted, having a pair of blue camlet sleeves bound at the wrists with four yellow laces, closed afore very richly with a dozen of pewter buttons. His hose was of gray kersey, with a large slop, barred[146] overthwart the

---

[143]*gear:* matter, affair.

[144]*trapped:* covered with trappings; adorned.

[145]*couch:* The sense is "coach" (the 1598 emendation) or "carriage," but the intent may be to suggest a particularly comfortable and luxurious coach.

[146]*with a large slop, barred:* Here is an example of an "accidental" (a whim of punctuation or spelling) that turns out to be "substantive" in its effects. The 1596 edition inserts a comma after "slop"; if we accept the comma, then "slop" refers to "hose" and the sense probably is that each leg of the hose fits loosely. Without the comma, "slop" need not refer to "hose" and could mean "tunic" or "outer garment"; a "slop" could also be a kind of sash or scarf worn from shoulder to hip or around the waist. "Barred" means "trimmed"; to discover what is trimmed, we come back once again to the comma.

pocket holes with three fair guards[147] stitched of either side with red thread; his stock was of the own, sewed close to his breech,[148] and for to beautify his hose he had trussed himself round with a dozen of new threaden points[149] of medley color; his bonnet was green whereon stood a copper brooch with the picture of St. Denis; and, to want nothing that might make him amorous in his old days, he had a fair shirt band of fine lockram, whipped over[150] with Coventry blue of no small cost. Thus attired, Corydon bestirred himself as chief stickler in these actions and had strowed all the house with flowers, that it seemed rather some of Flora's choice bowers than any country cottage.

Thither repaired Phoebe with all the maids of the forest to set out the bride in the most seemliest sort that might be; but howsoever she helped to prank out Aliena, yet her eye was still on Ganymede, who was so neat in a suit of gray that he seemed Endymion when he won Luna with his looks, or Paris when he played the swain to get the beauty of the nymph Oenone. Ganymede, like a pretty page, waited on his mistress Aliena and overlooked that all was in a readiness against the bridegroom should come. Who, attired in a forester's suit, came accompanied with Gerismond and his brother Rosader early in the morning; where, arrived, they were solemnly entertained by Aliena and the rest of the country swains, Gerismond very highly commending the fortunate choice of Saladyne, in that he had chosen a shepherdess, whose virtues appeared in her outward beauties, being no less fair than seeming modest.

Ganymede coming in and, seeing her father, began to blush, nature working affects by her secret effects. Scarce could she abstain from tears to see her father in so low fortunes—he that was wont to sit in his royal palace attended on by twelve noble peers, now to be contented with a simple cottage and a troop of reveling woodmen for his train. The consideration of his fall made Ganymede full of sorrows;

[147]*guards:* ornamental borders; "barred" and "guards" refer to the same thing.

[148]*his stock was of the own, sewed close to his breech:* Possibly the reference is to close-fitting boots, "the own" suggesting his own design or the shoemaker's attempt to fit him in some way appropriate only to him.

[149]*threaden points:* string laces (of the kind still found on some jackets and, of course, in shoes); points were made of twisted yarn, silk, or leather, and their primary function was to attach the hose to the doublet.

[150]*lockram, whipped over:* a linen fabric, embroidered over (with some kind of trim or ornament).

yet that she might triumph over fortune with patience, and not any way dash that merry day with her dumps, she smothered her melancholy with a shadow of mirth and very reverently welcomed the king, not according to his former degree but to his present estate, with such diligence as Gerismond began to commend the page for his exquisite person and excellent qualities.

As thus the king with his foresters frolicked it among the shepherds, Corydon came in with a fair mazer full of cider and presented it to Gerismond with such a clownish salute that he began to smile and took it of the old shepherd very kindly, drinking to Aliena and the rest of her fair maids, amongst whom Phoebe was the foremost. Aliena pledged the king and drunk to Rosader, so the carouse went round from him to Phoebe, etc.

As they were thus drinking and ready to go to church, came in Montanus appareled all in tawny to signify that he was forsaken. On his head he wore a garland of willow, his bottle hanged by his side whereon was painted despair, and on his sheep hook hung two sonnets as labels of his loves and fortunes. Thus attired came Montanus in, with his face as full of grief as his heart was of sorrows, showing in his countenance the map of extremities. As soon as the shepherds saw him they did him all the honor they could, as being the flower of all the swains in Arden; for a bonnier boy was there not seen since the wanton wag of Troy that kept sheep in Ida. He, seeing the king and guessing it to be Gerismond, did him all the reverence his country courtesy could afford; insomuch that the king, wondering at his attire, began to question what he was. Montanus, overhearing him, made this reply:

"I am, sir," quoth he, "love's swain, as full of inward discontents as I seem fraught with outward follies. Mine eyes, like bees, delight in sweet flowers; but sucking their full on the fair of beauty, they carry home to the hive of my heart far more gall than honey, and for one drop of pure dew a tun full of deadly aconiton.[151] I hunt with the fly to pursue the eagle,[152] that, flying too nigh the sun, I perish with the sun;[153] my thoughts are above my reach and my desires more than my fortunes, yet neither greater than my loves. But daring with

---

[151]*aconiton:* that is, "aconitine" or "aconitum" (a drug).

[152]*I hunt with the fly to pursue the eagle:* Montanus emphasizes his own folly and perversity when he completely changes a well-known proverb (Tilley, E1): "The eagle does not catch flies."

[153]*with the sun:* The sense is "by (or because of) the sun"; the 1604 edition emended to "by."

Phaëthon I fall with Icarus, and seeking to pass the mean I die for being so mean. My nights' sleeps are waking slumbers, as full of sorrows as they be far from rest; and my days' labors are fruitless amours, staring at a star and stumbling at a straw, leaving reason to follow after repentance. Yet every passion is a pleasure though it pinch, because love hides his wormseed in figs, his poisons in sweet potions, and shadows prejudize[154] with the mask of pleasure. The wisest counselors are my deep discontents, and I hate that which should salve my harm, like the patient which, stung with the tarantula, loathes music and yet the disease incurable but by melody. Thus, sir, restless I hold myself remediless, as loving without either reward or regard and yet loving, because there is none worthy to be loved but the mistress of my thoughts. And that I am as full of passions as I have discoursed in my plaints, sir, if you please, see my sonnets and by them censure of my sorrows."

These words of Montanus brought the king into a great wonder, amazed as much at his wit as his attire; insomuch that he took the papers off his hook and read them to this effect:

Montanus' First Sonnet

Alas, how wander I amidst these woods,
Whereas no day bright shine doth find access,
But where the melancholy fleeting floods,
Dark as the night my night of woes express.
Disarmed of reason, spoiled of nature's goods,
Without redress to salve my heaviness
  I walk, whilst thought, too cruel to my harms,
  With endless grief my heedless judgment charms.

My silent tongue assailed by secret fear,
My traitorous eyes imprisoned in their joy,
My fatal peace devoured in feigned cheer,
My heart enforced to harbor in annoy,
My reason robbed of power by yielding ear,
My fond opinions slave to every toy.
  Oh, Love, thou guide in my uncertain way,
  Woe to thy bow, thy fire, the cause of my decay.
                             Et florida pungunt.

When the king had read this sonnet, he highly commended the device of the shepherd that could so wittily wrap his passions in a

---

[154]*prejudize:* related to "prejudiced," but the primary sense seems to be "covered over."

shadow and so covertly conceal that which bred his chiefest discontent
—affirming that, as the least shrubs have their tops, the smallest hairs
their shadows, so the meanest swains had their fancies and in their
kind were as chary of love as a king. Whetted on with this device, he
took the second and read it; the effects were these:

Montanus' Second Sonnet

When the Dog,[155]
Full of rage,
   With his ireful eyes
   Frowns amidst the skies,
The shepherd, to assuage
   The fury of the heat,
   Himself doth safely seat
By a fount
Full of fair,
   Where a gentle breath
   Mounting from beneath,
Temp'reth the air.
There his flocks
Drink their fill,
   And with ease repose
   Whilest sweet sleep doth close
Eyes from toilsome ill.
But I burn
Without rest,
   No defensive power
   Shields from Phoebe's lower.
Sorrow is my best.
Gentle love,
Lower no more,
   If thou wilt invade,
   In the secret shade,
Labor not so sore.
I myself
And my flocks,
   They their love to please,
   I myself to ease,
Both leave the shady oaks,
   Content to burn in fire,
   Sith love doth so desire.
            Et florida pungunt.

[155]*Dog:* Sirius (the "Dog Star").

Gerismond, seeing the pithy vein of those sonnets, began to make further inquiry what he was. Whereupon Rosader discoursed unto him the love of Montanus to Phoebe, his great loyalty and her deep cruelty, and how in revenge the gods had made the curious nymph amorous of young Ganymede. Upon this discourse the king was desirous to see Phoebe, who, being brought before Gerismond by Rosader, shadowed the beauty of her face with such a vermilion teinture that the king's eyes began to dazzle at the purity of her excellence. After Gerismond had fed his looks awhile upon her fair, he questioned with her why she rewarded Montanus' love with so little regard, seeing his deserts were many and his passions extreme. Phoebe, to make reply to the king's demand, answered thus:

"Love, sir, is chary in his laws; and whatsoever he sets down for justice, be it never so unjust, the sentence cannot be reversed. Women's fancies lend favors not ever by desert, but as they are enforced by their desires; for fancy is tied to the wings of fate, and what the stars decree stands for an infallible doom. I know Montanus is wise, and women's ears are greatly delighted with wit, as hardly escaping the charm of a pleasant tongue as Ulysses the melody of the Sirens. Montanus is beautiful, and women's eyes are snared in the excellence of objects as desirous to feed their looks with a fair face as the bee to suck on a sweet flower. Montanus is wealthy, and an ounce of give-me persuades a woman more than a pound of hear-me. Danae was won with a golden shower when she could not be gotten with all the entreaties of Jupiter. I tell you, sir, the string of a woman's heart reacheth to the pulse of her hand, and let a man rub that with gold and 'tis hard but she will prove his heart's gold. Montanus is young, a great clause in fancy's court; Montanus is virtuous, the richest argument that love yields; and yet knowing all these perfections, I praise them and wonder at them, loving the qualities but not affecting the person because the destinies have set down a contrary censure. Yet Venus, to add revenge, hath given me wine of the same grape, a sip of the same sauce, and, firing me with the like passion, hath crossed me with as ill a penance. For I am in love with a shepherd's swain as coy to me as I am cruel to Montanus, as peremptory in disdain as I was perverse in desire; and that is," quoth she, "Aliena's page, young Ganymede."

Gerismond, desirous to prosecute the end of these passions, called in Ganymede, who, knowing the case, came in graced with such a blush as beautified the crystal of his face with a ruddy brightness. The king noting well the physiognomy of Ganymede, began by his favors[156] to call to mind the face of his Rosalind, and with that fetched a deep sigh. Rosader, that was passing familiar with Gerismond, demanded of him why he sighed so sore.

"Because, Rosader," quoth he, "the favor of Ganymede puts me in mind of Rosalind."

At this word Rosader sighed so deeply as though his heart would have burst.

"And what's the matter," quoth Gerismond, "that you quite[157] me with such a sigh?"

"Pardon me, sir," quoth Rosader, "because I love none but Rosalind."

"And upon that condition," quoth Gerismond, "that Rosalind were here, I would this day make up a marriage betwixt her and thee."

At this Aliena turned her head and smiled upon Ganymede, and she could scarce keep countenance. Yet she salved all with secrecy, and Gerismond, to drive away such dumps, questioned with Ganymede what the reason was he regarded not Phoebe's love, seeing she was as fair as the wanton that brought Troy to ruin. Ganymede mildly answered:

"If I should affect the fair Phoebe, I should offer poor Montanus great wrong to win that from him, in a moment, that he hath labored for so many months. Yet have I promised to the beautiful shepherdess to wed myself never to woman except unto her; but with this promise —that if I can, by reason, suppress Phoebe's love towards me, she shall like of none but of Montanus."

"To that," quoth Phoebe, "I stand; for my love is so far beyond reason as it will admit no persuasion of reason."

"For justice," quoth he, "I appeal to Gerismond."

"And to his censure will I stand," quoth Phoebe.

"And in your victory," quoth Montanus, "stands the hazard of my fortunes; for if Ganymede go away with conquest, Montanus is in conceit love's monarch; if Phoebe win, then am I in effect most miserable."

"We will see this controversy," quoth Gerismond, "and then we will to church. Therefore, Ganymede, let us hear your argument."

"Nay, pardon my absence awhile," quoth she, "and you shall see one in store."

In went Ganymede and dressed herself in woman's attire, having

[156]*favors:* The singular, "favor," meant "face" or "countenance"; perhaps the plural implies specific features (eyes, nose, etc.).
[157]*quite:* requite.

on a gown of green with kirtle of rich sendal so quaint that she seemed Diana triumphing in the forest. Upon her head she wore a chaplet of roses, which gave her such a grace that she looked like Flora perked in the pride of all her flowers. Thus attired came Rosalind in and presented herself at her father's feet, with her eyes full of tears, craving his blessing and discoursing unto him all her fortunes—how she was banished by Torismond and how ever since she lived in that country disguised.

Gerismond, seeing his daughter, rose from his seat and fell upon her neck, uttering the passions of his joy in watery plaints, driven into such an ecstasy of content that he could not utter one word. At this sight, if Rosader was both amazed and joyful, I refer myself to the judgment of such as have experience in love, seeing his Rosalind before his face whom so long and deeply he had affected. At last Gerismond recovered his spirits and in most fatherly terms entertained his daughter, Rosalind, after many questions demanding of her what had passed between her and Rosader.

"So much, sir," quoth she, "as there wants nothing but your grace to make up the marriage."

"Why, then," quoth Gerismond, "Rosader, take her, she is thine; and let this day solemnize both thy brother's and thy nuptials."

Rosader, beyond measure content, humbly thanked the king and embraced his Rosalind, who, turning towards Phoebe, demanded if she had shown sufficient reason to suppress the force of her loves.

"Yea," quoth Phoebe, "and so great a persuasive that please it you, madam, and Aliena to give us leave, Montanus and I will make this day the third couple in marriage."

She had no sooner spake this word but Montanus threw away his garland of willow, his bottle (where was painted despair), and cast his sonnets in the fire, showing himself as frolic as Paris when he handseled his love with Helena.

At this Gerismond and the rest smiled and concluded that Montanus and Phoebe should keep their wedding with the two brethren. Aliena, seeing Saladyne stand in a dump, to wake him from his dream began thus:

"Why, how now, my Saladyne, all amort? What, melancholy, man, at the day of marriage? Perchance thou art sorrowful to think on thy brother's high fortunes and thine own base desires to choose so mean a shepherdess. Cheer up thy heart, man, for this day thou shalt be married to the daughter of a king; for know, Saladyne, I am not Aliena, but Alinda, the daughter of thy mortal enemy, Torismond."

At this all the company was amazed, especially Gerismond, who, rising up, took Alinda in his arms and said to Rosalind:

"Is this that fair Alinda, famous for so many virtues, that forsook her father's court to live with thee exiled in the country?"

"The same," quoth Rosalind.

"Then," quoth Gerismond, turning to Saladyne, "jolly forester, be frolic, for thy fortunes are great and thy desires excellent; thou hast got a princess as famous for her perfection as exceeding in proportion."

"And she hath with her beauty won," quoth Saladyne, "an humble servant as full of faith as she of amiable favor."

While everyone was amazed with these comical events, Corydon came skipping in and told them that the priest was at the church and tarried for their coming. With that, Gerismond led the way and the rest followed, where to the admiration of all the country swains in Arden their marriages were solemnly solemnized. As soon as the priest had finished, home they went with Alinda, where Corydon had made all things in readiness. Dinner was provided, and—the tables being spread and the brides set down by Gerismond—Rosader, Saladyne, and Montanus that day were servitors. Homely cheer they had such as their country could afford, but to mend their fare they had mickle good chat and many discourses of their loves and fortunes. About mid dinner, to make them merry, Corydon came in with an old crowd[158] and played them a fit of mirth, to which he sung this pleasant song:

Corydon's Song

A blithe and bonny country lass,
   heigh-ho, the bonny lass,
Sat sighing on the tender grass
   and weeping said, "Will none come woo me?"[159]
A smicker boy, a lither[160] swain,
   heigh-ho, a smicker swain,
That in his love was wanton fain,
   with smiling looks straight came unto her.

[158]*crowd:* violin-like instrument.

[159]*me:* Greg omits the quotation marks (also omitted, of course, in the original) and emends "me" to "her," apparently to give the effect of indirect discourse and also to make a rhyme with "her" in the eighth line. He also rearranges the five stanzas (given here as they are in the 1590 edition) into four stanzas of 8, 8, 12, and 8 lines, respectively.

[160]*smicker . . . lither:* handsome . . . agile.

Whenas the wanton wench espied,
   heigh-ho, when she espied,
The means to make herself a bride,
   she simpered smooth like bonny bell.[161]
The swain that saw her squint-eyed kind,
   heigh-ho, so squint-eyed kind,
His arms about her body twined,
   and said, "Fair lass, how fare ye—well?"

The country kit said, "Well, forsooth,
   heigh-ho, well, forsooth.
But that I have a longing tooth,
   a longing tooth that makes me cry."
"Alas," said he, "what gars[162] thy grief?
   heigh-ho, what gars thy grief?"
"A wound," quoth she, "without relief,
   I fear a maid that I shall die."

"If that be all," the shepherd said,
   heigh-ho, the shepherd said.
"I'll make thee wive it, gentle maid,
   and so recure thy malady."
Hereon they kissed with many a oath,
   heigh-ho, with many a oath,
And 'fore god Pan did plight their troth,
   and to the church they hied them fast.

And God send every pretty peat,[163]
   heigh-ho, the pretty peat,
That fears to die of this conceit,
   so kind a friend to help at last.

Corydon having thus made them merry, as they were in the midst of all their jollity, word was brought in to Saladyne and Rosader that a brother of theirs, one Fernandyne, was arrived and desired to speak with them. Gerismond, overhearing this news, demanded who it was.

"It is, sir," quoth Rosader, "our middle brother that lives a scholar in Paris; but what fortune hath driven him to seek us out I know not."

---

[161]*bonny bell:* a common phrase for "fair maid" or "bonny lass" (perhaps from the French *bonne et belle*).

[162]*gars:* causes.

[163]*peat:* pet.

With that, Saladyne went and met his brother, whom he welcomed with all courtesy, and Rosader gave him no less friendly entertainment; brought he was by his two brothers into the parlor where they all sat at dinner. Fernandyne, as one that knew as many manners as he could[164] points of sophistry and was as well brought up as well lettered, saluted them all. But when he espied Gerismond, kneeling on his knee he did him what reverence belonged to his estate and with that burst forth into these speeches:

"Although, right mighty prince, this day of my brothers' marriage be a day of mirth, yet time craves another course; and therefore from dainty cates rise to sharp weapons. And you, the sons of Sir John of Bordeaux, leave off your amours and fall to arms; change your loves into lances, and now this day show yourselves as valiant as hitherto you have been passionate. For know, Gerismond, that hard by the edge of this forest the twelve peers of France are up in arms to recover thy right; and Torismond, trooped with a crew of desperate runagates, is ready to bid them battle. The armies are ready to join; therefore show thyself in the field to encourage thy subjects. And you, Saladyne and Rosader, mount you and show yourselves as hardy soldiers as you have been hearty lovers; so shall you for the benefit of your country discover the idea of your father's virtues to be stamped in your thoughts, and prove children worthy of so honorable a parent."

At this alarum given by Fernandyne, Gerismond leaped from the board, and Saladyne and Rosader betook themselves to their weapons.

"Nay," quoth Gerismond, "go with me. I have horse and armor for us all; and then, being well mounted, let us show that we carry revenge and honor at our falchion points."

Thus they leave the brides full of sorrow, especially Alinda, who desired Gerismond to be good to her father. He, not returning a word because his haste was great, hied him home to his lodge, where he delivered Saladyne and Rosader horse and armor and, himself armed, royally led the way; not having ridden two leagues before they discovered where in a valley both the battles[165] were joined. Gerismond, seeing the wing wherein the peers fought, thrust in there

---

[164]*he could:* Something may have been omitted after these words, possibly the word "tell" or "recite." Or perhaps "knew," used earlier in the sentence, is to be understood as carrying over into "he could"; in that case "he could" is a variation of "he knew" and is used the way "he did" might be used now.

[165]*battles:* armies.

and cried "'St. Denis!"—Gerismond laying on such load upon his enemies that he showed how highly he did estimate of a crown. When the peers perceived that their lawful king was there, they grew more eager; and Saladyne and Rosader so behaved themselves that none durst stand in their way nor abide the fury of their weapons. To be short, the peers were conquerors, Torismond's army put to flight, and himself slain in battle. The peers then gathered themselves together and, saluting their king, conducted him royally into Paris, where he was received with great joy of all the citizens. As soon as all was quiet and he had received again the crown, he sent for Alinda and Rosalind to the court, Alinda being very passionate for the death of her father, yet brooking it with the more patience in that she was contented with the welfare of her Saladyne.

Well, as soon as they were come to Paris, Gerismond made a royal feast for the peers and lords of his land, which continued thirty days, in which time, summoning a parliament, by the consent of his nobles he created Rosader heir apparent to the kingdom; he restored Saladyne to all his father's land and gave him the dukedom of Nameurs;[166] he made Fernandyne principal secretary to himself; and that fortune might every way seem frolic, he made Montanus lord over all the forest of Arden, Adam Spencer captain of the king's guard, and Corydon master of Alinda's flocks.

Here, gentlemen, may you see in Euphues' golden legacy that such as neglect their fathers' precepts incur much prejudice; that division in nature as it is a blemish in nurture so 'tis a breach of good fortunes; that virtue is not measured by birth but by action; that younger brethren, though inferior in years, yet may be superior to honors; that concord is the sweetest conclusion and amity betwixt brothers more forcible than fortune. If you gather any fruits by this legacy, speak well of Euphues for writing it and me for fetching it. If you grace me with that favor, you encourage me to be more forward; and as soon as I have overlooked my labors, expect "The Sailor's Calendar."

T. Lodge

Finis

[166]*Nameurs:* Nemours, a town some forty miles south of Paris on the Loire.

♪ A Notable Discovery
of Cozenage

(1591)

ROBERT GREENE

Since Robert Greene was the most versatile as well as one of the most prolific writers of prose fiction in the Elizabethan period, he is represented in the present volume by two works—*Pandosto* (1588) and *A Notable Discovery of Cozenage* (1591). In each of these quite different forms (and also in the drama and in lyric poetry) he made important contributions. One virtue of *A Notable Discovery* is a simple, idiomatic prose style. Since the language of *Pandosto* is not especially simple, one asks: what happened in those three years between the publishing of *Pandosto* and *A Notable Discovery?* We do not know for sure. But the prefaces may contain one important clue: in *Pandosto* Greene had addressed himself only to gentlemen, while in *A Notable Discovery* he now writes "To the Young Gentlemen, Merchants, Apprentices, Farmers, and Plain Country Men" in a style that anyone could understand. The five different groups thus singled out in the dedication may not be so miscellaneous as they at first appear; the men of low birth, as well as the gentlemen, all have money jangling in their pockets. Sir Porrus in *Pandosto* was a plain country man made gentleman; possibly the implication is that his success is no longer exceptional—the Sir Porruses are now fairly typical of post-Armada prosperity, and no one should be surprised to see a good number of them becoming wealthy tradesmen, lord mayors of London, and members of parliament.[1]

---

[1] In *The Spanish Masquerado* (1589) Greene looks back on the Armada victory with relief but also with an awareness of what could have been if

A *Notable Discovery* has always been called a "cony-catching pamphlet." The term has the advantage of concreteness, but it is not entirely accurate, for it applies only to the first and largest section, "The Art of Cony-Catching," but not to the other four sections. "Criminal fiction" fits the whole work better; it suggests fictional or semifictional accounts of underworld activities, thus linking earlier Elizabethan works like Thomas Awdeley's *Fraternity of Vagabonds* (1565) and Thomas Harman's *Caveat for Common Cursitors* (1567) with several works of seventeenth-century criminal fiction that preceded Defoe's *Moll Flanders*.[2]

But although "cony-catching pamphlet" and "criminal fiction" are useful terms, they tell us nothing about the technique of *A Notable Discovery*. For that purpose "anatomy" and "short story" (if by the latter we mean only the short form of "novel") are useful. Greene's pamphlet is an anatomy in that its form is analytical, extroverted, and intellectual and the characters are occupational types, not individuals. At one point (pp. 418–19) the narrator classifies the different kinds of roguery being practiced in London in 1591, and under each of the eight kinds he lists the special skills required and then describes each skill in the slang of the underworld. But in addition to anatomy, another form emerges throughout: the scenes of *A Notable Discovery* are "realistic" in the manner of scenes in a novel or short story. The dialogue is not only idiomatic but is suggestive of the casual rhythms of ordinary speech; the action is strictly everyday and contemporary,

---

God had not sent the "gusts and storms to scatter their [the Spanish] navy" (Alexander B. Grosart, ed., *Works of Greene* [London, 1881–86], V, 287). But God did send them, and the English nation is therefore under his special protection. This line of thinking seems to offer Greene a new conception of the English nation; he writes of "our cities," "our children," "the Queen and her subjects" as though he understands a unity, a coherence among the different classes of people, he had not understood before. Mainly, however, *The Spanish Masquerado* is an attack on Spain. For an interesting analysis of the pro-English, anti-Catholic symbolism, see Esler, "Robert Greene and the Spanish Armada."

2*A Notable Discovery* is so vivid that it seems to be entirely the result of Greene's own personal observations of the underworld; but the fact is that Greene borrowed fairly heavily both from Harman and from *A Manifest Detection . . . of Dice Play* (1552). See Frank Aydelotte, *Elizabethan Rogues and Vagabonds*, vol. I in a series called *Oxford Historical and Literary Studies* (Oxford, 1913), pp. 86–129. For a collection of five seventeenth-century short works of criminal fiction, see Spiro Peterson, ed., *The Counterfeit Lady* (Garden City, N.Y., 1961).

the implication being that similar events are occurring in London even as Greene writes. Although the characters are types, the allusions are often to specific jails and poorhouses, and at one point (p. 422) we get a fairly explicit description of a whore's manner of dress.

A Notable Discovery is in one sense complementary to *Master F. J.*; where the latter is an exposé of the upper crust, the former is an exposé of the other end of the social structure. On p. 425 we are given the initials ("J. B." and "J. R.") of actual culprits; and on several other occasions the narrator hints that he could tell much more, but for personal reasons (such as the possible reform of the criminals if they are not embarrassed by exposure) he will not reveal all he knows. The narrator repeatedly avows that he has "seen with mine eyes" (as on p. 429) the events he describes, and we find no difficulty in believing him. The narrator of *Master F. J.*, on the other hand, is always saying "as Master F. J. has told me." Yet despite the indirection, the state of being at least once-removed from the action, *Master F. J.* is much more "inward" in its presentation than *A Notable Discovery*. We know F. J. as an individual, while the conies and cony-catchers are types illustrating classic underworld situations.

Since the characters of *A Notable Discovery* are types, the commentary is general and not focused on the analysis of any one particular person. But Greene sets up an interesting counterpoint between commentary on the one hand and scenes on the other; in the former the cony-catchers are described as "consuming moths of the commonwealth" and "worms" who maliciously prey upon innocent country men, while in the latter the cony-catchers tend to emerge as knaves for whom the narrator has a certain respect (if not sympathy). When he comments, the narrator stands at a great distance; from this view he is conservatively on the side of the law and of anyone who may be duped. When the narrator gives us a scene, he is still standing a little apart; we do not learn the characters' names, and we do not know what they are thinking. Nevertheless, we are close enough to hear dialogue. The narrator's eye naturally falls on movement, which means that he concentrates on the knaves, who are very fascinating in the way they go about their intricate business. They are professionals, each one good at his own particular specialty. Meanwhile we are allowed to forget that the poor country man is a victim. The narrator emerges, in other words, as two "persons," each one presenting one element of Greene's ambiguous attitude toward his subject: the judger of the knaves' actions is conservative and puritan, while the describer of the action is uncommitted, worldly wise, calmly and objectively analytical.[3]

An unpleasant survey of human nature gradually emerges; some of the glimpses are bluntly direct and frank, while others are subtly ironic and suggestive. The erstwhile innocent cony learns how to cozen before he is himself cozened, and he enjoys the tricks so much that he intends to use them on his neighbors back home. For the moment the cony is similar to the knaves; he cheats as they do, and he enjoys with them a feeling of superiority. But in his case the feeling is illusory; although he has lost his innocence, he is still an innocent to the knaves. The cony is unaware of the total situation, while the knaves have created that situation, step by patient step, including the cony's momentary exhilaration at cheating and winning. Finally the cony loses all, even his temporary status as a knave.

Toward the end of the cony-catching section, the narrator gives us the results of an interview with one of the knaves, who is outside the law and without any standard of conduct unless it is anti-law. Whatever the law is at any given time, he means to circumvent it. Although one side of the narrator hopes to reform such knaves, the other side of him knows that they are not reformable because they recognize no moral or legal code. Their amorality is an advantage against law-bound constables and judges; the best of them have other advantages —"a quick eye, a sharp wit, and a reaching head." Since "each day

---

[3]G. R. Hibbard contends that Greene "writes from the point of view of the citizen, but he does not like him" (*Three Elizabethan Pamphlets* [London, 1951], pp. 15–16). Hibbard probably is right about Greene's not liking the citizen; but, strictly speaking, the point of view is no more the citizen's than it is the cony-catchers'. The narrator observes the action in the third person: now A does one thing, and now B does another; C, suddenly entering the picture, does something else. The narrator all the while, in the scenes at least, is standing apart (rarely entering into anyone's thoughts and feelings). The significant aspect of the technique is not really a matter of point of view: it is a matter of focus. In the scenes the narrator concentrates on the knaves. Possibly the only reason for doing so is a kind of accident; the knaves happen to be the ones who are doing things, controlling all the action. Since the cony is merely passive, he therefore plays a minor role in the action; yet his responses are given. If the presentation had been from the cony's point of view, then the narrator would have given us more of a cony-oriented context (where the cony was going when he was accosted, what was on his mind at the time, what his response was to the verser's approach, etc.); the whole fleecing episode, in that case, would have been one big interruption in the cony's plans. Compare the first section of *A Notable Discovery* with tale 11 in *The Sackful of News*; there is the same concentration on the knaves' action.

they invent new tricks," the law always will be at least one step behind them.

The three short sections at the end of *A Notable Discovery* have their own subtitles—"A Pleasant Discovery of the Cozenage of Colliers," "How a Cook's Wife in London Did Lately Serve a Collier for His Cozenage," and "How a Flax Wife and Her Neighbors Used a Cozening Collier." The word "cony" is no longer used, and the characters are all city people. Now the verdict goes entirely against the knaves, who are not very clever and whose machinations, therefore, are no longer fascinating. The action focuses on the victims, who do not remain victims for long. These "poor whom God loves" (p. 430) take the law into their own hands and serve up a democratic and poetic justice to the offenders.

In the five sections there are at least two references to "a merry jest" (pp. 414 and 432), a term that we may take literally: *A Notable Discovery*, like *The Unfortunate Traveler* and *Jack of Newbury*, derives in part from the jest-biography, only instead of one character binding all the jests together, in Greene's pamphlet it is the subject—petty crime in London—that unifies.

৵৾৻৾৵

To the Young Gentlemen, Merchants, Apprentices, Farmers, and Plain Country Men: Health

Diogenes, gentlemen, from a counterfeit coiner of money became a current corrector of manners, as absolute in the one as dissolute in the other. Time refineth men's affects, and their humors grow different by the distinction of age. Poor Ovid, that amorously writ in his youth *The Art of Love*, complained in his exile amongst the Getes of his wanton follies. And Socrates' age was virtuous, though his prime was licentious.

So, gentlemen, my younger years had uncertain thoughts; but now my ripe days calls on to repentant deeds, and I sorrow as much to see others willful as I delighted once to be wanton. The odd madcaps I have been mate to, not as a companion but as a spy to have an insight into their knaveries, that, seeing their trains,[4] I might eschew their snares. Those mad fellows I learned at last to loathe by their own graceless villainies, and what I saw in them to their confusion I can forewarn in others to my country's commodity.

None could decipher tyrannism better than Aristippus; not that his nature was cruel, but that he was nurtured with Dionysius. The simple swain that cuts the lapidaries' stones can distinguish a ruby from a diamond only by his labor. Though I have not practiced their deceits, yet conversing by fortune and talking upon purpose with such copes-mates hath given me light into their conceits, and I can decipher their qualities, though I utterly mislike of their practices.

To be brief, gentlemen, I have seen the world and rounded it; though not with travel, yet with experience. And I cry out with Solomon, *Omnia sub sole vanitas*.[5] I have smiled with the Italian and worn the viper's head in my hand, and yet stopped his venom. I have eaten Spanish mirabolanes[6] and yet am nothing the more metamorphosed. France, Germany, Poland, Denmark—I know them all, yet not affected to any in the form of my life. Only I am English born, and I have English thoughts—not a devil incarnate because I am Italianate, but hating the pride of Italy because I know their peevishness.

Yet in all these countries where I have traveled I have not seen more excess of vanity than we Englishmen practice through vainglory. For as our wits be as ripe as any, so our wills are more ready than they all to put in effect any of their licentious abuses. Yet amongst the rest, letting ordinary sins pass because custom hath almost made them a law, I will only speak of two such notable abuses, which the practitioners of them shadow with the name of arts, as never have been heard in any age before.

The first and chief is called the art of cony-catching; the second, the art of cross-biting—two such pestilent and prejudicial practices as of late have been the ruin of infinite persons and the subversion and overthrow of many merchants, farmers, and honest-minded yeomen. The first is a deceit at cards, which, growing by enormity into a cozenage, is able to draw, by the subtle show thereof, a man of great judgment to consent to his own confusion. Yet, gentlemen, when

[4]*trains:* tricks; see note 77 in *Euphues.*
[5]*Omnia sub sole vanitas:* Everything under the sun is vanity.
[6]*mirabolanes:* myrobalan (a dried, astringent, plum-like fruit resembling a prune).

you shall read this book, written faithfully to discover[7] these cozening practices, think I go not about to disprove or disallow the most
ancient and honest pastime or recreation of card play. For thus much
I know by reading: when the city of Thebes was besieged by them
of Lacedemonia,[8] being girt within strong-fenced walls and having
men enough and able to rebate the enemy, they found no inconvenience of force to breed their ensuing bane but famine, in that
when victuals waxed scant, hunger would make them either yield by
a fainting composition or a miserable death. Whereupon, to weary
the foe with wintering at the siege, the Thebans devised this policy:
they found out the method of cards and dice and so busied their
brains with the pleasantness of that new invention, passing away the
time with strange recreations and pastimes, beguiling hunger with
the delight of the new sports, and eating but every third day and
playing two. So their frugal sparing of victuals kept them from famine,
the city from sacking, and raised the foe from such a mortal siege.

Thus was the use of cards and dice first invented and since among
princes highly esteemed and allowed in all commonwealths as a necessary recreation for the mind. But as time and malice of man's nature
hatcheth abuse, so good things by ill wits are wrested to the worse.
And so in cards. For from an honest recreation it is grown to a prejudicial practice and most high degree of cozenage, as shall be discovered in my *Art of Cony-Catching*. For not only simple swains,
whose wits is[9] in their hands, but young gentlemen and merchants are
all caught like conies in the hay and so led like lambs to their confusion. The poor man that cometh to the term[10] to try his right and
layeth his hand to mortgage to get some crowns in his purse to see
his lawyer, is drawn in by these devilish cony-catchers, that, at one
cut at cards, loseth all his money, by which means he, his wife, and
children is brought to utter ruin and misery. The poor prentice,
whose honest mind aimeth only at his master's profits, by these pestilent vipers of the commonwealth is smoothly enticed to the hazard
of this game at cards and robbed of his master's money, which forceth
him oft times either to run away or bankrout[11] all, to the overthrow
of some honest and wealthy citizen.

[7]*discover:* reveal, make known.
[8]*Lacedemonia:* Lacedaemon (ancient Sparta).
[9]*wits is:* The fourth edition, printed in 1592, emends "is" to "are"; but
Greene probably had nothing to do with the change. A lack of agreement
between subject and verb is fairly common in Elizabethan grammar.
[10]*term:* a session of the courts of law; there were four sessions during
the year—Hilary, Easter, Trinity, and Michaelmas.
[11]*bankrout:* bankrupt.

Seeing, then, such a dangerous enormity groweth by them to the discredit of the estate of England, I would wish the justices appointed as severe censors of such fatal mischiefs, to show themselves *patres patriae*[12] by weeding out such worms as eat away the sap of the tree and rooting this base degree of cozeners out so peaceable and prosperous a country. For of all devilish practices, this is the most prejudicial. The high lawyer (that challengeth a purse by the highway side), the foist, the nip, the stale, the snap—I mean the pickpockets and cutpurses—are nothing so dangerous to meet withal as these cozening cony-catchers. The cheaters that with their false dice make a hand and strike in at hazard or passage with their dice of advantage are nothing so dangerous as these base-minded caterpillars. For they have their vies and their revies upon the poor cony's back till they so ferret beat him that they leave him neither hair on his skin nor hole to harbor in.[13]

There was before this, many years ago, a practice, put in use by such shifting companions, which was called the Barnard's Law, wherein, as in the art of cony-catching, four persons were required to perform their cozening commodity—the taker-up, the verser, the barnard, and the rutter. And the manner of it in deed was thus: the taker-up is a skillful man in all things, who hath by long travail[14] learned without book a thousand policies to insinuate himself into a man's acquaintance. Talk of matters in law, he hath plenty of[15] cases at his fingers' ends, and he hath seen and tried and ruled in the king's courts. Speak of grazing and husbandry, no man knoweth more shires[16] than he nor better which way to raise a gainful commodity and how the abuses and overture[17] of prices might be redressed. Finally, enter into what

[12]*patres patriae:* fathers of their country.

[13]*ferret beat . . . hole to harbor in:* Ferrets (weasels) were used to "ferret out" rabbits from their holes.

[14]*travail:* The first two editions read "trauail" (modernized here to "travail"), while the third and fourth editions read "trauell"; "travail" (hard work) is perhaps what Greene intended, but "travel" (journeying) is a possible sense. The spelling often is not a clue as to the sense; later, on p. 416, the sense is clearly "travel" despite the spelling in the first three editions of "trauail."

[15]*plenty of:* changed to "twenty" in the fourth edition (1592); it is an improvement, but we cannot be sure that Greene made it.

[16]*shires:* counties, regions (the implication being that he knows the kind of soil in each region). The fourth edition emends "shires" to "shifts" (tricks), which also makes good sense of a different kind.

[17]*overture:* overturning, upsetting.

discourse they list, were it into a broom man's[18] faculty, he knoweth what gains they have for old boots and shoes. Yea, and it shall scape him hardly but that ere your talk break off he will be your countryman at least and, peradventure, either of kin, ally, or some stale sib to you, if your reach far surmount not his. In case he bring to pass that you be glad of his acquaintance, then doth he carry you to the taverns. And with him goes the verser, a man of more worship[19] than the taker-up; and he hath the countenance of a landed man. As they are set, comes in the barnard stumbling into your company, like some aged farmer of the country, a stranger unto you all, that had been at some market town thereabout buying and selling, and there tippled so much malmsey that he had never a ready word in his mouth, and is so careless of his money that he throweth some forty angels on the board's end and, standing somewhat aloof, calleth for a pint of wine and saith, "Masters, I am somewhat bold with you. I pray you be not aggrieved if I drink my drink by you" and ministers such idle, drunken talk that the verser, who counterfeiteth the landed man, comes and draws more near to the plain, honest-dealing man and prayeth him to call the barnard more near to laugh at his folly. Between them two the matter shall be so workmanly conveyed and finely argued that out cometh an old pair[20] of cards, whereat the barnard teacheth the verser a new game that he says cost him for the learning two pots of ale not two hours ago. The first wager is drink; the next, two pence or a groat.[21] And lastly, to be brief, they use the matter so, that he that were a hundred year old and never played in his life for a penny cannot refuse to be the verser's half.[22] And consequently at one game at cards he loseth all they play for, be it a hundred pound. And if perhaps when the money is lost (to use their word of art),[23] the poor country man begin to smoke[24] them and swears the drunken knave shall not get his money so, then standeth the rutter at the door and draweth his sword and picketh a quarrel at his own shadow, if he lack an ostler or a tapster, or some other to brabble with, that, while

---

[18]*broom man's:* A "broom man" apparently is not only a street sweeper, but also a dealer in old shoes and clothes.

[19]*more worship:* The verser is dressed to appear as though he is of a higher social standing than the taker-up.

[20]*pair:* deck.

[21]*groat:* A "groat" was a coin worth four pence; "pence" was the plural of "penny," twelve of which made a shilling.

[22]*half:* partner.

[23]*to use their word of art:* The sense of this phrase may be "to use the word they customarily use themselves in the art of cony-catching."

[24]*smoke:* suspect.

the street and company gather to the fray, as the manner is, the barnard steals away with all the coin and gets him to one blind tavern
or other, where these cozeners had appointed to meet.

Thus, gentlemen, I have glanced at the Barnard's Law, which,
though you may perceive it to be a prejudicial, insinuating cozenage,
yet is the art of cony-catching so far beyond it in subtlety as the devil
is more dishonest than the holiest angel. For so unlikely is it for the
poor cony to leese,[25] that, might he pawn his stake to a pound, he
would lay it that he cannot be cross-bitten in the cut at cards, as you
shall perceive by my present discovery. Yet, gentlemen, am I sore
threatened by the hacksters of that filthy faculty that if I set their
practices in print, they will cut off that hand that writes the pamphlet.
But how I fear their bravadoes you shall perceive by my plain painting out of them. Yea, so little do I esteem such base-minded braggarts
that were it not I hope of their amendment, I would in a schedule set
down the names of such cozening cony-catchers.

Well, leaving them and their course of life to the honorable and
the worshipful of the land to be censors of with justice, have about for
a blow at the art of cross-biting. I mean not cross-biters at dice, when
the cheater, with a langret,[26] cut contrary to the vantage, will cross-
bite a barred cater trey.[27] Nor I mean not when a broking[28] knave
cross-bites a gentleman with a bad commodity, nor when the foist
(the pickpocket, sir reverence,[29] I mean) is cross-bitten by the snap
and so smoked for his purchase. Nor when the nip, which the common people call a cutpurse, hath a cross-bite by some bribing officer
who, threatening to carry him to prison, takes away all the money and
lets him slip without any punishment. But I mean a more dishonorable
art, when a base rogue either keepeth a whore as his friend or
marries one to be his maintainer and with her not only cross-bites

---

[25]*leese:* lose. Usually the spelling is "loose," which has been modernized
to "lose" when the sense, as in this case, is clearly "fail to win."

[26]*langret:* a false or loaded die (the singular of "dice").

[27]*barred cater trey:* On the cube-shaped die, the four ("cater") and
three ("trey") are opposite each other; if the axis between the four and
three is made slightly longer than the other axis, then the die is said to
be "barred cater trey"—meaning that the four and three are barred, or prevented, from ever showing in the up position when the die is rolled.

[28]*broking:* fraudulent.

[29]*sir reverence:* begging your pardon; the narrator begs the reader's
pardon for using the word "foist" instead of "pickpocket," the term the
reader is more likely to be familiar with.

men of good calling but especially poor, ignorant country farmers, who, Got wot, be by them led like sheep to the slaughter.

Thus, gentle readers, have I given you a light in brief what I mean to prosecute at large. And so with an humble suit to all justices that they will seek to root out these two roguish arts, I commit you to the Almighty.

Yours,
Rob. Greene

A Notable Discovery of Cozenage

[1] *The Art of Cony-Catching*

There be requisite effectually to act the art of cony-catching three several parties—the setter, the verser, and the barnacle. The nature of the setter is to draw in any person familiarly to drink with him, which person they call the cony. And their method is according to the man they aim at. If a gentleman, merchant, or apprentice, the cony is the more easily caught in that they are soon induced to play; and therefore I omit the circumstance they use in catching of them. And for because the poor country farmer or yeoman is the mark they most shoot at, who they know comes not empty to the term, I will discover the means they put in practice to bring in some honest, simple, and ignorant men to their purpose.

The cony-catchers, appareled like honest, civil gentlemen or good fellows, with a smooth face, as if butter would not melt in their mouths, after dinner, when the clients are come from Westminster Hall and are somewhat at leisure to walk up and down Paul's, Fleet Street, Holborne, the Strand, and such common haunted places where these cozening companions attend only to spy out a prey: who, as soon as they see a plain country fellow well and cleanly appareled either in a coat of home-spun russet or of frieze, as the time requires, and a side pouch at his side, "There is a cony," saith one.

At that word out flies the setter and, overtaking the man, begins to salute him thus: "Sir, God save you. You are heartily welcome to London. How doth all our good friends in the country? I hope they be all in health?"

The country man, seeing a man so courteous that he knows not, half in a brown study at this strange salutation, perhaps makes him this answer: "Sir, all our friends in the country are well, thanks be to God. But truly I know you not. You must pardon me."

"Why, sir," saith the setter, guessing by his tongue what country-man he is, "are ye not a Yorkshireman, or such a countryman?" If he say yes, then he creeps upon him closely; if he say no, then straight the setter comes over him thus: "In good sooth, sir, I know you by your face and have been in your company before. I pray you, if without offense, let me crave your name and the place of your abode."

The simple man straight tells him where he dwells, his name, and who be his next neighbors, and what gentlemen dwell about him. After he hath learned all of him, then he comes over his fallows[30] kindly: "Sir, though I have been somewhat bold to be inquisitive of your name, yet hold me excused, for I took you for a friend of mine. But since by mistaking I have made you slack your business, we'll drink a quart of wine or a pot of ale together."

If the gentle fool be so ready as to go, then the cony is caught. But if he smack the setter and smells a rat by his clawing and will not drink with him, then away goes the setter and discourseth to the verser the name of the man, the parish he dwells in, and what gentle-men are his near neighbors. With that away goes he[31] and, crossing the man at some turning, meets him full in the face and greets him thus:

"What, Goodman Barton? How fares all our friends about you? You are well met. I have a pint of wine for you. You are welcome to town."

The plain country man, hearing himself named by a man he knows not, marvels and answers him that he knows him not and craves pardon.

"Not me, Goodman Barton? Have you forgot me? Why, I am such a man's kinsman—your neighbor not far off. How doth this or that good gentleman, my friend? Good Lord, that I should be out of your remembrance! I have been at your house divers times."

"Indeed, sir," saith the farmer, "are you such a man's kinsman? Surely, sir, if you had not challenged acquaintance of me, I should never have known you. I have clean forgot you, but I know the good gentleman your cousin well. He is my very good neighbor."

"And for his sake," saith the verser, "we'll drink afore we part."

---

[30]*fallows:* plowed and arable land; the innocent cony is ready for the setter's seeds of deceit, which, once planted, will yield the setter a good crop.

[31]*away goes he:* that is, the verser.

Happely[31a] the man thanks him, and to the wine or ale they go. Then, ere they part they make him a cony, and so ferret-claw him at cards that they leave him as bare of money as an ape of a tail.

Thus have these filthy fellows their subtle fetches, to draw on poor men to fall into their cozening practices. Thus, like consuming moths of the commonwealth, they prey upon the ignorance of such plain souls as measure all by their own honesty, not regarding either conscience or the fatal revenge that is threatened for such idle and licentious persons, but do employ all their wits to the overthrow of such as with their handy thrift satisfy their hearty thirst, they preferring cozenage before labor and choosing an idle practice before any honest form of good living.

Well, to the method again of taking up their conies. If the poor country man smoke them still and will not stoop unto either of these lures, then one, either the verser or the setter or some of their crew— for there is a general fraternity betwixt them—steppeth before the cony as he goeth and letteth drop twelve pence in the highway, that of force the cony must see it. The country man, spying the shilling, maketh not dainty—for *quis nisi mentis inops oblatum respuit aurum*[32]—but stoopeth very mannerly and taketh it up. Then one of the cony-catchers behind crieth half part and so challengeth half of the finding. The country man, content, offereth to change the money. "Nay, faith, friend," saith the verser "'tis ill luck to keep found money. We'll go spend it in a pottle[33] of wine or in a breakfast, dinner, or supper, as the time of the day requires."

If the cony say he will not, then answers the verser, "Spend my part." If still the cony refuse, he taketh half and away. If they spy the country man to be of a having and covetous humor, then have they a further policy to draw him on: another that knoweth the place of his abode meeteth him and saith, "Sir, well met. I have run hastily to overtake you. I pray you, dwell you not in Derbyshire, in such a village?"

"Yes, marry, do I, friend," saith the cony.

Then replies the verser, "Truly, sir, I have a suit unto you. I am going out of town and must send a letter to the parson of your parish. You shall not refuse to do a stranger such a favor as to carry it him. Happely, as men may in time meet, it may lie in my lot to do you as

[31a]*Happely:* The primary sense is "haply" (perhaps), but "happily" (joyfully) may also be suggested for the particular case of an unusually naïve victim.

[32]*quis nisi mentis inops oblatum respuit aurum:* for who but a halfwit would refuse an offer of gold.

[33]*pottle:* half a gallon.

good a turn. And, sir, for your pains I will give you twelve pence."

The poor cony, in mere simplicity, saith, "Sir, I will do so much for you with all my heart. Where is your letter?"

"I have it not, good sir, ready written. But may I entreat you to step into some tavern or alehouse? We'll drink the while and I will write but a line or two."

At this the cony stoops, and for greediness of the money and upon kind courtesy goes with the setter unto the tavern. As they walk they meet the verser, and then they all three go into the tavern together.

See, gentlemen, what great logicians these cony-catchers be that have such rhetorical persuasions to induce the poor country man to his confusion and what variety of villainy they have to strip the honest farmer of his money? Well, imagine the cony is in the tavern. Then sits down the verser and saith to the setter, "What, sirrah? Wilt thou give me a quart of wine or shall I give thee one?"

"We'll drink a pint," saith the setter, "and we'll play a game at cards for it, respecting more the sport than the loss."

"Content," saith the verser. "Go call for a pair."

And while he is gone to fetch them, he saith to the cony, "You shall see me fetch over my young master for a quart of wine finely, but this you must do for me: when I cut the cards, as I will not cut above five off, mark then of all the great pack which is undermost.[34] And when I bid you call a card for me, name that, and you shall see we'll make him pay for a quart of wine straight."

"Truly," saith the cony, "I am no great player at cards, and I do not well understand your meaning."

"Why," saith he, "it is thus: I will play at mumchance, or decoy, that he shall shuffle the cards and I will cut. Now, either of us must call a card. You shall call for me and he for himself, and whose card comes first wins. Therefore, when I have cut the cards, then mark the nethermost of the greatest heap that I set upon the cards which I cut off and always call that for me."

"Oh, now," saith the cony, "I understand you. Let me alone. I warrant I'll fit your turn."

With that, in comes the setter with his cards and asketh at what game they shall play.

"Why," saith the verser, "at a new game called mumchance, that hath no policy nor knavery but plain as a pikestaff. You shall shuffle

[34]*great pack which is undermost:* The "great pack" is the larger of the two stacks (after the deck has been cut); "which is undermost" means "which card is on the bottom."

and I'll cut. You shall call a card, and this honest man, a stranger almost to us both, shall call another for me. And which of our cards comes first shall win."

"Content," saith the setter. "For that's but mere hazard."

And so he shuffles the cards, and the verser cuts off some four cards. And then, taking up the heap to set upon them, giveth the cony a glance of the bottom card of that heap, then saith, "And now, sir, call for me."

The cony, to blind the setter's eyes, asketh, as though he were not made privy to the game, "What, shall I cut? What card saith the verser?"

"Why, what you will—either heart, spade, club, or diamond, coat card[35] or other."

"Oh, is it so?" saith the cony. "Why then you shall have the four of hearts"—which was the card he had the glance of.

And saith the setter, holding the cards in his hand and turning up the uppermost card as though he knew not well the game, "I'll have the knave of trumps."

"Nay," saith the verser, "there is no trump. You may call what card you will."

Then saith he, "I'll have the ten of spades." With that he draws, and the four of hearts comes first. "Well," saith the setter, " 'tis but hazard. Mine might have come as well as yours. Five is up. I fear not the set."

So they shuffle and cut, but the verser wins. "Well," saith the setter, "no butter will cleave on my bread. What, not one draught amongst five? Drawer, a fresh pint! I'll have another bout with you. But, sir, I believe," saith he to the cony, "you see some card that it goes so cross on my side."

"I?" saith the cony. "Nay, I hope you think not so of me. 'Tis but hazard and chance, for I am but a mere stranger to the game. As I am an honest man, I never saw it before."

Thus this simple cony closeth up smoothly to take the verser's part, only for greediness to have him win the wine. "Well," answers the setter, "then I'll have one cast more." And to it they go, but he loseth all and beginneth to chafe in this manner: "Were it not," quoth he, "that I care not for a quart of wine, I could swear as many oaths for anger as there be hairs on my head. Why should not my luck be as good as yours and fortune favor me as well as you? What, not one called card in ten cuts? I'll forswear the game forever."

---

[35]*coat card:* a "picture" card; the figure (king, queen, or jack) wears a coat.

"What, chafe not, man," saith the verser. "Seeing we have your quart of wine, I'll show you the game." And with that discovereth all to him, as if he knew it not.

The setter, as simply as if the knave were ignorant, saith, "Aye, marry, I think so. You must needs win when he knows what card to call. I might have played long enough before I got a set."

"Truly," saith the cony, " 'tis a pretty game, for 'tis not possible for a man to lose that cuts the cards. I warrant, the other, that shuffles, may lose St. Peter's cope if he had it. Well, I'll carry this home with me into the country and win many a pot of ale with it."

"A fresh pint," saith the verser, "and then we'll away. But seeing, sir, you are going homeward, I'll learn you a trick worth the noting that you shall win many a pot with in the winter's nights."

With that he culls out the four knaves and pricks one in the top, one in the midst, and one in the bottom. "Now, sir," saith he, "you see these three knaves apparently. Thrust them down with your hand and cut where you will, and though they be so far asunder, I'll make them all come together."

"I pray you, let's see that trick," saith the cony. "Methinks it should be impossible."

So the verser draws, and all the three knaves come in one heap. This he doth once or twice, that the cony wonders at it and offers him a pint of wine to teach it him.

"Nay," saith the verser, "I'll do it for thanks, and therefore mark me where you have taken out the four knaves. Lay two together above and draw up one of them that it may be seen. Then prick the other in the midst and the third in the bottom, so when any cuts, cut he never so warily, three knaves must of force come together. For the bottom knave is cut to lie upon both the upper knaves."

"Aye, marry," saith the setter, "but then the three knaves you showed comes not together."

"Truth," saith the verser, "but one among a thousand marks not that. It requires a quick eye, a sharp wit, and a reaching head to spy at the first."

"Now, gramercy, sir, for this trick," saith the cony, "I'll domineer with this amongst my neighbors."

Thus doth the verser and the setter feign a kind friendship to the cony, offering him no show of cozenage nor once to draw him in for a pint of wine, the more to shadow their intended villainy. But now begins the sport. As thus they sit tippling, comes the barnacle and thrusts open the door, looking into the room where they are and, as one bashful, steps back again and very mannerly saith, "I cry you mercy, gentlemen. I thought a friend of mine had been here. I pray you pardon my boldness."

"No harm, sir," saith the verser. "I pray you, drink a cup of wine with us and welcome."

So in comes the barnacle and, taking the cup, drinks to the cony and then saith, "What, at cards, gentlemen? Were it not I should be offensive to your company, I would play for a pint till my friend come that I look for."

"Why, sir," saith the verser, "if you will sit down, you shall be taken up for a quart of wine."

"With all my heart," saith the barnacle. "What will you play at— at primero, primo visto, sant, one and thirty, new cut, or what shall be the game?"

"Sir," saith the verser, "I am but an ignorant man at cards, and I see you have them at your fingers' end. I'll play with you at a game wherein can be no deceit. It is called mumchance at cards, and it is thus: you shall shuffle the cards, and I will cut. You shall call one, and this plain, honest country yeoman shall call a card for me. And which of our cards comes first shall win. Here, you see, is no deceit; and at this I'll play."

"No, truly," saith the cony, "methinks there can be no great craft in this."

"Well," saith the barnacle, "for a pint of wine have at you."

So they play as before, five up, and the verser wins. "This is hard luck," saith the barnacle, "and I believe the honest man spies some card in the bottom. And therefore I'll make this: always to prick the bottom card."[36]

"Content," saith the verser.

And the cony, to cloak the matter, saith, "Sir, you offer me injury to think that I can see a card when I neither touch them, shuffle, cut, nor draw them."

"Ah, sir," saith the barnacle, "give losers leave to speak."

Well, to it they go again; and then the barnacle, knowing the game better than they all, by chopping[37] a card wins two of the five but lets the verser win the set. Then in a chafe he sweareth 'tis but his ill luck, and he can see no deceit at it, and therefore he will play twelve pence

---

[36]*I'll make this: always to prick the bottom card:* I'll make this rule: always bury the bottom card in the middle of the deck (and then it won't matter whether the honest country yeoman sees it or not).

[37]*chopping:* changing (secretly substituting one card for another).

a cut. The verser is content and wins two or three shillings of the barnacle, whereat he chafes and saith, "I came hither in an evil hour, but I will win my money again or lose all in my purse."

With that he draws out a purse with some three or four pound and claps it on the board. The verser asketh the cony secretly by signs if he will be his half. He says aye and straight feels for his purse. Well, the barnacle shuffles the cards thoroughly, and the verser cuts as before.

The barnacle, when he hath drawn one card, saith, "I'll either win something or lose something. Therefore I'll vie and revie every card at my pleasure till either yours or mine come out. And therefore twelve pence upon this card. My card comes first for twelve pence."

"No," saith the verser.

"Aye," saith the cony, "and I durst hold twelve pence more."

"Why, I hold you," saith the barnacle.

And so they vie and revie till some ten shillings be on the stake. And then next comes forth the verser's card that the cony called, and so the barnacle loseth. Well, this flesheth the cony. The sweetness of gain maketh him frolic, and no man is more ready to vie and revie than he.

Thus for three or four times the barnacle loseth. At last to whet on the cony he striketh his chopped card and winneth a good stake. "Away with the witch!" cries the barnacle. "I hope the cards will turn at last."

"Aye, much," thinketh the cony, " 'twas but a chance that you asked so right, to ask one of the five that was cut off. I am sure there was forty to one on my side, and I'll have you on the lurch by and by."

So still they vie and revie, and for once that the barnacle wins the cony gets five. At last, when they mean to shave the cony clean of all his coin, the barnacle chafeth and, upon a pawn, borroweth some money of the tapster and swears he will vie it to the uttermost. Then, thus he chops his card to cross-bite the cony. He first looks on the bottom card and shuffles often, but still keeping that bottom card, which he knows to be uppermost. Then sets he down the cards; and the verser, to encourage the cony, cuts off but three cards, whereof the barnacle's card must needs be the uppermost. Then shows he the bottom card of the other heap cut off to the cony and sets it upon the barnacle's card, which he knows. So that of force the card that was laid uppermost must come forth first. And then the barnacle calls that card. They draw a card, and then the barnacle vies and the country man vies upon him. For this is the law: as often as one vies or revies, the other must see it or else he loseth the stake.

Well, at last the barnacle plies it so that perhaps he vies more money than the cony hath in his purse. The cony, upon this, knowing his card is the third or fourth card and that he hath forty to one against the barnacle, pawns his rings if he hath any, his sword, his cloak, or else what he hath about him, to maintain the vie. And when he laughs in his sleeve, thinking he hath fleeced the barnacle of all, then the barnacle's card comes forth and strikes such a cold humor to his heart that he sits as a man in a trance, not knowing what to do, and sighing while his heart is ready to break, thinking on the money that he hath lost.

Perhaps the man is very simple and patient and, whatsoever he thinks, for fear goes his way quiet with his loss while the cony-catchers laugh and divide the spoil. And being out of doors, poor man, goeth to his lodging with a heavy heart and watery eyes, pensive and sorrowful. But too late, for perhaps the man's state did depend on that money; and so he, his wife, his children, and his family are brought to extreme misery. Another, perhaps more hardy and subtle, smokes the cony-catchers and smelleth cozenage and says they shall not have his money so. But they answer him with braves; and though he bring them before an officer, yet the knaves are so favored that the man never recovers his money, and yet they are[38] let slip without punishment.

Thus are the poor conies robbed by these base-minded caterpillars. Thus are servingmen oft enticed to play and lose all. Thus are prentices induced to be conies and so are cozened of their masters' money. Yea, young gentlemen, merchants, and others are fetched in by these damnable rakehells, a plague as ill as hell, which is present loss of money and ensuing misery. A lamentable case in England when such vipers are suffered to breed and are not cut off with the sword of justice. This enormity is not only in London but now generally dispersed through all England, in every shire, city, and town of any receipt.[39] And many complaints are heard of their egregious cozenage.

The poor farmer simply going about his business or to his attorney's

---

[38]*they are:* All four of the early editions read "he is"; but the reference is to the knaves, not to the cony or the officer.

[39]*town of any receipt:* any town big or important enough to have an inn or tavern in which strangers may stay for the night.

chamber is caught up and cozened of all. The servingman, sent with his lord's treasure, loseth ofttimes most part to these worms of the commonwealth. The prentice, having his master's money in charge, is spoiled by them, and from an honest servant either driven to run away or to live in discredit forever. The gentleman loseth his land, the merchant his stock, and all to these abominable cony-catchers whose means is as ill as their living. For they are all either wedded to whores or so addicted to whores that what they get from honest men they spend in bawdy houses amongst harlots and consume it as vainly as they get it villainously. Their ears are of adamant, as pitiless as they are treacherous; for be the man never so poor, they will not return him one penny of his loss.

I remember a merry jest done of late to a Welchman who, being a mere stranger in London and not well acquainted with the English tongue, yet chanced amongst certain cony-catchers who, spying the gentleman to have money, they so dealt with him that what by signs and broken English they got him in for a cony and fleeced him of every penny that he had and of his sword. At last the man smoked them and drew his dagger upon them at Ludgate, for thereabouts they had catched him, and would have stabbed one of them for his money but people came and stopped him, and the rather because they could not understand him although he had a card in one hand and his dagger in the other and said as well as he could, "A card, a card, mon dieu!" In the meanwhile the cony-catchers were gotten into Paul's and so away. The Welchman followed them and sought them there and went up and down the church, still with his naked dagger and the card in his hand. And gentlemen marveled what he meant thereby. At last one of his countrymen met him and inquired the cause of his choler. And then he told him how he was cozened at cards and robbed of all his money. But as his loss was voluntary, so his seeking them was mere vanity, for they were stepped into some blind alehouse to divide the shares.

Near to St. Edmondsbury, in Suffolk, there dwelt an honest man, a shoemaker, that, having some twenty marks in his purse long gathered and nearly kept,[40] came to the market to buy a dicker of hides[41] and by chance fell amongst cony-catchers, whose names I omit because I hope of their amendment. This plain country man, drawn in by these former devices, was made a cony and so straight stripped of his twenty mark, to all his utter undoing. The knaves scaped, and he

[40]*nearly kept:* kept close by, so that he could have his eye on it all the time.

[41]*a dicker of hides:* a lot or package of ten hides.

went home a sorrowful man. Shortly after, one of these cony-catchers was taken for a suspected person and laid in Bury Gaol, the sessions coming and he produced to the bar. It was the fortune of this poor shoemaker to be there, who, espying this rogue to be arraigned, was glad and said nothing unto him but looked what would be the issue of his appearance. At the last he was brought before the justices where he was examined of his life. And, being demanded what occupation he was, said "None."

"What profession then are you of, and how live you?"

"Marry," quoth he, "I am a gentleman and live of my friends."

"Nay, that is a lie," quoth the poor shoemaker. "Under correction of the worshipful of the bench, you have a trade and are by your art a cony-catcher."

"A cony-catcher?" said one of the justices, and smiled. "What, is he a warrener fellow? Whose warren doth he keep, canst thou tell?"

"Nay, sir, your worship mistaketh me," quoth the shoemaker. "He is not a warrener, but a cony-catcher."

The bench, that never heard this name before, smiled and attributed the name to the man's simplicity, thinking he meant a warrener. Which the shoemaker espying, made answer that some conies this fellow catched were worth twenty mark apiece. "And for proof," quoth he, "I am one of them" and so discoursed the whole order of the art and the baseness of the cozening. Whereupon the justices, looking into his life, appointed him to be whipped. And the shoemaker desired he might give him his payment, which was granted. So when he came to his punishment, the shoemaker laughed and said, " 'Tis a mad world when poor conies are able to beat their cony-catchers." But he lent him so friendly lashes that almost he made him pay an ounce of blood for every pound of silver.

Thus we see how the generation of these vipers increase, to the confusion of many honest men, whose practices to my poor power I have discovered and set out, with their villainous sleights that they use to the entrapping the simple. Yet have they cloaks for the rain and shadows for their villainies, calling it by the name of art or law, as Cony-Catching Art or Cony-Catching Law. And hereof it riseth that like as law, when the term is truly considered, signifieth an ordinance of good men, established for the commonwealth to repress all vicious living. So these cony-catchers turn the cat in the pan,[42] giving to diverse vile patching shifts an honest and godly title, calling it by

---

[42]*turn the cat in the pan:* a proverb (Tilley, C172); the literal sense is lost, but the figurative sense is that the cony-catchers are so clever they can make things appear to be the very opposite of what they are.

the name of a law because by a multitude of hateful rules, as it were
in good learning, they exercise their villainies to the destruction of
sundry honest people. Thus and hereupon do they give their false
conveyance the name of Cony-Catching Law, as there be also other
laws, as: High Law, Sacking Law, Figging Law, Cheating Law, Barnard's Law. If you marvel at these mysteries and quaint words, consider, as the carpenter hath many terms familiar enough to his
prentices that others understand not at all, so have the cony-catchers,
not without great cause; for a falsehood once detected can never
compass the desired effect.

Therefore will I presently acquaint you with the signification of the
terms in a table. But leaving them till time and place, coming down
the other day Turnmill Street I met with one whom I suspected a
cony-catcher—and, indeed, missed not of my mark. After salutations
and some chat, I drew him on to the tavern, and there, after a cup of
wine or two, I began to treat with him of the manner of his life and
told him I was sorry for his friends' sake that he took so bad a course
as to live upon the spoil of poor men and especially to deserve the
name of cony-catching, dissuading him from that base kind of life
that was so ignominious in the world and so loathsome in the sight
of God.

"Tut, sir," quoth he, calling me by my name, "as my religion is
small, so my devotion is less. I leave God to be disputed on by divines.
The two ends I aim at is gain and ease, but by what honest means I
may get never comes within the compass of my thoughts. Though
your experience in travel be great, yet in home matters mine is more.
Yea, I am sure you are not so ignorant but you know that few men
can live uprightly unless he have some pretty way, more than the
world is witness to, to help himself withal. Think you some lawyers
could be such purchasers if all their pleas were short and their proceedings justice and conscience? That offices would be so dearly
bought and the buyers so soon enriched if they counted not pillage an
honest kind of purchase? Or do you think that men of handy trades
do make all their commodities without falsehood when so many of
them are become daily purchasers? Nay, what will you more? Who
so hath not some sinister way to help himself, but followeth his nose
always straight forward, may well hold up the head for a year or two,
but the third he must needs sink and gather the wind into beggars'
haven.[43] Therefore, sir, cease to persuade me to the contrary, for

---

[43]*gather the wind into beggars' haven:* This metaphorical expression for
"become a beggar" is quoted word-for-word from A *Manifest Detection of
Dice Play* (c. 1552); see Judges, ed., *Elizabethan Underworld,* pp. 38,
492ff.

my resolution is to beat my wits and spare not to busy all my brains to save and help me by what means so ever I care not, so I may avoid the danger of the law."

Whereupon, seeing this cony-catcher resolved in his form of life, leaving him to his lewdness I went my ways, wondering at the baseness of their minds that would spend their time in such detestable sort. But no marvel, for they are given up into a reprobate sense and are in religion mere atheists, as they are in trade flat dissemblers. If I should spend many sheets in deciphering their shifts it were frivolous, in that they be many and are full of variety; for every day they invent new tricks and such quaint devices as are secret and yet passing[44] dangerous that if a man had Argus' eyes he could scarcely pry into the bottom of their practices.

Thus, for the benefit of my country I have briefly discovered the law of cony-catching, desiring all justices if such cozeners light in their precinct, even to use *summum jus*[45] against them because it is the basest of all villainies. And that London prentices, if they chance in such cony-catchers' company, may teach them London law—that is, to defend the poor men that are wronged and learn the caterpillars the high way to Newgate, where if Hind[46] favor them with the heaviest irons in all the house and give them his unkindest entertainment, no doubt his other petty sins shall be half pardoned for his labor. But I would it might be their fortune to happen into Nobles Northward in White Chapel. There, in faith, Round Robin, his deputy, would make them, like wretches, feel the weight of his heaviest fetters. And so, desiring both honorable and worshipful, as well justices as other officers, and all estates, from the prince to the beggar, to rest professed enemies to these base-minded cony-catchers, I take my leave.

Nascimur pro patria.[47]

---

[44]*passing:* surpassing; very.

[45]*summum jus:* the utmost rigor of the law.

[46]*Hind:* The word "hind," with a small "h," meant bailiff or steward; by capitalizing the word, Greene personified the generic term. Newgate was the principal jail in London.

[47]*Nascimur pro patria:* We are born for our country.

A Table of the Words of Art Used in the Effecting These Base
Villainies, Wherein is Discovered the Nature of Every Term,
Being Proper to None But to the Professors Thereof

1. High Law: robbing by the highway side.
2. Sacking Law: lechery.
3. Cheating Law: play at false dice.
4. Cross-Biting Law: cozenage by whores.
5. Cony-Catching Law: cozenage by cards.
6. Versing Law: cozenage by false gold.
7. Figging Law: cutting of purses and picking of pockets.
8. Barnard's Law: a drunken cozenage by cards.

These are the eight laws of villainy, leading the high way to infamy:

In High Law

The thief is called a high lawyer.
He that setteth the watch, a scripper.
He that standeth to watch, an oak.
He that is robbed, the martin.
When he yieldeth, stooping.

In Sacking Law

The bawd, if it be a woman, a pander.
The bawd, if a man, an apple squire.
The whore, a commodity.
The whorehouse, a trugging place.

In Cheating Law

Pardon me, gentlemen, for although no man could better than
myself discover this law and his terms and the name of their
cheats, barred dice, flats, forgers, langrets, gourds, demies, and
many others, with their nature, and the crosses and contraries to
them upon advantage, yet for some special reasons herein I will
be silent.

In Cross-Biting Law

The whore, the traffic.
The man that is brought in, the simpler.
The villains that take them, the cross-biters.

In Cony-Catching Law

The party that taketh up the cony, the setter.
He that placeth the game, the verser.
He that is cozened, the cony.
He that comes in to them, the barnacle.
The money that is won, purchase.

In Versing Law

He that bringeth him in, the verser.
The poor country man, the cousin.[48]
And the drunkard that comes in, the suffler.[49]

In Figging Law

The cutpurse, a nip.
He that is half with him, the snap.
The knife, a cuttle-bung.[50]
The pickpocket, a foist.
He that faceth the man, the stale.
Taking the purse, drawing.
Spying of him, smoking.
The purse, the bung.
The money, the shells.
The act doing, striking.

In Barnard's Law

He that fetcheth in the man, the taker.
He that is taken, the cousin.
The landed man, the verser.
The drunken man, the barnard.
And he that makes the fray, the rutter.

Cum multis aliis quae nunc praescribere longum est.[51]

These quaint terms do these base arts use to shadow their villainy
withal, for *multa latent quae non patent*[52]—obscuring their filthy

---

[48]*cousin:* Note the similarity—in spelling, sound, and connotation—between "cousin" and "cozen."

[49]*suffler:* probably from "suffle," a commotion or disturbance.

[50]*cuttle-bung:* a knife used for cutting purses.

[51]*Cum multis . . . longum est:* With many others, which it would take a long time to write down.

[52]*multa . . . patent:* many things lie hidden which are not exposed.

crafts with these fair colors, that the ignorant may not espy what their subtlety is. But their end will be like their beginning, hatched in Cain and consumed in Judas. And so, bidding them adieu to the devil and you farewell in God, I end. And now to the art of cross-biting.

[2] *The Art of Cross-Biting*

The cross-biting law is a public profession of shameless cozenage, mixed with incestuous whoredoms, as ill as was practiced in Gomorrha or Sodom, though not after the same unnatural manner. For the method of their mischievous art (with blushing cheeks and trembling heart let it be spoken) is that these villainous vipers, unworthy the name of men, base rogues (yet why do I term them so well?) being outcasts from God, vipers of the world and an excremental reversion of sin, doth consent—nay, constrain—their wives to yield the use of their bodies to other men, that, taking them together, he may cross-bite the party of all the crowns he presently can make. And that the world may see their monstrous practices, I will briefly set down the manner.

They have sundry preys that they call simplers, which are men fondly and wantonly given, whom for a penalty of their lust they fleece of all that ever they have:[53] some merchants, prentices, serving-men, gentlemen, yeomen, farmers, and of all degrees.

And this is their form: There are resident in London and the suburbs certain men attired like gentlemen, brave fellows but basely minded, who, living in want, as their last refuge fall unto this cross-biting law and to maintain themselves either marry with some stale whore or else forsooth keep one as their friend. And these persons be commonly men of the eight laws before rehearsed: either high lawyers, versers, nips, cony-catchers, or such of the like fraternity. These, when their other trades fail (as the cheater when he hath no cousin to grime with his stop dice, or the high lawyer when he hath no set match to ride about,[54] and the nip when there is no term, fair, nor time of great assembly) then to maintain the main chance, they use the benefit of their wives or friends to the cross-biting of such as

---

[53]*their lust they fleece . . . they have:* their (the simplers') lust they (the cross-biters) fleece . . . they (the simplers) have.

[54]*when he hath no set match to ride about:* when there are no travelers on the highway for the "high lawyer" to ride to (and rob).

lust after their filthy enormities. Some simple men are drawn on by subtle means, which never intended such a bad matter.

In summer evenings and in winter nights these traffics—these common trulls, I mean—walk abroad, either in the fields or streets that are commonly haunted, as stales to draw men unto hell. And afar off, as their attending apple squires, certain cross-biters stand aloof, as if they knew them not. Now, so many men, so many affections. Some unruly mates that place their content in lust, letting slip the liberty of their eyes on their painted faces, feed upon their unchaste beauties till their hearts be set on fire. Then come they to these dishonest minions and court them with many sweet words. Alas, their loves need no long suits, for they are forthwith entertained; and either they go to the tavern to seal up the match with a pottle of hippocras,[55] or straight she carries him to some bad place and there picks his pocket. Or else the cross-biters comes swearing in and so outface the dismayed companion that rather than he would be brought in question he would disburse all that he present hath, or possible may get, to their content.

But this is but an easy cozenage. Some other meeting with one of that profession in the street will question if she will drink with him a pint of wine. Their trade is never to refuse, and if for manners they do, it is but once. And then scarce shall they be warm in the room but in comes a terrible fellow with a side hair and a fearful beard, as though he were of Polyphemus' cut.[56] And he comes frowning in and saith, "What hast thou to do, base knave, to carry my sister (or my wife) to the tavern? By his 'ouns,[57] you infamous whore, 'tis some of your companions, and I will have you both before the justice, deputy, or constable to be examined."

The poor servingman, apprentice, farmer, or whatsoever he is, seeing such a terrible huff-snuff, swearing with his dagger in his hand, is fearful both of him and to be brought in trouble, and therefore speaks kindly and courteously to him and desires him to be content; he meant no harm. The whore, that hath tears at command, falls aweeping and cries him mercy. At this submission of them both, he

[55]*hippocras:* a cordial made of strained wine mixed with spices (from Hippocrates, a Greek physician of the fifth century B.C. who supposedly invented "Hippocrates' sleeve," a sleeve or bag through which the wine was strained to make it clear).

[56]*side hair . . . Polyphemus' cut:* a reference to the one-eyed giant in Book IX of the *Odyssey,* "side hair" probably meaning a beard.

[57]*By his 'ouns:* By his (Christ's) wounds.

triumphs like a braggart and will take no composition.[58] Yet at the last, through the entreaty of other his companions that comes in like strangers, he is pacified with some forty shillings; and the poor man goes sorrowful away, sighing out that which Solomon said in his proverbs:

> A shameless woman hath honey in her lips and her throat as sweet as honey, her throat as soft as oil. But the end of her is more bitter than aloes, and her tongue is more sharp than a two-edged sword. Her feet go unto death, and her steps lead unto hell.[59]

Again, these trulls, when they have gotten in a novice then straight they pick his purse. And then have they their cross-biters ready, to whom they convey the money, and so offer themselves to be searched. But the poor man is so outfaced by these cross-biting ruffians that he is glad to go away content with his loss. Yet are these easy practices. Ah, might the justices send out espials[60] in the night, they should see how these streetwalkers will jet in rich-guarded gowns,[61] quaint periwigs, ruffs of the largest size (quarter and half deep),[62] gloried richly with blue starch, their cheeks dyed with surfuling[63] water. And thus are they tricked up, and either walk like stales up and down the streets or else stand like the devil's *siquis*[64] at a tavern or alehouse, as if who should say, "If any be so minded for to satisfy his filthy lust, to lend me his purse and the devil his soul, let him come in and be welcome."

Now, sir, comes by a country farmer, walking from his inn to perform some business. And seeing such a gorgeous damsel, he, wondering at such a brave wench, stands staring her on the face. Or perhaps doth but cast a glance and bid her good speed (as plain, simple

---

[58]*will take no composition:* will not settle by mutual agreement; the change from "composition" to "compassion" in the second edition may be an improvement, but, once again, we cannot be sure that Greene was responsible for it.

[59]*A shameless . . . unto hell:* quoted from Proverbs, V, 3–5.

[60]*espials:* spies.

[61]*jet in rich-guarded gowns:* strut in gowns trimmed with costly and elegant materials.

[62]*ruffs . . . quarter and half deep:* The ruff or ruffle, made of starched linen, was a garment worn around the wrist or neck. The reference here is to the horizontal flutings or frills, and the unit of measurement is the yard; presumably a quarter and a half would be 13½ inches.

[63]*surfuling water:* surfling water; water with coloring in it, to be used as a rouge.

[64]*siquis:* public notice, bill, or advertisement.

swains have their lusting humors as well as others). The trull, straight beginning her *exordium*[65] with a smile, saith, "How now, my friend, what want you? Would you speak with anybody here?"

If the fellow hath any bold spirit, perhaps he will offer the wine. And then he is caught; 'tis enough. In he goes, and they are chambered. Then sends she for her husband or her friend, and there either the farmer's pocket is stripped or else the cross-biters fall upon him and threaten him with Bridewell[66] and the law. Then, for fear, he gives them all in his purse and makes them some bill to pay a sum of money at a certain day.

If the poor farmer be bashful and passeth by one of these shameless strumpets, then will she verse it[67] with him and claim acquaintance of him and by some policy or other fall aboard on him and carry him into some house or other. If he but enter in at doors with her, though the poor farmer never kissed her, yet then the cross-biters, like vultures, will prey upon his purse and rob him of every penny. If there be any young gentleman that is a novice and hath not seen their trains, to him will some common filth that never knew love feign an ardent and honest affection till she and her cross-biters have versed him to the beggar's estate.

Ah, gentlemen, merchants, yeomen, and farmers, let this to you all and to every degree else be a caveat to warn you from lust, that your inordinate desire be not a means to impoverish your purses, discredit your good names, condemn your souls, but also that your wealth, gotten with the sweat of your brows or left by your parents as a patrimony, shall be a prey to those cozening cross-biters. Some fond men are so far in with these detestable trugs that they consume what they have upon them and find nothing but a Neapolitan favor[68] for their labor. Read the seventh of Solomon's proverbs[69] and there at large view the description of a shameless and impudent courtezan.

[65]*exordium:* The opening part of a speech, with certain other well-known parts to follow in a prescribed order; here the reference is not to a speech, but to a well-laid plan, according to which the smile and the innocent-sounding question have their important functions.

[66]*Bridewell:* Stow notes that in 1553 Bridewell became "a Workhouse for the poore and idle persons of the Citie" (*Survey of London,* ed. C. L. Kingsford [Oxford, 1908], II, 44–45).

[67]*verse it:* cozen (by means of sweet talk).

[68]*Neapolitan favor:* syphilis—easily contractible in Naples, according to the English, who thought of syphilis as an Italian or French disease.

[69]*seventh of Solomon's proverbs:* the seventh chapter, verses 5–27; see note 59 referring to Proverbs, V, 3–5 (also a "description of a shameless and impudent courtezan").

Yet is there another kind of cross-biting which is most pestilent, and that is thus: there lives about this town certain householders, yet mere shifters and cozeners, who, learning some insight in the civil law, walk abroad like paritors, summoners, and informers,[70] being none at all either in office or credit. And they go spying about where any merchant or merchant's prentice, rich citizen, wealthy farmer, or other of good credit, either doth accompany with any woman familiarly or else hath gotten some maid with child. As men's natures be prone to sin, straight they come over his fallows thus: they send for him to a tavern and there open the matter unto him which they have cunningly learned out and tell him he must be presented to the Arches,[71] and the citation shall be peremptorily served in his parish church. The party, afraid to have his credit cracked with the worshipful of the city and the rest of his neighbors, and grieving highly his wife should hear of it, straight takes composition with this cozener for some twenty mark—nay, I have heard of three-score[72] pound cross-bitten at one time. And then the cozening informer or cross-biter promiseth him to wipe him out of the court[73] and discharge him from the matter when it was neither known nor presented. So go they to the woman and fetch her off, if she be married. And though they have this gross sum, yet oftentimes they cross-bite her for more. Nay, thus do they fear citizens, prentices, and farmers that they find but any way suspicious of the like fault.

These cross-biting bawds, for no better I can term them, in that for lucre they conceal the sin and smother up lust, do not only enrich themselves mightily but also discredit, hinder, and prejudice the Court of the Arches and the officers belonging to the same. There are some purblind patches[74] of that faculty that have their tenements purchased and their plate on their board very solemnly, who only get

---

[70]*paritors, summoners, and informers:* A paritor (now spelled "apparitor"), a summoner, and an informer performed roughly the same function; each was an officer of the government who served a summons or informed a person that he was to appear in court at a certain time.

[71]*Arches:* The Court of Arches was the ecclesiastical court of appeal (handling such matters as marriage and divorce) for Canterbury; the word "Arches" comes from St. Mary of the Arches, the church where the court sat.

[72]*three-score:* The second edition emended to "forty."

[73]*court:* The third edition emended to "book."

[74]*purblind patches:* completely blind fools; the word "patch" may be derived from *pazzo,* the Italian word for "fool." Cardinal Wolsey's fool was named Patch; see Chapter VI of Deloney's *Jack of Newbury.*

this gains by cross-biting, as afore is rehearsed. But leaving them to
the deep insight and consideration of such as are appointed with
justice to correct vice, again to the crew of my former cross-biters,
whose fee simple to live upon is nothing but the following of common,
dishonest, and idle trulls, and thereby they maintain themselves brave
and the strumpets in handsome furniture.[75]

And to end this art[76] with an English demonstration, I will tell you
a pretty tale alate performed in Bishopsgate Street. There was there
five traffics, pretty but common huswives,[77] that stood fast by a tavern
door, looking if some prey would pass by for their purpose. Straight
the eldest of them and most experienced in that law, named Mal B.,
spied a master of a ship coming all along.

"Here is a simpler," quoth she. "I'll verse him or hang me. Sir,"
quoth she, "God even.[78] What, are you so liberal as to bestow on
three good wenches that are dry a pint of wine?"

"In faith, fair women," quoth he, "I was never niggard for so
much." And with that he takes one of them by the hand and carries
them all into the tavern. There he bestowed cheer and hippocras
upon them, drinking hard till the shot came to a noble, so that they
three carousing to the gentleman made him somewhat tipsy; and then
Et venus in vinis, ignis in igne fuit.[79] Well, night grew on and he
would away, but this Mistress Mal B. stopped his journey thus:
"Gentleman," quoth she, "this undeserved favor of yours makes us
so deeply beholding unto you that our ability is not able any ways to
make sufficient satisfaction. Yet, to show us kind in what we can, you
shall not deny me this request to see my simple house before you go."

The gentleman, a little whittled,[80] consented and went with them.
So the shot was paid and away they go. Without the tavern door
stood two of their husbands, J. B. and J. R.; and they were made
privy to the practice. Well, home goes this gentleman with these jolly

---

[75]*brave . . . furniture:* "brave" means "handsomely" and "furniture" means
"clothes"; in other words, the cross-biter and his trull wear their gains on
their backs, preferring not to spend them on a fixed place to live (fee
simple).

[76]*this art:* the art of cross-biting; the fourth edition changes "art" to
"act."

[77]*huswives:* hussies.

[78]*God even:* God give you good evening.

[79]*Et venus in vinis, ignis in igna fuit:* And just as Venus was in wine, so
fire (the glow of passion) was in fire.

[80]*whittled:* drunk.

huswives, stumbling; and at last he was welcome to Mistress Mal's house; and one of the three went into a chamber and got her to bed, whose name was A. B. After they had chatted awhile, the gentleman would have been gone, but she told him that before he went he should see all the rooms of her house and so led the gentleman up to the chamber where the party lay in bed.

"Who is here?" said the gentleman.

"Marry," saith Mal, "a good pretty wench, sir, and if you be not well, lie down by her. You can take no harm of her."

Drunkenness desires lust, and so the gentleman begins to dally. And away goes she with the candle, and at last he put off his clothes and went to bed. Yet he was not so drunk but he could after awhile remember his money; and feeling for his purse, all was gone and three links of his whistle[81] were broken off. The sum that was in his purse was, in gold and silver, twenty nobles. As thus he was in a maze, though his head were well laden, in comes J. B., goodman of the house, and two other with him, and speaking somewhat loud.

"Peace, husband," quoth she, "there's one in bed. Speak not so loud."

"In bed!" saith he. "Gog's nouns,[82] I'll go see."

"And so will I," saith the other.

"You shall not," saith his wife, and strove against him.

But up goes he and his cross-biters with him, and seeing the gentleman in bed, out with his dagger and asked what base villain it was that there sought to dishonest his house. Well, he sent one of them for a constable and made the gentleman rise, who, half drunk, yet had that remembrance to speak fair and to entreat him to keep his credit. But no entreaty could serve, but to the Counter[83] he must; and the constable must be sent for. Yet at last one of them entreated that the gentleman might be honestly used, and carried to a tavern to talk of the matter till a constable came.

"Tut," saith J. B., "I'll have the law upon him."

But the base cross-biter at last stooped, and to the tavern they go, where the gentleman laid his whistle to pawn for money and there bestowed as much of them as came to ten shillings and sat drinking and talking until the next morrow.

[81]*links of his whistle:* links of the chain holding his whistle.

[82]*Gog's nouns:* an oath—by God's (Christ's) wounds.

[83]*Counter:* a city jail for debtors. There were two in London in the sixteenth century—the Poultry Counter and the Bread Street Counter.

By that the gentleman had stolen a nap and, waking, it was daylight. And then, seeing himself compassed with these cross-biters, and remembering his night's work, soberly smiling, asked them if they knew what he was. They answered, "Not well."

"Why, then," quoth he, "you base, cozening rogues, you shall ere we part." And with that, drawing his sword, kept them into the chamber, desiring that the constable might be sent for. But this brave of his could not dismay Mistress Mal, for she had bidden a sharper brunt before. Witness the time of her martyrdom, when upon her shoulders was engraven the history of her whorish qualities. But she, replying, swore, seeing he was so lusty her husband should not put it up by no means.

"I will tell thee, thou base, cross-biting bawd," quoth he, "and you cozening companions, I serve a nobleman; and for my credit with him, I refer me to the penalty he will impose on you. For by God, I will make you an example to all cross-biters ere I end with you. I tell you, villains, I serve ——" And with that he named his lord.

When the guilty whores and cozeners heard of his credit and service, they began humbly to entreat him to be good to them.

"Then," quoth he, "first deliver me my money."

They, upon that, gladly gave him all and restored the links of his chain. When he had all, he smiled and sware afresh that he would torment them for all this, that the severity of their punishment might be a caveat to others to beware of the like cozenage; and upon that knocked with his foot and said he would not let them go till he had a constable. Then, in general they humbled themselves, and so recompensed the party that he agreed to pass over the matter, conditionally beside that[84] they would pay the sixteen shillings he had spent in charges—which they also performed. The gentleman stepped his way and said, "You may see the old proverb fulfilled, *Fallere fallentem non est fraus.*"[85] But the poor cross-biters sat sighing a sorrowful heigh-ho.

Thus have I deciphered an odious practice not worthy to be named. And now, wishing all of what estate soever to beware of filthy lust and such damnable stales as draws men on to disordinate desires, and rather to spend their coin amongst honest company than to bequeath

[84]*conditionally beside that:* on condition that they pay in addition to the recompense.

[85]*Fallere fallentem non est fraus:* Cheating a cheat is no deceit.

it unto such base cross-biters as prey upon men like ravens on dead carcasses, I end with this prayer—that cross-biting and cony-catching may be as little known in England as the eating of swine's flesh was among the Jews. Farewell.

Nascimur pro patria.

Finis

[3] *A Pleasant Discovery of the Cozenage of Colliers*

Although, courteous readers, I did not put in amongst the laws of cozening the law of legering, which is a deceit that colliers abuse the commonwealth withal in having unlawful sacks, yet take it for a petty kind of craft or mystery as prejudicial to the poor as any of the other two. For I omitted divers other devilish vices—as the nature of the lift, the black art, and the curbing[86] law, which is the filchers and thieves that come into houses or shops and lift away anything; or picklocks, or hookers at windows, although they be as species and branches to the table before rehearsed. But omitting them, again to our law of legering.

Know, therefore, that there be inhabiting in and about London certain caterpillars (colliers, I should say) that do term themselves (amongst themselves) by the name of legers, who for that the honorable, the Lord Mayor of the city of London, and his officers, look straightly[87] to the measuring of coals, do, to prevent the execution of his justice, plant themselves in and about the suburbs of London, as Shoreditch, White Chapel, Southwark, and such places. And there they have a house or yard that hath a back gate because it is the more convenient for their cozening purpose. And the reason is this: the leger, the crafty collier I mean, riseth very early in the morning and either goeth towards Croydon, Whetstone, Greenwich, or Romford and there meeteth with country colliers who bring coals to serve the market. There, in a forestalling manner, this leger bargaineth with the country collier for his coals and payeth for them some nineteen shillings, or twenty at the most, but commonly fifteen and sixteen, and there is in the load thirty-six sacks. For that they pay for

---

[86]*curbing:* probably a branch of the Figging Law, one of the eight laws given in the table on p. 418, above. The curber is a person who pulls clothing, etc., out of a window by means of a hook, presumably on a long stick.

[87]*straightly:* straitly (strictly, closely).

every couple about fourteen pence.[88] Now, having bought his coals, every sack containing full four bushels, he carryeth the country collier home to his legering place and there, at the back gate, causeth him to unload and, as they say, shoot the coals down. As soon as the country collier hath dispatched and is gone, then the leger, who hath three or four hired men under him, bringeth forth his own sacks, which be long and narrow, holding at the most not three bushels, so that they gain in the change of every sack a bushel for their pains.

Tush, yet this were somewhat to be borne withal, although the gain and usury is monstrous. But this sufficeth not, for they fill not these sacks full by far but put into them some two bushels and a half, laying in the mouth of their sack certain great, choice coals, which they call fillers, to make the sack show fair, although all the rest be small willow coal and half dross. When they have thus not filled their sacks but thrust coals into them, that which they lay uppermost is best filled for to make the greater show. Then a tall, sturdy knave that is all ragged and dirty on his legs, as though he came out of the country (for they dirty their hose and shoes upon purpose to make themselves seem country colliers).[89] Thus, with two sacks apiece they either go out at the back gate or steal privily out at the street side, and so go up and down the suburbs and sell their coals in summer for fourteen and sixteen pence a couple and in winter for eighteen or twenty. The poor cooks and other citizens that buy them think they be country colliers that have left some coals of their load and would gladly have money, supposing, as the statute is, they be good and lawful sacks, are thus cozened by the legers and have but two bushels and a half for four bushels and yet are extremely racked in the price. Which is not only a great hindrance to her majesty's poor commons,[90] but greatly prejudicial to the master colliers that bring true sacks and measure out of the country.

Then consider, gentle readers, what a kind of cozenage these legers use, that can make of thirty sacks some six and fifty—which I have seen with mine eyes, for I have set down with my pen how many turns they have made of a load. And they made eight and twenty

---

[88]*fourteen pence:* actually, a little less than that, even at the maximum price of twenty shillings; there are twelve pence to the shilling, and therefore the leger pays only 6.6 pence per sack or 13.2 pence for two sacks.

[89]*Then a tall, sturdy knave . . . colliers:* The predicate of this sentence seems to have been lost in the shift from singular to plural subject.

[90]*her majesty's poor commons:* Queen Elizabeth's poor common people.

turns, every turn being two sacks, so that they have gotten an intolerable gains by their false measure. I could not be silent seeing this
abuse, but thought to reveal it for my country's commodity and to
give light to the worshipful justices and other her majesty's officers in
Middlesex, Surrey, and elsewhere. To look to such a gross cozenage
as contrary to a direct statute doth defraud and impoverish her
majesty's poor commons. Well may the honorable and worshipful of
the city of London flourish, who carefully look to the country coals.
And if they find not four bushels in every sack, do sell them to the
poor as forfeit and distribute the money to them that have need,
burning the sack and honoring, or rather dishonoring, the pillory with
the colliers' dirty faces. And well may the honorable and worshipful of
the suburbs live and prosper if they look in justice to these legers,
who deserve more punishment than the statute appoints for them—
which is whipping at a cart's tail or, with favor, the pillory. For, fuel
or firing being a thing necessary in a commonwealth, and charcoal
used more than any other, the poor, not able to buy by the load, are
fain to get in their fire by the sack and so are greatly cozened by the
retail.

Seeing, therefore, the careful laws her majesty hath appointed for
the wealth of her commons and succor of the poor, I would humbly
entreat all her majesty's officers to look into the life of these legers
and to root them out, that the poor feel not the burden of their unconscionable gains. I heard with my ears a poor woman of Shoreditch
who had bought coals of a leger, with weeping tears complain and
rail against him in the street, in her rough eloquence calling him
cozening knave and saying, " 'Tis no marvel, villain," quoth she, "if
men compare you colliers to the devil, seeing your consciences are
worser than the devil's. For he takes none but those souls whom God
hates, and you undo the poor whom God loves."

"What is the matter, good wife," quoth I, "that you use such invective words against the collier?"

"A collier, sir!" saith she. "He is a thief and a robber of the common people. I'll tell you, sir, I bought of a country collier two sacks
for thirteen pence, and I bought of this knave three sacks, which cost
me two and twenty pence. And, sir, when I measured both their
sacks, I had more in the two sacks by three pecks than I had in his
three. I would," quoth she, "the justices would look into this abuse
and that[91] my neighbors would join with me in a supplication, and by
God I would kneel before the Queen and entreat that such cozening

___

[91]*the justices . . . and that:* omitted in the fourth edition.

colliers might not only be punished with the bare pillory—for they have such black faces that no man knows them again, and so are they careless—but that they might leave their ears behind them for a forfeit. And if that would not mend them, that bull with a fair halter might root them out of the world that live in the world by such gross and dishonest cozenage."

The collier hearing this went smiling away because he knew his life was not looked into, and the woman wept for anger that she had not someone by that might with justice revenge her quarrel.

There be also certain colliers that bring coals to London by water in barges, and they be called gripers. To these comes the leger and bargains with him for his coals and sells by retail with the like cozenage of sacks as I rehearsed before. But these mad legers, not content with this monstrous, extorting gains, do besides mix amongst their other sacks of coals store of shruff dust[92] and small coal, to their great advantage. And for proof hereof, I will recite you a matter of truth lately performed by a cook's wife upon a cozening collier.

[4] *How a Cook's Wife in London Did Lately Serve a Collier for His Cozenage*

It chanced this summer that a load of coals came forth of Kent to Billingsgate. And a leger brought them, who, thinking to deceive the citizens as he did those in the suburbs, furnished himself with a couple of sacks and comes up St. Mary Hill to sell them. A cook's wife bargained with the collier for his coals, and they agreed upon fourteen pence for the couple. Which done, he carried in the coals and shot[93] them. And when the wife saw them, and perceiving there was scarce five bushels for eight, she calls a little girl to her and bade her go for the constable.

"For thou, cozening rogue," quoth she, speaking to the collier, "I will teach thee how thou shalt cozen me with thy false sacks—whatsoever thou dost to others; and I will have thee before my lord mayor."

With that she caught a spit in her hand and swore if he offered to stir she would therewith broach him. At which word the collier was amazed, and the fear of the pillory put him in such a fright that he said he would go to his boat and return again to answer whatsoever she durst object against him.

---

[92]*shruff dust:* light refuse wood or cinders.
[93]*shot:* dumped (into the coalhouse, so that he could take the empty sacks away with him).

"And for pledge thereof," quoth the collier, "keep my sacks, your money, and the coals also."

Whereupon the woman let him go. But as soon as the collier was out of doors, it was needless to bid him run; for down he gets to his boat and away he thrusts from Billingsgate and so immediately went down to Wapping and never after durst return to the cook's wife to demand either the money, sacks, or coals.

[5] *How a Flax Wife and Her Neighbors Used a Cozening Collier*

Now, gentlemen, by your leave, and hear a merry jest. There was in the suburbs of London a flax wife that wanted coals. And seeing a leger come by with a couple of sacks that had before deceived her, in like sort cheaped, bargained, and bought them and so went in with her to shoot them in her coalhouse. As soon as she saw her coals, she easily guessed there was scarce[94] six bushels. Yet, dissembling the matter, she paid him for them and bade him bring her two sacks more. The collier went his way, and in the meantime the flax wife measured the coals; and there was just five bushels and a peck. Hereupon she called in her neighbors, being a company of women that before time had also been pinched in their coals, and showed them the cozenage and desired their aid to her in tormenting the collier—which they promised to perform. And thus it fell out.

She conveyed them into a back room—some sixteen of them—every one having a good cudgel under her apron. Straight comes the collier and saith, "Mistress, here by your coals."

"Welcome, good collier," quoth she. "I pray thee, follow me into the back side and shoot them in another room."

The collier was content and went with her; but as soon as he was in, the goodwife locked the door. And the collier, seeing such a troop of wives in the room, was amazed, yet said, "God speed you all, shrews."

"Welcome," quoth one jolly dame, being appointed by them all to give sentence against him. Who, so soon as the collier had shot his sacks, said, "Sirra, collier, know that we are here all assembled as a grand jury to determine of thy villainies, for selling us false sacks of coals. And know that thou art here indicted upon cozenage. Therefore, hold up thy hand at the bar and either say guilty or not guilty

[94]*there was scarce:* Unfortunately, with these words at the bottom of sig. F4ᵛ, the only extant copy of the first edition comes to an end; the last leaf, sig. G1, is missing. The copytext for the missing part is the second edition.

and by whom thou wilt be tried. For thou must receive condign punishment for the same ere thou depart."

The collier, who thought they had but jested, smiled and said, "Come on, which of you all shall be my judge?"

"Marry, sir," quoth one jolly dame, "that is I. And by God, you knave, you shall find I will pronounce sentence against you severely, if you be found guilty."

When the collier saw they were in earnest, he said, "Come, come, open the door and let me go."

With that, five or six wives started up and fell upon the collier and gave unto him half a score of sound lambeaks[95] with their cudgels and bade him speak more reverently to their principal. The collier, feeling it smart, was afraid and thought mirth and courtesy would be the best mean to make amends for his villainy and therefore said he would be tried by the verdict of the smock. Upon this they paneled a jury, and the flax wife gave evidence. And because this unaccustomed jury required witness, she measured the coals before the collier's face; upon which he was found guilty. And she that sat as principal to give judgment upon him began as followeth:

"Collier, thou art condemned here by proof of flat cozenage. And I am now appointed in conscience to give sentence against thee, being not only moved thereunto because of this poor woman but also for the general commodity of my country. And, therefore, this is my sentence: we have no pillory for thee nor cart to whip thee at, but here I do award that thou shalt have as many bastinadoes[96] as thy bones will bear and then to be turned out of doors without sacks or money."

This sentence being pronounced, she rose up and gave no respite of time for the execution; but according to the sentence before expressed, all the women fell upon him, beating him extremely, among whom he lent some lusty buffets. But might overcomes right, and therefore *ne Hercules contra duos*.[97] The women so crushed him that he was not able to lift his hands to his head, and so with a broken pate or two he was paid and, like Jack Drum, fair and orderly thrust out of doors.[98]

[95]*lambeaks:* heavy blows (often spelled "lambacks"); cf. "lambaste," "lambast."

[96]*bastinadoes:* a Spanish word meaning "blows with a stick or cudgel."

[97]*ne Hercules contra duos:* not [even] Hercules [could win] against two.

[98]*Jack Drum ... thrust out of doors:* Compare Tom Drum in Chapter VIII of Deloney's *The Gentle Craft, Part II,* where Drum's "entertainment" consists of his being thrown out of doors as an unwelcome guest.

This was the reward that the collier had, and I pray God all such colliers be so served and that goodwives, when they buy such sacks, may give them such payments and that the honorable and worshipful of the land may look into this gross abuse of colliers as well for charity sake as also for the benefit of the poor. And so, wishing colliers to amend their deceitful and disordered dealings herein, I end.

Finis

℁ The Unfortunate Traveler

OR

The Life of Jack Wilton
(1594)

Thomas Nashe

Thomas Nashe's *The Unfortunate Traveler* ends with "June 27, 1593." By that time Nashe had put away euphuistic language as a childish thing, even though he had regarded it as *"ipse ille"* when he was a "little ape in Cambridge."[1] By the middle of 1593 there is little trace of euphuism in his style except when he is mocking it; yet the subtleties of language remained his one great, lifelong preoccupation. Before we turn to Nashe's style, however, we should consider first the larger matter of the form his narrative takes.

What we find is a form so thoroughly mixed that we cannot assign it to any one genre in particular. *The Unfortunate Traveler* has elements of romance, confession, anatomy, and novel, with emphasis on the latter two. It is anatomy because it is fundamentally analytical and satirical; but it is also a novel in that it operates within the actual structure of society, which we come to know intimately by sight, sound, and smell. The other two forms, romance and confession, are less basic. The romance element is inverted, becoming really anti-romance, and is not an extensive part of the work as a whole. Confession seems more extensive than it really is; the first-person point of view helps to give a sense of immediacy, but we do not come to know Jack very well. He is not at all introspective, and therefore we tend to know him from the outside through scenes, many of which could have been presented just as well from the third-person point of view.

Certainly Nashe is right to say in his dedication that *The Unfortu-*

[1] See Nashe's *Strange News* in *The Works of Thomas Nashe,* ed. Mc-Kerrow, I, 319.

nate Traveler is "a clean different vein from other my former courses of writing." Individual passages may remind us of earlier works, from *The Anatomy of Absurdity* (1589) to *Christ's Tears over Jerusalem* (1593), but as a whole it is quite different. Various comments in the dedication and in the text seem to indicate Nashe's intention to write a kind of history. Sometimes the word "history" simply means "story," but often it also carries the modern sense, a writing about past events. There is one reference (p. 512) to Lanquet's *Chronicle*, from which Nashe takes the information that 100,000 people died in 1522 of the plague in Rome. McKerrow probably is right that Nashe makes use of other chroniclers besides Lanquet, especially Sleidan, Hall, and Holinshed. All in all, there are enough references to historical persons and places for us to consider Nashe, along with Deloney, as antecedents of Sir Walter Scott in the "historical novel" or "historical romance." But Nashe takes great liberties with history, even with well-known persons such as Erasmus and the Earl of Surrey (to say nothing of the pope). Toward the end Jack refers to himself as an "outlandish chronicler." It is not a recognizable past that Nashe evokes so much as the Elizabethan present; no other creative writer of the period is such a mine of factual information about the 1580's and 1590's. McKerrow's index to Nashe's works can take us back easily into everyday Elizabethan life—what people then wore, ate, drank; what diseases they caught and what remedies were applied; their beliefs and superstitions; the ways they actually expressed themselves, including the colloquialisms and slang. Nashe was, in other words, a first-rate reporter. He "covered" a plague, a war, or a simple drinking bout with an eye to explicit detail.

Like many a subsequent newspaperman, Nashe's eye is somewhat jaundiced by what he regards as human folly. In each section of his narrative he is debunking something—an idea, a person, a religion, a sect, a way of writing, a pattern of conduct. Our response usually is laughter at the object (and hardly ever laughter with or compassion for).[2]

[2]Agnes M. C. Latham is right in suggesting that Nashe is not a journalist in the usual modern sense; Nashe makes no effort to give us detached and accurate reporting. He constantly exaggerates, but he often exaggerates in order to more fully reveal and expose the true nature of the object. Miss Latham argues persuasively that most of *The Unfortunate Traveler* is humorous parody of which the Surrey–Geraldine episode is merely the most obvious. See her "Satire on Literary Themes and Modes in Nashe's 'The Unfortunate Traveller,'" which is listed in the Nashe section of the Select Bibliography.

Jack's travels through different European countries and through different levels of society have led some critics to see *The Unfortunate Traveler* as a picaresque story, perhaps modeled on the anonymous *Lazarillo de Tormes* (1555), a Spanish picaresque novel.[3] There are striking similarities in the structure of the individual episodes, each with beginning, middle, and end; in the hero, who provides a unifying link among the episodes; and in a prevailing satiric thrust, which also unifies. Yet Nashe may have gotten the first two elements from the jest-biography, and he needed no model for the third.

Since the unit of Nashe's narrative is an attack or exposé, the jestbook offered in many ways an ideal model for an individual episode. Again and again, beginning with the cider merchant (the "lord of misrule") and the practical joke that Wilton plays on him, we are reminded of jests like the ones in *The Sackful of News*.

But the jestbook is only one of many narrative sources, for *The Unfortunate Traveler* is one of the most eclectic works of prose fiction in the entire Renaissance. Nashe seems to be perfectly aware that he is combining many forms. "History" and "jest" are the most frequent words that Jack Wilton employs to describe sections of his narrative; but he also uses "treatise," "pamphlet," "life," "tale," "elegiacal history," and "tragical matter." The episode about Surrey and Geraldine is excellent parody of the Petrarchan sonnet and medieval romance,[4] and it was written a dozen years before Part I of *Don Quixote* appeared in 1605. Like Cervantes, Nashe seems to have in mind a *tour de force*, a deliberate mingling of medieval and Renaissance forms with the ancient forms—epic, lyric, comedy, and tragedy—all in the same work.[5]

Nashe's bold attempt to mix genres probably is related to (and may be responsible for) the one serious flaw in the narrative structure of *The Unfortunate Traveler*—a blurred conception of the nar-

[3]See Bowers, "Thomas Nashe and the Picaresque Novel."

[4]G. R. Hibbard finds it "hard to resist the conclusion that this part of *The Unfortunate Traveller* is an intermediate stage between *Rosalynde* and *As You Like It*, that Shakespeare read it and was influenced by it, and that Rosalind herself owes something to Nashe's witty page." See Hibbard's *Thomas Nashe*, p. 162.

[5]The dialogue between the canon and the curate in *Don Quixote*, Part I, Chapters 47 and 48, probably shows an awareness on Cervantes' part that his own narrative is an ambitious composite of several genres. See the Samuel Putnam translation of *Don Quixote* (New York, 1949), pp. 426–428.

rator-protagonist. In our discussion of *Master F. J.* we have noted how well Gascoigne solved the problem of "authority." As G. T. narrates the story of F. J., we are never allowed to forget that G. T. gets all his information second and third hand; but that never seems to us a disadvantage because G. T. himself is a very interesting person who gives to the whole story a unity and perspective that the young and confused F. J. could never have given it. In *The Unfortunate Traveler,* on the other hand, Jack Wilton tells his own story; the protagonist and the narrator are one person. Since we do not get much of Jack's thoughts and feelings, there seems to be little advantage to his telling his own story. He rarely emerges as anyone we can visualize; in fact, from one episode to another he becomes a different kind of person, as though Nashe has forgotten his original conception or has not yet made up his mind. Late in the story Zadoch refers to Jack as "of the age of eighteen, of stature tall, straight limbed, of as clear a complexion as any painter's fancy can imagine" (p. 528). Zadoch's description seems reliable enough at the moment, but his is the only concrete description of Jack in the whole work (despite the fact that we are given exceptionally concrete descriptions of many other persons). In most episodes our impression of the protagonist is vague, but he seems older than eighteen. Occasionally the narrator's voice seems so much older than eighteen that we suspect Nashe himself of breaking in to give us a brief "elegiacal history"— as, for example, the story of the "noble and chaste matron called Heraclide" (pp. 513–20). In that episode Jack is largely forgotten. If we read closely, we find (p. 519) that Jack is upstairs looking through a "cranny" down at the rape, which occurs on the first floor. But we do not see the action from above (from Jack's point of view); we see it from close and level range. Similarly, later on, when we find Diamante "deliberating with herself in what hellish servitude she lived with the Jew" (p. 535), we do not have Jack's point of view, for, unlike an omniscient narrator, he cannot know anyone's thoughts but his own.

G. R. Hibbard has observed that *The Unfortunate Traveler* "embodies nothing that can be called a view of life."[6] Nashe analyzes or parodies a great many views that he cannot accept, without piecing together a positive view of his own (or Jack Wilton's own). But his implied view seems to be that of the Establishment; he accepts the *via media* of Queen Elizabeth, and his repeated attacks on Puritans

[6] *Thomas Nashe,* p. 179.

reflect a consistent, if narrowly conservative, view. He was also a humanist, especially with regard to the Latin classics, Ovid in particular; but, unlike Elyot and Ascham, he does not give us a sense of what it meant to be a humanist in the sixteenth century.

Yet if we are looking specifically for "content," we are not meeting Nashe on the ground he has chosen. While he makes no claim to having original ideas, he does make claim to forging something new in the way of a style in English. McKerrow probably is right when he suggests (V, 129) that Nashe's references to Aretino indicate a desire to create a style in English with the same force and vivacity that Aretino, the "scourge of princes," had shown possible in the Italian language early in the sixteenth century. We may call Nashe the "English Aretino." Perhaps we may also think of him as the "English Rabelais." Whether Nashe actually studied Rabelais, whose works began appearing in French as early as 1532, is debatable; but their robust and hyperbolic styles are similar.

One of the most obvious characteristics of Nashe's language is a listing of adjectives, one after another, as in "big, swollen, large face" (p. 480). In isolation the device seems to be merely a kind of repetition and overlapping, but the cumulative effect is visual clarity and strong emphasis. The overflowing style is to indicate an excess in the object. Thus the wine merchant is a "miser and a snudge" (p. 450). "Miser" and "snudge" mean the same thing, but the effect of the colloquial and onomatopoeic "snudge" is to emphasize and exaggerate the miserliness.

If just the right word is not current, Nashe invents it. Again and again when one looks in the *OED* to find the sense of a Nashe expression, one finds that Nashe was the first to use it. A. J. Kirkman, in an article called "Word Coinage,"[7] lists some of the new words that may be found in *Christ's Tears* alone: abhorrent, adumbrate, ambiguity, articulate; balderdash; circumduct, concise, congestion, controvert; devastation, diminutive, dislocated; epitomize, excruciating, expiate; multifarious; niggling; pinckany [piccaninni], progeniture; vociferate. A comparative study might reveal that Nashe has the largest vocabulary of all the Elizabethans, including Shakespeare. Many of his words are of three and four syllables; he apparently likes to hear the sounds roll and reverberate.

Writing for an age accustomed to reading aloud, Nashe makes clever use of sound effects. Alliteration he likes particularly well; in

[7]*TLS*, 4 May 1962, p. 325.

expressions like "none cared for covetous clientry" (p. 512) the hard "c's" emphasize a negative and derogatory trait. Nashe is especially good at describing a type of abhorrent person. His etching of Vanderhulk is a brilliant "character" of the kind that became popular early in the seventeenth century with Joseph Hall's *Characters of Virtues and Vices* (1608). Besides alliteration, Nashe's storehouse includes a whole bagful of puns, *double entendres,* and free word associations. "Cimices" (bedbugs) suggests "Cimbrians" (p. 507) and the very incongruity makes the sparks of humor fly. Doubtless many of the puns are lost to us since they depend upon connotations and allusions no longer traceable, but the ones that we can understand reveal a sensitivity to wordplay that is unusual even among the Elizabethans.

But in the end it may be the rhythm of Nashe's language that is his strongest point; almost at random one comes across a paragraph like this:

> Alas, our Englishmen are the plainest dealing souls that ever God put life in. They are greedy of news and love to be fed in their humors and hear themselves flattered the best that may be. Even as Philemon, a comic poet, died with extreme laughter at the conceit of seeing an ass eat figs, so have the Italians no such sport as to see poor English asses, how soberly they swallow Spanish figs, devour any hook baited for them. He is not fit to travel that cannot, with the Candians, live on serpents, make nourishing food even of poison. Rats and mice engender by licking one another. He must lick, he must crouch, he must cog, lie, and prate, that either in the court or a foreign country will engender and come to preferment. Be his feature what it will, if he be fair spoken he winneth friends. *Non formosus erat, sed erat facundus Ulysses:* Ulysses, the long traveler, was not amiable but eloquent (pp. 522–23).

Most of the sentences begin with nouns or pronouns; but the first, third, and next to the last begin with another part of speech. Toward the middle of the paragraph there is a long sentence, which is followed by a fairly short and then a very short sentence. The effect is a supple and athletic rhythm. One is reminded of Lyly in the similes, but the total effect—with the hard "c" and explosive "p" sounds; the repetitions ("must" three times, "engender" twice); the strong verbs, overlapping in sense ("cog," "lie," and "prate")—is a more dynamic style than Lyly's, more visceral and less strictly intellectual.

Like Lyly, Nashe gives every appearance of enjoying the process of creating a style. Style is the man; and verbal expression is the index of reason, man's special gift. But precisely why Nashe should enjoy pinning to the wall a naïve Englishman, a scheming foreigner, or a whole religious movement is difficult to say. Nothing that we know from his life suggests a good enough motive for so thorough a negativism. Perhaps he regards himself a verbal warrior, no less professional because he is using a pen in London rather than a sword on some distant battlefield.

To the Right Honorable Lord Henry Wriothesley,[8]
Earl of Southampton and Baron
of Titchfield

Ingenuous honorable lord, I know not what blind custom methodical antiquity hath thrust upon us, to dedicate such books as we publish to one great man or other. In which respect, lest any man should challenge these my papers as goods uncustomed and so extend upon them as forfeit to contempt, to the seal of your excellent censure, lo, here I present them to be seen and allowed. Prize them as high or as low as you list. If you set any price on them, I hold my labor well satisfied. Long have I desired to approve my wit unto you. My reverent dutiful thoughts, even from their infancy, have been retainers to your glory. Now at last I have enforced an opportunity to plead my devoted mind. All that in this fantastical treatise, I can promise, is some reasonable conveyance of history and variety of mirth. By divers of my good friends have I been dealt with to employ my dull pen in this kind, it being a clean different vein from other my former courses of writing. How well or ill I have done in it, I am ignorant: the eye that sees round about itself sees not into itself. Only your honor's applauding encouragement hath power to make me arrogant.

Incomprehensible is the height of your spirit both in heroical reso-

---

[8]*Wriothesley:* This dedication to the third Earl of Southampton (1573–1624) was omitted in the second edition; naturally, the *errata* list following the dedication was also omitted in the second edition (and all the corrections made). Wriothesley was the young man of nineteen and twenty to whom Shakespeare dedicated "Venus and Adonis" (1593) and "Lucrece" (1594); he was imprisoned in 1601–03 for complicity in Essex's rebellion, but James I restored him to favor.

lution and matters of conceit. Unreprievably perisheth that book whatsoever to wastepaper which on the diamond rock of your judgment disasterly chanceth to be shipwrecked. A dear lover and cherisher you are, as well of the lovers of poets as of poets themselves. Amongst their sacred number I dare not ascribe myself, though now and then I speak English. That small brain I have, to no further use I convert save to be kind to my friends and fatal to my enemies. A new brain, a new wit, a new style, a new soul will I get me to canonize your name to posterity if, in this my first attempt, I be not taxed of presumption.

Of your gracious favor I despair not, for I am not altogether fame's outcast. This handful of leaves I offer to your view, to the leaves on trees I compare, which, as they cannot grow of themselves except they have some branches or boughs to cleave to and with whose juice and sap they be evermore recreated and nourished, so except these unpolished leaves of mine have some branch of nobility whereon to depend and cleave and with the vigorous nutriment of whose authorized commendation they may be continually fostered and refreshed, never will they grow to the world's good liking, but forthwith fade and die on the first hour of their birth. Your lordship is the large spreading branch of renown from whence these my idle leaves seek to derive their whole nourishing. It resteth you either scornfully shake them off, as worm-eaten and worthless, or in pity preserve them and cherish them for some little summer fruit you hope to find amongst them.

Your honor's in all humble service,
Tho. Nashe

The Induction to the Dapper Monsieur
Pages of the Court

Gallant squires, have amongst you. A mumchance[9] I mean not (for so I might chance come to short commons) but at *novus, nova, no-*

---

[9]*mumchance*: a game at dice similar to "hazard," from which "craps" is derived; one theory is that in mumchance the players had to observe strict silence. See Raleigh, *Shakespeare's England,* II, 470–471. However, in *A Notable Discovery,* above, pp. 408 ff., mumchance is a card game, not a dice game, and the players speak up whenever they like; but the verser and setter are so full of tricks that we probably should not trust them even to give the correct name of the "game" that they "teach" the poor cony.

vum,[10] which is, in English, news of the maker. A proper fellow page of yours, called Jack Wilton, by me commends him unto you, and hath bequeathed for wastepaper here amongst you certain pages of his misfortunes. In any case, keep them previously as a privy token of his good will towards you. If there be some better than other, he craves you would honor them in their death so much as to dry and kindle tobacco with them. For a need he permits you to wrap velvet pantofles in them also—so they be not woebegone at the heels, or weatherbeaten like a black head with gray hairs, or mangy at the toes like an ape about the mouth. But as you love good fellowship and ambs-ace,[11] rather turn them to stop mustard pots than the grocers should have one patch of them to wrap mace in—a strong, hot, costly spice it is which, above all things, he hates. To any use about meat or drink put them, too, and spare not, for they cannot do their country better service. Printers are mad whoresons; allow them some of them for napkins.

Just a little nearer to the matter and the purpose. Memorandum: every one of you, after the perusing of this pamphlet, is to provide him a case of poniards that, if you come in company with any man which shall dispraise it or speak against it, you may straight cry, "*Sic, respondeo!*" and give him the stockado.[12] It stands not with your honors, I assure ye, to have a gentleman and a page abused in his absence. Secondly, whereas you were wont to swear men on a pantofle to be true to your puissant order, you shall swear them on nothing but this chronicle of the king of pages henceforth. Thirdly, it shall be lawful for any whatsoever to play with false dice in a corner on the cover of this foresaid acts and monuments.[13] None of the

---

[10]*novum:* a pun: (1) the neuter Latin word for "news," and (2) a game at dice for five or six persons. Nashe loves puns, but there will be no space in this edition to call attention to more than a fraction of them.

[11]*ambs-ace:* double ace, the lowest throw at dice (also spelled "ames-ace"); possibly here the name of a game.

[12]*"Sic respondeo!"* . . . *stockado:* Thus I reply . . . the thrust (with a dagger).

[13]*acts and monuments:* probably a reference to John Foxe's *Acts and Monuments* (1563), a very serious book detailing the violent deaths of religious martyrs. *The Unfortunate Traveler* is hardly a monument to religious martyrs; in fact, by linking "false dice" and "acts and monuments," Nashe may be preparing us for the essentially sacrilegious nature of his story. He may also be suggesting that Foxe's book is false, or at least that it deserves to be made light of.

fraternity of the minorites[14] shall refuse it for a pawn in the times of famine and necessity. Every stationer's stall they pass by, whether by day or by night, they shall put off their hats, too, and make a low leg, in regard their grand printed capitano is there entombed. It shall be flat treason for any of this forementioned catalogue of the point trussers once to name him within forty foot of an alehouse. Marry, the tavern is honorable.

Many special grave articles more had I to give you in charge, which your wisdoms, waiting together at the bottom of the great chamber stairs, or sitting in a porch (your parliament house), may better consider of than I can deliver. Only let this suffice for a taste to the text and a bit to pull on a good wit with, as a rasher on the coals is to pull on a cup of wine. Heigh pass, come aloft! Every man of you take your places and hear Jack Wilton tell his own tale.

The Unfortunate Traveler
[1. *Turney and Turwin*]

About that time that the terror of the world and fever quartan of the French, Henry the Eighth, the only true subject of chronicles, advanced his standard against the two hundred and fifty towers of Turney and Turwin,[15] and had the emperor and all the nobility of Flanders, Holland, and Brabant as mercenary attendants on his fullsailed fortune, I, Jack Wilton, a gentleman at least, was a certain kind of an appendix or page, belonging, or appertaining in, or unto, the confines of the English court, where what my credit was a number of my creditors that I cozened can testify. *Caelum petimus stultitia:*[16] which of us all is not a sinner?

[14]*minorites:* probably a pun: (1) class of persons of low (minor) rank; (2) a certain order of friars. Foxe writes: "the order of the Minors or Minorite Friars descended from one Francis . . . . These Franciscans or begging friars [are all alike in their] superstition and hypocrisy" (*Acts and Monuments*, 1583 ed., I, 259: sig. Y4).

[15]*Turney and Turwin:* Nashe's spelling, in this instance also the popular pronunciation and spelling. "Turney" is an anglicization of "Tournai," a Belgian city some 50 miles southwest of Brussels. "Turwin" is "Thérouanne, a town a few miles south of St. Omer on the Lys River. In 1513 both were besieged and captured by Henry VIII in his war with France.

[16]*Caelum petimus stultitia:* In our folly we even aim at the sky. Jack shortens a line from Horace, *Odes*, I, 3.38. Four lines earlier Horace refers

Be it known to as many as will pay money enough to peruse my story that I followed the camp, or the court, or the court and the camp, when Turwin lost her maidenhead and opened her gates to more than Jane Trosse[17] did. There did I (soft, let me drink before I go any further) reign sole king of the cans and blackjacks, prince of the pigmies, county palatine of clean straw and provant,[18] and, to conclude, lord high regent of rashers of the coals and red-herring cobs.[19] *Paulô maiora canamus.*

Well, to the purpose. What stratagemical acts and monuments do you think an ingenious infant of my age might enact? You will say, "It were sufficient if he slur a die,[20] pawn his master to the utmost penny, and minister the oath on the pantofle artificially."

These are signs of good education, I must confess, and arguments of "In grace and virtue to proceed."[21] Oh, but *aliquid latet quod non patet*: there's a further path I must trace. Examples confirm. List, lordings, to my proceedings.

Whosoever is acquainted with the state of a camp understands that in it be many quarters, and yet not so many as on London Bridge. In those quarters are many companies. Much company, much knavery—as true as that old adage, "Much courtesy, much subtlety." Those companies, like a great deal of corn, do yield some chaff. The corn are cormorants; the chaff are good fellows which are quickly blown to nothing with bearing a light heart in a light purse. Amongst this chaff was I winnowing my wits to live merrily and, by my troth,

---

to Daedalus, and the implication is that man is arrogant and defiant. Unfortunately, there will not be space enough to translate all of Jack's Latin phrases. For the most part they are from Ovid, Horace, Virgil, Cicero, Terence, and Erasmus; sometimes Jack quotes from his source exactly, but usually he adapts it slightly to his own context. Occasionally he translates the Latin for us. In this case "which of us all is not a sinner?" is a question arising from an implied translation.

[17]*Jane Trosse:* apparently a well-known London prostitute.

[18]*provant:* provisions (for the troops and the horses).

[19]*cobs:* a pun—the lord high regent (the head or chief of something), and the heads ("cobs") of red herrings. Since the head of a fish is hardly a very important matter, the quotation from Virgil, *"Paulô maiora canamus"* (Let us sing of somewhat greater things), comes as an amusing transition.

[20]*slur a die:* throw a die without turning it over; a slang expression for cheating at dice.

[21]*"In grace and virtue to proceed:"* Probably Jack is mocking what he regards as a cant phrase often used by self-righteous Puritans.

so I did. The prince could but command men spend their blood in his service. I could make them spend all the money they had for my pleasure. But poverty in the end parts friends. Though I was prince of their purses, and exacted of my unthrift subjects as much liquid allegiance as any kaiser in the world could do, yet where it is not to be had the king must lose his right.[22] Want cannot be withstood. Men can do no more than they can do. What remained, then, but the fox's case must help when the lion's skin is out at the elbows?

There was a lord in the camp. Let him be a lord of misrule, if you will, for he kept a plain alehouse without welt or guard of any ivybush[23] and sold cider and cheese by pint and by pound to all that came (at that very name of cider I can but sigh, there is so much of it in Rhenish wine nowadays). Well, *tendit ad sydera virtus:*[24] there's great virtue belongs (I can tell you) to a cup of cider, and very good men have sold it, and at sea it is *aqua coelestis*. But that's neither here nor there. If it had no other patron but this peer of quart pots to authorize it, it were sufficient. This great lord, this worthy lord, this noble lord thought no scorn (Lord have mercy upon us) to have his great velvet breeches larded with the droppings of this dainty liquor; and yet he was an old servitor, a cavalier of an ancient house, as it might appear by the arms of his ancestry, drawn very amiably in chalk on the inside of his tent door.

He, and no other, was the man I chose out to damn with a lewd moneyless device; for coming to him on a day as he was counting his barrels, and setting the price in chalk on the head of every one of them, I did my duty very devoutly and told his aley[25] honor I had matters of some secrecy to impart unto him, if it pleased him to grant me private audience.

"With me, young Wilton," quoth he. "Marry, and shalt. Bring us a pint of cider of a fresh tap into The Three Cups here. Wash the pot."

---

[22]*where it is . . . lose his right:* a proverb (Tilley, N338).

[23]*without welt or guard of any ivybush:* The Elizabethans used "without welt or guard" to mean "without ornamentation" (literally, without a frill or fringe sewn on the edge of a garment). A sprig of ivy was the recognized sign or symbol of a tavern, but the "lord of misrule" does without that ornament. See note 16 in *Euphues*.

[24]*tendit ad sydera virtus:* virtue extends to the stars (with a pun on "cider").

[25]*aley:* The sense seems to be "ale" plus "y" (pertaining to ale).

So into a back room he led me, where, after he had spit on his finger and picked off two or three motes of his old moth-eaten velvet cap and sponged and wrung all the rheumatic drivel from his ill-favored goat's beard, he bade me declare my mind. And thereupon he drank to me on the same.

I up with a long circumstance—alias, a cunning shift of the seventeens[26]—and discoursed unto him what entire affection I had borne him time out of mind, partly for the high descent and lineage from whence he sprung and partly for the tender care and provident respect he had of poor soldiers, that, whereas the vastity of that place (which afforded them no indifferent supply of drink or of victuals) might humble them to some extremity and so weaken their hands, he vouchsafed in his own person to be a victualer to the camp (a rare example of magnificence and honorable courtesy) and diligently provided that, without far travel, every man might for his money have cider and cheese his bellyful.

Nor did he sell his cheese by the way only, or his cider by the great,[27] but abased himself with his own hands to take a shoemaker's knife, a homely instrument for such a high personage to touch, and cut it out equally like a true justiciary, in little pennyworths, that it would do a man good for to look upon. So likewise of his cider; the poor man might have his moderate draught of it (as there is a moderation in all things) as well for his doit or his dandiprat as the rich man for his half-souse or his denier.[28]

"Not so much," quoth I, "but this tapster's linen apron, which you wear before you to protect your apparel from the imperfections of the spigot, most amply bewrays your lowly mind. I speak it with tears. Too few such humble-spirited noblemen have we that will draw drink in linen aprons. Why, you are every child's fellow; any man that comes under the name of a soldier and a good fellow you will sit and

---

[26]*a cunning shift of the seventeens:* If the literal reference is to a dance step, then the sense is that Jack dazzles his listener with a nimble and complicated discourse.

[27]*by the way . . . by the great:* Both expressions mean roughly the same thing—by great amounts, in great quantities.

[28]*doit . . . denier:* The sense is that the doit (a Dutch coin) and the dandiprat (English) are practically worthless coins to the poor man, while the half-souse and the denier (both French) are practically worthless to the rich man. The implication is that the latter two coins are the more valuable, but actually all four coins are of small value (a couple of pennies, more or less).

bear company to the last pot. Yea, and you take in as good part the homely phrase of 'Mine host, here's to you,' as if one saluted you by all the titles of your barony. These considerations, I say, which the world suffers to slip by in the channel of carelessness, have moved me, in ardent zeal of your welfare, to forewarn you of some dangers that have beset you and your barrels."

At the name of "dangers" he started up and bounced with his fist on the board so hard that his tapster, overhearing him, cried, "Anon, anon, sir," by and by, and came and made a low leg and asked him what he lacked. He was ready to have stricken his tapster for interrupting him in attention of this his so much desired relation, but for fear of displeasing me he moderated his fury and, only sending him for the other fresh pint, willed him look to the bar and come when he is called with a devil's name. Well, at his earnest importunity, after I had moistened my lips to make my lie run glib to his journey's end, forward I went as followeth:

"It chanced me the other night, amongst other pages, to attend where the king with his lords and many chief leaders sat in counsel. There, amongst sundry serious matters that were debated, and intelligences from the enemy given up, it was privily informed (no villains to these privy informers) that you, even you that I now speak to, had—(Oh, would I had no tongue to tell the rest; by this drink it grieves me so I am not able to repeat it.)"

Now was my drunken lord ready to hang himself for the end of the full point, and over my neck he throws himself very lubberly and entreated me, as I was a proper young gentleman and ever looked for pleasure at his hands, soon to rid him out of this hell of suspense and resolve him of the rest. Then fell he on his knees, wrung his hands, and I think (on my conscience) wept out all the cider that he had drunk in a week before, to move me to have pity on him. He rose and put his rusty ring on my finger, gave me his greasy purse with that single money[29] that was in it, promised to make me his heir, and a thousand more favors, if I would expire the misery of his unspeakable tormenting uncertainty. I being by nature inclined to mercy (for, indeed, I knew two or three good wenches of that name) bade him harden his ears and not make his eyes abortive before their time, and he should have the inside of my breast turned outward, hear such a tale as would tempt the utmost strength of life to attend it and not die in the midst of it.

"Why," quoth I, "myself, that am but a poor childish well-willer of

[29]*single money:* small change.

yours, with the very thought that a man of your desert and state by a number of peasants and varlets should be so injuriously abused in huggermugger, have wept all my urine upward. The wheels under our city bridge carries not so much water over the city as my brain hath welled forth gushing streams of sorrow. I have wept so immoderately and lavishly that I thought verily my palate had been turned to the pissing conduit[30] in London. My eyes have been drunk, outrageously drunk, with giving but ordinary intercourse through their sea-circled islands to my distilling dreariment. What shall I say? That which malice hath said is the mere overthrow and murder of your days. Change not your color. None can slander a clear conscience to itself. Receive all your fraught of misfortune in at once.

"It is buzzed in the king's head that you are a secret friend to the enemy; and, under pretense of getting a license to furnish the camp with cider and such like provant, you have furnished the enemy, and in empty barrels sent letters of discovery and corn innumerable."

I might well have left here, for by this time his white liver had mixed itself with the white of his eye, and both were turned upwards, as if they had offered themselves a fair white for death to shoot at. The troth was, I was very loath mine host and I should part to heaven with dry lips, wherefore the best means that I could imagine to wake him out of his trance was to cry loud in his ear, "Hough, host, what's to pay? Will no man look to the reckoning here?" And in plain verity, it took expected effect; for with the noise he started and bustled, like a man that had been seared with fire out of his sleep, and ran hastily to his tapster and all-to-belabored him about the ears for letting gentlemen call so long and not look in to them. Presently he remembered himself, and had like to have fallen into his memento again but that I met him half ways and asked his lordship what he meant to slip his neck out of the collar[31] so suddenly and, being revived, strike his tapster so rashly.

"Oh," quoth he, "I am bought and sold for doing my country such

---

[30]*pissing conduit:* the popular term, in a robust age, for a certain conduit or water fountain, probably the one near the Royal Exchange; needless to say, it ran with a small but steady stream (which, however, would be a large stream in weeping, Jack implies).

[31]*slip his neck out of the collar:* a proverb (Tilley, N69). The sense here is mentally to withdraw; the usual figurative meaning is to shrink from a task, and the literal image is of a horse withdrawing his neck from the collar against which he pushes to draw a load. "Memento" refers to the trance mentioned earlier.

good service as I have done. They are afraid of me because my good deeds have brought me into such estimation with the commonalty. I see, I see it is not for the lamb to live with the wolf."

The world is well amended, thought I, with your cidership; such another forty years' nap together, as Epimenides had, would make you a perfect wise man.

"Answer me," quoth he. "My wise young Wilton, is it true that I am thus underhand dead and buried by these bad tongues?"

"Nay," quoth I, "you shall pardon me, for I have spoken too much already. No definitive sentence of death shall march out of my well meaning lips. They have but lately sucked milk, and shall they so suddenly change their food and seek after blood?"

"Oh, but," quoth he, "a man's friend is his friend. Fill the other pint, tapster. What said the king? Did he believe it when he heard it? I pray thee say. I swear to thee by my nobility, none in the world shall ever be made privy that I received any light of this matter from thee."

"That firm affiance," quoth I, "had I in you before, or else I would never have gone so far over the shoes to pluck you out of the mire. Not to make many words, since you will needs know, the king says flatly you are a miser and a snudge,[32] and he never hoped better of you."

"Nay then," quoth he, "questionless some planet that loves not cider hath conspired against me."

"Moreover, which is worse, the king hath vowed to give Turwin one hot breakfast, only with the bungs that he will pluck out of your barrels. I cannot stay at this time to report each circumstance that passed, but the only counsel that my long cherished kind inclination can possibly contrive is now in your old days to be liberal. Such victuals or provision as you have, presently distribute it frankly amongst poor soldiers. I would let them burst their bellies with cider, and bathe in it, before I would run into my prince's ill opinion for a whole sea of it. The hunter pursuing the beaver for his stones, he bites them off and leaves them behind for him to gather up, whereby he lives quiet.[33] If greedy hunters and hungry telltales pursue you,

[32]*snudge:* miser (though the sneering sound of the word gives it greater force than "miser"); a good example of the redundant-overlapping-emphatic aspect of Nashe's style.

[33]*The hunter ... lives quiet:* one of many references in *The Unfortunate Traveler* that may be traced back to Pliny's *Natural History,* this one to Book VIII, Chapter 47. In "he bites" and "he lives," the "he" refers to the beaver.

it is for a little pelf which you have. Cast it behind you. Neglect it. Let them have it, lest it breed a further inconvenience. Credit my advice. You shall find it prophetical, and thus I have discharged the part of a poor friend."

With some few like phrases of ceremony—"Your honor's suppliant," and so forth, and "Farewell, my good youth; I thank thee and will remember thee"—we parted.

But the next day I think we had a dole of cider—cider in bowls, in scuppets,[34] in helmets; and, to conclude, if a man would have filled his boots full, there he might have had it. Provant thrust itself into poor soldiers' pockets whether they would or no. We made five peals of shot into the town together, of nothing but spigots and faucets of discarded empty barrels. Every underfoot soldier had a distenanted tun, as Diogenes had his tub to sleep in. I myself got as many confiscated tapster's aprons as made me a tent as big as any ordinary commander's in the field.

But, in conclusion, my well-beloved baron of double beer got him humbly on his marybones[35] to the king and complained he was old and stricken in years and had ne'er an heir to cast at a dog; wherefore, if it might please his majesty to take his lands into his hands and allow him some reasonable pension to live on, he should be marvelous well pleased. As for the wars, he was weary of them; and yet as long as his highness should venture his own person, he would not flinch a foot but make his withered body a buckler to bear off any blow that should be advanced against him.

The king, marveling at this strange alteration of his great merchant of cider, for so he would often pleasantly term him, with a little further talk bolted out the whole complotment. Then was I pitifully whipped for my holiday lie, although they made themselves merry with it many a fair winter's evening after.

Yet notwithstanding his good ass-headed honor, mine host persevered in his former simple request to the king to accept of the surrender of his lands and allow him a beadsmanry or out-brothership of brachet;[36] which at length, through his vehement instancy, took

---

[34]*scuppets:* spades, shovels.

[35]*marybones:* an obsolete spelling (and popular pronunciation) of "marrowbones," a humorous expression for the knees.

[36]*brachet:* "Brachet" or "brach" literally means "bitch-hound," but here it is a general term of abuse made all the more abusive by the contrast with "beadsmanry" (the praying for another's soul). The ironic juxtaposition is similar to "good ass-headed honor" at the beginning of the sentence.

effect. And the king jestingly said, since he would needs have it so, he would distrain on part of his land for impost of cider, which he was behindhand with him and never paid.

This was one of my famous achievements, insomuch as I never light upon the like famous fool, but I have done a thousand better jests if they had been booked in order as they were begotten.[37] It is pity posterity should be deprived of such precious records, and yet there is no remedy. And yet there is, too; for when all fails, welfare[38] a good memory. Gentle readers (look you be gentle now since I have called you so), as freely as my knavery was mine own, it shall be yours to use in the way of honesty.

Even in this expedition of Turwin (for the king stood not long thrumming of buttons there) it happened me fall out (I would it had fallen out otherwise for his sake) with an ugly mechanical captain. You must think in an army where truncheons are in their state house, it is a flat stab once to name a captain without cap in hand. Well, suppose he was a captain and had ne'er a good cap of his own, but I was fain to lend him one of my lord's cast velvet caps, and a weather-beaten feather, wherewith he threatened his soldiers afar off, as Jupiter is said, with the shaking of his hair, to make heaven and earth to quake. Suppose, out of the parings of a pair of false dice, I appareled both him and myself many a time and oft. And surely, not to slander the devil, if any man ever deserved the golden dice the king of the Parthians sent to Demetrius, it was I; I had the right vein of sucking up a die twixt the dints of my fingers. Not a crevice in my hand but could swallow a quater trey[39] for a need. In the line of life many a dead lift did there lurk, but it was nothing towards the maintenance of a family.

This Monsieur Capitano eat up the cream of my earnings; and *crede mihi, res est ingeniosa dare:* any man is a fine fellow as long as he hath any money in his purse. That money is like the marigold, which opens and shuts with the sun. If fortune smileth, or one be in favor, it floweth; if the evening of age comes on, or he falleth into

[37]*This was one . . . were begotten:* The shift from present to past tense is partly responsible for obscuring the exact meaning, which may perhaps be suggested by the following words in brackets: "This was [only] one of my [many] famous achievements . . . but [I reflect that] I have done . . . ."

[38]*welfare:* a verb, literally meaning "fare well"; the sense here is "may it go well with."

[39]*quater trey:* die (singular of dice); since the "quater" or "cater" (four) and the "trey" (three) are on opposite sides of a die, they include the whole die between them. For another use of "cater trey," see *A Notable Discovery,* note 27.

disgrace, it fadeth and is not to be found. I was my craft's master, though I was but young, and could as soon decline *nominativo: hic asinus* as a greater clerk; wherefore I thought it not convenient my soldado should have my purse any longer for his drum to play upon. But I would give him Jack Drum's entertainment,[40] and send him packing.

This was my plot: I knew a piece of service of intelligence, which was presently to be done, that required a man with all his five senses to effect it, and would overthrow any fool that should undertake it. To this service did I animate and egg my foresaid costs and charges, alias Senior Velvet-Cap, whose head was not encumbered with too much forecast. And coming to him in his cabin about dinner time, where I found him very devoutly paring of his nails for want of other repast, I entertained him with this solemn oration:

"Captain, you perceive how near both of us are driven. The dice of late are grown as melancholy as a dog. High men and low men both prosper alike; langrets, fulhams,[41] and all the whole fellowship of them will not afford a man his dinner. Some other means must be invented to prevent imminent extremity. My state, you are not ignorant, depends on trencher service;[42] your advancement must be derived from the valor of your arm. In the delays of siege, desert hardly gets a day of hearing. 'Tis gowns must direct and guns enact all the wars that is to be made against walls. Resteth no way for you to climb suddenly, but by doing some strange stratagem that the like hath not been heard of heretofore; and fitly at this instant occasion is ministered.

"There is a feat the king is desirous to have wrought on some great man of the enemy's side. Marry, it requireth not so much resolution as discretion to bring it to pass; and yet resolution enough shall be shown in it too, being so full of hazardous jeopardy as it is. Hark in your

[40]*Jack Drum's entertainment:* "Entertainment" is ironic, for it consists of being thrown out as an unwelcome guest; Deloney dramatizes this common Elizabethan expression in the person of Tom Drum (Chapter VIII, *The Gentle Craft, Part II*).

[41]*High men, low men . . . langrets, fulhams:* "High men" and "low men" are dice so loaded that high or low numbers always turn up; "langret" and "fulham" (or "fullam") are still other terms for loaded dice—a "high fulham" meaning dice loaded in such a way that a high number always turned up, and "low fulham" designating a throw of 1, 2, or 3 on each die.

[42]*trencher service:* The sense probably is "food supply" (from "trencher," the flat piece of wood, presumably a little concave, on which food was served).

ear; thus it is. Without more drumbling or pausing, if you will undertake it and work it through-stitch[43] (as you may ere the king hath determined which way to go about it), I warrant you are made while you live; you need not care which way your staff falls.[44] If it prove not so, then cut off my head."

Oh, my auditors, had you seen him how he stretched out his limbs, scratched his scabbed elbows at this speech, how he set his cap over his eyebrows like a politician, and then folded his arms one in another, and nodded with the head, as who should say, "Let the French beware, for they shall find me a devil." If, I say, you had seen but half the actions that he used of shrucking up his shoulders, smiling scornfully, playing with his fingers on his buttons, and biting the lip, you would have laughed your face and your knees together. The iron being hot, I thought to lay on load, for in any case I would not have his humor cool. As before I laid open unto him the brief sum of the service, so now I began to urge the honorableness of it, and what a rare thing it was to be a right politician, how much esteemed of kings and princes, and how divers of mean parentage have come to be monarchs by it.

Then I discoursed of the qualities and properties of him in every respect—how, like the wolf, he must draw the breath from a man before he be seen; how, like a hare, he must sleep with his eyes open; how, as the eagle in flying casts dust in the eyes of crows and other fowls for to blind them, so he must cast dust in the eyes of his enemies, delude their sight by one means or other, that they dive not into his subtleties; how he must be familiar with all and trust none, drink, carouse, and lecher with him out of whom he hopes to wring any matter, swear and forswear rather than be suspected; and, in a word, have the art of dissembling at his fingers' ends as perfect as any courtier.

"Perhaps," quoth I, "you may have some few greasy cavaliers that will seek to dissuade you from it; and they will not stick to stand on their three halfpenny honor, swearing and staring that a man were better be an hangman than an intelligencer, and call him a sneaking eavesdropper, a scraping hedgecreeper, and a piperly pickthank. But you must not be discouraged by their talk, for the most part of those beggarly contemners of wit are huge burly-boned butchers like Ajax—

[43]*through-stitch:* thoroughly; literally, in sewing, "through-stitch" meant to stitch all the way through the material.

[44]*which way your staff falls:* a proverb (Tilley, W142); the sense is "no matter what happens."

good for nothing but to strike right down blows on a wedge with a cleaving beetle, or stand hammering all day upon bars of iron.

"The whelps of a bear never grow but sleeping; and these bearwards, having big limbs, shall be preferred though they do nothing. You have read stories (I'll be sworn he never looked in book in his life) how many of the Roman worthies were there that have gone as spies into their enemy's camp? Ulysses, Nestor, Diomed went as spies together in the night into the tents of Rhaesus and intercepted Dolon, the spy of the Trojans. Never any discredited the trade of intelligencers but Judas, and he hanged himself. Danger will put wit into any man. Architas made a wooden dove to fly, by which proportion I see no reason that the veriest block in the world should despair of anything.

"Though nature be contrary inclined, it may be altered. Yet usually those whom she denies her ordinary gifts in one thing, she doubles them in another. That which the ass wants in wit, he hath in honesty. Who ever saw him kick or winch, or use any jade's tricks? Though he live an hundred years, you shall never hear that be breaks pasture. Amongst men, he that hath not a good wit likely hath a good iron memory; and he that hath neither of both hath some bones to carry burthens. Blind men have better noses than other men. The bull's horns serve him as well as hands to fight withal. The lion's paws are as good to him as a pole-ax to knock down any that resists him. So the boar's tusks serve him in better stead than a sword and buckler. What need the snail care for eyes when he feels the way with his two horns as well as if he were as sharp sighted as a decipherer? There is a fish that, having no wings, supports herself in the air with her fins.

"Admit that you had neither wit nor capacity, as sure, in my judgment, there is none equal unto you in idiotism. Yet if you have simplicity and secrecy, serpents themselves will think you a serpent. For what serpent is there but hideth his sting? And yet whatsoever be wanting, a good plausible, alluring tongue in such a man of employment can hardly be spared. Which as the forenamed serpent, with his winding tail fetcheth in those that come near him; so with a ravishing tale, it gathers all men's hearts unto him. Which if he have not, let him never look to engender by the mouth, as ravens and doves do—that is, mount or be great by undermining.

"Sir, I am ascertained that all these imperfections I speak of in you have their natural resiance.[45] I see in your face that you were born, with the swallow, to feed flying, to get much treasure and honor by

[45]*resiance:* abode, residence.

travel. None so fit as you for so important an enterprise; our vulgar reputed politicians are but flies swimming on the stream of subtlety superficially. In comparison of your singularity their blind narrow eyes cannot pierce into the profundity of hypocrisy. You alone, with Palamed, can pry into Ulysses' mad counterfeiting; you can discern Achilles from a chambermaid, though he be decked with his spindle and distaff. As Jove dining with Lycaon could not be beguiled with human flesh dressed like meat, so no human brain may go beyond you, none beguile you. You gull all. All fear you, love you, stoop to you. Therefore, good sir, be ruled by me; stoop your fortune so low as to bequeath yourself wholly to this business."

This silver-sounding tale made such sugared harmony in his ears that with the sweet meditation what a more than miraculous politician he should be, and what kingly promotion should come tumbling on him thereby, he could have found in his heart to have packed up his pipes and to have gone to heaven without a bait. Yea, he was more inflamed and ravished with it than a young man called Taurimontanus was with the Phrygian melody, who was so incensed and fired therewith that he would needs run presently upon it and set a courtesan's house on fire that had angered him.

No remedy there was but I must help to furnish him with money. I did so, as who will not make his enemy a bridge of gold to fly by? Very earnestly he conjured me to make no man living privy to his departure in regard of his place and charge, and on his honor assured me his return should be very short and successful. (Aye, aye, shorter by the neck, thought I. In the meantime, let this be thy posy: I live in hope to 'scape the rope.)

Gone he is. God send him good shipping to Wapping; and by this time, if you will, let him be a pitiful poor fellow and undone forever. For mine own part, if he had been mine own brother, I could have done no more for him than I did. For straight after his back was turned I went in all love and kindness to the marshal general of the field and certified him that such a man was lately fled to the enemy, and got his place begged for another immediately. What became of him after, you shall hear. To the enemy he went and offered his service. Railing egregiously on the king of England, he swore, as he was a gentleman and a soldier, he would be revenged on him; and let but the king of France follow his counsel, he would drive him from Turwin walls yet ere three[46] days to an end. All these were good humors, but the tragedy followeth.

[46]*three:* an emendation of the second edition; in the first edition the figure was "ten," thus conflicting with "from the siege of Turwin in three

The French king, hearing of such a prating fellow that was come, was desirous to see him; but yet he feared treason, wherefore he willed one of his minions to take upon him his person and he would stand by as a private man whilst he was examined. Why should I use any idle delays? In was Captain Gog's Wounds[47] brought, after he was thoroughly searched. Not a louse in his doublet was let pass but was asked, "*Quevela?*"[48] and charged to stand in the king's name. The molds of his buttons they turned out, to see if they were not bullets covered over with thread. The codpiece in his devil's breeches (for they were then in fashion) they said plainly was a case for a pistol.[49] If he had had ever a hobnail in his shoes it had hanged him, and he should never have known who had harmed him. But as luck was, he had not a mite of any metal about him. He took part with none of the four ages—neither the golden age, the silver age, the brazen, nor the iron age. Only his purse was aged in emptiness, and I think verily a Puritan, for it kept itself from any pollution of crosses.[50] Standing before the supposed king, he was asked what he was and wherefore he came.

To the which, in a glorious bragging humor, he answered that he was a gentleman, a captain commander, a chief leader that came away from the king of England upon discontentment. Questioned particular of the cause of his discontentment, he had not a word to bless himself with; yet fain he would have patched out a poltfoot tale.[51] But (God he knows) it had not one true leg to stand on. Then began he to smell on the villain so rammishly that none there but was ready to rent him in pieces; yet the minion king kept in his choler and

---

days," two paragraphs below. It seems impossible to say whether Nashe meant one figure or the other, but it is unlikely that the typesetter made the change: he probably would not have seen the difficulty until he came to the second figure, and then he would have changed "three" to "ten."

[47]*Gog's Wounds:* God's Wounds (a play on a common oath, "by Gog's wounds")—an apt name or alias, in view of the swearing to the French king, above.

[48]*Quevela?:* Who goes there?

[49]*codpiece . . . pistol:* "Devil's" breeches were unusually close-fitting. The "codpiece" was a covering for the opening in the front of a man's breeches; it served also as a pocket to carry various and assorted items—though not usually an item as big as a pistol (which may be a sexual pun).

[50]*Puritan . . . crosses:* one of several very unsympathetic references to Puritans. Jack is accusing Puritans not only of reacting against the cross as a religious symbol, but also of having empty purses (the latter sense from "cross," a coin with the figure of the cross stamped on it).

[51]*poltfoot tale:* lame tale (literally, "clubfoot tale").

propounded unto him further. What of the king of England's secrets, so advantageable, he was privy to, as might remove him from the siege of Turwin in three days? He said divers, divers matters, which asked longer conference, but in good honesty they were lies, which he had not yet stamped. Hereat the true king stepped forth and commanded to lay hands on the losel and that he should be tortured to confess the truth, for he was a spy and nothing else.

He no sooner saw the wheel and the torments set before him, but he cried out like a rascal and said he was a poor captain in the English camp, suborned by one Jack Wilton, a nobleman's page, and no other, to come and kill the French king in a bravery and return, and that he had no other intention in the world.

This confession could not choose but move them all to laughter, in that he made it as light a matter to kill their king and come back as to go to Islington and eat a mess of cream[52] and come home again. Nay, and besides, he protested that he had no other intention, as if that were not enough to hang him.

Adam never fell till God made fools. All this could not keep his joints from ransacking on the wheel, for they vowed either to make him a confessor or a martyr in a trice. When still he sung all one song, they told the king he was a fool and some shrewd head had knavishly wrought on him; wherefore it should stand with his honor to whip him out of the camp and send him home. That persuasion took place, and soundly was he lashed out of their liberties and sent home by a herald with this message—that so the king his master hoped to whip home all the English fools very shortly. Answer was returned that that "shortly" was a long lie, and they were shrewd fools that should drive the Frenchman out of his kingdom and make him glad, with Corinthian Dionysius, to play the schoolmaster.

The herald being dismissed, our afflicted intelligencer was called *coram nobis*. How he sped, judge you; but something he was adjudged to.[53] The sparrow for his lechery liveth but a year; he for his treachery was turned on the toe.[54] *Plura dolor prohibet.*

---

[52]*Islington ... mess of cream:* Islington, a suburb north of London, was popular for an outing; a "mess" was a bowl or serving, and a "cream" probably was any sweet or fancy concoction that had cream in it.

[53]*How he sped ... but something he was adjudged to:* The sense is "How he fared ... but he was sentenced to something."

[54]*turned on the toe:* McKerrow (IV, 263) suggests that the sense may be "flogged." We expect the English to inflict a punishment similar to the one

Here let me triumph a while, and ruminate a line or two on the excellence of my wit; but I will not breathe neither till I have disfraughted[55] all my knavery.

Another Switzer captain, that was far gone for want of the wench, I led astray most notoriously; for he being a monstrous unthrift of battle-axes (as one that cared not in his anger to bid, "Fly out scuttles!"[56] to five score of them) and a notable emboweler of quart pots, I came disguised unto him in the form of a half-a-crown wench, my gown and attire according to the custom then in request. Iwis, I had my courtesies in cue[57]—or in quart pot, rather—for they dived into the very entrails of the dust, and I simpered with my countenance like a porridge pot on the fire when it first begins to seethe. The sobriety of the circumstance is that after he had courted me and all, and given me the earnest penny of impiety, some six crowns at the least for an antepast[58] to iniquity, I feigned an impregnable excuse to be gone and never came at him after.

Yet left I not here, but committed a little more scutchery. A company of coistrel clerks (who were in hand with Satan, and not of any soldier's collar nor his hatband) pinched a number of good minds to Godward of their provant. They would not let a dram of dead pay

---

the captain had received from the French. But another sense is more likely —"to turn off the ladder in hanging" (OED, under "toe"). If that is the sense, the parallelism with the sparrow's death is to be taken literally; and *Plura dolor prohibit* (grief prevents my saying more) means that Jack has a reason for grief even if he is only pretending it. (Incidentally, the part about the sparrow's lust is proverbial; see Tilley, S715.)

[55]*disfraughted:* unloaded.

[56]*fly out scuttles:* The word "scuttle" had several meanings—a trencher or plate on which one ate, a basket, and a small hatchway or porthole in a ship. Jack's exact sense is not clear, though we may be sure that it is ironic. Perhaps the "Switzer captain" sends plates sailing through the air at the enemy (instead of standing man-to-man with his battle-ax); or perhaps he gives orders to flee out the portholes.

[57]*courtesies in cue:* Jack intends a pun on "cue"; one sense is correct timing (as in the theater), and the other sense is quart pot (abbreviation "q."). "Courtesies," the reading of the first edition, has been retained because the intended meaning seems to be larger than "curtseys," the emendation of the second edition (though the change in the second edition may have been intended only as a variant in spelling).

[58]*antepast:* whetting of the appetite (from the Italian, *antipasto*).

overslip them.[59] They would not lend a groat of the week to come to him that had spent his money before this week was done. They outfaced the greatest and most magnanimous servitors in their sincere and finigraphical clean shirts and cuffs. A louse that was any gentleman's companion they thought scorn of; their ne'er-bitten[60] beards must, in a devil's name, be dewed every day with rose water; hogs could have ne'er a hair on their backs, for making them rubbing brushes to rouse their crab lice. They would in no wise permit that the motes in the sunbeams should be full-mouthed beholders of their clean, finified apparel. Their shoes shined as bright as a slickstone; their hands troubled and soiled[61] more water with washing than the camel doth, that ne'er drinks till the whole stream be troubled. Summarily, never any were so fantastical the one half as they. My masters, you may conceive of me what you list, but I think confidently I was ordained God's scourge from above for their dainty finicality.

The hour of their punishment could no longer be prorogued, but vengeance must have at them at all a-ventures. So it was that the most of these above-named goosequill braggadocios were mere cowards and cravens, and durst not so much as throw a penful of ink into the enemy's face, if proof were made; wherefore on the experience of their pusillanimity I thought to raise the foundation of my roguery. What did I now but one day made a false alarm, in the quarter where they lay, to try how they would stand to their tackling; and with a pitiful outcry warned them to fly, for there was treason afoot, they were environed and beset.

Upon the first watchword of treason that was given, I think they betook them to their heels very stoutly, left their pen and inkhorns and papers behind them for spoil, resigned their desks, with the money that was in them to the mercy of the vanquisher—and, in fine, left me and my fellows, their fool-catchers, lords of the field. How we dealt with them, their disburdened desks can best tell; but

[59]*coistrel . . . pinched a number of good minds to Godward of their provant . . . would not let a dram of dead pay overslip them:* rascally . . . murdered a number of soldiers and took their food and valuables . . . would not miss the opportunity of collecting all the dead soldiers' pay.

[60]*ne'er-bitten:* The word "nere" appears three times within a few lines in the first edition; all three times the sense probably is "never," and not "near." If "never" is correct, "ne'er-bitten" probably means "never-shaved" (though since the clerks are finicky, their beards may be carefully trimmed).

[61]*soiled:* McKerrow (II, 226) accepts "foiled," the emendation of the second edition; but "soiled," the reading of the Huntington copy of the first edition, makes better sense.

this I am assured: we fared the better for it a fortnight of fasting days after.

[2. *England*]

I must not place a volume in the precincts of a pamphlet. Sleep an hour or two, and dream that Turney and Turwin is won, that the king is shipped again into England, and that I am close at hard meat[62] at Windsor or at Hampton Court. What, will you in your indifferent opinions allow me for my travel no more seigniory over the pages than I had before? Yes, whether you will part with so much probable friendly suppose or no, I'll have it in spite of your hearts.

For your instruction and Godly consolation, be informed that at that time I was no common squire, no undertrodden torchbearer. I had my feather in my cap as big as a flag in the foretop; my French doublet gelt in the belly as though (like a pig ready to be spitted) all my guts had been plucked out; a pair of side-paned hose[63] that hung down like two scales filled with Holland cheeses; my long stock that sat close to my dock[64] and smothered not a scab or a lecherous hairy sinew on the calf of my leg; my rapier pendant like a round stick fastened in the tacklings for skippers the better to climb by; my cape cloak of black cloth overspreading my back like a thornback or an elephant's ear (that hangs on his shoulders like a country house-wife's banskin, which she thirleth her spindle on); and, in consummation of my curiosity, my hands without gloves, all a-more French, and a black budge[65] edging of a beard on the upper lip, and the like sable aglet of excrements in the first rising of the angle of my chin.

I was the first that brought in the order of passing into the court, which I derived from the common word *"qui passa?"* and the herald's phrase of arms, "passant"—thinking, in sincerity, he was not a gentleman nor his arms current who was not first passed by the pages. If any prentice or other came into the court that was not a gentleman, I thought it was an indignity to the preeminence of the court to include such a one, and could not be salved except we gave him arms passant to make him a gentleman. Besides, in Spain, none compass any far way but he must be examined what he is and give three pence for his pass.

---

[62]*close at hard meat:* in close confinement.
[63]*side-paned hose:* possibly hose with a strip or section down each side made of a different material or color.
[64]*stock . . . dock:* hose . . . buttocks.
[65]*banskin . . . budge:* leather apron . . . fur.

In which regard it was considered of by the common table of the cupbearers what a perilsome thing it was to let any stranger or outdweller approach so near the precincts of the prince as the great chamber without examining what he was, and giving him his pass; whereupon we established the like order, but took no money of them as they did. Only for a sign that he had not passed our hands unexamined, we set a red mark on either of his ears, and so let him walk as authentical.

I must not discover what ungodly dealing we had with the blackjacks, or how oft I was crowned king of the drunkards with a court cup. Let me quietly descend to the waning of my youthful days and tell a little of the sweating sickness that made me in a cold sweat take my heels and run out of England.

[3. *Milan and Münster*]

This sweating sickness was a disease that a man then might catch and never go to a hothouse.[66] Many masters desire to have such servants as would work till they sweat again, but in those days he that sweat never wrought again. That Scripture then was not thought so necessary which says, "Earn thy living with the sweat of thy brows," for then they earned their dying with the sweat of their brows. It was enough if a fat man did but truss his points[67] to turn him over the perch.[68] Mother Cornelius' tub[69]—why, it was like hell; he that came into it never came out of it. Cooks that stand continual-

---

[66]*hothouse:* brothel.

[67]*truss his points:* tie his laces; probably he is attaching his hose to his doublet.

[68]*turn him over the perch:* push him over the edge (kill him).

[69]*Mother Cornelius' tub:* As Jack has pointed out in the first sentence of the paragraph, the sweating sickness and syphilis are two separate diseases; but the victims of both diseases were treated by soaking in a tub, which apparently was supposed to sweat out the impurities. "Mother Cornelius" seems to have been a kind of generic name for women who operated amateur "clinics" for the treatment of syphilis. For an account of several epidemics of the often fatal sweating sickness in 1485, 1508, 1517, 1528, 1529, and 1551, see Charles Creighton, *A History of Epidemics in Britain* (Cambridge, 1891), Vol. I, Chapter V. It is possible that "Cornelius" is related to "cornelian" (also spelled "cornelius"), a semitransparent quartz of a deep, dull red color. According to a contemporary description (given in Creighton, I, 241), one of the symptoms of the virus infection known as the sweating sickness was a "redness of the face and of all the body."

ly basting their faces before the fire were now all cashiered with this sweat into kitchen stuff;[70] their hall[71] fell into the king's hands for want of one of the trade to uphold it. Feltmakers and furriers, what the one with the hot steam of their wool new taken out of the pan, and the other with the contagious heat of their slaughter budge[72] and cony skins, died more thick than of the pestilence. I have seen an old woman at that season, having three chins, wipe them all away one after another, as they melted to water, and left herself nothing of a mouth but an upper chap. Look how in May or the heat of summer we lay butter in water for fear it should melt away; so then were men fain to wet their clothes in water, as dyers do, and hide themselves in wells from the heat of the sun.

Then happy was he that was an ass, for nothing will kill an ass but cold; and none died but with extreme heat. The fishes called sea stars, that burn one another by excessive heat, were not so contagious as one man that had the sweat was to another. Masons paid nothing for hair to mix their lime, nor glovers to stuff their balls with, for then they had it for nothing. It dropped off men's heads and beards faster than any barber could shave it. Oh, if hair breeches had then been in fashion, what a fine world had it been for tailors! And so it was a fine world for tailors nevertheless, for he that could make a garment slightest and thinnest carried it away. Cutters, I can tell you, then stood upon it to have their trade one of the twelve companies;[73] for who was it then that would not have his doublet cut to the skin, and his shirt cut into it too, to make it more cold. It was as

[70]*kitchen stuff:* drippings (of fat, from cooking meat).

[71]*their hall:* Having their own trade guild, the cooks also had a building on Aldersgate Street where they met regularly.

[72]*slaughter budge:* "Budge" was fur from the lamb, but what "slaughter" adds is not clear; McKerrow (IV, 265) suggests fur obtained from slaughter houses.

[73]*twelve companies:* What Jack anachronistically refers to is the gradual emergence of the Twelve Great Livery Companies; the process was not complete until the middle of the sixteenth century, though for some time there had been a distinction between lesser and greater guilds (or "companies" as they came to be called). The Twelve Great Companies were the Clothmakers, Drapers, Fishmongers, Goldsmiths, Grocers, Haberdashers, Ironmongers, Mercers, Merchant Tailors, Salters, Skinners, and Vintners. The Cutlers ("cutters," as Jack calls them) never made the grade; they were incorporated in the reign of Henry V but remained a lesser company. (See George Unwin, *Gilds and Companies of London,* 4th ed. [New York, 1963], pp. 160–1).

much as a man's life was worth once to name a frieze jerkin;[74] it was treason for a fat, gross man to come within five miles of the court. I heard where they died up all in one family, and not a mother's child escaped. Insomuch as they had but an Irish rug locked up in a press, and not laid upon any bed neither; if those that were sick of this malady slept on it, they never waked more.

Physicians with their simples in this case were simple fellows and knew not which way to bestir them. Galen might go shoe the gander[75] for any good he could do; his secretaries had so long called him divine that now he had lost all his virtue upon earth. Hippocrates might well help almanac makers, but here he had not a word to say. A man might sooner catch the sweat with plodding over him to no end than cure the sweat with any of his impotent principles. Paracelsus, with his spirit of the buttery and his spirits of minerals,[76] could not so much as say "God amend him" to the matter. *Plus erat in artifice quam arte:* there was more infection in the physician himself than his art could cure.

This mortality first began amongst old men, for they, taking a pride to have their breasts loose basted with tedious beards, kept their houses so hot with these hairy excrements that not so much but their very walls sweat out saltpeter with the smothering perplexity. Nay a number of them had marvelous hot breaths which, sticking in the briers of their bushy beards, could not choose but (as close air long imprisoned) engender corruption. Wiser was our brother Banks of these latter days, who made his juggling horse a cut, for fear if at any time he should foist, the stink sticking in his thick bushy tail might be noisome to his auditors.[77] Should I tell you how many pursevants[78] with red noses, and sergeants with precious faces,

---

[74]*once to name a frieze jerkin:* to mention (say aloud) once the term, "frieze jerkin" (which was a short jacket made of coarse woolen cloth). Note the pun on "freeze." The sentence following contains several problems: whether "dide" in the original means "died" or "did"; the sense of "Irish rug . . . press"; and whether "it" in "slept on it" refers to "Irish rug," "press," "bed," or "malady."

[75]*shoe the gander:* an idiomatic expression meaning "to attempt an impossibility." Our word "shoe" is always spelled "shoo" in the first edition; but here there may be a pun—"shoe" and "shoo" (scare away).

[76]*spirit of the buttery . . . spirits of minerals:* Possibly both expressions mean what we mean by "intoxicating liquor."

[77]*Banks . . . horse a cut . . . auditors:* Banks (fl. 1588–1637) was a famous showman whose horse "Morocco" became something of a legend for dancing and doing tricks. Obviously, the reason Jack gives was hardly the real reason why Banks had his horse's tail cut short.

[78]*pursevants:* pursuivants, attendants.

shrunk away in this sweat, you would not believe me. Even as the salamander with his very sight blasteth apples on the trees, so a pursevant or a sergeant at this present, with the very reflex of his fiery facias,[79] was able to spoil a man afar off. In some places of the world there is no shadow of the sun; *diebus illis* if it had been so in England, the generation of Brut had died all and some. To knit up this description in a purse-net,[80] so fervent and scorching was the burning air which enclosed them that the most blessed man then alive would have thought that God had done fairly by him if he had turned him to a goat, for goats take breath not at the mouth or nose only but at the ears also.

Take breath how they would, I vowed to tarry no longer amongst them. As at Turwin I was a demisoldier in jest, so now I became a martialist in earnest. Oversea with my implements I got me, where, hearing the king of France and the Switzers were together by the ears, I made towards them as fast as I could, thinking to thrust myself into that faction that was strongest. It was my good luck or my ill, I know not which, to come just to the fighting of the battle where I saw a wonderful spectacle of bloodshed on both sides—here the unwieldy Switzers wallowing in their gore like an ox in his dung, there the sprightly French sprawling and turning on the stained grass like a roach new taken out of the stream. All the ground was strewed as thick with battle-axes as the carpenter's yard with chips. The plain appeared like a quagmire, overspread as it was with trampled dead bodies. In one place might you behold a heap of dead murdered men overwhelmed with a falling steed instead of a tombstone; in another place a bundle of bodies fettered together in their own bowels. And as the tyrant Roman emperors used to tie condemned living caitiffs face to face to dead corpses, so were the half living here mixed with squeezed carcasses long putrified. Any man might give arms that was an actor in that battle, for there were more arms and legs scattered in the field that day than will be gathered up till doomsday. The French king himself in this conflict was much distressed—the brains of his own men sprinkled in his face, thrice was his courser slain under him, and thrice was he struck on the breast with a spear. But in the end, by the help of the Venetians, the Helvetians or Switzers

[79]*fiery facias:* a pun—"fiery faces" and *"fieri-facias"* (the latter a writ used by the sheriff to command the defendant to sell enough goods to pay a debt). Note the look backward to "precious faces"; "precious" is to suggest that a sergeant's fiery face, from drinking, resembles a precious stone.

[80]*purse-net:* a bag-shaped net, drawn together with a cord, used to catch rabbits or fish. We are to notice the play on "pursevant."

were subdued, and he crowned victor, a peace concluded, and the city of Milan surrendered unto him as a pledge of reconciliation.[81]

That war thus blown over and the several bands dissolved, like a crow that still follows aloof where there is carrion, I flew me over to Münster in Germany, which an Anabaptistical brother named John Leyden kept at that instant against the emperor and the Duke of Saxony.[82] Here I was in good hope to set up my staff for some reasonable time, deeming that no city would drive it to a siege except they were able to hold out. And prettily well had these Münsterians held out, for they kept the emperor and the Duke of Saxony sound play[83] for the space of a year, and longer would have done but that Dame Famine came amongst them. Whereupon they were forced by messengers to agree upon a day of fight, when according to their Anabaptistical error they might be all new christened in their own blood.

That day come, flourishing entered John Leyden the botcher into the field with a scarf made of lists,[84] like a bow case; a cross on his breast like a thread bottom;[85] a round, twilted[86] tailor's cushion buckled like a tankard bearer's device to his shoulders for a target, the pike whereof was a pack needle;[87] a tough prentice's club for his

[81]*The French king ... Milan ... reconciliation:* The historical battle for Milan between King Francis I of France and the Swiss occurred in 1515.

[82]*John Leyden ... emperor ... Duke of Saxony:* Jan Beuckelssen, popularly known as Jan of Leyden, and other Anabaptists gained control of Münster in 1534, but Emperor Charles V and various other German leaders, including the Duke of Saxony, overthrew the insurrectionists in 1535 and restored Münster to Catholicism.

[83]*kept ... sound play:* an idiom meaning "kept well occupied."

[84]*lists:* the edges of some material, like broadcloth; these edges were so woven that they were unusually strong and did not come unraveled easily. John's bow case and scarf (the latter worn diagonally from shoulder to opposite hip, and designed so that he could carry things on it) were made of such material.

[85]*a cross on his breast like a thread bottom:* A "thread bottom" was a reel on which thread was wound; presumably the bottom itself was cross-shaped, or else the thread was wound on it in such a shape. At any rate, Jan of Leyden apparently has something cross-shaped (sewn?) on his breast.

[86]*twilted:* quilted; the padding of the cushion is held in place by sewing, as in a quilt.

[87]*target ... pack needle:* shield ... large needle used to sew up packages in heavy cloth (but still ludicrously small to be used as a pike or pick-ax).

spear; a great brewer's cow[88] on his back for a corselet; and on his head for a helmet a huge high shoe with the bottom turned upward, embossed as full of hobnails as ever it might stick.

His men were all base handicrafts, as cobblers and curriers and tinkers, whereof some had bars of iron, some hatchets, some cool staves,[89] some dung forks, some spades, some mattocks, some wood knives, some adzes for their weapons. He that was best provided had but a piece of a rusty brown bill[90] bravely fringed with cobwebs to fight for him. Perchance here and there you might see a fellow that had a canker-eaten skull[91] on his head, which served him and his ancestors for a chamber pot two hundred years; and another that had bent a couple of iron dripping pans armor-wise, to fence his back and his belly; another that had thrust a pair of dry old boots as a breast plate before his belly of his doublet, because he would not be dangerously hurt; another that had twilted all his truss full of counters,[92] thinking if the enemy should take him he would mistake them for gold and so save his life for his money.

Very devout asses they were, for all they were so dunstically set forth, and such as thought they knew as much of God's mind as richer men. Why, inspiration was their ordinary familiar, and buzzed in their ears like a bee in a box every hour—what news from heaven, hell, and the land of Whipperginny?[93] Displease them who durst; he should have his mittimus to damnation *ex tempore*. They would vaunt there was not a pea's difference twixt them and the Apostles. They were as poor as they, of as base trades as they, and no more inspired than they; and with God there is no respect of persons.

Only herein may seem some little diversity to lurk—that Peter wore a sword, and they count it flat hellfire for any man to wear a

[88]*brewer's cow:* possibly a wooden tub or cowl in which malt liquors were made (the point being that although a tub would be most unsuitable as armor, Leyden "the botcher" nevertheless so used it).

[89]*cool staves:* probably cowl or tub staves (the strips of wood that, set edge to edge, form the sides of a tub or barrel).

[90]*brown bill:* halberd (combination spear and battle-ax).

[91]*skull:* skull-cap (of steel).

[92]*twilted . . . truss . . . counters:* sewn up . . . trousers . . . tokens used to represent real money.

[93]*Whipperginny:* a word of several meanings (all of which Jack may mean to suggest): purgatory, loose woman, and a card game. The last sense may be intended to bring out another sense of "counters"—objects used, like poker chips today, in keeping the score of a card game.

dagger. Nay, so grounded and graveled were they in this opinion that, now when they should come to battle, there's ne'er a one of them would bring a blade (no, not an onion blade) about him, to die for it. It was not lawful, said they, for any man to draw the sword but the magistrate. And in fidelity (which I had well-nigh forgot) Jack Leyden, their magistrate, had the image or likeness of a piece of a rusty sword like a lusty lad by his side. Now I remember me, it was but a foil neither; and he wore it to show that he should have the foil of his enemies, which might have been an oracle for his two-hand interpretation. *Quid plura?* His battle is pitched. By "pitched" I do not mean set in order, for that was far from their order. Only as sailors do pitch their apparel, to make it stormproof, so had most of them pitched their patched clothes, to make them impierceable. A nearer way than to be at the charges of armor by half. And in another sort he might be said to have pitched the field, for he had pitched or set up his rest whither to fly if they were discomfited.

Peace, peace there in the belfry;[94] service begins. Upon their knees before they join false John Leyden and his fraternity, very devoutly they pray, they howl, they expostulate with God to grant them victory, and use such unspeakable vehemence a man would think them the only well-bent men under heaven.

Wherein let me dilate a little more gravely than the nature of this history requires, or will be expected of so young a practitioner in divinity, that not those that intermissively cry, "Lord, open unto us! Lord, open unto us!" enter first into the kingdom of heaven; that not the greatest professors have the greatest portion in grace; that all is not gold that glisters. When Christ said the kingdom of heaven must suffer violence, he meant not the violence of long babbling prayers to no purpose, nor the violence of tedious invective sermons without wit, but the violence of faith, the violence of good works, the violence of patient suffering. The ignorant arise and snatch the kingdom of heaven to themselves with greediness, when we with all our learning sink down into hell.

Where did Peter and John, in the third of the Acts, find the lame cripple but in the gate of the temple called Beautiful? In the beautifullest gates of our temple, in the forefront of professors, are many lame cripples—lame in life, lame in good works, lame in everything.

[94]*Peace ... belfry:* The poor people sat or stood under the tower in church; cf. disparaging remarks in plays to "groundlings."

Yet will they always sit at the gates of the temple. None be more forward than they to enter into matters of reformation, yet none more behindhand to enter into the true temple of the Lord by the gates of good life.

You may object that those which I speak against are more diligent in reading the Scriptures, more careful to resort unto sermons, more sober in their looks and modest in their attire than any else. But I pray you let me answer you. Doth not Christ say that before the latter day the sun shall be turned into darkness and the moon into blood? Whereof what may the meaning be but that the glorious sun of the Gospel shall be eclipsed with the dim cloud of dissimulation, that that which is the brightest planet of salvation shall be a means of error and darkness, and the moon shall be turned into blood? Those that shine fairest, make the simplest show, seem most to favor religion, shall rent out the bowels of the church, be turned into blood, and all this shall come to pass before the notable day of the Lord, whereof this age is the eve.

Let me use a more familiar example, since the heat of a great number hath outraged so excessively. Did not the devil lead Christ to the pinnacle or highest part of the temple to tempt him? If he lead Christ, he will lead a whole army of hypocrites to the top or highest part of the temple, the highest step of religion and holiness, to seduce them and subvert them. I say unto you that which this our tempted Savior with many other words besought his disciples; save yourselves from this froward generation. Verily, verily, the servant is not greater than his master; verily, verily, sinful men are not holier than holy Jesus, their maker. That holy Jesus again repeats this holy sentence: "Remember the words I said unto you; the servant is not holier or greater than his master"—as if he should say, remember, then, imprint in your memory; your pride and singularity will make you forget them; the effects of them many years hence will come to pass. "Whosoever will seek to save his soul shall lose it."[95] Whosoever seeks by headlong means to enter into heaven, and disannul God's ordinance, shall, with the giants that thought to scale heaven in contempt of Jupiter, be overwhelmed with Mount Ossa and Pelion, and dwell with the devil in eternal desolation.

Though the high priest's office was expired when Paul said unto

[95]*Whosoever will . . . lose it"*: Luke, XVII, 33; in the King James version the key word is "life," not "soul."

one of them, "God rebuke thee, thou painted sepulcher,"[96] yet when a stander by reproved him, saying, "Revilest thou the high priest?" he repented and asked forgiveness.

That which I suppose I do not grant. The lawfulness of the authority they oppose themselves against is sufficiently proved. Far be it my underage arguments should intrude themselves as a green, weak prop to support so high a building. Let it suffice if you know Christ, you know his father also. If you know Christianity, you know the fathers of the Church also. But a great number of you, with Philip,[97] have been long with Christ and have not known him, have long professed yourselves Christians and not known his true ministers. You follow the French and Scottish fashion and faction, and in all points are like the Switzers—*qui quaerunt cum qua Gente cadunt:* that seek with what nation they may first miscarry.

In the days of Nero there was an odd fellow that had found out an exquisite way to make glass as hammer proof as gold. Shall I say that the like experiment he made upon glass we have practiced on the Gospel? Aye, confidently will I. We have found out a sleight to hammer it to any heresy whatsoever. But those furnaces of falsehood and hammer heads of heresy must be dissolved and broken as his was, or else I fear me the false glittering glass of innovation will be better esteemed of than the ancient gold of the Gospel. The fault of faults is this: that your dead born faith is begotten by too, too infant fathers. Cato, one of the wisest men Roman histories canonized, was not born till his father was four score years old; none can be a perfect father of faith and beget men aright unto God but those that are aged in experience, have many years imprinted in their mild conversation, and have, with Zacchaeus,[98] sold all their possessions of vanities to enjoy the sweet fellowship not of the human but spiritual messiahs.

[96]*God . . . sepulcher:* Acts, XXIII, 3. In the King James version of 1611 the wording is less colorful: "God shall smite thee, thou whited wall." According to McKerrow (IV, 215) Nashe used on one occasion the Bishops' Bible and on another the Geneva, both of which had been printed in many editions before 1594. But for this particular verse (Acts, XXIII, 3) the Bishops' Bible (1568 ed.) is exactly the same as the King James, and the Geneva Bible (1560 ed.) differs only in having "painted wall" for "whited wall." In this case Nashe (Jack) prefers his own version, which surely is better English.

[97]*Philip:* John Berryman surely is right here in his edition of *The Unfortunate Traveler* (New York, 1960), p. 156: Philip the Apostle (John, XIV, 8–9) is the primary reference, with also a snide glance at Philip II, the Catholic king of Spain.

[98]*Zacchaeus:* See Luke XIX, 2–10.

Ministers and pastors, sell away your sects and schisms to the decrepit churches in contention beyond sea. They have been so long inured to war, both about matters of religion and regiment, that now they have no peace of mind but in troubling all other men's peace. Because the poverty of their provinces will allow them no proportionable maintenance for higher callings of ecclesiastical magistrates, they would reduce us to the precident of their rebellious persecuted beggary—much like the sect of philosophers called cynics, who, when they saw they were born to no lands or possessions (nor had any possible means to support their desperate estates, but they must live despised and, in misery, do what they could) they plotted and consulted with themselves how to make their poverty better esteemed of than rich dominion and sovereignty.

The upshot of their plotting and consultation was this: that they would live to themselves, scorning the very breath or company of all men. They professed (according to the rate of their lands) voluntary poverty, thin fare, and lying hard, contemning and inveighing against all those as brute beasts whatsoever whom the world had given any reputation for riches or prosperity. Diogenes was one of the first and foremost of the ringleaders of this rusty morosity; and he, for all his nice dogged disposition and blunt deriding of worldly dross and the gross felicity of fools, was taken notwithstanding a little after very fairly coining money in his cell.

So fares it up and down with our cynical reformed foreign churches. They will disgest no grapes of great bishoprics, forsooth, because they cannot tell how to come by them. They must shape their coats, good men according to their cloth, and do as they may, not as they would. Yet they must give us leave here in England, that are their honest neighbors, if we have more cloth than they, to make our garment somewhat larger. What was the foundation or groundwork of this dismal declining of Münster but the banishing of their bishop; their confiscating and casting lots for church livings, as the soldiers cast lots for Christ's garments; and, in short terms, their making the house of God a den of thieves?

The house of God a number of hungry church robbers in these days have made a den of thieves. Thieves spend loosely what they have got lightly. Sacrilege is no sure inheritance. Dionysius was ne'er the richer for robbing Jupiter of his golden coat; he was driven in the end to play the schoolmaster at Corinth. The name of religion, be it good or bad that is ruinated, God never suffers unrevenged. I'll say of it as Ovid said of eunuchs:

Qui primus pueris genitalia membra recidit
Vulnera quae fecit debuit ipse pati.

Who first deprived young boys of their best part,
With selfsame wounds he gave he ought to smart.

So would he that first gelt religion or church livings had been first gelt himself or never lived. Cardinal Wolsey is the man I aim at, *qui in suas poenas ingeniosus erat*, first gave others a light to his own overthrow. How it prospered with him and his instruments that after wrought for themselves, chronicles largely report though not apply; and some parcel of their punishment, yet unpaid, I do not doubt but will be required of their posterity.

To go forward with my story of the overthrow of that usurper John Leyden, he and all his army (as I said before) falling prostrate on their faces, and fervently given over to prayer, determined never to cease, or leave soliciting of God, till he had showed them from heaven some manifest miracle of success. Note that it was a general received tradition, both with J. Leyden and all the crew of Cnipperdolings and Müncers,[99] if God at any time at their vehement outcries and clamors did not condescend to their requests, to rail on him and curse him to his face; to dispute with him and argue him of injustice for not being so good as his word with them; and to urge his many promises in the Scripture against him. So that they did not serve God simply, but that he should serve their turns. And after that tenure are many content to serve as bondmen to save the danger of hanging. But he that serves God aright, whose upright conscience hath for his mot, *amor est mihi causa sequendi:* I serve because I love; he says, *egote potius domine quam tua dona sequar:* I'll rather follow thee, Oh Lord, for thine own sake, than for any covetous respect of that thou canst do for me.

Christ would have no followers but such as forsook all and follow him, such as forsake all their own desires; such as abandon all expectations of reward in this world; such as neglected and contemned their lives, their wives, and children in comparison of him; and were content to take up their cross and follow him. These Anabaptists had not yet forsook all and followed Christ. They had not forsook their own desires of revenge and innovation. They had not abandoned their

[99]*Cnipperdolings and Müncers:* Knipperdolinck was a leader, with Jan of Leyden, at the Münster insurrection. Thomas Münzer apparently had the most extreme views of all these reformers. See *The Cambridge Modern History,* II, 186.

expectation of the spoil of their enemies. They regarded their lives. They looked after their wives and children. They took not up their cross of humility and followed him, but would cross him, upbraid him, and set him at naught if he assured not by some sign their prayers and supplications. *Deteriora sequuntur:* they followed God as daring him. God heard their prayers, *quod petitur poena est:* it was their speedy punishment that they prayed for. Lo, according to the sum of their impudent supplications, a sign in the heavens appeared—the glorious sign of the rainbow, which agreed just with the sign of their ensign that was a rainbow likewise. Whereupon, assuring themselves of victory—*miseri quod volunt, facile credunt:* that which wretches would have they easily believe—with shouts and clamors they presently ran headlong on their well-deserved confusion.

Pitiful and lamentable was their unpitied and well-performed slaughter. To see even a bear (which is the most cruelest of all beasts) too, too bloodily overmatched and deformedly rent in pieces by an unconscionable number of curs, it would move compassion against kind and make those that, beholding him at the stake yet uncoped with, wished him a suitable death to his ugly shape, now to recall their hardhearted wishes and moan him suffering as a mild beast, in comparison of the foul-mouthed mastiffs his butchers. Even such compassion did those overmatched ungracious Münsterians obtain of many indifferent eyes, who now thought them, suffering, to be as sheep brought innocent to the shambles, whenas before they deemed them as a number of wolves up in arms against the shepherds.

The imperials themselves that were their executioners (like a father that weeps when he beats his child, yet still weeps and still beats) not without much ruth and sorrow prosecuted that lamentable massacre. Yet drums and trumpets, sounding nothing but stern revenge in their ears, made them so eager that their hands had no leisure to ask counsel of their effeminate eyes. Their swords, their pikes, their bills, their bows, their calivers[100] slew, empierced, knocked down, shot through, and overthrew as many men every minute of the battle as there falls ears of corn before the scythe at one blow. Yet all their weapons so slaying, empiercing, knocking down, shooting through, overthrowing, dis(soul)joined not half so many as the hailing thunder of their great ordnance. So ordinary at every footstep was the imbruement of iron in blood that one could hardly discern heads from bullets, or clottered hair from mangled flesh hung with gore.

[100]*calivers:* light-weight, smoothbore muskets; the caliver was the lightest of all the portable sixteenth-century firearms except the pistol.

This tale must at one time or other give up the ghost, and as good now as stay longer. I would gladly rid my hands of it cleanly if I could tell how, for what with talking of cobblers and tinkers and ropemakers and botchers and dirt daubers, the mark is clean gone out of my muse's mouth; and I am, as it were, more than duncified twixt divinity and poetry. What is there more as touching this tragedy that you would be resolved of? Say quickly, for now my pen is got upon his feet again. How J. Leyden died? Is that it? He died like a dog. He was hanged and the halter paid for. For his companions, do they trouble you? I can tell you they troubled some men before, for they were all killed, and none escaped—no, not so much as one to tell the tale of the rainbow.[101] Hear what it is to be Anabaptists, to be Puritans, to be villains. You may be counted illuminate botchers for a while; but your end will be, "Good people, pray for me."

[4. *Middleburgh, Rotterdam, Wittenberg,*
and the Emperor's Court]

With the tragical catastrophe of this Münsterian conflict did I cashier the new vocation of my cavaliership. There was no more honorable wars in Christendom then towards. Wherefore, after I had learned to be half an hour in bidding a man *bon jour* in German sunonimas,[102] I traveled along the country towards England as fast as I could. What with wagons and bare ten toes having attained to Middleborough (good Lord, see the changing chances of us knight-errant infants) I met with the right honorable Lord Henry Howard, Earl of Surrey,[103] my late master. Jesu, I was persuaded I should not be more glad to see heaven than I was to see him. Oh, it was a right noble lord, liberality itself (if in this iron age there were any such creature as liberality left on the earth) a prince in content because a poet without peer.

[101]*tale of the rainbow:* See the passage three paragraphs above—"the glorious sign of the rainbow . . . rainbow likewise."

[102]*bon jour in German sunonimas:* that is, saying what is synonymous to "good day" in German.

[103]*Henry Howard, Earl of Surrey:* The Earl of Surrey (1517?–1547) was one of the two or three notable English poets in the first half of the sixteenth century. But there is little that is historical in Nashe's characterization. The Surrey-Geraldine love affair Nashe created out of one little sonnet, "A Description and Praise of His Love, Geraldine," which Surrey seems to have addressed to an Irish girl, Elizabeth Fitzgerald (1528?–1589), who may really have had Italian ancestors. It is possible that Surrey actually had a romantic interest in Elizabeth; Ruth Hughey contends that Elizabeth may

Destiny never defames herself but when she lets an excellent poet die; if there be any spark of Adam's paradised perfection yet embered up in the breasts of mortal men, certainly God hath bestowed that, his perfectest image, on poets. None come so near to God in wit, none more contemn the world. *Vatis avarus non temere est animus,* saith Horace; *versus amat, hoc studet unum:* seldom have you seen any poet possessed with avarice; only verses he loves, nothing else he delights in. And as they contemn the world, so contrarily of the mechanical world are none more contemned. Despised they are of the world because they are not of the world; their thoughts are exalted above the world of ignorance and all earthly conceits.

As sweet angelical queristers,[104] they are continually conversant in the heaven of arts; heaven itself is but the highest height of knowledge. He that knows himself and all things else knows the means to be happy. Happy, thrice happy are they whom God hath doubled his spirit upon, and given a double soul unto to be poets.

My heroical master exceeded in this supernatural kind of wit. He entertained no gross earthly spirit of avarice, nor weak womanly spirit of pusillanimity and fear that are fained to be of the water, but admirable, airy, and fiery spirits, full of freedom, magnanimity and bountihood. Let me not speak any more of his accomplishments for fear I spend all my spirits in praising him and leave myself no vigor of wit, or effects of a soul, to go forward with my history.

Having thus met him I so much adored, no interpleading was there of opposite occasions; but back I must return and bear half stakes with him in the lottery of travel. I was not altogether unwilling to walk along with such a good purse bearer; yet musing what changeable humor had so suddenly seduced him from his native soil to seek

---

· have been thirteen or fourteen years old when the sonnet was written—and not merely a child of nine, as previous scholars have thought (*The Arundel Harington Manuscript of Tudor Poetry* [Columbus, Ohio, 1960], II, 76–84). There seems to be no record of Surrey's having talked to Erasmus in Rotterdam, and he probably never set foot in Italy. But he did have a boisterous servant, Pickering, with whom he was arrested for having broken the windows of certain London houses and churches. (See the *DNB* article). Possibly these escapades suggested to Nashe the much more violent and profane adventures of the fictional Surrey and Jack Wilton.

[104]*queristers:* Probably here, and certainly later in "a young querister to keep time" (p. 483), Jack has in mind "chorister" (literally, singer in a choir); but he may think of a poet not only as a singer, but also as a "querist," one who asks questions.

out needless perils in these parts beyond sea, one night very boldly I demanded of him the reason that moved him thereto.

"Ah," quoth he, "my little page, full little canst thou perceive how far metamorphosed I am from myself since I last saw thee. There is a little god called Love that will not be worshiped of any leaden brains—one that proclaims himself sole king and emperor of piercing eyes, and chief sovereign of soft hearts. He it is that, exercising his empire in my eyes, hath exorcised and clean conjured me from my content.

"Thou knowest stately Geraldine—too stately, I fear, for me to do homage to her statue or shrine. She it is that is come out of Italy to bewitch all the wise men of England. Upon Queen Katherine, Dowager,[105] she waits, that hath a dowry of beauty sufficient to make her wooed of the greatest kings in Christendom. Her high exalted sunbeams have set the phoenix nest of my breast on fire, and I myself have brought Arabian spiceries of sweet passions and praises to furnish out the funeral flame of my folly. Those who were condemned to be smothered to death by sinking down into the soft bottom of an high-built bed of roses never died so sweet a death as I should die if her rose-colored disdain were my deathsman. Oh, thrice imperial Hampton Court, Cupid's enchanted castle, the place where I first saw the perfect omnipotence of the Almighty expressed in mortality; 'tis thou alone that, tithing all other men solace in thy pleasant situation, affordest me nothing but an excellent begotten sorrow out of the chief treasury of all thy recreations.

"Dear Wilton, understand that there it was where I first set eye on my more than celestial Geraldine. Seeing her I admired her, all the whole receptacle of my sight was unhabited with her rare worth. Long suit and uncessant protestations got me the grace to be entertained. Did never unloving servant so prentice-like obey his never-pleased mistress as I did her. My life, my wealth, my friends, had all their destiny depending on her command.

"Upon a time I was determined to travel. The fame of Italy, and an especial affection I had unto poetry, my second mistress, for which Italy was so famous, had wholly ravished me unto it. There was no dehortment[106] from it, but needs thither I would. Wherefore, coming

---

[105]*Queen Katherine, Dowager:* presumably Catherine of Aragon, Henry VIII's first wife, but there is no record of Elizabeth Fitzgerald's having served her. The "dowry of beauty" applies to Geraldine.

[106]*dehortment:* exhortation, urging.

to my mistress as she was then walking with other ladies of estate in Paradise[107] at Hampton Court, I most humbly besought her of favor, that she would give me so much gracious leave to absent myself from her service as to travel a year or two into Italy.

"She very discreetly answered me that if my love were so hot as I had often avouched, I did very well to apply the plaster of absence unto it. For absence, as they say, causeth forgetfulness.

" 'Yet, nevertheless, since it is Italy, my native country, you are so desirous to see, I am the more willing to make my will yours. *Aye, pete Italiam:* go and seek Italy, with Aeneas; but be more true than Aeneas. I hope that kind, wit-cherishing climate will work no change in so witty a breast. No country of mine shall it be more if it conspire with thee in any new love against me. One charge I will give thee, and let it be rather a request than a charge: when thou comest to Florence, the fair city from whence I fetched the pride of my birth, by an open challenge defend my beauty against all comers.

" 'Thou hast that honorable carriage in arms that it shall be no discredit for me to bequeath all the glory of my beauty to thy well-governed arm. Fain would I be known where I was born; fain would I have thee known where fame sits in her chiefest theater. Farewell, forget me not; continued deserts will eternize me unto thee. Thy full wishes shall be expired when thy travel shall be once ended.'

"Here did tears step out before words, and intercepted the course of my kind-conceived speech, even as wind is allayed with rain. With heart-scalding sighs I confirmed her parting request, and vowed myself hers while living heat allowed me to be mine own. *Hinc illae lachrimae:* here hence proceedeth the whole cause of my peregrination."

Not a little was I delighted with this unexpected love story, especially from a mouth out of which was nought wont to march but stern precepts of gravity and modesty. I swear unto you I thought his company the better by a thousand crowns because he had discarded those nice terms of chastity and continency. Now I beseech God love me so well as I love a plain-dealing man. Earth is earth, flesh is flesh; earth will to earth, and flesh unto flesh; frail earth, frail flesh, who can keep you from the work of your creation.

Dismissing this fruitless annotation *pro et contra*, towards Venice we progressed, and took Rotterdam in our way, that was clean out of

---

[107]*Paradise:* probably the name given a particular garden or room at Hampton Court, a palace near London built by Wolsey and later presented by him to Henry VIII.

our way. There we met with aged learning's chief ornament, that abundant and superingenious clerk, Erasmus, as also with merry Sir Thomas More, our countryman, who was come purposely over a little before us to visit the said grave father, Erasmus. What talk, what conference we had then it were here superfluous to rehearse. But this I can assure you: Erasmus in all his speeches seemed so much to mislike the indiscretion of princes in preferring of parasites and fools that he decreed with himself to swim with the stream and write a book forthwith in commendation of folly.[108]

Quick-witted Sir Thomas More traveled in a clean contrary province, for he—seeing most commonwealths corrupted by ill custom; and that principalities were nothing but great piracies which, gotten by violence and murder, were maintained by private undermining and bloodshed; that in the chiefest flourishing kingdoms there was no equal or well-divided weal one with another, but a manifest conspiracy of rich men against poor men, procuring their own unlawful commodities under the name and interest of the commonwealth—he concluded with himself to lay down a perfect plot of a commonwealth or government, which he would entitle his *Utopia*. So left we them to prosecute their discontented studies, and made our next journey to Wittenberg.

At the very point of our entrance into Wittenberg, we were spectators of a very solemn scholastical entertainment of the Duke of Saxony thither. Whom, because he was the chief patron of their university and had took Luther's part in banishing the mass and all like papal jurisdiction out of their town, they crouched unto extremely. The chief ceremonies of their entertainment were these: first, the heads of their university (they were great heads of certainty) met him in their hooded hypocrisy and doctorly accouterments; *secundum formam statuti*, whereby the orator of the university, whose pickerdevant[109] was very plentifully besprinkled with rose water, a very learned—or, rather, ruthful—oration was delivered (for it rained all the while)

---

[108]*a book . . . in commendation of folly:* a reference to Erasmus' ironic book *The Praise of Folly*, first published in Latin, the international language of the Renaissance, in 1511; Thomas Chaloner's English translation appeared in 1549. More's *Utopia* likewise first appeared in Latin (1516) and then in Ralph Robinson's English translation (1551). More and Erasmus were great friends, but Erasmus was the traveler; there is no record of More's visiting Erasmus in Rotterdam—or of Surrey's talking to either one of them there.

[109]*pickerdevant:* often spelled "picke-devant" or "pique devant" and meaning "peak in front"; a Vandyke beard, short and trimmed to a point.

signifying thus much, that it was all by patch and by piecemeal stolen out of Tully. And he must pardon them, though in emptying their phrasebooks the air emptied his entrails,[110] for they did it not in any ostentation of wit (which they had not) but to show the extraordinary good will they bare the duke (to have him stand in the rain till he was thorough wet). A thousand *quemadmodums* and *qua propters* he came over him with; every sentence he concluded with *esse posse videatur;* through all the nine worthies he ran with praising and comparing him; Nestor's years he assured him of under the broad seal of their supplications. And with that crow-trodden verse in Virgil, *dum juga montis aper,* he packed up his pipes and cried, "*Dixi.*"

That pageant overpassed, there rushed upon him a miserable rabblement of junior graduates that all cried out upon him mightily in their gibrige[110a] like a company of beggars, "God save your grace! God save your grace! Jesus preserve your highness, though it be but for an hour!"

Some three halfpenny worth of Latin here also had he thrown at his face; but it was choice stuff, I can tell you, as there is a choice even amongst rags gathered up from the dunghill. At the town's end met him the burghers and dunstical incorporationers of Wittenberg in their distinguished liveries—their distinguished livery faces I mean, for they were most of them hot-livered drunkards, and had all the coat colors of sanguine, purple, crimson, copper, carnation that were to be had in their countenances. Filthy knaves, no cost had they bestowed on the town for his welcome—saving new painted their houghs[111] and boozing houses, which commonly are built fairer than their churches; and over their gates set the town arms,[112] which sounded

---

[110]*he must . . . their phrasebooks . . . his entrails:* Both "he" and "his" refer to Tully (Cicero); "their phrasebooks" refers to notebooks in which the "heads" of the university copied down phrases from Cicero. The satire on Wittenberg has several implications; one has to do with Wittenberg as the place where Luther posted his 95 theses in 1517—an action which, to Nashe, the anti-Puritan and defender of the Church of England, simply was "dunstical."

[110a]*gibrige:* gibberish.

[111]*houghs:* Probably "houghs" is just another name for "boozing houses"; Jack's manner of expressing himself often involves such a doubling up or overlapping. Cf. "hofs and tap houses," a phrase in another work by Nashe (McKerrow, III, 386.22).

[112]*town arms:* At this point—after "town arms" and before "which sounded"—the following clause, omitted from the first edition, was inserted into the second edition: "carousing a whole health to the duke's arms." There is some doubt whether Nashe was responsible for the insertion; if he

gulping after this sort: *vanhotten, slotten, irk bloshen glotten gelder-like*. Whatever the words were, the sense was this: good drink is a medicine for all diseases.

A bursten-belly inkhorn orator called Vanderhulk they picked out to present him with an oration, one that had a sulphurous, big, swollen, large face like a Saracen, eyes like two Kentish oysters, a mouth that opened as wide every time he spake as one of those old knit[113] trap doors, a beard as though it had been made of a bird's nest plucked in pieces which consisteth of straw, hair, and dirt mixed together. He was appareled in black leather new liquored, and a short gown without any gathering in the back, faced before and behind with a boisterous bearskin, and a red nightcap on his head. To this purport and effect was this broccing,[114] double-beer oration.

"Right noble duke (*ideo nobilis quasi no bilis*), for you have no bile or choler in you, know that our present incorporation of Wittenberg by me—the tongue-man of their thankfulness, a townsman by birth, a free German by nature, an orator by art, and a scrivener by education—in all obedience and chastity most bountifully bid you welcome to Wittenberg. Welcome, said I? Oh, orifficial rhetoric, wipe thy everlasting mouth and afford me a more Indian metaphor than that for the brave princely blood of a Saxon. Oratory, uncask the barred hutch of thy compliments, and with the triumphantest trope in thy treasury do trewage[115] unto him. What impotent speech, with his eight parts, may not specify this unestimable gift, holding his peace, shall, as it were (with tears I speak it), do whereby, as it may seem or appear, to manifest or declare, and yet it is, and yet it is not, and yet it may be a diminutive oblation meritorious to your high pusillanimity and

---

did write it, then of course we should think of it as part of the text. The general sense of the passage, without the insertion, is that the German words on the town's coat of arms make gulping sounds when pronounced aloud— or at least an Englishman might think so. With the insertion, there are two coats of arms, one belonging to the town and one to the duke, each presumably with gutteral German words on it; but apparently we are also to visualize actual arms, and hands, in the act of offering a toast to the duke.

[113]*knit:* The sense is not clear; possibly "knit" goes with "old," meaning something like "old-fashioned"; "folding" is also a possibility.

[114]*broccing:* Probably the sense is "brocking" (stinking), with reference to the orator's breath. Nashe would be delighted that to the modern reader there is an additional sense—the low quality of the oration itself.

[115]*hutch . . . trewage:* storage chest . . . tribute.

indignity? Why should I go gadding and fizgigging after firking, flantado amphibologies?[116] Wit is wit, and good will is good will. With all the wit I have, I here, according to the premises, offer up unto you the city's general good will, which is a gilded can, in manner and form following for you and the heirs of your body lawfully begotten, to drink healths in. The scholastical squitter-books[117] clout you up canopies and footcloths of verses. We that are good fellows, and live as merry as cup and can, will not verse upon you as they do but must do as we can, and entertain you if it be but with a plain empty can. He hath learning enough that hath learned to drink to his first man.

"Gentle duke, without paradox be it spoken, thy horses at our own proper costs and charges shall kneed[118] up to the knees all the while thou art here in spruce beer and Lübeck liquor.[119] Not a dog thou bringest with thee but shall be banqueted with Rhenish wine and sturgeon. On our shoulders we wear no lambskin or miniver like these academics, yet we can drink to the confusion of all thy enemies. Good lamb's wool have we for their lambskins; and for their miniver, large minerals in our coffers. Mechanical men they call us, and not amiss; for most of us being *Maechi*—that is, cuckolds and whoremasters— fetch our antiquity from the temple of *Maecha*,[120] where Mahomet is hung up. Three parts of the world, America, Africa, and Asia, are of this our mechanic religion. Nero, when he cried, "*O, quantus artifex pereo!*"[121] professed himself of our freedom, insomuch as *artifex* is a citizen or craftsman, as well as *carnifex* a scholar or hangman. Pass on by leave into the precincts of our abomination. Bonny duke, frolic in our bower and persuade thyself that even as garlic hath three prop-

[116]*fizgigging . . . firking, flantado amphibologies:* gadding about . . . moving about briskly, flaunted ambiguities.

[117]*squitter-books:* literally, diarrhea-books; books written by scribblers who are copious but worthless writers.

[118]*kneed:* The word is to sound like "knees" and perhaps to mean "knead" (tread).

[119]*spruce beer . . . Lübeck liquor:* beer made of fermented spruce leaves . . . strong beer made in Lübeck.

[120]*Maechi . . . Maecha:* One sense is "people of Mecca . . . Mecca"; but, as Robert Ashley and Edwin M. Moseley have pointed out, *Elizabethan Fiction* (New York, 1953), p. 427, there is a pun on the Latin *moechus* (adulterer) and also an echo of "mechanical men."

[121]*"O, quantus artifex pereo!":* "Oh, what an artist is lost in me!" Then the orator plays upon *"artifex"* and *"carnifex"* in a way that is difficult to fathom. *"Carnifex"* means "hangman" or "murderer," which fits Nero well

erties (to make a man wink, drink, and stink), so we will wink on thy imperfections, drink to thy favorites, and all thy foes shall stink before us. So be it. Farewell."

The duke laughed not a little at this ridiculous oration. But that very night as great an ironical occasion was ministered, for he was bidden to one of the chief schools to a comedy handled by scholars. *Acolastus, the Prodigal Child*[122] was the name of it, which was so filthily acted, so leathernly set forth, as would have moved laughter in Heraclitus. One, as if he had been planing a clay floor, stampingly trod the stage so hard with his feet that I thought verily he had resolved to do the carpenter that set it up some utter shame. Another flung his arms like cudgels at a pear tree, insomuch as it was mightily dreaded that he would strike the candles that hung above their heads out of their sockets and leave them all dark. Another did nothing but wink and make faces. There was a parasite, and he with clapping his hands and thripping his fingers seemed to dance an antic to and fro. The only thing they did well was the prodigal child's hunger, most of their scholars being hungrily kept; and surely you would have said they had been brought up in hogs' academy, to learn to eat acorns, if you had seen how sedulously they fell to them. Not a jest had they to keep their auditors from sleep but of swill and draff. Yes, now and then the servant put his hand into the dish before his master and almost choked himself, eating slovenly and ravenously to cause sport.

The next day they had solemn disputations where Luther and Carolostadius scolded level coil.[123] A mass of words I wot well they heaped up against the mass and the pope, but further particulars of their disputations I remember not. I thought verily they would have worried one another with words, they were so earnest and vehement. Luther had the louder voice; Carolostadius went beyond him in beat-

---

enough; perhaps the sense in which *"carnifex"* can also mean "scholar" has to do with the orator himself—a "scholar" in the process of "murdering" an oration. Presumably this latter sense would be unconscious on the part of the orator but conscious and deliberate on the part of Jack and Nashe. Notice the phrase "handled by scholars" when Jack speaks of the presentation of *Acolastus*.

[122]*Acolastus, the Prodigal Child*: the title of a play by a Dutch writer, Gulielmus Fullonius, and translated into English in 1540 (STC 11470).

[123]*Carolostadius . . . coil*: Carlstadt was a German reformer whose name was often linked with Luther's as a bitter critic of the Catholic Church; see *Cambridge Modern History*, II, 165 ff. "Scolded level coil" means "scolded in a noisy, rough manner" (from *lever le cul*, to raise the buttocks, a boisterous game something like musical chairs, in which each player is driven from his seat and his place taken by another player).

ing and bouncing with his fists, *quae supra no nihil ad nos*. They uttered nothing to make a man laugh; therefore I will leave them. Marry, their outward gestures now and then would afford a man a morsel of mirth. Of those two I mean not so much as of all the other train of opponents and respondents.

One pecked like a crane with his forefinger at every half syllable he brought forth, and nodded with his nose like an old singing man teaching a young querister to keep time. Another would be sure to wipe his mouth with his handkerchief at the end of every full point. And ever when he thought he had cast a figure so curiously, as he dived over head and ears into his auditors' admiration, he would take occasion to stroke up his hair and twine up his mustachios twice or thrice over while they might have leisure to applaud him. A third wavered and waggled his head like a proud horse playing with his bridle, or as I have seen some fantastical swimmer at every stroke train his chin sidelong over his left shoulder. A fourth sweat and foamed at the mouth for very anger his adversary had denied that part of his syllogism which he was not prepared to answer. A fifth spread his arms like an usher that goes before to make room, and thripped with his finger and his thumb when he thought he had tickled it with a conclusion. A sixth hung down his countenance like a sheep, and stutted and slavered very pitifully when his invention was swept aside out of the way. A seventh gasped and gaped for wind, and groaned in his pronunciation as if he were hard bound with some bad argument.

Gross plodders they were all, that had some learning and reading but no wit to make use of it. They imagined the duke took the greatest pleasure and contentment under heaven to hear them speak Latin, and as long as they talked nothing but Tully he was bound to attend them. A most vain thing it is in many universities at this day that they count him excellent eloquent who stealeth not whole phrases but whole pages out of Tully. If of a number of shreds of his sentences he can shape an oration, from all the world he carries it away—although in truth it be no more than a fool's coat of many colors. No invention or matter have they of their own, but tack up a style of his stale gallimaufry. The leaden-headed Germans first began this, and we Englishmen have surfeited of their absurd imitation. I pity Nizolius[124] that had nothing to do but pick threads' ends out of an old overworn garment.

[124]*Nizolius:* an Italian scholar who compiled *Thesaurus Ciceronianus* (1535), a thesaurus based on words and phrases from Cicero's writings; Jack finds that kind of scholarship sterile and derivative.

This is but by the way. We must look back to our disputants. One amongst the rest, thinking to be more conceited than his fellows, seeing the duke have a dog he loved well, which sat by him on the terrace, converted all his oration to him, and not a hair of his tail but he combed out with comparisons. So to have courted him if he were a bitch had been very suspicious. Another commented and descanted on the duke's staff, new tipping it with many quaint epithets. Some cast his nativity and promised him he should not die till the day of judgment.

Omitting further superfluities of this stamp, in this general assembly we found intermixed that abundant scholar Cornelius Agrippa.[125] At that time he bare the fame to be the greatest conjurer in Christendom. Scoto, that did the juggling tricks here before the queen, never came near him one quarter in magic reputation. The doctors of Wittenberg, doting on the rumor that went of him, desired him before the duke and them to do something extraordinary memorable.

One requested to see pleasant Plautus and that he would show them in what habit he went, and with what countenance he looked when he ground corn in the mill. Another had half a month's mind to Ovid and his hook nose. Erasmus, who was not wanting to that honorable meeting, requested to see Tully in that same grace and majesty he pleaded his oration *pro Roscio Amerino*. Affirming that till in person he beheld his importunity of pleading, he would not be persuaded any man could carry away a manifest case with rhetoric so strangely. To Erasmus' petition he easily condescended and (willing the doctors at such an hour to hold their convocation, and everyone to keep him in his place without moving) at the time prefixed, in entered Tully, ascended his pleading place, and declaimed verbatim the forenamed oration, but with such astonishing amazement, with such fervent

[125]*Cornelius Agrippa:* Forgotten today but famous in his lifetime (1486–1535) as a soldier, physician, and writer. With Erasmus and Ovid, he is the most important of Nashe's direct sources. From Agrippa's *De Incertitude et Vanitate Scientiarum et Artium* (first published in 1531, translated into English by James Sanford in 1569) come little tidbits of miscellaneous but striking, often fantastic, information. A careful comparison of Nashe's work with Agrippa's may reveal a significant meeting of minds. Agrippa was perhaps the most learned anti-intellectual in the Renaissance; one by one he ticks off the arts and sciences as useless and corrupting. The influence on Nashe seems to take the form of a constant tendency to debunk or be-little; Nashe's satiric thrust, his delight in reducing to the absurd, may have gained its central confidence from Agrippa (though the strictly verbal pyrotechnics owe little to him).

exaltation of spirit, with such soul-stirring gestures, that all his auditors were ready to install his guilty client for a god.

Great was the concourse of glory Agrippa drew to him with this one feat. And indeed he was so cloyed with men which came to behold him that he was fain sooner than he would to return to the emperor's court from whence he came, and leave Wittenberg before he would. With him we traveled along, having purchased his acquaintance a little before. By the way as we went, my master and I agreed to change names. It was concluded betwixt us that I should be the Earl of Surrey and he my man, only because in his own person, which he would not have reproached, he meant to take more liberty of behavior. As for my carriage, he knew he was to tune it at a key, either high or low or as he list.

To the emperor's court we came, where our entertainment was every way plentiful. Carouses we had in whole gallons instead of quart pots. Not a health was given us but contained well near a hogshead. The customs of the country we were eager to be instructed in, but nothing we could learn but this: that ever at the emperor's coronation there is an ox roasted with a stag in the belly, and that stag in his belly hath a kid, and that kid is stuffed full of birds. Some courtiers to weary out time would tell us further tales of Cornelius Agrippa, and how when Sir Thomas More, our countryman, was there, he showed him the whole destruction of Troy in a dream. How the Lord Cromwell, being the king's ambassador there, in like case, in a perspective glass he set before his eyes King Henry the Eighth with all his lords hunting in his forest at Windsor. And when he came into his study and was very urgent to be partaker of some rare experiment that he might report when he came into England, he willed him amongst two thousand great books to take down which he list and begin to read one line in any place, and without book he would rehearse twenty leaves following. Cromwell did so, and in many books tried him, when in everything he exceeded his promise and conquered his expectation. To Charles the Fifth, then emperor, they reported how he showed the nine worthies (David, Solomon, Gideon, and the rest) in that similitude and likeness that they lived upon earth.

My master and I, having by the highway side gotten some reasonable familiarity with him, upon this access of miracles imputed to him, resolved to request him something in our own behalves. I, because I was his suborned lord and master, desired him to see the lively image of Geraldine, his love, in the glass, and what at that instant she

did, and with whom she was talking. He showed her us without more
ado, sick weeping on her bed, and resolved all into devout religion for
the absence of her lord. At the sight thereof he could in no wise
refrain, though he had took upon him the condition of a servant, but
he must forthwith frame this extemporal ditty:

All soul, no earthly flesh, why dost thou fade?
All gold, no worthless dross, why look'st thou pale?
Sickness, how dar'st thou one so fair invade,
Too base infirmity to work her bale?
 Heaven be distempered since she grieved pines,
 Never be dry these my sad plaintive lines.

Perch thou my spirit on her silver breasts,
And with their pain-redoubled music beatings,
Let them toss thee to world where all toil rests,
Where bliss is subject to no fear's defeatings;
 Her praise I tune whose tongue doth tune the spheres,
 And gets new muses in her hearer's ears.

Stars fall to fetch fresh light from her rich eyes,
Her bright brow drives the sun to clouds beneath,
Her hairs reflex with red streaks paints the skies,
Sweet morn and evening dew flows from her breath;
 Phoebe rules tides, she my tears' tides forth draws,
 In her sickbed love sits and maketh laws.

Her dainty limbs tinsel her silk soft sheets,
Her rose-crowned cheeks eclipse my dazzled sight,
Oh, glass with too much joy my thoughts thou greets,
And yet thou show'st me day but by twilight.
 I'll kiss thee for the kindness I have felt,
 Her lips one kiss would unto nectar melt.

[5. Venice]

Though the emperor's court, and the extraordinary edifying company
of Cornelius Agrippa, might have been arguments of weight to have
arrested us a little longer there, yet Italy still stuck as a great mote
in my master's eye. He thought he had traveled no farther than Wales
till he had took survey of that country which was such a curious
molder of wits.

To cut off blind ambages by the highway side, we made a long
stride and got to Venice in short time. Where, having scarce looked
about us, a precious supernatural pander, appareled in all points like
a gentleman and having half a dozen several languages in his purse,

entertained us in our own tongue very paraphrastically and eloquently and, maugre all other pretended acquaintance, would have us in a violent kind of courtesy to be the guests of his appointment. His name was Petro de Campo Frego, a notable practitioner in the policy of bawdry. The place whither he brought us was a pernicious courtesan's house named Tabitha the Temptress', a wench that could set as civil a face on it as chastity's first martyr, Lucrecia. What will you conceit to be in any saint's house that was there to seek? Books, pictures, beads, crucifixes—why, there was a haberdasher's shop of them in every chamber. I warrant you should not see one set of her necker-cher perverted or turned awry, not a piece of a hair displaced. On her beds there was not a wrinkle of any wallowing to be found; her pillows bare out as smooth as a groaning wife's belly. And yet she was a Turk and an infidel and had more doings than all her neighbors besides. Us, for our money, they used like emperors. I was master, as you heard before, and my master the earl was but as my chief man whom I made my companion. So it happened, as iniquity will out at one time or other, that she, perceiving my expense had no more vents than it should have, fell in with my supposed servant, my man, and gave him half a promise of marriage if he would help to make me away, that she and he might enjoy the jewels and wealth that I had.

The indifficulty of the condition thus she explained unto him. Her house stood upon vaults which in two hundred years together were never searched; who came into her house none took notice of. His fellow servants that knew of his master's abode there should be all dispatched by him as from his master, into sundry parts of the city about business; and when they returned, answer should be made that he lay not there any more but had removed to Padua since their de-parture, and thither they must follow him.

"Now," quoth she, "if you be disposed to make him away in their absence, you shall have my house at command. Stab, poison, or shoot him through with a pistol—all is one. Into the vault he shall be thrown when the deed is done."

On my bare honesty it was a crafty quean, for she had enacted with herself, if he had been my legitimate servant, as he was one that served and supplied my necessities, when he had murdered me, to have accused him of the murder and made all that I had hers—as I carried all my master's wealth, money, jewels, rings, or bills of ex-change continually about me. He very subtly consented to her strat-agem at the first motion: kill me he would (that heavens could not withstand), and a pistol was the predestinate engine which must deliver the parting blow. God wot I was a raw young squire and my master dealt Judasly with me, for he told me but[126] everything that she and he agreed of. Wherefore I could not possibly prevent it but, as a man would say, avoid it. The execution day aspired to his utmost devolution. Into my chamber came my honorable attendant, with his pistol charged by his side, very suspiciously and sullenly; Lady Tabitha and Petro de Campo Frego, her pander, followed him at the hard heels. At their entrance I saluted them all very familiarly and merrily, and began to impart unto them what disquiet dreams had disturbed me the last night.

"I dreamed," quoth I, "that my man Brunquell here (for no better name got he of me) came into my chamber with a pistol charged under his arm to kill me, and that he was suborned by you, Mistress Tabitha, and my very good friend here, Petro de Campo Frego. God send it turn to good, for it hath affrighted me above measure."

As they were ready to enter into a colorable commonplace of the deceitful frivolousness of dreams, my trusty servant Brunquell stood quivering and quaking every joint of him and, as it was before compacted between us, let his pistol drop from him on the sudden. Wherewith I started out of my bed and drew my rapier and cried, "Murder! Murder!" which made Goodwife Tabitha ready to bepiss her.

My servant (or my master, which you will) I took roughly by the collar and threatened to run him through incontinent if he confessed not the truth. He, as it were, stricken with remorse of conscience (God be with him, for he could counterfeit most daintily) down on his knees, asked me forgiveness, and impeached Tabitha and Petro de Campo Frego as guilty of subornation. I very mildly and gravely gave him audience. Rail on them I did not after his tale was ended, but said I would try what the law could do. Conspiracy, by the custom of their country, was a capital offense, and what custom or justice might afford they should be all sure to feel.

"I could," quoth I, "acquit myself otherwise, but it is not for a stranger to be his own carver[127] in revenge."

Not a word more with Tabitha but die she would before God or

---

[126]*but:* absolutely; a rare usage, at least in writing, though perhaps as common colloquially then as now.

[127]*to be his own carver:* a proverb (Tilley, C110); the sense is "to take or choose for oneself, at one's own discretion."

the devil would have her. She swooned[128] and revived, and then swooned again. And after she revived again sighed heavily, spoke faintly and pitifully; yea, and so pitifully as, if a man had not known the pranks of harlots before, he would have melted in commiseration. Tears, sighs, and doleful-tuned words could not make any forcible claim to my stony ears. It was the glistering crowns that I hungered and thirsted after; and with them, for all her mock holy day gestures,[129] she was fain to come off before I would condescend to any bargain of silence. So it fortuned (fie upon that unfortunate word of "fortune") that this whore, this quean, this courtesan, this common of ten thousand, so bribing me not to bewray her, had given me a great deal of counterfeit gold which she had received of a coiner to make away a little before, amongst the gross sum of my bribery. I, silly milksop, mistrusting no deceit, under an angel of light took what she gave me—ne'er turned it over—for which (oh, falsehood in fair show) my master and I had like to have been turned over.[130]

He that is a knight-errant, exercised in the affairs of ladies and gentlewomen, hath more places to send money to than the devil hath to send his spirits to. There was a delicate wench called Flavia Aemilia lodging in St. Mark's Street at a goldsmith's, which I would fain have had to the grand test, to try whether she were current in alchemy or no. Aye me, she was but a counterfeit slip, for she not only gave me the slip but had well-nigh made me a slipstring.[131] To her I sent my gold to beg an hour of grace. Ah, graceless fornicatress, my hostess and she were confederate, who, having gotten but one

---

[128]*swooned:* In the first edition the spelling of this word is "sounded"; later on Heraclide falls "in a sowne," and still later we find Juliana "in a swound." Modernizing to "swooned" and "swoon" is not perhaps taking too much liberty with the text.

[129]*holy day gestures:* There is a question here whether the sense is "holy day gestures" (gestures appropriate to a religious celebration) or "holiday gestures" (gestures suggestive of recreation, with perhaps a hint that we remember Tabitha's profession). McKerrow in his index indicates "holiday," but most modern editors prefer "holy day." The context would seem to bear out the latter spelling: "Tears, sighs, and doleful-tuned words" seem to indicate that Tabitha may have her hands clasped in a mock attitude of prayer; "holiday" gestures she probably would not have to feign. Both senses may be intended.

[130]*turned over:* killed. Note the play on words—"angel" (the coin *vs.* the outwardly attractive quean, who outwardly may also look like a queen), and "turn it [the coin] over" (examine it) *vs.* "turn over" (to put to death).

[131]*counterfeit slip ... gave me the slip ... made me a slipstring:* counterfeit coin ... escaped me ... made me a person fit to be hanged (was the death of me).

piece of my ill gold into their hands, devised the means to make me immortal. I could drink for anger till my head ached, to think how I was abused. Shall I shame the devil and speak the truth? To prison was I sent as principal, and my master as accessory. Nor was it to a prison neither, but to the master of the mint's house, who, though partly our judge, and a most severe upright justice in his own nature, extremely seemed to condole our ignorant estate. And without all peradventure a present redress, he had ministered, if certain of our countrymen hearing an English earl was apprehended for coining, had not come to visit us. An ill planet brought them thither; for at the first glance they knew the servant of my secrecies to be the Earl of Surrey and I (not worthy to be named), I, an outcast of his cup or his pantofles. Thence, thence sprung the full period of our infelicity. The master of the mint, our whilom refresher and consolation, now took part against us; he thought we had a mint in our head of mischievous conspiracies against their state. Heavens bear witness with us it was not so (heavens will not always come to witness when they are called).

To a straiter ward were we committed: that which we have imputatively transgressed must be answered. Oh, the heathen hey-pass,[132] and the intrinsical legerdemain of our special approved good pander, Petro de Campo Frego. He, although he dipped in the same dish with us every day, seeming to labor our cause very importunately, and had interpreted for us to the state from the beginning, yet was one of those treacherous Brother Trulies and abused us most clerkly. He interpreted to us with a pestilence, for whereas we stood obstinately upon it, we were wrongfully detained, and that it was naught but a malicious practice of sinful Tabitha, our late hostess, he, by a fine cony-catching corrupt translation, made us plainly to confess and cry, "*Miserere!*" ere we had need of our neck verse.[133]

Detestable, detestable, that the flesh and the devil should deal by their factors. I'll stand to it; there is not a pander but hath vowed paganism. The devil himself is not such a devil as he, so be he perform his function aright. He must have the back of an ass, the snout

[132]*hey-pass:* The sense is reinforced by "legerdemain" and "pander." "Hey, pass!" literally was the call of a magician when he commanded an object to move.

[133]*neck verse:* Ben Jonson and many another Elizabethan literally saved their necks by claiming "benefit of clergy," Jonson after he had killed a fellow actor in a duel. The "benefit" was exemption from trial by a secular court; all the accused had to do was show that he could read a verse or two of Latin, usually from the beginning of Psalms, Chapter 51.

of an elephant, the wit of a fox, and the teeth of a wolf; he must fawn like a spaniel, crouch like a Jew, leer like a sheepbiter.[134] If he be half a Puritan, and have Scripture continually in his mouth, he speeds the better. I can tell you it is a trade of great promotion, and let none ever think to mount by service in foreign courts, or creep near to some magnifique lords, if they be not seen in this science. Oh, it is the art of arts, and ten thousand times goes beyond the intelligencer. None but a staid, grave, civil man is capable of it; he must have exquisite courtship in him or else he is not old who;[135] he wants the best point in his tables.[136]

God be merciful to our pander (and that were for God to work a miracle), he was seen in all the seven liberal deadly sciences; not a sin but he was as absolute in as Satan himself. Satan could never have supplanted us so as he did. I may say to you he planted in us the first Italianate wit that we had.

During the time we lay close and took physic in this castle of contemplation, there was a magnifico's wife of good calling sent in to bear us company. Her husband's name was Castaldo; she hight Diamante. The cause of her committing was an ungrounded jealous suspicion which her doting husband had conceived of her chastity.

One Isaac Medicus, a Bergomast,[137] was the man he chose to make him a monster, who (being a courtier and repairing to his house very often, neither for love of him nor his wife, but only with a drift to borrow money of a pawn of wax and parchment) when he saw his expectation deluded, and that Castaldo was too chary for him to close with, he privily, with purpose of revenge, gave out amongst his copesmates[138] that he resorted to Castaldo's house for no other end but to cuckold him. And doubtfully he talked that he had and he had not obtained his suit. Rings which he borrowed of a light courtesan that he used, too, he would feign to be taken from her fingers. And, in sum, so handled the matter that Castaldo exclaimed, "Out, whore, strumpet, six-penny hackster! Away with her to prison!"

---

[134]*sheepbiter:* a thieving, sneaky person (literally, a dog that bites or worries sheep).

[135]*old who:* somebody (a person of importance); perhaps the expression should be capitalized, "Old Who."

[136]*point in his tables:* a reference to the game of backgammon; a "point" is one of the twelve tapered divisions on each "table" of the backgammon board.

[137]*Bergomast:* Bergamask (a native of Bergamo, near Venice).

[138]*copesmates:* associates (either in business or pleasure).

As glad were we almost as if they had given us liberty that fortune lent us such a sweet pew fellow. A pretty round-faced wench was it, with black eyebrows, a high forehead, a little mouth, and a sharp nose; as fat and plump every part of her as a plover, a skin as slick and soft as the back of a swan. It doth me good when I remember her. Like a bird she tripped on the ground, and bare out her belly as majestical as an ostrich. With a licorous,[139] rolling eye fixed piercing on the earth, and sometimes scornfully darted on the tone[140] side, she figured forth a high discontented disdain, much like a prince puffing and storming at the treason of some mighty subject fled lately out of his power. Her very countenance repiningly wrathful, and yet clear and unwrinkled, would have confirmed the clearness of her conscience to the austerest judge in the world.

If in anything she were culpable, it was in being too melancholy chaste, and showing herself as covetous of her beauty as her husband was of his bags. Many are honest because they know not how to be dishonest. She thought there was no pleasure in stolen bread because there was no pleasure in an old man's bed. It is almost impossible that any woman should be excellently witty and not make the utmost penny of her beauty. This age and this country of ours admits of some miraculous exceptions, but former times are my constant informers. Those that have quick motions of wit have quick motions in everything. Iron only needs many strokes, only iron wits are not won without a long siege of entreaty. Gold easily bends; the most ingenious minds are easiest moved. *Ingenium nobis molle Thalia dedit*, saith Sapho to Phao. Who hath no merciful, mild mistress, I will maintain, hath no witty but a clownish, dull, phlegmatic puppy to his mistress.

This magnifico's wife was a good loving soul that had mettle enough in her to make a good wit of; but being never removed from under her mother's and her husband's wing, it was not molded and fashioned as it ought. Causeless distrust is able to drive deceit into a simple woman's head. I durst pawn the credit of a page, which is worth ambs-ace[141] at all times, that she was immaculate honest till she met with us in prison. Marry, what temptations she had then when fire and flax were put together, conceit with yourselves; but hold my master excusable.

[139]*licorous:* lickerish (wanton).
[140]*the tone:* used for "the one" up to *c*. 1600.
[141]*ambs-ace:* both aces (the lowest throw at dice).

Alack, he was too virtuous to make her vicious; he stood upon religion and conscience. What a heinous thing it was to subvert God's ordinance. This was all the injury he would offer her: sometimes he would imagine her in a melancholy humor to be his Geraldine, and court her in terms correspondent. Nay, he would swear she was his Geraldine and take her white hand and wipe his eyes with it, as though the very touch of her might stanch his anguish. Now would he kneel and kiss the ground as holy ground which she vouchsafed to bless from barrenness by her steps. Who would have learned to write an excellent passion, might have been a perfect tragic poet, had he but attended half the extremity of his lament. Passion upon passion would throng one on another's neck. He would praise her beyond the moon and stars, and that so sweetly and ravishingly as I persuade myself he was more in love with his own curious forming fancy than her face. And truth it is, many become passionate lovers only to win praise to their wits.

He praised, he prayed, he desired and besought her to pity him that perished for her. From this his entranced mistaking ecstasy could no man remove him. Who loveth resolutely will include everything under the name of his love. From prose he would leap into verse, and with these or suchlike rhymes assault her:

> If I must die, oh, let me choose my death;
> Suck out my soul with kisses, cruel maid,
> In thy breast's crystal balls enbalm my breath;
> Dole it all out in sighs when I am laid.
> Thy lips on mine like cupping glasses clasp;
> Let our tongues meet and strive as they would sting;
> Crush out my wind with one strait, girting grasp;
> Stabs on my heart keep time whilst thou dost sing.
> Thy eyes like searing irons burn out mine;
> In thy fair tresses stifle me outright;
> Like Circes, change me to a loathsome swine,
> So I may live forever in thy sight.
>> Into heaven's joys can none profoundly see,
>> Except that first they meditate on thee.

Sadly and verily, if my master said true, I should, if I were a wench, make many men quickly immortal. What is't, what is't for a maid fair and fresh to spend a little lip salve on a hungry lover? My master beat the bush and kept a coil and a prattling, but I caught the bird. Simplicity and plainness shall carry it away in another world. God wot he was Petro Desperato when I, stepping to her with a dunstable[142] tale, made up my market. A holy requiem to their souls that think to woo women with riddles. I had some cunning plot, you must suppose, to bring this about. Her husband had abused her, and it was very necessary she should be revenged. Seldom do they prove patient martyrs who are punished unjustly. One way or other they will cry quittance whatsoever it cost them. No other apt means had this poor she-captived Cicely[143] to work her hoddypeak[144] husband a proportionable plague to his jealousy but to give his head his full loading of infamy. She thought she would make him complain for something that now was so hard bound with an heretical opinion. How I dealt with her, guess, gentle reader: *subaudi*[145] that I was in prison and she was my jailer.

Means there was made after a month's or two durance by Mr. John Russell, a gentleman of King Henry the Eighth's chamber, who then lay ledger[146] at Venice for England, that our cause should be favorably heard. At that time was Monsieur Petro Aretino searcher and chief inquisitor for the college of courtesans. Diverse and sundry ways was this Aretino beholding to the King of England, especially for by this aforesaid Mr. Russell; a little before, he had sent him a pension of four hundred crowns yearly during his life. Very forcibly was he dealt withal to strain the utmost of his credit for our delivery. Nothing at his hands we sought, but that the courtesan might be more narrowly sifted and examined. Such and so extraordinary was his care and industry herein that within few days after Mistress Tabitha and her pander cried, "*Peccavi, confiteor!*" and we were presently discharged, they (for example sake) executed. Most honorably, after our enlargement, of the state were we used, and had sufficient recompense for all our troubles and wrongs.

---

[142]*dunstable:* plain, direct (originally referring to the road between London and Dunstable, in Bedfordshire).

[143]*Cicely:* a common name for a girl; also the popular name of a plant, of which there were several varieties, such as Sweet Cicely, Wild Cicely, and Fool's Cicely (all of which apply to Diamante).

[144]*hoddypeak:* simpleton.

[145]*subaudi:* it being understood (Berryman's translation).

[146]*John Russell . . . lay ledger:* another historical character, though described, as usual, with little regard for history. Russell (1486?–1555) was apparently "lay ledger" (resident ambassador) to Pope Clement at Rome. Russell's duties took him to many Italian cities, but Venice was not one of them. Neither did he have any connection with Henry Howard, Earl of Surrey; but he did serve with Surrey's father, Thomas Howard, third Duke of Norfolk, in a naval expedition against France in 1522.

Before I go any further, let me speak a word or two of this Aretino. It was one of the wittiest knaves that ever God made. If out of so base a thing as ink there may be extracted a spirit, he writ with nought but the spirit of ink; and his style was the spirituality of arts, and nothing else, whereas all others of his age were but the lay temporalty of inkhorn terms.[147] For indeed they were mere temporizers, and no better. His pen was sharp pointed like a poniard. No leaf he wrote on but was like a burning glass to set on fire all his readers. With more than musket shot did he charge his quill, where he meant to inveigh. No one hour but he sent a whole legion of devils into some herd of swine or other. If Martial had ten muses (as he saith of himself) when he but tasted a cup of wine, he had ten score when he determined to tyrannize. Ne'er a line of his but was able to make a man drunken with admiration. His sight pierced like lightning into the entrails of all abuses. This I must needs say, that most of his learning he got by hearing the lectures at Florence. It is sufficient that learning he had, and a conceit exceeding all learning, to quintessence everything which he heard.

He was no timorous, servile flatterer of the commonwealth wherein he lived. His tongue and his invention were forborne; what they thought, they would confidently utter. Princes he spared not that in the least point transgressed. His life he contemned in comparison of the liberty of speech. Whereas some dull-brain maligners of his accuse him of that treatise, *De Tribus Impostoribus Mundi*,[148] which was never contrived without a general counsel of devils, I am verily

[147]*lay temporalty of inkhorn terms:* "Lay temporalty" seems to mean something like "users" or "possessors," and "inkhorn terms" are bookish, pedantic expressions. The ensuing description of the style of Pietro Aretino (1492–1556) is quite accurate; his language was indeed "pointed," and he was widely called "the scourge of princes" (*Il flagello de principi*, as Jack says later on); some of the princes he bribed into favors. He probably had no connection with John Russell, but Henry VIII seems to have given Aretino about 200 crowns (T. C. Chubb, *Aretino* [New York, 1940], p. 403). Note that Jack's portrait of Aretino as a kind of intellectual Robin Hood is consistent with his own sense of values; to Jack, imaginative knavery is heroic.

[148]*De Tribus Impostoribus Mundi:* Aretino was one of many who were accused of writing *De Tribus;* Boccaccio, Machiavelli, Erasmus, and Milton were some others. The treatise was supposed to have offered proof that Christ, Moses, and Mohammed were imposters. Actually, although allusions to an alleged author are frequent during the Renaissance (and the accusers usually are "sincere"), there is no proof that *De Tribus* ever existed—and certainly it does not exist now. See Don Cameron Allen, *Doubt's Boundless Sea* (Baltimore, 1964), pp. 224–243.

persuaded it was none of his; and of my mind are a number of the most judicial Italians. One reason is this: because it was published forty years after his death. And he never in all his life wrote anything in Latin. Certainly I have heard that one of Machiavel's followers and disciples was the author of that book, who, to avoid discredit, filched it forth under Aretino's name a great while after he had sealed up his eloquent spirit in the grave. Too much gall did that wormwood of Ghibelline wits put in his ink, who engraved that rhubarb epitaph on this excellent poet's tombstone. Quite forsaken of all good angels was he, and utterly given over to an artless envy. Four universities honored Aretino with these rich titles: *Il flagello de principi, Il veritiero, Il devino,* and *L'unico Aretino.*

The French king, Francis the First, he kept in such awe that, to chain his tongue, he sent him a huge chain of gold in the form of tongues fashioned. Singularly hath he commented of the humanity of Christ. Besides, as Moses set forth his Genesis, so hath he set forth his Genesis also, including the contents of the whole Bible. A notable treatise hath he compiled, called *Il sette Psalmi poenetentiarii.* All the Thomasos have cause to love him because he hath dilated so magnificently of the life of Saint Thomas. There is a good thing that he hath set forth, *La Vita della Virgine Maria,* though it somewhat smell of superstition, with a number more which here for tediousness I suppress.

If lascivious he were, he may answer, with Ovid, *vita verecunda est, musa jocosa mea est:* my life is chaste, though wanton be my verse. Tell me, who is most traveled in histories: what good poet is, or ever was there, who hath not had a little spice of wantonness in his days? Even Beza himself, by your leave. Aretino, as long as the world lives shalt thou live. Tully, Virgil, Ovid, Seneca were never such ornaments to Italy as thou hast been. I never thought of Italy more religiously than England till I heard of thee. Peace to thy ghost, and yet methinks so indefinite a spirit should have no peace or intermission of pains, but be penning ditties to the archangels in another world. Puritans spew forth the venom of your dull inventions, A toad swells with thick, troubled poison. You swell with poisonous perturbations; your malice hath not a clear dram of any inspired disposition.

[6. *Florence*]

My principal subject plucks me by the elbow. Diamante, Castaldo's the magnifico's wife, after my enlargement, proved to be with child, at which instant there grew an insatiable famine in Venice; wherein, whether it were for mere niggardise, or that Castaldo still ate out his heart with jealousy, St. Anne be our record, he turned up the heels very devoutly. To Master Aretino, after this, once more very dutifully I appealed, requested him of favor, acknowledged former gratuities. He made no more humming or halting but, in despite of her husband's kinfolks, gave her her *nunc dimittis* and so established her free of my company.

Being out, and fully possessed of her husband's goods, she invested me in the state of a monarch. Because the time of childbirth drew nigh, and she could not remain in Venice but discredited, she decreed to travel whithersoever I would conduct her. To see Italy throughout was my proposed scope. And that way if she would travel, have with her, I had wherewithal to relieve her.

From my master, by her full-hand provokement, I parted without leave. The state of an earl he had thrust upon me before, and now I would not bate him an inch of it. Through all the cities passed I by no other name but the young Earl of Surrey. My pomp, my apparel, train, and expense was nothing inferior to his; my looks were as lofty, my words as magnifical.

Memorandum: that Florence being the principal scope of my master's course, missing me, he journeyed thither without interruption. By the way as he went, he heard of another Earl of Surrey besides himself, which caused him make more haste to fetch me in, whom he little dreamed of had such art in my budget to separate the shadow from the body.

Overtake me at Florence he did, where, sitting in my pontificalibus[149] with my courtesan at supper (like Anthony and Cleopatra, when they quaffed standing bowls of wine spiced with pearl together) he stole in ere we sent for him, and bade much good it us, and asked us whether we wanted any guests. If he had asked me whether I would have hanged myself, his question had been more acceptable. He that had then ungartered me might have plucked out my heart at my hams.

My soul, which was made to soar upward, now sought for passage downward; my blood, as the blushing Sabine maids surprised on the sudden by the soldiers of Romulus, ran to the noblest of blood amongst them for succor, that were in no less (if not greater) danger,

---

[149]*pontificalibus:* literally, the ceremonial robes of a bishop; here it means the same as "My pomp, my apparel," two paragraphs above (that is, what Jack wears to impersonate the Earl of Surrey).

so did it run for refuge to the noblest of his blood about my heart assembled, that stood in more need itself of comfort and refuge. A trembling earthquake or shaking fever assailed either of us, and I think unfeignedly. If he, seeing our faint-heart agony, had not soon cheered and refreshed us, the dogs had gone together by the ears under the table for our fear-dropped limbs.

Instead of menacing or affrighting me with his sword or his frowns for my superlative presumption, he burst out into a laughter above E-la[150], to think how bravely napping he had took us, and how notably we were damped and struck dead in the nest with the unexpected view of his presence.

"Ah," quoth he, "my noble lord" (after his tongue had borrowed a little leave of his laughter) "is it my luck to visit you thus unlooked for? I am sure you will bid me welcome, if it be but for the name's sake. It is a wonder to see two English earls of one house, at one time together in Italy."

I, hearing him so pleasant, began to gather up my spirits, and replied as boldly as I durst.

"Sir, you are welcome; your name which I have borrowed I have not abused. Some large sums of money this my sweet mistress Diamante hath made me master of, which I knew not how better to employ for the honor of my country than by spending it munificently under your name. No Englishman would I have renowned for bounty, magnificence, and courtesy but you. Under your colors all my meritorious works I was desirous to shroud. Deem it no insolence to add increase to your fame. Had I basely and beggarly, wanting ability to support any part of your royalty, undertook the estimation of this high calling, your allegement of injury had been the greater, and my defense less authorized. It will be thought but a policy of yours thus to send one before you who, being a follower of yours, shall keep and uphold the estate and port of an earl. I have known many earls myself that in their own persons would go very plain but delighted to have one that belonged to them (being laden with jewels, appareled in cloth of gold and all the rich embroidery that might be) to stand bareheaded unto him. Arguing thus much: that if the greatest men went not more sumptuous, how more great than the greatest was he that could command one going so sumptuous. A nobleman's glory appeareth in nothing so much as in the pomp of his attendants. What is the glory of the sun but that the moon and

---

[150]*E-la:* a high, treble note in music.

so many millions of stars borrow their light from him? If you can reprehend me of any one illiberal, licentious action I have disparaged your name with, heap shame on me prodigally. I beg no pardon or pity."

Non veniunt in idem pudor et amor: he was loath to detract from one that he loved so. Beholding with his eyes that I clipped not the wings of his honor, but rather increased them with additions of expense, he entreated me as if I had been an ambassador. He gave me his hand and swore he had no more hearts but one and I should have half of it, in that I so enhanced his obscured reputation.

"One thing," quoth he, "my sweet Jack, I will entreat thee (it shall be but one) that though I am well pleased thou shouldst be the ape of my birthright (as what nobleman hath not his ape and his fool) yet that thou be an ape without a clog,[151] not carry thy courtesan with thee.

I told him that a king could do nothing without his treasury; this courtesan was my purse bearer, my countenance, and supporter.

"My earldom I would sooner resign than part with such a special benefactress. Resign it I will, however, since I am thus challenged of stolen goods by the true owner. Lo, into my former state I return again; poor Jack Wilton and your servant am I, as I was at the beginning, and so will I persevere to my life's ending."

That theme was quickly cut off, and other talk entered in place. Of what I have forgot, but talk it was, and talk let it be. And talk it shall be, for I do not mean here to remember it. We supped, we got to bed, we rose in the morning. On my master I waited; and the first thing he did after he was up, he went and visited the house where his Geraldine was born. At sight whereof he was so impassioned that in the open street, but for me, he would have made an oration in praise of it. Into it we were conducted and showed each several room thereto appertaining. Oh, but when he came to the chamber where his Geraldine's clear sunbeams first thrust themselves into this cloud of flesh and acquainted mortality with the purity of angels, then did his mouth overflow with magnificats. His tongue thrust the stars out of heaven, and eclipsed the sun and moon with comparisons. Geraldine was the soul of heaven, sole daughter and heir to *primus motor*. The alchemy of his eloquence, out of the incomprehensible drossy matter of clouds and air, distilled no more quintessence than would make his Geraldine complete fair.

[151]*clog:* a heavy object (usually a block of wood) attached to an ape's leg to prevent escape.

In praise of the chamber that was so illuminatively honored with her radiant conception, he penned this sonnet:

Fair room, the presence of sweet beauty's pride,
The place the sun upon the earth did hold,
When Phaëthon his chariot did misguide,
The tower where Jove rained down himself in gold.
Prostrate as holy ground I'll worship thee;
Our Lady's chapel henceforth be thou nam'd;
Here first love's queen put on mortality,
And with her beauty all the world inflam'd.
Heav'n's chambers harboring fiery cherubines,
Are not with thee in glory to compare;
Lightning it is not light which in thee shines,
None enter thee but straight entranced are.
Oh, if Elysium be above the ground,
Then here it is where nought but joy is found.

Many other poems and epigrams in that chamber's patient alabaster enclosure, which her melting eyes long sithence had softened, were curiously engraved. Diamonds thought themselves *dii mundi* if they might but carve her name on the naked glass. With them on it did he anatomize these body-wanting mots: *dulce puella malum est. Quod fugit ipse sequor. Amor est mihi causa sequendi. O infoelix ego. Cur vidi, cur perii. Non patienter amo. Tantum patiatur amari.* After the view of these venereal monuments, he published a proud challenge in the Duke of Florence's court against all comers (whether Christians, Turks, Cannibals,[152] Jews, or Saracens) in defense of his Geraldine's beauty. More mildly was it accepted, in that she whom he defended was a townborn child of that city; or else the pride of the Italian would have prevented him ere he should have come to perform it. The Duke of Florence nevertheless sent for him and demanded him of his estate, and the reason that drew him thereto; which, when he was advertised of to the full, he granted all countries whatsoever (as well enemies and outlaws as friends and confederates) free access and regress into his dominions unmolested, until that insolent trial were ended.

The right honorable and ever renowned Lord Henry Howard, Earl of Surrey, my singular good lord and master, entered the lists after this order. His armor was all intermixed with lilies and roses, and

[152]*Cannibals:* capitalized because Columbus, Montaigne, and others in the Renaissance thought of cannibals as natives of the Caribbean area, not just as eaters of human flesh. "Cannibals" was omitted in the second edition and also by McKerrow in his edition.

the bases thereof bordered with nettles and weeds (signifying stings, crosses, and overgrowing encumbrances in his love); his helmet round proportioned like a gardener's waterpot, from which seemed to issue forth small threads of water, like cithern strings, that not only did moisten the lilies and roses but did fructify as well the nettles and weeds, and made them overgrow their liege lords. Whereby he did import thus much, that the tears that issued from his brain, as those artificial distillations issued from the well-counterfeit waterpot on his head, watered and gave life as well to his mistress' disdain (resembled to nettles and weeds) as increase of glory to her care-causing beauty (comprehended under the lilies and roses). The symbol thereto annexed was this: *ex lachrimis lachrimae.*

The trappings of his horse were pounced and bolstered out with rough-plumed silver plush, in full proportion and shape of an ostrich. On the breast of the horse were the foreparts of this greedy bird advanced. Whence, as his manner is, he reached out his long neck to the reins of the bridle, thinking they had been iron, and still seemed to gape after the golden bit and, ever as the courser did raise or curvet, to have swallowed it half in. His wings, which he never useth but running, being spreaded full sail, made his lusty steed as proud under him as he had been some other Pegasus. And so quiveringly and tenderly were these his broad wings bound to either side of him that, as he paced up and down the tiltyard in his majesty ere the knights were entered, they seemed wantonly to fan in his face and make a flickering sound, such as eagles do, swiftly pursuing their prey in the air. On either of his wings, as the ostrich hath a sharp goad or prick wherewith he spurreth himself forward in his sail-assisted race, so this artificial ostrich, on the inbent knuckle of the pinion of either wing, had embossed chrystal eyes affixed, wherein wheelwise were circularly engrafted sharp pointed diamonds, as rays from those eyes derived, that, like the rowels of a spur, ran deep into his horse's sides and made him more eager in his course.

Such a fine, dim shine did these chrystal eyes and these round-enranked diamonds make through their bollen,[153] swelling bowers of feathers, as if it had been a candle in a paper lantern, or a glow-worm in a bush by night glistering through the leaves and briers. The tail of the ostrich, being short and thick, served very fitly as a plume to trick up his horse's tail with, so that every part of him was as naturally coapted as might be. The word to this device was *aculeo alatus:* I spread my wings only spurred with her eyes.

[153]*bollen:* swollen.

The moral of the whole is this: that as the ostrich, the most burning-sighted bird of all others, insomuch as the female of them hatcheth not her eggs by covering them but by the effectual rays of her eyes—as he, I say, outstrippeth the nimblest trippers of his feathered condition in footmanship, only spurred on with the needle-quickening goad under his side, so he no less burning-sighted than the ostrich, spurred on to the race of honor by the sweet rays of his mistress' eyes, persuaded himself he should outstrip all other in running to the goal of glory only animated and incited by her excellence. And as the ostrich will eat iron, swallow any hard metal whatsoever, so would he refuse no iron adventure, no hard task whatsoever, to sit in the grace of so fair a commander.

The order of his shield was this: it was framed like a burning glass, beset round with flame-colored feathers; on the outside whereof was his mistress' picture adorned as beautiful as art could portraiture; on the inside a naked sword tied in a true love knot; the mot, *militat omnis amans,* signifying that in a true love knot his sword was tied to defend and maintain the high features of his mistress.

Next him entered the black knight, whose beaver was pointed[154] all torn and bloody, as though he had new come from combatting with a bear. His headpiece seemed to be a little oven fraught full with smothering flames, for nothing but sulphur and smoke voided out at the clefts of his beaver. His bases were all embroidered with snakes and adders, engendered of the abundance of innocent blood that was shed. His horse's trappings were throughout bespangled with honey-spots,[155] which are no blemishes, but ornaments. On his shield he bare the sun full shining on a dial at his going down; the word, *sufficit tandem.*

After him followed the knight of the owl, whose armor was a stubbed tree overgrown with ivy; his helmet fashioned like an owl sitting on the top of this ivy; on his bases were wrought all kind of birds as on the ground wandering about him; the word, *ideo mirum quia monstrum.* His horse's furniture was framed like a cart, scattering whole sheaves of corn amongst hogs; the word, *liberalitas liberalitate perit.* On his shield a bee entangled in sheep's wool; the mot, *frontis nulla fides.*

The fourth that succeeded was a well-proportioned knight in an

---

[154]*pointed:* that is, appointed (designed or made to appear).

[155]*honey spots:* Usually the expression meant "moles in the flesh," which are blemishes; but here the sense is "honey-colored spots" deliberately painted, or otherwise placed, on the trappings of a horse as ornaments.

armor imitating rust, whose headpiece was prefigured like flowers growing in a narrow pot where they had not any space to spread their roots or disperse their flourishing. His bases embellished with open armed hands scattering gold amongst truncheons; the word, *cura futuri est.* His horse was harnessed with leaden chains having the outside gilt, or at least saffroned instead of gilt, to decipher a holy or golden pretense of a covetous purpose; the sentence, *cani capilli mei compedes.* On his target he had a number of crawling worms kept under by a block; the faburden,[156] *speramus lucent.*

The fifth was the forsaken knight, whose helmet was crowned with nothing but cypress and willow garlands. Over his armor he had on Hymen's nuptial robe dyed in a dusky yellow, and all to be defaced and discolored with spots and stains. The enigma, *nos quoque florimus* as who should say, we have been in fashion. His steed was adorned with orange, tawny eyes, such as those have that have the yellow jaundice, that make all things yellow they look upon; with this brief, *qui invident egent:* those that envy are hungry.

The sixth was the knight of the storms, whose helmet was round molded like the moon, and all his armor like waves whereon the shine of the moon, sleightly[157] silvered, perfectly represented moonshine in the water; his bases were the banks or shores that bounded in the streams. The spoke was this, *frustra pius:* as much to say, as fruitless service. On his shield he set forth a lion driven from his prey by a dunghill cock. The word, *non vi sed voce:* not by violence but by his voice.

The seventh had, like the giants that sought to scale heaven in despite of Jupiter, a mount overwhelming his head and whole body. His bases outlaid with arms and legs which the skirts of that mountain left uncovered. Under this did he characterize a man, desirous to climb to the heaven of honor, kept under with the mountain of his prince's command; and yet had he arms and legs exempted from the suppression of that mountain. The word, *tu mihi criminis author* (alluding to his prince's command): thou are the occasion of my imputed cowardice. His horse was trapped in the earthy strings of tree roots; which, though their increase was stubbed down to the ground, yet were they not utterly deaded, but hoped for an after resurrection. The word, *spe alor:* I hope for a spring. Upon his shield

[156]*faburden:* word, motto (with perhaps also the suggestion that the motto is "high sounding"); literally, a musical term with several meanings, one of which is "refrain."
[157]*sleightly:* a pun: (1) deftly, and (2) slightly.

he bare a ball stricken down with a man's hand that it might mount. The word, *ferior ut efferar:* I suffer myself to be contemned because I will climb.

The eighth had all his armor throughout engrailed like a crabbed, briery hawthorn bush out of which, notwithstanding, sprung (as a good child of an ill father) fragrant blossoms of delightful may-flowers that made (according to the nature of May) a most odorif-erous smell. In midst of this his snowy, curled top, round wrapped together, on the ascending of his crest sat a solitary nightingale close encaged, with a thorn at her breast, having this mot in her mouth: *luctus monumenta manebunt.* At the foot of this bush represented on his bases lay a number of black, swollen toads gasping for wind, and summer-lived grasshoppers gaping after dew, both which were choked with excessive drought and for want of shade. The word, *non sine vunere viresco:* I spring not without impediments—alluding to the toads and suchlike, that erst lay sucking at his roots but now were turned out and near choked with drought. His horse was suited in black, sandy earth (as adjacent to this bush) which was here and there patched with short-burnt grass, and as thick ink dropped[158] with toiling ants and emmets as ever it might crawl, who, in the full of the summer moon (ruddy garnished on his horse's forehead) hoarded up their provision of grain against winter. The word, *victrix fortunae sapientia:* providence prevents misfortune. On his shield he set forth the picture of death doing alms deeds to a number of poor, desolate children. The word, *nemo alius explicat:* no other man takes pity upon us. What his meaning was herein I cannot imagine, except death had done him and his brethren some great good turn in rid-ding them of some untoward parent or kinsman that would have been their confusion; for else I cannot see how death should have been said to do alms deeds, except he had deprived them suddenly of their lives to deliver them out of some further misery Which could not in any wise be, because they were yet living.

The ninth was the infant knight, who on his armor had enameled a poor young infant put into a ship without tackling, masts, furniture, or anything. This weather-beaten and ill-appareled ship was shad-owed on his bases, and the slender compass of his body set forth the

---

[158]*as thick ink dropped:* The sense through here is obscure; McKerrow inserts a hyphen between "ink" and "dropped," but it is difficult to see how that clears up the sense. Perhaps something has been omitted; surely the punctuation is faulty.

right picture of an infant. The waves wherein the ship was tossed were fretted on his steed's trappings so movingly that, ever as he offered to bound or stir, they seemed to bounce and toss and sparkle brine out of their hoary, silver billows. Their mot, *inopem me copia fecit:* as much to say, as the rich prey makes the thief. On his shield he expressed an old goat that made a young tree to wither only with biting it. The word thereto, *primo extinguor in aevo:* I am frostbitten ere I come out of the blade.

It were here too tedious to manifest all the discontented or amorous devices that were used in that tournament. The shields only of some few I will touch to make short work. One bare for his impress the eyes of young swallows coming again after they were plucked out, with this mot, *et addit et addimit*: your beauty both bereaves and restores my sight. Another, a siren smiling when the sea rageth and ships are overwhelmed, including a cruel woman that laughs, sings, and scorns at her lover's tears and the tempests of his despair; the word, *cuncta pereunt*: all my labor is ill employed. A third, being troubled with a curst, a treacherous, and wanton, wanton wife, used this similitude: on his shield he caused to be limned Pompey's ordinance for parricides, as namely a man put into a sack with a cock, a serpent, and an ape—interpreting that his wife was a cock for her crowing, a serpent for her stinging, and an ape for her unconstant wantonness—with which ill qualities he was so beset that thereby he was thrown into a sea of grief. The word, *extremum malorum mulier*: the utmost of evils is a woman. A fourth, who, being a person of suspected religion, was continually haunted with intelligencers and spies that thought to prey upon him for that he had, he could not devise which way to shake them off but by making away that he had. To obscure this, he used no other fancy but a number of blind flies whose eyes the cold had closed; the word, *aurum reddit acutissimum:* gold is the only physic for the eyesight. A fifth, whose mistress was fallen into a consumption, and yet would condescend to no treaty of love, emblazoned for his complaint grapes that withered for want of pressing. The ditty to the mot, *quid regna sine usu.*

I will rehearse no more, but I have an hundred other. Let this be the upshot of those shows: they were the admirablest that ever Florence yielded. To particularize their manner of encounter were to describe the whole art of tilting. Some had like to have fallen over their horse's neck and so break their necks in breaking their staves. Others ran at a buckle instead of a button, and peradventure whetted their spears' points, idly gliding on their enemies' sides, but did no other harm. Others ran across at their adversaries' left elbow; yea, and by your leave sometimes let not the lists 'scape scot-free, they were so eager. Others, because they would be sure not to be unsaddled with the shock, when they came to the spear's utmost proof, they threw it over the right shoulder and so tilted backward, for forward they durst not. Another had a monstrous spite at the pommel of his rival's saddle and thought to have thrust his spear twixt his legs without raising any skin, and carried him clean away on it as a cool-staff.[159] Another held his spear to his nose, or his nose to his spear, as though he had been discharging a caliver, and ran at the right foot of his fellow's steed. Only the Earl of Surrey, my master, observed the true measures of honor and made all his encounterers new scour their armor in the dust. So great was his glory that day as Geraldine was thereby eternally glorified. Never such a bountiful master came amongst the heralds—not that he did enrich them with any plentiful purse-largess, but that by his stern assaults he tithed them more rich offals of bases, of helmets, of armor than the rent of their offices came to in ten years before.

What would you have more? The trumpets proclaimed him master of the field; the trumpets proclaimed Geraldine the exceptionless fairest of women. Everyone strived to magnify him more than other. The Duke of Florence, whose name (as my memory serveth me) was Paschal de Medices,[160] offered him such large proffers to stay with him as it were incredible to report. He would not. His desire was, as he had done in Florence, so to proceed throughout all the chief cities in Italy. If you ask why he began not this at Venice first, it was because he would let Florence, his mistress' native city, have the maidenhead of his chivalry. As he came back again he thought to have enacted something there worthy the annals of posterity, but he was debarred both of that and all his other determinations. For continuing in feasting and banqueting with the Duke of Florence and the princes of Italy there assembled, posthaste letters came to him from the king his master to return as speedily as he could pos-

---

[159]*cool-staff:* cowl-staff (a long stick); two men carried a "cowl" or tub by placing the stick on their shoulders after inserting it through the handles of the tub.

[160]*Paschal de Medices:* Jack's "memory" does not serve him very well, since there was no Paschal de' Medici (in the Medici family that ruled Florence off and on all through the Renaissance); but probably Nashe is deliberately inventing a fictitious first name.

sible into England. Whereby his fame was quite cut off by the shins and there was no reprieve but, *bazelus manus,*[161] he must into England, and I with my courtesan traveled forward in Italy.

[7. Rome]

What adventures happened him after we parted I am ignorant, but Florence we both forsook. And I, having a wonderful ardent inclination to see Rome (the queen of the world and metropolitan mistress of all other cities) made thither with my bag and baggage as fast as I could.

Attained thither, I was lodged at the house of one Johannes de Imola, a Roman cavaliero. Who, being acquainted with my courtesan's deceased, doting husband, for his sake used us with all the familiarity that might be. He showed us all the monuments that were to be seen, which are as many as there have been emperors, consuls, orators, conquerors, famous painters, or players in Rome. Till this day not a Roman (if he be a right Roman indeed) will kill a rat but he will have some registered remembrance of it. There was a poor fellow during my remainder there that, for a new trick he had invented of killing cimices and scorpions, had his mountebank banner hung up on a high pillar, with an inscription about it longer than the King of Spain's style. I thought these cimices, like the Cimbrians,[162] had been some strange nation he had brought under, and they were no more but things like sheep lice which, alive, have the venomost sting that may be and, being dead, do stink out of measure. St. Austen[163] compareth heretics unto them.

The chiefest thing that my eyes delighted in was the Church of the Seven Sibyls,[164] which is a most miraculous thing. All their prophecies and oracles being there enrolled, as also the beginning

[161]*bazelus manus:* that is, *beso las manos,* Spanish for "good-by" (literally, "kiss the hands").

[162]*cimices . . . Cimbrians:* The cimex (plural, cimices) is a bedbug; Jack chooses the learned-sounding word "Cimbrians" (an ancient Germanic tribe) because the sound is similar to "cimices."

[163]*St. Austen:* St. Augustine, Bishop of Hippo.

[164]*Church of the Seven Sibyls:* probably another example of fictitious naming (though it may be worth noting that the Sistine Chapel fresco, painted by Michelangelo, 1508–1512, has five sibyls and seven prophets in it). Traditionally, one sibyl was called the Cimmerian Sibyl; if Jack has her in mind, it probably is by a process of sound association (cimices–Cimbrians–Cimmerian).

and ending of their whole catalogue of the heathen gods, with their manner of worship. There are a number of other shrines and statues also dedicated to their emperors, and withal some statues of idolatry reserved for detestation. I was at Pontius Pilate's house and pissed against it.[165] There is the prison yet packed up together (an old rotten thing) where the man that was condemned to death, and could have nobody come to him and succor him but was searched, was kept alive a long space by sucking his daughter's breasts.

These are but the shop dust of the sights that I saw, and in truth I did not behold with any care hereafter to report but contented my eye for the present. And so let them pass. Should I memorize half the miracles which they there told me had been done about martyrs' tombs, or the operations of the earth of the sepulcher, and other relics brought from Jerusalem, I should be counted the monstrost[166] liar that ever came in print.

The ruins of Pompey's theater, reputed one of the nine wonders of the world; Gregory the Sixth's tomb; Priscilla's grate; or the thousands of pillars arreared amongst the razed foundations of old Rome—it were here frivolous to specify since he that hath but once drunk with a traveler talks of them. Let me be a historiographer of my own misfortunes and not meddle with the continued trophies of so old a triumphing city.

At my first coming to Rome, I being a youth of the English cut, wore my hair long, went appareled in light colors, and imitated four or five sundry nations in my attire at once. Which no sooner was noted, but I had all the boys of the city in a swarm wondering about me. I had not gone a little farther but certain officers crossed the way of me and demanded to see my rapier; which when they found

---

[165]*against it:* At this point—after "against it" and before "There is"—the following sentence, omitted from the first edition, was inserted in the second edition: "The name of the place I remember not, but it is as one goes to St. Paul's Church, not far from the iemmes Piazza." What "iemmes" refers to is not clear. Ashley and Moseley suggest "Gems"; if that is correct, possibly the reference is to the *Scalae Gemoniae* (the *Gemonies*). Berryman likes the emendation, "Jews'" (in which case "Jews' Piazza" would be the "Piazza Giudea" near or in the ghetto in Rome).

[166]*the monstrost:* an emendation of "the monstrous" in both early editions. It is possible, as Grosart thinks, that "most" was omitted by mistake before "monstrous"; but it seems more likely, on the analogy of "venomost" (most venomous), two paragraphs above, that Nashe intended "monstrost" (as McKerrow suggests).

(as also my dagger) with his point unblunted, they would have haled me headlong to the strappado but that with money I appeased them. And my fault was more pardonable in that I was a stranger, altogether ignorant of their customs.

Note, by the way, that it is the use in Rome for all men whatsoever to wear their hair short; which they do not so much for conscience's sake, or any religion they place in it, but because the extremity of the heat is such there that, if they should not do so, they should not have a hair left on their heads to stand upright when they were scared with sprites.[167] And he is counted no gentleman amongst them that goes not in black; they dress their jesters and fools only in fresh colors, and say variable garments do argue unstayedness and unconstancy of affection.

The reason of their strait ordinance for carrying weapons without points is this: the bandettos, which are certain outlaws that lie betwixt Rome and Naples and besiege the passage, that none can travel that way without robbing. Now and then, hired for some few crowns, they will steal to Rome and do a murder and betake them to their heels again. Disguised as they go, they are not known from strangers; sometimes they will shroud themselves under the habit of grave citizens. In this consideration neither citizen nor stranger, gentleman, knight, marquis, or any, may wear any weapon endamageable upon pain of the strappado. I bought it out; let others buy experience of me better cheap.

To tell you of the rare pleasures of their gardens, their baths, their vineyards, their galleries were to write a second part of the *Gorgeous Gallery of Gallant Devices*.[168] Why, you should not come into any man's house of account but he had fishponds and little orchards on the top of his leads.[169] If by rain or any other means those ponds were so full they need to be sluiced[170] or let out, even of

[167]*the extremity of the heat . . . sprites:* The humorous exaggeration here is perhaps our cue as to how we should take Jack's claim as an "historiographer."

[168]*Gorgeous . . . Devices:* So that he can play on the word "gallery," Jack quotes the title of an Elizabethan poetical miscellany, by Thomas Procter, published in 1578.

[169]*leads:* roof (made of sheets or strips of lead).

[170]*sluiced:* In the first edition the word is either "sluste" or "fluste," it seems impossible to tell which; McKerrow probably is right that the intended word, in modern spelling, is "sluiced" (though "flushed" would also make good sense).

their superfluities they made melodious use; for they had great wind instruments, instead of leaden spouts, that went duly in consort, only with this water's rumbling descent.

I saw a summer banqueting house, belonging to a merchant, that was the marvel of the world and could not be matched except God should make another paradise. It was built round of green marble, like a theater without; within, there was a heaven and earth comprehended both under one roof. The heaven was a clear, overhanging vault of crystal, wherein the sun and moon and each visible star had his true similitude, shine, situation, and motion; and, by what enwrapped[171] art I cannot conceive, these spheres in their proper orbs observed their circular wheelings and turnings, making a certain kind of soft, angelical, murmuring music in their often windings and going about. Which music the philosophers say in the true heaven, by reason of the grossness of our senses, we are not capable of.

For the earth, it was counterfeited in that likeness that Adam lorded it out before his fall. A wide, vast spacious room it was, such as we would conceit Prince Arthur's hall to be, where he feasted all his knights of the Round Table together every Pentecost. The floor was painted with the beautifullest flowers that ever man's eye admired, which so lineally[172] were delineated that he that viewed them afar off, and had not directly stood poringly over them, would have sworn they had lived indeed. The walls round about were hedged with olives and palm trees, and all other odoriferous, fruit-bearing plants, which at any solemn entertainment dropped myrrh and frankincense. Other trees, that bare no fruit, were set in just order one against another and divided the room into a number of shady lanes, leaving but one overspreading pine tree arbor, where we sat and banqueted.

On the well-clothed boughs of this conspiracy of pine trees against the resembled sunbeams were perched as many sorts of shrill-breasted birds as the summer hath allowed for singing men in her sylvan chapels. Who, though there were bodies without souls, and sweet-resembled substances without sense, yet by the mathematical experiments of long silver pipes secretly inrinded[173] in the entrails of the

---

[171]*enwrapped:* Possibly the intent is "enrapt" (absorbed and inspired) rather than "enwrapped," the word in both the early editions. Yet the two words could mean practically the same thing; see the *OED*, "enwrap," 2a.

[172]*lineally:* The context appears to make the word mean "in vivid detail"; McKerrow may be right that "lineally" is a printer's error for "lively."

[173]*inrinded:* inserted.

boughs whereon they sat, and undiscernibly conveyed unto their bellies into their small throats' sloping, they whistled and freely caroled their natural field note. Neither went those silver pipes straight, but, by many-edged, unsundered writhings, and crankled wanderings aside, strayed from bough to bough into an hundred throats. But into this silver pipe so writhed and wandering aside, if any demand how the wind was breathed, forsooth the tail of the silver pipe stretched itself into the mouth of a great pair of bellows, where it was close soldered and baled about with iron; it could not stir or have any vent betwixt. Those bellows, with the rising and falling of leaden plummets wound up on a wheel, did beat up and down incessantly, and so gathered in wind, serving with one blast all the snarled pipes to and fro of one tree at once. But so closely were all those organizing implements obscured in the corpulent trunks of the trees that every man there present renounced conjectures of art and said it was done by enchantment.

One tree for his fruit bare nothing but enchained, chirruping birds, whose throats being conduit piped with squared, narrow shells, and charged syringe-wise with searching sweet water, driven in by a little wheel for the nonce that fed it afar off, made a spirting sound, such as chirping is, in bubbling upwards through the rough crannies of their closed bills.

Under tuition of the shade of every tree that I have signified to be in this round hedge, on delightful leafy cloisters, lay a wild, tyrannous beast asleep, all prostrate; under some, two together—as the dog nuzzling his nose under the neck of the deer, the wolf glad to let the lamb lie upon him to keep him warm, the lion suffering the ass to cast his leg over him (preferring one honest, unmannerly friend before a number of crouching pickthanks). No poisonous beast there reposed (poison was not before our parent Adam transgressed). There were no sweet-breathing panthers that would hide their terrifying heads to betray, no men imitating hyenas that changed their sex to seek after blood. Wolves as now when they are hungry eat earth, so then did they feed on earth only and abstained from innocent flesh. The unicorn did not put his horn into the stream to chase away venom before he drunk, for there was no such thing as venom extant in the water or on the earth. Serpents were as harmless to mankind as they are still one to another. The rose had no cankers, the leaves no caterpillars, the sea no sirens, the earth no usurers. Goats then bare wool, as it is recorded in Sicily they do yet. The torrid zone was habitable. Only jays loved to steal gold and silver to build their nests withal, and none cared for covetous clientry or running to the Indies.[174] As the elephant understands his country speech, so every beast understood what men spoke. The ant did not hoard up against winter, for there was no winter but a perpetual spring, as Ovid saith. No frosts to make the green almond tree counted rash and improvident, in budding soonest of all other; or the mulberry tree a strange politician, in blooming late and ripening early. The peach tree at the first planting was fruitful and wholesome, whereas now, till it be transplanted, it is poisonous and hateful. Young plants for their sap had balm; for their yellow gum, glistering amber. The evening dewed not water on flowers, but honey. Such a golden age, such a good age, such an honest age was set forth in this banqueting house.

Oh, Rome, if thou hast in thee such soul-exalting objects, what a thing is heaven in comparison of thee, of which Mercator's globe is a perfecter model than thou art? Yet this I must say to the shame of us Protestants: if good works may merit heaven, they do them; we talk of them. Whether superstition or no makes them unprofitable servants, that let pulpits decide. But there you shall have the bravest ladies in gowns of beaten gold washing pilgrims' and poor soldiers' feet, and doing nothing, they and their waiting maids, all the year long, but making shirts and bands for them against they come by in distress. Their hospitals are more like noblemen's houses than otherwise—so richly furnished, clean kept, and hot perfumed that a soldier would think it a sufficient recompense, for his travel and his wounds, to have such a heavenly retiring place. For the pope and his pontificalibus, I will not deal with; only I will dilate unto you what happened whiles I was in Rome.

So it fell out that, it being a vehement hot summer when I was a sojourner there, there entered such a hotspurred plague as hath not been heard of. Why, it was but a word and a blow, Lord have mercy upon us, and he was gone. Within three quarters of a year in that one city there died of it a hundred thousand. Look in Lanquet's chronicle and you shall find it.[175] To smell of a nosegay that was poisoned, and

---

[174]*clientry . . . Indies:* The sense of "clientry" ("client" plus "ry") is simply "people" and probably is chosen for the alliteration with "cared" and "covetous." To the Renaissance Englishman both the East and the West Indies were sources of fabulous wealth.

[175]*Look in Lanquet's chronicle and you shall find it:* Jack is right; look under the year 1522, on sig. 3Z4ᵛ of the 1549 edition. But there is only one sentence, giving the number of dead; the rest of Jack's description is not from Lanquet, whose chronicle, incidentally, was left incomplete at his death in 1545. Thomas Cooper, later Bishop of Winchester, brought it to completion; after publication in 1549 as *An Epitome of Chronicles,* it was often referred to as "Cooper's chronicle."

turn your nose to a house that had the plague—it was all one. The clouds, like a number of cormorants that keep their corn till it stink and is musty, kept in their stinking exhalations till they had almost stifled all Rome's inhabitants. Physicians' greediness of gold made them greedy of their destiny. They would come to visit those with whose infirmities their art had no affinity; and even as a man with a fee should be hired to hang himself, so would they quietly go home and die presently after they had been with their patients. All day and all night long car men did nothing but go up and down the streets with their carts and cry, "Have you any dead to bury? Have you any dead to bury?" and had many times out of one house their whole loading. One grave was the sepulcher of seven score ; one bed was the altar whereon whole families were offered.

The walls were hoared and furred with the moist, scorching steam of their desolation. Even as before a gun is shot off, a stinking smoke funnels out and prepares the way for him; so before any gave up the ghost, death (arrayed in a stinking smoke) stopped his nostrils and crammed itself full into his mouth that closed up his fellow's eyes, to give him warning to prepare for his funeral. Some died sitting at their meat, others as they were asking counsel of the physician for their friends. I saw, at the house where I was hosted, a maid bring her master warm broth for to comfort him and she sink down dead herself ere he had half eat it up.

During this time of visitation, there was a Spaniard, one Esdras of Granada, a notable bandetto authorized by the pope because he assisted him in some murders. This villain, colleagued with one Bartol, a desperate Italian, practiced to break into those rich men's houses in the night where the plague had most rained; and if there were none but the mistress and maid left alive, to ravish them both and bring away all the wealth they could fasten on. In a hundred chief citizens' houses where the hand of God had been, they put this outrage *in ure*.[176] Though the women so ravished cried out, none durst come near them for fear of catching their deaths by them; and some thought they cried out only with the tyranny of the malady.

Amongst the rest, the house where I lay he invaded; where, all being snatched up by the sickness but the good wife of the house, a noble and chaste matron called Heraclide, and her zany, and I and my courtesan, he, knocking at the door late in the night, ran in to the matron and left me and my love to the mercy of his companion.

[176]*in ure:* into practice (that is, his "system" of breaking into houses and raping women).

Who, finding me in bed (as the time required) ran at me full with his rapier, thinking I would resist him; but as good luck was, I escaped him and betook me to my pistol in the window uncharged. He, fearing it had been charged, threatened to run her through if I once offered but to aim at him. Forth the chamber he dragged her, holding his rapier at her heart, whilst I still cried out, "Save her, kill me, and I'll ransom her with a thousand ducats." But lust prevailed; no prayers would be heard. Into my chamber I was locked, and watchmen charged (as he made semblance when there was none there) to knock me down with their halberds if I stirred but a foot down the stairs. So threw I myself pensive again on my pallet and dared all the devils in hell, now I was alone, to come and fight with me one after another in defense of that detestable rape. I beat my head against the walls and called them bawds, because they would see such a wrong committed and not fall upon him.

To return to Heraclide below, whom the ugliest of all bloodsuckers, Esdras of Granada, had under shrift.[177] First he assailed her with rough means, and slew her zany at her foot that stepped before her in rescue. Then when all armed resist was put to flight, he assayed her with honey speech and promised her more jewels and gifts than he was able to pilfer in an hundred years after. He discoursed unto her how he was countenanced and borne out by the pope, and how many execrable murders with impunity he had executed on them that displeased him.

"This is the eighth-score house," quoth he, "that hath done homage unto me; and here I will prevail, or I will be torn in pieces."

"Ah," quoth Heraclide with a heart-rending sigh, "art thou ordained to be a worse plague to me than the plague itself? Have I escaped the hands of God to fall into the hands of man? Hear me, Jehovah, and be merciful in ending my misery. Dispatch me incontinent, dissolute homicide, death's usurper. Here lies my husband stone cold on the dewy floor. If thou beest of more power than God to strike me speedily, strike home. Strike deep. Send me to heaven with my husband. Aye me, it is the spoil of my honor thou seekest in my soul's troubled departure; thou art some devil sent to tempt me. Avoid from me, Satan; my soul is my Savior's. To him I have be-

---

[177]*below . . . shrift:* Apparently Jack and Diamante are on the second floor or level, while Heraclide and her servant (zany) are on the first; also, Heraclide is below Esdras, in an attitude of confession or penance (though actually she is begging for her life); ironically, Esdras is the one who should be confessing.

queathed it; from him can no man take it. Jesu, Jesu spare me undefiled for thy spouse. Jesu, Jesu never fail those that put their trust in thee."

With that she fell in a swoon; and her eyes in their closing seemed to spawn forth in their outward sharp corners new created seed pearl, which the world before never set eye on. Soon he rigorously revived her and told her that he had a charter above Scripture. She must yield; she should yield. See who durst remove her out of his hands. Twixt life and death thus she faintly replied:

"How thinkest thou? Is there a power above thy power? If there be, he is here present in punishment; and on thee will take present punishment if thou persistest in thy enterprise. In the time of security every man sinneth. But when death substitutes one friend his special baily to arrest another by infection, and disperseth his quiver into ten thousand hands at once, who is it but looks about him? A man that hath an inevitable huge stone hanging only by a hair over his head, which he looks every paternoster-while to fall and pash him in pieces, will not he be submissively sorrowful for his transgressions, refrain himself from the least thought of folly, and purify his spirit with contrition and penitence? God's hand, like a huge stone, hangs inevitably over thy head. What is the plague but death playing the provost marshal, to execute all those that will not be called home by any other means? This my dear knight's body is a quiver of his arrows, which already are shot into thee invisible.

"Even as the age of goats is known by the knots in their horns, so think the anger of God apparently visioned or shown unto thee in the knitting of my brows. A hundred have I buried out of my house, at all whose departures I have been present. A hundred's infection is mixed with my breath; lo, now I breathe upon thee, a hundred deaths come upon thee. Repent betimes; imagine there is a hell though not a heaven. That hell thy conscience is thoroughly acquainted with, if thou hast murdered half so many as thou unblushingly braggest. As Maecenas in the latter end of his days was seven years without sleep, so these seven weeks have I took no slumber. My eyes have kept continual watch against the devil, my enemy. Death I deemed my friend (friends fly from us in adversity). Death, the devil, and all the ministering spirits of temptation are watching about thee to entrap thy soul by my abuse to eternal damnation. It is thy soul only thou mayest save by saving mine honor. Death will have thy body infallibly for breaking into my house, that he had selected for his private habitation.

"If thou ever camest of a woman, or hopest to be saved by the seed of a woman, spare a woman. Deers oppressed with dogs, when they cannot take soil, run to men for succor. To whom should women in their disconsolate and desperate estate run but to men, like the deer, for succor and sanctuary? If thou be a man, thou wilt succor me; but if thou be a dog and a brute beast, thou wilt spoil me, defile me, and tear me. Either renounce God's image or renounce the wicked mind that thou bearest."

These words might have moved a compound heart of iron and adamant. But in his heart they obtained no impression; for he sitting in his chair of state against the door all the while that she pleaded, leaning his overhanging, gloomy eyebrows on the pommel of his unsheathed sword, he never looked up or gave her a word. But when he perceived she expected his answer of grace or utter perdition, he started up and took her currishly by the neck, and asked her how long he should stay for her ladyship.

"Thou tellest me," quoth he, "of the plague, and the heavy hand of God, and thy hundred infected breaths in one. I tell thee I have cast the dice an hundred times for the galleys in Spain and yet still missed the ill chance. Our order of casting is this: if there be a general or captain new come home from the wars, and hath some four or five hundred crowns overplus of the king's in his hand, and his soldiers all paid, he makes proclamation that whatsoever two resolute men will go to dice for it, and win the bridle or lose the saddle,[178] to such a place let them repair and it shall be ready for them. Thither go I and find another such needy squire resident. The dice run, I win, he is undone. I, winning, have the crowns; he, losing, is carried to the galleys. This is our custom, which a hundred times and more hath paid me custom of crowns, when the poor fellows who have gone to Gehenna[179] had coarse bread and whipping cheer all their life after.

"Now thinkest thou that I, who so oft have escaped such a number of hellish dangers (only depending on the turning of a few pricks), can be scare-bugged with the plague? What plague canst thou name worse than I have had? Whether diseases, imprisonment, poverty, banishment—I have passed through them all. My own mother gave I a box of the ear to, and broke her neck down a pair of stairs, be-

---

[178]*win ... saddle:* perhaps a conscious variation of the proverb (Tilley, H693): "Steal the horse and carry home the bridle."

[179]*Gehenna:* prison; or, in this case, the galleys (from Gehenna in the Bible, meaning "hell" or "hellfire").

cause she would not go in to a gentleman when I bade her. My sister I sold to an old leno[180] to make his best of her. Any kinswoman that I have, knew I she were not a whore, myself would make her one. Thou art a whore; thou shalt be a whore in spite of religion or precise ceremonies."

Therewith he flew upon her and threatened her with his sword, but it was not *that* he meant to wound her with. He grasped her by the ivory throat and shook her as a mastiff would shake a young bear, swearing and staring[181] he would tear out her weasand if she refused. Not content with that savage constraint, he slipped his sacrilegious hand from her lily lawn-skinned[182] neck and enscarfed it in her long silver locks, which with struggling were unrolled. Backward he dragged her even as a man backward would pluck a tree down by the twigs. And then, like a traitor that is drawn to execution on a hurdle, he traileth her up and down the chamber by those tender, untwisted braids; and, setting his barbarous foot on her bare, snowy breast, bade her yield or have her wind stamped out.

She cried, "Stamp! Stifle me in my hair, hang me up by it on a beam, and so let me die rather than I should go to heaven with a beam in my eye."

"No," quoth he, "nor stamped, nor stifled, nor hanged, nor to heaven shalt thou go till I have had my will of thee. Thy busy arms in these silken fetters I'll enfold."

Dismissing her hair from his fingers and pinioning her elbows therewithal, she struggled, she wrested, but all was in vain. So struggling and so resisting, her jewels did sweat, signifying there was poison coming towards her. On the hard boards he threw her and used his knee as an iron ram to beat open the two-leaved gate of her chastity. Her husband's dead body he made a pillow to his abomination.

Conjecture the rest. My words stick fast in the mire and are clean tired; would I had never undertook this tragical tale. Whatsoever is born is born to have end. Thus endeth my tale: his boorish lust was glutted, his beastly desire satisfied; what in the house of any worth was carriageable, he put up and went his way.

Let not your sorrow die, you that have read the proem and narration of this elegiacal history. Show you have quick wits in sharp

---

[180]*leno:* pimp (from the Italian, *lenone*).

[181]*swearing and staring:* an idiom, with the connotation of uncontrollable rage.

[182]*lawn-skinned:* soft-skinned (like the texture of fine lawn or linen).

conceit of compassion. A woman that hath viewed all her children sacrificed before her eyes, and after the first was slain wiped the sword with her apron to prepare it for the cleanly murder of the second, and so on forward till it came to the empiercing of the seventeenth of her loins—will you not give her great allowance of anguish? This woman, this matron, this forsaken Heraclide, having buried fourteen children in five days, whose eyes she howlingly closed and caught many wrinkles with funeral kisses. Besides having her husband within a day after laid forth as a comfortless corpse, a carrionly block that could neither eat with her, speak with her, nor weep with her, is she not to be borne withal though her body swells with a tympany of tears, though her speech be as impatient as unhappy Hecuba's, though her head raves and her brain dotes? Devise with yourselves that you see a corpse rising from his bier after he is carried to church, and such another suppose Heraclide to be, rising from the couch of enforced adultery.

Her eyes were dim, her cheeks bloodless, her breath smelled earthy, her countenance was ghastly. Up she rose after she was deflowered; but loath she arose, as a reprobate soul rising to the day of judgment. Looking on the tone side as she rose, she spied her husband's body lying under her head. Ah, then she bewailed as Cephalus when he had killed Procris unwittingly, or Oedipus when ignorant he had slain his own father and known his mother incestuously. This was her subdued reason's discourse:

"Have I lived to make my husband's body the bier to carry me to hell? Had filthy pleasure no other pillow to lean upon but his spreaded limbs? On thy flesh my fault shall be imprinted at the day of resurrection. Oh, beauty, the bait ordained to ensnare the irreligious! Rich men are robbed for their wealth; women are dishonested for being too fair. No blessing is beauty, but a curse. Curst be the time that ever I was begotten; curst be the time that my mother brought me forth to tempt. The serpent in paradise did no more; the serpent in paradise is damned sempiternally. Why should not I hold myself damned (if predestination's opinions be true) that am predestinate to this horrible abuse? The hog dieth presently if he loseth an eye; with the hog have I wallowed in the mire, I have lost my eye of honesty, it is clean plucked out with a strong hand of unchastity. What remaineth but I die? Die I will, though life be unwilling. No recompense is there for me to redeem my compelled offense, but with a rigorous, compelled death. Husband, I'll be thy wife in heaven; let not thy pure, deceasing spirit despise me when we meet because I am tyrannously polluted. The devil, the belier of our frailty and common accuser of mankind, cannot accuse me though he would of unconstrained submitting. If any guilt be mine, this is my fault—that I did not deform my face ere it should so impiously allure."

Having passioned thus a while, she hastily ran and looked herself in her glass to see if her sin were not written on her forehead. With looking she blushed though none looked upon her but her own reflected image.

Then began she again: *"Heu quam difficile est crimen non prodere vultu:* How hard is it not to bewray a man's fault by his forehead. Myself do but behold myself, and yet I blush. Then God beholding me, shall not I be ten times more ashamed? The angels shall hiss at me, the saints and martyrs fly from me; yea, God himself shall add to the devil's damnation because he suffered such a wicked creature to come before him. Agamemnon, thou wert an infidel; yet when thou wentest to the Trojan war thou leftest a musician at home with thy wife who, by playing the foot spondaeus till thy return, might keep her in chastity. My husband, going to war with the devil and his enticements, when he surrendered, left no musician with me but mourning and melancholy. Had he left any, as Aegisthus killed Agamemnon's musician ere he could be successful, so surely would he have been killed ere this Aegisthus surceased.

"My distressed heart, as the hart when he loseth his horns is astonied and sorrowfully runneth to hide himself, so be thou afflicted and distressed; hide thyself under the Almighty's wings of mercy. Sue, plead, entreat; grace is never denied to them that ask. It may be denied; I may be a vessel ordained to dishonor. The only repeal we have from God's undefinite chastisement is to chastise ourselves in this world. And so I will. Nought but death be my penance; gracious and acceptable may it be. My hand and my knife shall manumit me out of the horror of mind I endure. Farewell life that hast lent me nothing but sorrow; farewell sin-sowed flesh that hast more weeds than flowers, more woes than joys. Point pierce, edge enwiden; I patiently afford thee a sheath. Spur forth my soul to mount post to heaven. Jesu forgive me; Jesu receive me."

So, throughly stabbed, fell she down and knocked her head against her husband's body; wherewith, he not having been aired his full four and twenty hours, started as out of a dream (whiles I, through a cranny of my upper chamber unsealed, had beheld all this sad spectacle). Awaking, he rubbed his head to and fro and, wiping his eyes with his hand, began to look about him. Feeling something lie heavy on his breast, he turned it off and, getting upon his legs, lighted a candle.

Here beginneth my purgatory. For he, good man, coming into the hall with the candle and spying his wife with her hair about her ears, defiled and massacred, and his simple zany Capestrano run through, took a halberd in his hand and, running from chamber to chamber to search who in his house was likely to do it, at length found me lying on my bed, the door locked to me on the outside and my rapier unsheathed on the window. Wherewith he straight conjectured it was I. And calling the neighbors hard by, said I had caused myself to be locked into my chamber after that sort, sent away my courtesan whom I called my wife, and made clean my rapier, because I would not be suspected. Upon this was I laid in prison, should have been hanged, was brought to the ladder, had made a ballad for my farewell in a readiness called "Wilton's Wantonness"—and yet, for all that, scaped dancing in a hempen circle. He that hath gone through many perils and returned safe from them makes but a merriment to dilate them.

I had the knot under my ear; there was fair play; the hangman had one halter, and another about my neck which was fastened to the gallows; the riding device[183] was almost thrust home, and his foot on my shoulder to press me down, when I made my faint-like confession, as you have heard before, that such and such men at such an hour brake into the house, slew the zany, took my courtesan, locked me into my chamber, ravished Heraclide, and, finally, how she slew herself.

Present at the execution was there a banished English earl who, hearing that a countryman of his was to suffer for such a notable murder, came to hear his confession and see if he knew him. He had not heard me tell half of that I have recited but he craved audience and desired the execution might be stayed.

"Not two days since it is, gentlemen and noble Romans," said he, "since going to be let blood in a barber's shop against the infection, all on a sudden in a great tumult and uproar was there brought in one Bartol, an Italian, grievously wounded and bloody.[184] I seeming to commiserate his harms, courteously questioned him with what ill

---

[183]*riding device:* slip knot.

[184]*barber's shop . . . Bartol . . . wounded and bloody:* A barber in those days was also a surgeon; his shop was the natural place to bring a wounded man.

debtors he had met, or how or by what casualty he came to be so arrayed.

"'Oh,' quoth he, 'long I have lived sworn brothers in sensuality with one Esdras of Grenada. Five hundred rapes and murders have we committed betwixt us. When our iniquities were grown to the height, and God had determined to countercheck our amity, we came to the house of Johannes de Imola' (whom this young gentleman hath named); there did he justify all those rapes in manner and form as the prisoner here hath confessed.

"But lo, an accident after, which neither he nor this audience is privy to. Esdras of Granada, not content to have ravished the matron Heraclide and robbed her, after he had betook him from thence to his heels, lighted on his companion Bartol with his courtesan; whose pleasing face he had scarce winkingly glanced on but he picked a quarrel with Bartol to have her from him. On this quarrel they fought. Bartol was wounded to the death, Esdras fled, and the fair dame left to go whither she would. This Bartol in the barber's shop freely acknowledged (as both the barber and his man and other here present can amply depose)." Deposed as they were; their oaths went for current; I was quit by proclamation. To the banished earl I came to render thanks, when thus he examined me and schooled me:

"Countryman, tell me; what is the occasion of thy straying so far out of England to visit this strange nation? If it be languages, thou mayest learn them at home. Nought but lasciviousness is to be learned here. Perhaps to be better accounted of than other of thy condition thou ambitiously undertakest this voyage. These insolent fancies are but Icarus' feathers, whose wanton wax, melted against the sun, will betray thee into a sea of confusion. The first traveler was Cain, and he was called a vagabond runagate on the face of the earth. Travel, like the travail[185] wherein smiths put wild horses when they shoe them, is good for nothing but to tame and bring men under. God had no greater curse to lay upon the Israelites than by leading them out of their own country to live as slaves in a strange land. That which was their curse we Englishmen count our chief blessedness; he is nobody that hath not traveled. We had rather live as slaves in another land—crouch and cap, and be servile to

---

[185]*Travel . . . travail:* Apparently to make his point that "travel" *is* "travail" (that is, full of pain), Jack punningly spells both words "travail." Here the first is emended to read "travel." By "travail wherein smiths put wild horses," however, he means also a device for holding a horse still while a shoe is nailed on.

every jealous Italian's and proud Spaniard's humor, where we may neither speak, look, nor do anything but what pleaseth them—than live as free men and lords in our own country. He that is a traveler must have the back of an ass to bear all, a tongue like the tail of a dog to flatter all, the mouth of a hog to eat what is set before him, the ear of a merchant to hear all and say nothing. And if this be not the highest step of thraldom, there is no liberty or freedom.

"It is but a mild kind of subjection to be the servant of one master at once; but when thou hast a thousand thousand masters—as the veriest botcher, tinker, or cobbler freeborn will domineer over a foreigner, and think to be his better or master in company—then shalt thou find there's no such hell as to leave thy father's house, thy natural habitation, to live in the land of bondage. If thou dost but lend half a look to a Roman's or Italian's wife, thy porridge shall be prepared for thee and cost thee nothing but thy life. Chance some of them break a bitter jest on thee, and thou retortest it severely or seemest discontented; go to thy chamber and provide a great banquet, for thou shalt be sure to be visited with guests in a mask the next night when, in kindness and courtship, thy throat shall be cut and the doers return undiscovered. Nothing so long of memory as a dog; these Italians are old dogs and will carry an injury a whole age in memory. I have heard of a box on the ear that hath been revenged thirty year after. The Neapolitan carrieth the bloodiest, wreakful mind and is the most secret, fleering murderer. Whereupon it is grown to a common proverb, "I'll give him the Neapolitan shrug," when one means to play the villain and makes no boast of it.

"The only precept that a traveler hath most use of, and shall find most ease in, is that of Epicharchus[186]—*vigila, et memor sis ne quid credas:* believe nothing, trust no man; yet seem thou as thou swallowedest all, suspectedest none, but wert easy to be gulled by everyone. *Multi fallere docuerunt,* as Seneca saith, *dum timent falli:* many by showing their jealous suspect of deceit have made men seek more subtle means to deceive them.

"Alas, our Englishmen are the plainest dealing souls that ever God put life in. They are greedy of news and love to be fed in their humors and hear themselves flattered the best that may be. Even as

[186]*Epicharchus:* presumably Epicharmus, the Greek playwright of the fifth century B.C.

Philemon, a comic poet, died with extreme laughter at the conceit of seeing an ass eat figs, so have the Italians no such sport as to see poor English asses, how soberly they swallow Spanish figs,[187] devour any hook baited for them. He is not fit to travel that cannot, with the Candians, live on serpents, make nourishing food even of poison. Rats and mice engender by licking one another. He must lick, he must crouch, he must cog, lie, and prate, that either in the court or a foreign country will engender and come to preferment. Be his feature what it will, if he be fair spoken he winneth friends. *Non formosus erat, sed erat facundus Ulysses:* Ulysses, the long traveler, was not amiable but eloquent.

"Some allege they travel to learn wit; but I am of this opinion: that as it is not possible for any man to learn the art of memory— whereof Tully, Quintillian, Seneca, and Hermannus Buschius have written so many books—except he have a natural memory before, so it is not possible for any man to attain any great wit by travel, except he have the grounds of it rooted in him before. That wit which is thereby to be perfected or made staid, is nothing but *experientia longa malorum* (the experience of many evils)—the experience that such a man lost his life by this folly, another by that; such a young gallant consumed his substance on such a courtesan; these courses of revenge a merchant of Venice took against a merchant of Ferrara; and this point of justice was showed by the duke upon the murderer. What is here but we may read in books, and a great deal more, too, without stirring our feet out of a warm study?

> *Vobis alii ventorum praelia narrent* (saith Ovid)
>   *Quasque Scilla infestat, quasue Charybdis aquas.*
> Let others tell you wonders of the wind,
>   How Scilla or Charybdis is inclined.
> . . . *vos quod quisque loquetur*
>   *Credite.*[188]
> Believe you what they say, but never try.

"So let others tell you strange accidents, treasons, poisonings, close packings in France, Spain, and Italy. It is no harm for you to hear

[187]*Spanish figs:* poisoned figs; the English also used "Italian figs" in exactly the same sense.

[188]*Vobis alii . . . Credite:* The first two lines of Latin are from Ovid's *The Amores,* II, xi, 17–18; the last two lines of Latin are the end of line 21 and the beginning of line 22 (the three periods or ellipsis indicating that lines 19 and 20 have been omitted).

of them, but come not near them. What is there in France to be
learned more than in England, but falsehood in fellowship, perfect
slovenry, to love no man but for my pleasure, to swear *"Ah, par la
mort Dieu"* when a man's hams are scabbed? For the idle traveler, I
mean not for the soldier, I have known some that have continued
there by the space of half a dozen year; and when they come home,
they have hid a little wearish,[189] lean face under a broad French hat,
kept a terrible coil with the dust in the street in their long cloaks of
gray paper, and spoke English strangely. Nought else have they
profited by their travel, save learned to distinguish of the true Bordeaux grape, and know a cup of neat Gascoygne wine,[190] from wine
of Orleans. Yea, and peradventure this also: to esteem of the pox as
a pimple, to wear a velvet patch on their face, and walk melancholy
with their arms folded.

"From Spain what bringeth our traveler? A skull-crowned hat of
the fashion of an old deep porringer; a diminutive alderman's ruff
with short strings, like the droppings of a man's nose; a close-belted
doublet coming down with a peak behind as far as the crupper and
cut off before by the breast bone, like a partlet or neckerchief; a
wide pair of gascoynes[191] which, ungathered, would make a couple
of women's riding kirtles; huge hangers[192] that have half a cowhide
in them; a rapier that is lineally descended from half a dozen dukes
at the least. Let his cloak be as long or as short as you will. If long,
it is faced with Turkey grogeran raveled;[193] if short, it hath a cape
like a calf's tongue, and is not so deep in his whole length, nor hath
so much cloth in it I will justify, as only the standing cape of
a Dutchman's cloak. I have not yet touched all, for he hath in either
shoe as much taffeta for his tyings as would serve for an ancient;
which serveth him, if you will have the mystery of it, of the own

[189]*wearish:* sickly looking (lean and pale).

[190]*Gascoygne wine:* that is, Gascon wine (from Gascony in southwestern
France).

[191]*gascoynes:* that is, "gaskins" or "galligaskins," loose-fitting hose or
breeches (perhaps originally worn in Gascony).

[192]*hangers:* Usually a hanger is a short sword, but here the reference is
to a loop, made of leather and fastened to the sword belt, in which the
sword is hung or suspended.

[193]*Turkey grogeran raveled:* "Grogran" was a coarse-grained fabric (from
the French, *gros grain*); the implication here is that it was made in Turkey.
"Raveled" means "ragged, having frayed edges."

accord for a shoe rag.[194] A soldier and a braggart he is, that's concluded; he jetteth strutting, dancing on his toes with his hands under his sides. If you talk with him, he makes a dish cloth of his own country in comparison of Spain; but if you urge him more particularly wherein it exceeds, he can give no instance. But in Spain they have better bread than any we have; when (poor hungry slaves) they may crumble it into water well enough and make misers[195] with it, for they have not a good morsel of meat except it be salt pilchers to eat with it all the year long; and, which is more, they are poor beggars, and lie in foul straw every night.

"Italy, the paradise of the earth, and the epicure's heaven; how doth it form our young master? It makes him to kiss his hand like an ape, cringe his neck like a starveling, and play at hey-pass-repass-come-aloft[196] when he salutes a man. From thence he brings the art of atheism, the art of epicurizing, the art of whoring, the art of poisoning, the art of sodomitry. The only probable good thing they have to keep us from utterly condemning it is that it maketh a man an excellent courtier, a curious carpet knight—which is, by interpretation, a fine, close lecher, a glorious hypocrite. It is now a privy note amongst the better sort of men, when they would set a singular mark or brand on a notorious villain, to say he hath been in Italy.

"With the Dane and the Dutchman I will not encounter, for they are simple, honest men that, with Danaus' daughters, do nothing but fill bottomless tubs and will be drunk and snort in the midst of dinner. He hurts himself only that goes thither. He cannot lightly be damned, for the vintners, the brewers, the malt men and alewives pray for him. Pitch and pay,[197] they will pray all day; score and borrow, they will wish him much sorrow. But lightly a man is ne'er the

[194]*taffeta for his tyings . . . shoe rag:* Probably the reference is derogatory in two ways: (1) using a fancy material like taffeta for mere shoelaces, and (2) using so much material that it can serve, in addition, as a cloth for wiping off the shoes. "Serve for an ancient" means "enough taffeta material to make a standard or flag." If "ancient" means "ensign" (the officer who carries the flag), then the sense would be "enough material to outfit an ensign."

[195]*misers:* the emendation of the second edition, meaning "sop made of bread crumbs"; "misons" (mushrooms or truffles), the reading of the first edition, does not quite fit the context.

[196]*hey-pass . . . aloft:* See note 132.

[197]*Pitch and pay:* a proverb (Tilley, P360); the sense is "pay cash" (actually throw the money on the table). To "score" is to drink on credit.

better for their prayers, for they commit all deadly sin for the most part of them in mingling their drink, the vintners in the highest degree.

"Why jest I in such a necessary persuasive discourse? I am a banished exile from my country, though near linked in consanguinity to the best—an earl born by birth, but a beggar now, as thou seest. These many years in Italy have I lived an outlaw. A while I had a liberal pension of the pope, but that lasted not, for he continued not; one succeeded him in his chair that cared neither for Englishmen nor his own countrymen. Then was I driven to pick up my crumbs amongst the cardinals, to implore the benevolence and charity of all the dukes of Italy; whereby I have since made a poor shift to live, but so live as I wish myself a thousand times dead.

> *Cum patriam amisi, tunc me periisse putato.*
> When I was banished, think I caught my bane.

"The sea is the native soil to fishes; take fishes from the sea, they take no joy nor thrive, but perish straight. So likewise the birds removed from the air, the abode whereto they were born, the beasts from the earth, and I from England. Can a lamb take delight to be suckled at the breasts of a she-wolf? I am a lamb nourished with the milk of wolves, one that, with the Ethiopians inhabiting over against Meroe, feed on nothing but scorpions. Use is another nature, yet ten times more contentive, were nature restored to her kingdom from whence she is excluded. Believe me, no air, no bread, no fire, no water agree with a man or doth him any good out of his own country. Cold fruits never prosper in a hot soil, nor hot in a cold. Let no man for any transitory pleasure sell away the inheritance of breathing he hath in the place where he was born. Get thee home, my young lad; lay thy bones peaceably in the sepulcher of thy fathers, wax old in overlooking thy grounds, be at hand to close the eyes of thy kindred. The devil and I am desperate—he of being restored to heaven, I of being recalled home."

Here he held his peace and wept. I, glad of any opportunity of a full point to part from him, told him I took his counsel in worth; what lay in me to requite in love should not be lacking. Some business that concerned me highly called me away very hastily, but another time I hoped we should meet. Very hardly he let me go; but I earnestly overpleading my occasions, at length he dismissed me, told me where his lodging was, and charged me to visit him without excuse very often.

Here's a stir, thought I to myself after I was set at liberty, that is worse than an upbraiding lesson after a britching. Certainly if I had bethought me like a rascal as I was, he should have had an Ave Maria of me for his cynic exhortation. God plagued me for deriding such a grave, fatherly advertiser.

List the worst throw of ill lucks. Tracing up and down the city to seek my courtesan till the evening began to grow well in age, it fortuned the element, as if it had drunk too much in the afternoon, poured down so profoundly that I was forced to creep, like one afraid of the watch, close under the pentices,[198] where the cellar door of a Jew's house called Zadoch (over which in my direct way I did pass) being unbarred on the inside, over head and ears I fell into it, as a man falls in a ship from the orlop into the hold (or as in an earthquake the ground should open and a blind man come feeling pad, pad over the open gulf with his staff, should stumble on sudden into hell). Having worn out the anguish of my fall a little with wallowing up and down, I cast up mine eyes to see under what continent I was; and lo (oh, destiny) I saw my courtesan kissing very lovingly with a prentice. My back and my sides I had hurt with my fall, but now my head swelled and ached worse than both. I was even gathering wind to come upon her with a full blast of contumely when the Jew (awaked with the noise of my fall) came bustling down the stairs and, raising his other servants, attached both the courtesan and me for breaking his house and conspiring with his prentice to rob him.

It was then the law in Rome, that if any man had a felon fallen into his hands, either by breaking into his house or robbing him by the highway, he might choose whether he would make him his bondman or hang him. Zadoch (as all Jews are covetous) casting with himself he should have no benefit by casting me off the ladder, had another policy in his head. He went to one Dr. Zachary, the pope's physician, that was a Jew and his countryman likewise, and told him he had the finest bargain for him that might be.

"It is not concealed from me," saith he, "that the time of your accustomed yearly anatomy is at hand, which it behooves you under forfeiture of the foundation of your college very carefully to provide for. The infection is great, and hardly will you get a sound body to deal upon. You are my countryman; therefore, I come to you first. Be it known unto you, I have a young man at home fallen to me for

---

[198]*pentices:* eaves.

my bondman, of the age of eighteen, of stature tall, straight limbed, of as clear a complexion as any painter's fancy can imagine. Go to, you are an honest man and one of the scattered children of Abraham; you shall have him for five hundred crowns."

"Let me see him," quoth Dr. Zachary, "and I will give you as much as another."

Home he sent for me. Pinioned and shackled, I was transported alongst the street; where, passing under Juliana's, the Marquis of Mantua's wife's window, that was a lusty *Bona Roba*,[199] one of the pope's concubines, as she had her casement half open, she looked out and spied me.

At the first sight she was enamored with my age and beardless face, that had in it no ill sign of physiognomy fatal to fetters. After me she sent to know what I was, wherein I had offended, and whither I was going. My conducts resolved them all. She, having received this answer—with a lustful collachrymation[200] lamenting my Jewish praemunire[201] that, body and goods, I should light into the hands of such a cursed generation—invented the means of my release.

But first I'll tell you what betided me after I was brought to Dr. Zachary's. The purblind doctor put on his spectacles and looked upon me; and when he had thoroughly viewed my face, he caused me to be stripped naked, to feel and grope whether each limb were sound, and my skin not infected. Then he pierced my arm to see how my blood ran; which assays and searchings ended, he gave Zadoch his full price and sent him away, then locked me up in a dark chamber till the day of anatomy.

Oh, the cold sweating cares which I conceived after I knew I should be cut like a French summer doublet. Methought already the blood began to gush out at my nose; if a flea on the arm had but bit me, I deemed the instrument had pricked me. Well, well, I may scoff at a shrowd[202] turn, but there's no such ready way to make a man a true Christian as to persuade himself he is taken up for an anatomy.

---

[199]*Bona Roba:* literally, "good robe"; but in Elizabethan usage a "sexy wench" (probably overdressed and overpainted). One suspects a pun in "casement."

[200]*collachrymation:* tearfulness.

[201]*praemunire:* The sense seems to be "penalty" or "punishment"; "Jewish" apparently means "at the hands of the Jews" (Zadoch and Dr. Zachary).

[202]*shrowd:* The original spelling of both early editions is an obsolete spelling of two modern words, "shrewd" and "shroud"—and thus conveys the pun.

I'll depose I prayed then more than I did in seven year before. Not a drop of sweat trickled down my breast and my sides but I dreamed it was a smooth-edged razor tenderly slicing down my breast and my sides. If any knocked at door, I supposed it was the beadle of Surgeon's Hall come for me. In the night I dreamed of nothing but phlebotomy, bloody fluxes, incarnatives,[203] running ulcers. I durst not let out a wheal for fear through it I should bleed to death.

For meat in this distance I had plum porridge of purgations ministered me one after another to clarify my blood, that it should not lie cloddered[204] in the flesh. Nor did he it so much for clarifying physic as to save charges. Miserable is that mouse that lives in a physician's house; Tantalus lives not so hunger starved in hell as she doth there. Not the very crumbs that fall from his table but Zachary sweeps together, and of them molds up a manna. Of the ashy parings of his bread he would make conserve of chippings. Out of bones, after the meat was eaten off, he would alchemize an oil that he sold for a shilling a dram. His snot and spittle a hundred times he hath put over to his apothecary for snow water. Any spider he would temper to perfect mithridate. His rheumatic eyes, when he went in the wind or rose early in a morning, dropped as cool alum water as you would request. He was Dame Niggardize's sole heir and executor.

A number of old books had he, eaten with the moths and worms; now all day would not he study a dodkin,[205] but pick those worms and moths out of his library and of their mixture make a preservative against the plague. The liquor out of his shoes he would wring to make a sacred balsamum[206] against barrenness.

Spare we him a line or two, and look back to Juliana, who, conflicted in her thoughts about me very debatefully, adventured to send a messenger to Dr. Zachary in her name, very boldly to beg me of him and, if she might not beg me, to buy me with what sums of money so ever he would ask. Zachary jewishly and churlishly withstood both her suits, and said if there were no more Christians on the earth, he would thrust his incision knife into his throatbowl[207]

[203]*incarnatives:* medicines causing wounds or sores to heal.

[204]*cloddered:* clotted.

[205]*not . . . a dodkin:* not a jot, not one little bit; literally, a "dodkin" or "doit" is a small coin.

[206]*balsamum:* balsum; probably two meanings—"medicine as a curative" and "fragrance" (with full appreciation of the "fragrance" of well-worn shoes).

[207]*his throatbowl:* Jack's throat; indirect discourse serves, for the moment, as direct discourse.

immediately. Which reply she taking at his hands most despitefully, thought to cross him over the shins with as sore an overwhart[208] blow yet ere a month to an end.

The pope (I know not whether at her entreaty or no) within two days after fell sick. Dr. Zachary was sent for to minister unto him; who, seeing a little danger in his water, gave him a gentle conforta-tive[209] for the stomach and desired those near about him to persuade his holiness to take some rest, and he doubted not but he would be forthwith well. Who should receive this mild physic of him but the concubine, Juliana, his utter enemy. She, being not unprovided of strong poison at that instant, in the pope's outward chamber so mingled it that when his grand-sublimity-taster came to relish it he sunk down stark dead on the pavement.

Herewith the pope called Juliana and asked her what strong con-cocted broth she had brought him. She kneeled down on her knees and said it was such as Zachary the Jew had delivered her with his own hands, and therefore if it misliked his holiness she craved par-don. The pope, without further sifting into the matter, would have had Zachary and all Jews in Rome put to death; but she hung about his knees and with crocodile tears desired him the sentence might be lenified, and they be all but banished at most.

"For Dr. Zachary," quoth she, "your ten times ungrateful physi-cian, since, not withstanding his treacherous intent, he hath much art and many sovereign simples, oils, gargarisms,[210] and sirups in his closet and house that may stand your mightiness in stead, I beg all his goods only for your beatitude's preservation and good."

This request at the first was sealed with a kiss, and the pope's edict without delay proclaimed throughout Rome—namely that all foreskin clippers, whether male or female, belonging to the Old Jurie,[211] should depart and avoid upon pain of hanging, within twenty days after the date thereof.

Juliana, two days before the proclamation came out, sent her servants to extend upon Zachary's territories, his goods, his move-

[208]*overwhart:* usually spelled "overthwart"; the sense probably is "oblique" or "slantwise" (not a directly overhand or underhand blow).

[209]*confortative:* medicine, comfortive.

[210]*gargarisms:* gargles.

[211]*Old Jurie:* Old Jewry; the name given to a section or street in Lon-don inhabited by Jews. There was a ghetto in Rome, but presumably it did not go by this particular name.

ables, his chattels, and his servants; who performed their commission to the utmost title, and left him not so much as master of an urinal case or a candle box. It was about six o'clock in the evening when those boot halers[212] entered; into my chamber they rushed, when I sat leaning on my elbow, and my left hand under my side, devising what a kind of death it might be to be let blood till a man die. I called to mind the assertion of some philosophers who said the soul was nothing but blood; then, thought I, what a filthy thing were this, if I should let my soul fall and break his neck into a basin. I had but a pimple rose with heat in that part of the vein where they use to prick, and I fearfully misdeemed it was my soul searching for passage. Fie upon it, a man's breath to be let out a back door—what a villainy it is! To die bleeding is all one as if a man should die pissing. Good drink makes good blood, so that piss is nothing but blood underage. Seneca and Lucan were lobcocks[213] to choose that death of all other; a pig or a hog, or any edible brute beast a cook or a butcher deals upon, dies bleeding. To die with a prick, wherewith the faintest-hearted woman under heaven would not be killed—oh God, it is infamous!

In this meditation did they seize upon me; in my cloak they muffled me that no man might know me, nor I see which way I was carried. The first ground I touched, after I was out of Zachary's house, was the Countess Juliana's chamber. Little did I surmise that fortune reserved me to so fair a death. I made no other reckoning all the while they had me on their shoulders but that I was on horseback to heaven and carried to church on a bier, excluded forever from drinking any more ale or beer.

Juliana scornfully questioned them thus (as if I had fallen into her hands beyond expectation): "What proper apple squire[214] is this you bring so suspiciously into my chamber? What hath he done? Or where had you him?"

They answered, likewise afar off, that in one of Zachary's chambers they found him close prisoner, and thought themselves guilty of the breach of her ladyship's commandment if they should have left him behind.

"Oh," quoth she, "ye love to be double diligent, or thought peradventure that I, being a lone woman, stood in need of a love. Bring you me a princox beardless boy (I know not whence he is,

---

[212]*boot halers:* plunderers (literally, "booty" plus "haul").
[213]*lobcocks:* blundering fools.
[214]*apple squire:* pimp (also called an "apron squire").

nor whither he would) to call my name in suspense? I tell you, you have abused me, and I can hardly brook it at your hands. You should have led him to the magistrate; no commission received you of me but for his goods and his servants."

They besought her to excuse their overweening error; it proceeded from a zealous care of their duty, and no negligent default.

"But why should not I conjecture the worst?" quoth she. "I tell you troth. I am half in jealousy he is some fantastical amorous youngster who, to dishonor me, hath hired you to this stratagem. It is a likely matter that such a man as Zachary should make a prison of his house and deal in matters of state.

"By your leave, sir gallant, under lock and key shall you stay with me till I have inquired further of you; you shall be sifted thoroughly ere you and I part.

"Go, maid, show him to the further chamber at the end of the gallery that looks into the garden.

"You, my trim panders, I pray guard him thither as you took pains to bring him hither. When you have so done, see the doors be made fast and come your way."

Here was a wily wench had her liripoop without book;[215] she was not to seek in her knacks and shifts. Such are all women; not one of them but hath a cloak for the rain, and can blear her husband's eyes as she list.

Not too much of this madam marquise at once; we'll step a little back and dilate what Zadoch the Jew did with my courtesan after he had sold me to Zachary. Of an ill tree I hope you are not so ill sighted in grafting to expect good fruit. He was a Jew and entreated her like a Jew. Under shadow of enforcing her to tell how much money she had of his prentice so to be trained to his cellar, he stripped her and scourged her from top to toe tantara.[216] Day by day he digested his meat with leading her the measures. A diamond, Delphinical,[217] dry lecher it was.

[215]*liripoop without book:* often spelled "liriloop" or "liripipe" and meaning literally the long tail or loop on a graduate's hood; the sense here is that Juliana (in common with all women) knows by instinct certain subtle shifts that men must study to learn.

[216]*top to toe tantara:* with a flourish (suggested by the onomatopoeic sound of a flourish blown on a trumpet).

[217]*Delphinical:* Ashley and Moseley seem right in suggesting that the word is a combination of "Delphian" and "finical." But "Delphian" may not have the usual connotation of "oracular" or "obscure" so much as "arbitrary" or "all powerful," thus reinforcing "diamond" (hard) and "dry."

The ballad of the whipper[218] of late days here in England was but a scoff in comparison of him. All the colliers of Romford, who hold their corporation by yarking the blind bear at Paris Garden,[219] were but bunglers to him. He had the right agility of the lash; there were none of them could make the cord come aloft with a twang half like him.

Mark the ending, mark the ending. The tribe of Judah is adjudged from Rome to be trudging; they may no longer be lodged there. All the Albumazers, Rabisacks, Gedeons, Tebiths, Benhadads, Benrodans, Zedechiahs, Halies[220] of them were bankrupts and turned out of house and home. Zachary came running to Zadoch's in sackcloth and ashes presently after his goods were confiscated and told him how he was served, and what decree was coming out against them all.

Descriptions, stand by. Here is to be expressed the fury of Lucifer when he was turned over heaven bar for a wrangler.[221] There is a toad fish[222] which, taken out of the water, swells more than one would think his skin could hold and bursts in his face that toucheth him. So swelled Zadoch, and was ready to burst out of his skin and shoot his bowels like chain shot full at Zachary's face for bringing him such baleful tidings. His eyes glared and burned blue like brim-

[218]*The ballad of the whipper:* probably the ballad entered in the Stationers' Register for 16 February 1590/1 (Edward Arber, *A Transcript of the Registers of the Company of Stationers of London, 1554–1640,* II, 575); the revisers of A. W. Pollard and G. R. Redgrave, *Short-Title Catalogue . . . 1475–1640* report (January, 1966) that not a single copy is extant.

[219]*colliers of Romford . . . Paris Garden:* The picture we are to get is of Paris (or Parish) Garden, a bear-baiting amphitheater on the south bank of the Thames, that held 1,000 spectators; beginning at least as early as 1526 the performances were held on Sunday. "Yarking" usually meant holding the bear in place with a chain, but here it may have to do with what people did to him after he was "in place"—lash him with whips. The part about the colliers may be satirical: since the coal miners and porters had no real corporation (no "lesser" or "greater" company), they simply met at the Paris Garden for fellowship and "fun," instead of meeting in a regular hall across the river in London, the way the clothiers and the vintners did. (See note 73, above.)

[220]*Albumazers . . . Halies:* The spelling of the first edition has been retained in these names, some of which are easily recognizable as from the Bible; Nashe is making fun of the sounds of contemporary Jewish names.

[221]*turned over heaven bar for a wrangler:* pushed over the gate or edge of heaven because he was a quarreler (with God).

[222]*toad fish:* apparently the same fish Capt. John Smith saw a few years later in Virginia; when exposed to air, he said, it would "swell till it be like to burst" (*A Map of Virginia,* 1612, p. 15).

stone and *aqua vitae* set on fire in an eggshell. His very nose lightened glowworms; his teeth crashed and grated together, like the joints of a high building cracking and rocking like a cradle, when as a tempest takes her full butt against his broad side. He swore, he cursed, and said:

"These be they that worship that crucified God of Nazareth; here's the fruits of their newfound gospel. Sulphur and gunpowder carry them all quick to Gehenna.[223] I would spend my soul willingly to have this triple-headed pope with all his sin-absolved whores and oil-greased priests borne with a black sant[224] on the devils' backs in procession to the pit of perdition. Would I might sink presently into the earth, so I might blow up this Rome, this whore of Babylon, into the air with my breath. If I must be banished, if those heathen dogs will needs rob me of my goods, I will poison their springs and conduit heads, whence they receive all their water round about the city. I'll 'tice all the young children into my house that I can get and, cutting their throats, barrel them up in powdering beef tubs, and so send them to victual the pope's galleys. Ere the officers come to extend, I'll bestow a hundred pound on a dole of bread, which I'll cause to be kneaded with scorpion's oil that may kill more than the plague. I'll hire them that make their wafers or sacramentary gods to ming[225] them after the same sort, so in the zeal of their superstitious religion shall they languish and drop like carrion. If there be ever a blasphemous conjurer that can call the winds from their brazen caves and make the clouds travel before their time, I'll give him the other hundred pounds to disturb the heavens a whole week together with thunder and lightning, if it be for nothing but to sour all the wines in Rome and turn them to vinegar. As long as they have either oil or wine, this plague feeds but pinglingly upon them."

"Zadoch, Zadoch," said Dr. Zachary, cutting him off, "thou threatenest the air whiles we perish here on earth. It is the Countess Juliana, the Marquis of Mantua's wife, and no other, that hath complotted our confusion. Ask not how, but insist in my words and assist in revenge."

"As how? As how?" said Zadoch, shrugging and shrubbing. "More happy than the patriarchs were I if, crushed to death with the greatest torments Rome's tyrants have tried, there might be quintessenced

[223]*Gehenna:* hell.

[224]*black sant:* black sanctus, a deprecatory term applied to a particularly jarring and discordant hymn.

[225]*ming:* mix, blend.

out of me one quart of precious poison. I have a leg with an issue. Shall I cut it off, and from his fount of corruption extract a venom worse than any serpents? If thou wilt, I'll go to a house that is infected; where, catching the plague and having got a running sore upon me, I'll come and deliver her a supplication, and breathe upon her. I know my breath stinks so already that it is within half a degree of poison. I'll pay her home if I perfect it with any more putrefaction."

"No, no, brother Zadoch," answered Zachary, "that is not the way. Canst thou provide me ere a bondmaid, endued with singular and divine-qualified beauty, whom as a present from our synagogue thou mayest commend unto her, desiring her to be good and gracious unto us?"

"I have. I am for you," quoth Zadoch. "Diamante, come forth. Here's a wench," said he, "of as clear a skin as Susanna; she hath not a wem[226] on her flesh from the sole of the foot to the crown of the head. How think you, master doctor? Will she not serve the turn?"

"She will," said Zachary, "and therefore I'll tell you what charge I would have committed to her. But I care not if I disclose it only to her. Maid, if thou beest a maid, come hither to me; thou must be sent to the Countess of Mantua's about a small piece of service whereby, being now a bondwoman, thou shalt purchase freedom and gain a large dowry to thy marriage. I know thy master loves thee dearly though he will not let thee perceive so much. He intends after he is dead to make thee his heir, for he hath no children. Please him in that I shall instruct thee, and thou art made forever. So it is that the pope is far out of liking with the Countess of Mantua, his concubine, and hath put his trust in me, his physician, to have her quietly and charitably made away. Now I cannot intend it, for I have many cures in hand which call upon me hourly. Thou, if thou beest placed with her as her waiting maid or cupbearer, mayest temper poison with her broth, her meat, her drink, her oils, her sirups, and never be bewrayed. I will not say whether the pope hath heard of thee, and thou mayest come to be his leman in her place if thou behave thyself wisely. What, hast thou the heart to go through with it or no?"

Diamante, deliberating with herself in what hellish servitude she

---

[226]*Susanna . . . wem:* the beautiful wife of Joachim in the apocryphal Book of Susanna whom Daniel, as judge, delivers from a false charge of adultery; "wem" means "blemish" in both the physical and moral senses.

lived with the Jew, and that she had no likelihood to be released of it, but fall from evil to worse if she omitted this opportunity, resigned herself over wholly to be disposed and employed as seemed best unto them. Thereupon, without further consultation, her wardrobe was richly rigged, her tongue smooth-filed and new-edged on the whetstone, her drugs delivered her. And presented she was by Zadoch, her master, to the countess, together with some other slight newfangles, as from the whole congregation, desiring her to stand their merciful mistress and solicit the pope for them that, through one man's ignorant offense, were all generally in disgrace with him, and had incurred the cruel sentence of loss of goods and banishment.

Juliana, liking well the pretty, round face of my black-browed Diamante, gave the Jew better countenance than otherwise she would have done, and told him for her own part she was but a private woman and could promise nothing confidently of his holiness. For though he had suffered himself to be overruled by her in some humors, yet, in this that touched him so nearly, she knew not how he would be inclined. But what lay in her either to pacify or persuade him they should be sure of, and so craved his absence.

His back turned, she asked Diamante what countrywoman she was, what friends she had, and how she fell into the hands of that Jew?

She answered that she was a magnifico's daughter of Venice, stolen when she was young from her friends, and sold to this Jew for a bondwoman.

"Who," quoth she, "hath used me so jewishly and tyrannously that forever I must celebrate the memory of this day, wherein I am delivered from this jurisdiction. Alas," quoth she, deep sighing, "why did I enter into any mention of my own misusage? It will be thought that that which I am now to reveal proceeds of malice, not truth. Madam, your life is sought by these Jews that sue to you. Blush not, nor be troubled in your mind, for with warning I shall arm you against all their intentions.

"Thus and thus," quoth she, "said Dr. Zachary unto me; this poison he delivered me. Before I was called in to them, such and such consultation through the crevice of the door fast-locked did I hear betwixt them. Deny it if they can, I will justify it. Only, I beseech you to be favorable, lady, unto me, and let me not fall again into the hands of those vipers."

Juliana said little, but thought unhappily; only she thanked her for detecting it, and vowed though she were her bondwoman to be a mother unto her. The poison she took of her and set it up charily on a shelf in her closet, thinking to keep it for some good purposes—as, for example, when I was consumed and worn to the bones through her abuse, she would give me but a dram too much, and pop me into a privy. So she had served some of her paramours ere that, and if God had not sent Diamante to be my redeemer, undoubtedly I had drunk of the same cup.

In a leaf or two before was I locked up; here in this page the foresaid goodwife countess comes to me. She is no longer a judge but a client. How she came, in what manner of attire, with what immodest and uncomely words she courted me, if I should take upon me to enlarge, all modest ears would abhor me. Some inconvenience she brought me to by her harlot-like behavior, of which enough I can never repent me.

Let that be forgiven and forgotten; fleshly delights could not make her slothful or slumbering in revenge against Zadoch. She set men about him to incense and egg him on in courses of discontentment, and other supervising espials to ply, follow, and spur forward those suborning incensers. Both which played their parts so that Zadoch, of his own nature violent, swore by the ark of Jehovah to set the whole city on fire ere he went out of it. Zachary, after he had furnished the wench with the poison and given her instructions to go to the devil, durst not stay one hour for fear of disclosing, but fled to the Duke of Bourbon that, after, sacked Rome, and there practiced with his bastardship all the mischief against the pope and Rome that envy could put into his mind.

Zadoch was left behind for the hangman. According to his oath, he provided balls of wild fire in a readiness and laid trains of gunpowder in a hundred several places of the city to blow it up, which he had set fire to (as also bandied his balls abroad) if his attendant spies[227] had not taken him with the manner.[228] To the straightest[228a] prison in Rome he was dragged, where from top to toe he was clogged with fetters and manacles. Juliana informed the pope of Zachary's and his practice; Zachary was sought for but, *non est inventis*, he was packing long before. Commandment was given that Zadoch, whom they had under hand and seal of lock and key, should be executed with all the fiery torments that could be found out.

I'll make short work, for I am sure I have wearied all my readers. To the execution place was he brought, where first and foremost he

---

[227]*his attendant spies:* that is, Juliana's spies watching Zadoch.
[228]*with the manner:* in the act.
[228a]*straightest:* It is difficult to tell whether the sense is "straightest," "straitest," or both. See note 16 in *Pandosto.*

was stripped, then on a sharp iron stake fastened in the ground had he his fundament pitched, which stake ran up along into his body like a spit. Under his armholes two of like sort. A great bonfire they made round about him, wherewith his flesh roasted, not burned; and ever as with the heat his skin blistered, the fire was drawn aside, and they basted him with a mixture of *aqua fortis,* alum water, and mercury *sublimatum,* which smarted to the very soul of him, and searched him to the marrow. Then did they scourge his back parts, so blistered and basted, with burning whips of red hot wire; his head they 'nointed over with pitch and tar, and so enflamed it. To his privy members they tied streaming fireworks; the skin from the crest of his shoulder, as also from his elbows, his hucklebones, his knees, his ankles they plucked and gnawed off with sparkling pincers. His breast and his belly with seal skins they grated over, which, as fast as they grated and rawed, one stood over and laved with smiths' cindery water and *aqua vitae.* His nails they half raised up, and then under propped them with sharp pricks, like a tailor's shop window half open on a holiday. Every one of his fingers they rent up to the wrist; his toes they brake off by the roots, and let them still hang by a little skin. In conclusion, they had a small oil fire, such as men blow light bubbles of glass with and, beginning at his feet, they let him lingeringly burn up limb by limb, till his heart was consumed, and then he died. Triumph, women; this was the end of the whipping Jew, contrived by a woman in revenge of two women, herself and her maid.

I have told you, or should tell you, in what credit Diamante grew with her mistress. Juliana never dreamed but she was an authentical maid. She made her the chief of her bed chamber; she appointed none but her to look into me, and serve me of such necessaries as I lacked. You must suppose when we met there was no small rejoicing on either part—much like the three brothers that went three several ways to seek their fortunes, and at the year's end, at those three crossways, met again and told one another how they sped. So after we had been long asunder seeking our fortunes, we commented one to another most kindly what cross haps had encountered us.

Ne'er a six hours but the countess cloyed me with her company. It grew to this pass, that either I must find out some miraculous means of escape or drop away in a consumption, as one pined for lack of meat. I was clean spent and done; there was no hope of me.

The year held on his course to doomsday, when St. Peter's Day[229]

[229]*St. Peter's Day:* June 29.

dawned. That day is a day of supreme solemnity in Rome, when the ambassador of Spain comes and presents a milk-white jennet to the pope, that kneels down upon his own accord in token of obeisance and humility before him, and lets him stride on his back as easy as one strides over a block. With this jennet is offered a rich purse of a yard length, full of Peterpence. No music that hath the gift of utterance but sounds all the while. Copes and costly vestments deck the hoarsest and beggarliest singing man. Not a clerk or sexton is absent—no, nor a mule nor a footcloth belonging to any cardinal but attends on the tail of the triumph. The pope himself is borne in his pontificalibus through the Burgo (which is the chief street in Rome) to the ambassador's house to dinner, and thither resorts all the assembly; where, if a poet should spend all his lifetime in describing a banquet, he could not feast his auditors half so well with words as he doth his guests with junkets.

To this feast Juliana addressed herself like an angel—in a litter of green needlework wrought like an arbor, and open on every side, was she borne by four men, hidden under cloth rough-plushed and woven like eglantine and woodbine. At the four corners it was topped with four round chrystal cages of nightingales. For footmen, on either side of her went four virgins clad in lawn, with lutes in their hands playing. Next before her, two and two in order, a hundred pages in suits of white cypress, and long horsemen's coats of cloth of silver; who, being all in white, advanced every one of them her picture enclosed in a white, round screen of feathers, such as is carried over great princesses' heads when they ride in summer, to keep them from the heat of the sun. Before them went a four score beadwomen she maintained in green gowns, scattering, strewing herbs and flowers. After her followed the blind, the halt,[230] and the lame sumptuously appareled like lords; and thus passed she on to St. Peter's.

Interea quid agitur domi: how is't at home all this while? My courtesan is left my keeper; the keys are committed unto her; she is Mistress Factotum.[231] Against our countess we conspire—pack up all her jewels, plate, money that was extant, and to the waterside send them; to conclude, courageously rob her and run away. *Quid non auri sacra fames:* what defame will not gold salve? He mistook

---

[230]*the halt:* Jack seems to imply a difference between "the halt" and "the lame," but usually the terms were synonymous.

[231]*Factotum:* all powerful (not the usual sense today of "person hired to do all sorts of work").

himself that invented the proverb, *dimicandum est pro aris et focis;* for it should have been *pro auro et fama:* not for altars and fires we must contend, but for gold and fame.

[8. *Bologna*]

Oars nor wind could not stir nor blow faster than we toiled out of Tiber; a number of good fellows would give size, ace, and the dice[232] that with as little toil they could leave Tyburn behind them. Out of ken we were ere the countess came from the feast.

When she returned and found her house not so much pestered[233] as it was wont (her chests, her closets, and her cupboards broke open to take air, and that both I and my keeper was missing), oh, then she fared like a frantic bacchanal. She stamped; she stared; she beat her head against the walls, scratched her face, bit her fingers, and strewed all the chamber with her hair. None of her servants durst stay in her sight, but she beat them out in heaps, and bade them go seek, search they knew not where, and hang themselves, and never look her in the face more if they did not hunt us out. After her fury had reasonably spent itself, her breast began to swell with the mother, caused by her former fretting and chasing, and she grew very ill at ease.

Whereupon she knocked for one of her maids, and bade her run into her closet and fetch her a little glass that stood on the upper shelf, wherein there was *spiritus vini.* The maid went and, mistaking, took the glass of poison which Diamante had given her and she kept in store for me. Coming with it as fast as her legs could carry her, her mistress at her return was in a swoon and lay for dead on the floor; whereat she shrieked out, and fell a rubbing and chafing her very busily. When that would not serve, she took a key and opened her mouth and (having heard that *spiritus vini* was a thing of mighty operation, able to call a man from death to life) she took the poison and (verily thinking it to be *spiritus vini,* such as she was sent for) poured a large quantity of it into her throat, and jogged on her back to disgest it. It revived her with a merry venge-

---

[232]*give size, ace, and the dice:* the equivalent of saying that they would give a sure winner, a roll of seven ("size" probably being the French word for "six").

[233]*not so much pestered:* a humorous way of saying "not so crowded" (now that Jack and much of her belongings are gone).

ance, for it killed her outright. Only she awakened and lift up her hands, but spake ne'er a word.

Then was the maid in her grandame's beans,[234] and knew not what should become of her. I heard the pope took pity on her and, because her trespass was not voluntary but chance-medley, he assigned her no other punishment but this: to drink out the rest of the poison in the glass that was left, and so go scot-free.

We, careless of these mischances, held on our flight and saw no man come after us but we thought had pursued us. A thief, they say, mistakes every bush for a true man; the wind rattled not in any bush by the way as I rode, but I straight drew my rapier. To Bologna with a merry gale we posted, where we lodged ourselves in a blind street out of the way, and kept secret many days. But when we perceived we sailed in the haven, that the wind was laid, and no alarm made after us, we boldly came abroad. And one day, hearing of a more desperate murderer than Cain that was to be executed, we followed the multitude, and grudged not to lend him our eyes at his last parting.

Who should it be but one Cutwolf, a wearish,[235] dwarfish, writh-en-faced cobbler, brother to Bartol the Italian, that was confederate with Esdras of Granada and at that time stole away my courtesan when he ravished Heraclide.

It is not so natural for me to epitomize his impiety as to hear him in his own person speak upon the wheel where he was to suffer.

Prepare your ears and your tears, for never till this thrust I any tragical matter upon you. Strange and wonderful are God's judgments. Here shine they in their glory. Chaste Heraclide, thy blood is laid up in heaven's treasury; not one drop of it was lost, but lent out to usury. Water poured forth sinks down quietly into the earth, but blood spilled on the ground sprinkles up to the firmament. Murder is widemouthed and will not let God rest till he grant revenge. Not only the blood of the slaughtered innocent but the soul ascendeth to his throne, and there cries out and exclaims for justice and recompense. Guiltless souls that live every hour subject to violence, and with your despairing fears do much impair God's providence, fasten your eyes on this spectacle that will add to your faith. Refer all your oppressions, afflictions, and injuries to the even-balanced

---

[234]*in her . . . beans:* to be "in a bean patch" was roughly equivalent, in American slang, of being "up a creek."

[235]*wearish:* sickly looking (lean and pale).

eye of the Almighty. He it is that, when your patience sleepeth, will be most exceeding mindful of you.

This is but a gloss upon the text; thus Cutwolf begins his insulting oration:

"Men and people that have made holiday to behold my pained flesh toil on the wheel. Expect not of me a whining penitent slave, that shall do nothing but cry and say his prayers, and so be crushed in pieces. My body is little, but my mind is as great as a giant's; the soul which is in me is the very soul of Julius Caesar by reversion. My name is Cutwolf, neither better nor worse by occupation than a poor cobbler of Verona; cobblers are men and kings are no more. The occasion of my coming hither at this present is to have a few of my bones broken (as we are all born to die) for being the death of the emperor of homicides, Esdras of Granada.

"About two years since, in the streets of Rome, he slew the only and eldest brother I had, named Bartol, in quarreling about a courtesan. The news brought to me—as I was sitting in my shop under a stall knocking in of tacks, I think—I raised up my bristles; sold pritch-awl,[236] sponge, blacking tub, and punching iron; bought me rapier and pistol; and to go I went. Twenty months together I pursued him, from Rome to Naples, from Naples to Caiete[237] (passing over the river), from Caiete to Siena, from Siena to Florence, from Florence to Parma, from Parma to Pavia, from Pavia to Sion, from Sion to Geneva, from Geneva back again towards Rome; where in the way it was my chance to meet him in the nick here at Bologna, as I will tell you how.

"I saw a great fray in the streets as I passed along, and many swords walking; whereupon, drawing nearer, and inquiring who they were, answer was returned me it was that notable bandetto, Esdras of Granada. Oh, so I was tickled in the spleen with that word; my heart hopped and danced, my elbows itched, my fingers frisked, I wist not what should become of my feet, nor knew what I did for joy. The fray parted. I thought it not convenient to single him out (being a sturdy knave) in the street, but to stay till I had

[236]*pritch-awl:* a tool that the shoemaker uses to prick ("pritch") holes in leather.

[237]*Caiete:* Both the early editions spell this place name "Caiete," which suggests Caieta or Cajeta (now Gaeta), a city on the west coast of Italy between Naples and Rome. See Edward H. Sugden, *Topographical Dictionary* (Manchester, 1925), p. 89. By "passing over the river" Jack may mean passing over the Gulf of Gaeta.

got him at more advantage. To his lodging I dogged him, lay at the door all night where he entered—for fear he should give me the slip any way. Betimes in the morning I rung the bell and craved to speak with him; up to his chamber door I was brought, where knocking, he rose in his shirt and let me in and, when I was entered, bade me lock the door and declare my errand, and so he slipped to bed again.

"'Marry, this,' quoth I, 'is my errand. Thy name is Esdras of Granada, is it not? Most treacherously thou slewest my brother Bartol about two years ago in the streets of Rome; his death am I come to revenge. In quest of thee ever since above three thousand miles have I traveled. I have begged, to maintain me, the better part of the way, only because I would intermit no time from my pursuit in going back for money. Now have I got thee naked in my power; die thou shalt, though my mother and my grandmother dying did intreat for thee. I have promised the devil thy soul within this hour. Break my word I will not. In thy breast I intend to bury a bullet. Stir not, quinch[238] not, make no noise; for if thou dost it will be worse for thee.'

"Quoth Esdras, 'Whatever thou be at whose mercy I lie, spare me, and I will give thee as much gold as thou wilt ask. Put me to any pains my life reserved, and I willingly will sustain them. Cut off my arms and legs, and leave me as a lazar to some loathsome spittle,[239] where I may but live a year to pray and repent me. For thy brother's death the despair of mind that hath ever since haunted me, the guilty, gnawing worm of conscience I feel may be sufficient penance. Thou canst not send me to such a hell as already there is in my heart. To dispatch me presently is no revenge; it will soon be forgotten. Let me die a lingering death; it will be remembered a great deal longer. A lingering death may avail my soul, but it is the illest of ills that can befortune my body. For my soul's health I beg my body's torment; be not thou a devil to torment my soul, and send me to eternal damnation.

"'Thy overhanging sword hides heaven from my sight. I dare not look up, lest I embrace my death's wound unawares. I cannot pray to God and plead to thee both at once. Ah me, already I see my life buried in the wrinkles of thy brows. Say but I shall live,

---

[238]*quinch:* flinch.

[239]*spittle:* A "lazar-house" or "spittle-house" was a hospital for people with "foul diseases" and/or poor people.

though thou meanest to kill me. Nothing confounds like to sudden terror; it thrusts every sense out of office. Poison wrapped up in sugared pills is but half a poison. The fear of death's looks are more terrible than his stroke. The whilest I view death, my faith is deaded; where a man's fear is, there his heart is. Fear never engenders hope. How can I hope that heaven's father will save me from the hell everlasting when he gives me over to the hell of thy fury?

" 'Heraclide, now think I on thy fears sown in the dust, thy tears that my bloody mind made barren. In revenge of thee, God hardens this man's heart against me; yet I did not slaughter thee, though hundreds else my hand hath brought to the shambles. Gentle sir, learn of me what it is to clog your conscience with murder, to have your dreams, your sleeps, your solitary walks troubled and disquieted with murder. Your shadow by day will affright you. You will not see a weapon unsheathed, but immediately you will imagine it is predestinate for your destruction.

" 'This murder is a house divided within itself; it suborns a man's own soul to inform against him. His soul, being his accuser, brings forth his two eyes as witnesses against him. And the least eye-witness is unrefutable. Pluck out my eyes if thou wilt, and deprive my traitorous soul of her two best witnesses. Dig out my blasphemous tongue with thy dagger; both tongue and eyes will I gladly forgo to have a little more time to think on my journey to heaven.

" 'Defer a while thy resolution. I am not at peace with the world, for even but yesterday I fought and in my fury threatened further vengeance. Had I face to face asked forgiveness, I should think half my sins were forgiven. A hundred devils haunt me daily for my horrible murders. The devils, when I die, will be loath to go to hell with me, for they desired of Christ he would not send them to hell before their time. If they go not to hell, into thee they will go and hideously vex thee for turning them out of their habitation.

" 'Wounds I contemn. Life I prize light. It is another world's tranquility which makes me so timorous. Everlasting damnation, everlasting howling and lamentation. It is not from death I request thee to deliver me, but from this terror of torment's eternity. Thy brother's body only I pierced unadvisedly; his soul meant I no harm to at all. My body and soul both shalt thou cast away quite, if thou dost at this instant what thou mayst. Spare me, spare me I beseech thee! By thy own soul's salvation I desire thee seek not my soul's utter perdition; in destroying me, thou destroyest thyself and me.'

"Eagerly I replied after his long suppliant oration: 'Though I knew God would never have mercy on me except I had mercy on thee, yet of thee no mercy would I have. Revenge in our tragedies continually is raised from hell; of hell do I esteem better than heaven, if it afford me revenge. There is no heaven but revenge. I tell thee, I would not have undertook so much toil to gain heaven as I have done in pursuing thee for revenge. Divine revenge, of which (as of the joys above) there is no fullness or satiety. Look how my feet are blistered with following thee from place to place. I have riven my throat with overstraining it to curse thee. I have ground my teeth to powder with grating and grinding them together for anger, when any hath named thee. My tongue with vain threats is bollen,[240] and waxen too big for my mouth. My eyes have broken their strings with staring and looking ghastly, as I stood devising how to frame or set my countenance when I met thee. I have near spent my strength in imaginary acting on stone walls what I determined to execute on thee. Entreat not; a miracle may not reprieve thee. Villain, thus march I with my blade into thy bowels.'

" 'Stay, stay,' exclaimed Esdras, 'and hear me but one word further. Though neither for God nor man thou carest, but placest thy whole felicity in murder, yet of thy felicity learn how to make a greater felicity. Respite me a little from thy sword's point, and set me about some execrable enterprise that may subvert the whole state of Christendom, and make all men's ears tingle that hear of it. Command me to cut all my kindred's throats, to burn men, women, and children in their beds in millions, by firing their cities at midnight. Be it pope, emperor, or Turk that displeaseth thee, he shall not breathe on the earth. For thy sake will I swear and forswear, renounce my baptism, and all the interest I have in any other sacrament. Only let me live how miserable soever, be it in a dungeon amongst toads, serpents, and adders, or set up to the neck in dung. No pains I will refuse, however prorogued, to have a little respite to purify my spirit. Oh, hear me, hear me, and thou canst not be hardened against me!'

"At this his importunity I paused a little, not as retiring from my wreakful resolution, but going back to gather more forces of vengeance. With myself I devised how to plague him double for his base mind. My thoughts traveled in quest of some notable new Italianism, whose murderous platform might not only extend on his body but his soul also. The groundwork of it was this: that whereas he

[240] *bollen:* swollen.

had promised for my sake to swear and forswear and commit Italian-like violence on the highest seals of religion—if he would but thus far satisfy me he should be dismissed from my fury.

"First and foremost, he should renounce God and his laws, and utterly disclaim the whole title or interest he had in any covenant of salvation. Next, he should curse him to his face, as Job was willed by his wife, and write an absolute firm obligation of his soul to the devil, without condition or exception. Thirdly and lastly, having done this, he should pray to God fervently never to have mercy upon him, or pardon him.

"Scarce had I propounded these articles unto him but he was beginning his blasphemous abjurations. I wonder the earth opened not and swallowed us both, hearing the bold terms he blasted forth in contempt of Christianity. Heaven hath thundered when half less contumelies against it have been altered. Able they were to raise saints and martyrs from their graves, and pluck Christ himself from the right hand of his father. My joints trembled and quaked with attending them; my hair stood upright; and my heart was turned wholly to fire. So affectionately and zealously did he give himself over to infidelity, as if Satan had gotten the upper hand of our high maker. The vein in his left hand, that is derived from his heart, with no faint blow he pierced; and with the blood that flowed from it, writ a full obligation of his soul to the devil. Yea, more earnestly he prayed unto God never to forgive his soul than many Christians do to save their souls.

"These fearful ceremonies brought to an end, I bade him ope his mouth and gape wide. He did so—as what will not slaves do for fear? Therewith made I no more ado, but shot him full into the throat with my pistol. No more spake he after; so did I shoot him that he might never speak after, or repent him. His body, being dead, looked as black as a toad; the devil presently branded it for his own.

"This is the fault that hath called me hither. No true Italian but will honor me for it. Revenge is the glory of arms, and the highest performance of valor; revenge is whatsoever we call law or justice. The farther we wade in revenge, the nearer come we to the throne of the Almighty. To his scepter it is properly ascribed. His scepter he lends unto man, when he lets one man scourge another. All true Italians imitate me, in revenging constantly and dying valiantly. Hangman, to thy task, for I am ready for the utmost of thy rigor."

Herewith all the people, outrageously incensed, with one conjoined outcry yelled mainly, "Away with him! Away with him! Executioner, torture him! Tear him! Or we will tear thee in pieces if thou spare him!"

The executioner needed no exhortation hereunto, for of his own nature was he hackster good enough. Old Excellent he was, at a bone ache. At the first chop with his wood knife would he fish for a man's heart, and fetch it out as easily as a plum from the bottom of a porridge pot. He would crack necks as fast as a cook cracks eggs. A fiddler cannot turn his pin so soon as he would turn a man off the ladder. Bravely did he drum on this Cutwolf's bones—not breaking them outright but, like a saddler knocking in of tacks, jarring on them quaveringly with his hammer a great while together. No joint about him but with a hatchet he had for the nonce. He disjointed half, and then with boiling lead soldered up the wounds from bleeding. His tongue he pulled out, lest he should blaspheme in his torment. Venomous stinging worms he thrust into his ears, to keep his head ravingly occupied. With cankers scruzed[241] to pieces he rubbed his mouth and his gums. No limb of his but was lingeringly splintered in shivers. In this horror left they him on the wheel as in hell; where, yet living, he might behold his flesh legacied amongst the fowls of the air.

Unsearchable is the book of our destinies. One murder begetteth another; was never yet bloodshed barren from the beginning of the world to this day. Mortifiedly abjected and daunted was I with this trunculent tragedy of Cutwolf and Esdras. To such straight life did it thenceforward incite me that, ere I went out of Bologna, I married my courtesan, performed many alms deeds, and hasted so fast out of the Sodom of Italy that within forty days I arrived at the King of England's camp twixt Ardes and Guines[242] in France, where he with great triumphs met and entertained the emperor and the French king, and feasted many days.

And so, as my story began with the king at Turney and Turwin, I think meet here to end it with the king at Ardes and Guines. All the conclusive epilogue I will make is this: that if herein I have pleased any, it shall animate me to more pains in this kind. Otherwise, I will swear upon an English chronicle never to be outlandish chronicler more while I live. Farewell as many as wish me well. June 27, 1593.

Finis

[241]*scruzed:* squeezed.
[242]*Ardes and Guines:* Ardres and Guisnes; the meeting occurred in June, 1520.

Thomas of Reading

OR *The Six Worthy Yeomen of the West* (c. 1598)

THOMAS DELONEY

King Henry I perceives with a shock, in Chapter 1 of *Thomas of Reading* (c. 1598), that something truly revolutionary has happened to England's economic and social order. While on a journey to Wales, Henry's party must get off to the side of the highway to let a long train of wagons go by, each wagon loaded with cloth belonging to Thomas Cole of Reading. Naturally, the king is angry; but during the hour-long wait, he gradually realizes that the cloth represents prosperity not just for Cole, but for England. He sees plainly his own role: he will encourage the new economic trend, not thwart it. The narrator of *Thomas of Reading* strongly approves of the king's attitude, and he proceeds to tell the rest of the story from the center of a *laissez faire* economic view of life that is unique in Elizabethan prose fiction.

But if the view is economic, it is also idealistic. John Winchcomb in *Jack of Newbury* (c. 1597) and Thomas Cole in *Thomas of Reading* are not of gentle birth like Dorastus and Rosader in *Pandosto* and *Rosalind*; on the contrary, Jack and Thomas are plain men of humble birth who pull themselves up by their bootstraps. Their progress from apprentice to wealthy clothier (and in Jack's case to member of parliament representing Newbury) is a matter to be described in a new vocabulary of romance. They tend to ride horses only as a means of transportation, and their tremendous energy finds expression in hard and skillful work rather than in arms and love. Yet arms and love receive a secondary emphasis in the subplot concerning Duke Robert and Margaret; and in both plots the old values of medieval romance are still quite relevant. Courage now applies mainly to a competitive business world, but in times of national emergency it applies also to the battlefield and even hand-to-hand combat. Like most medieval romancers, Deloney pictures a world of action; he does not assume (as Lyly, Greene, Lodge, and Nashe do) that the Latin classics are an important cultural source that everyone should study and live by. Loyalty in Deloney's view is mainly to the commonwealth rather than to the king or liege lord, as in the old romances. Generosity is not of course a new value with Deloney, but the particular expression of it that Jack shows to Randoll Pert in Chapter 9 of *Jack of Newbury* is something new (and peculiarly appropriate to a world view that is frankly economic but not selfishly materialistic). What makes all Deloney's values hang together is his faith in human nature—or perhaps one should say faith in *English* human nature, with a consequent faith in the destiny of England. Dignity is a trait shared by apprentice and duke alike; but since the scene often focuses on the apprentice, the dignity is often accompanied by plainness, simplicity, and frugality. Frugality, like prowess at love, is important and appropriate in youth; with maturity and success, generosity tends to replace frugality, except where the latter is an aspect of plainness and simplicity (always good in themselves). Margaret comes to understand that her life as a servant is in some ways more satisfying than her former life among the nobility. She decides that "poverty with surety is better than honor mixed with fear." "Surety" is a favorite word with Deloney, as "blemish" is with Lyly; and the difference between the words is proportional to the difference between the two writers' values.

Unlike Nashe, Deloney never turns completely against Lyly's style. One or two passages in *Jack of Newbury* may be a parody of Lyly's use of Pliny, but usually Deloney's method is to do as Lodge had done and straightforwardly adapt euphuism to his own purposes. Deloney eliminates some of the alliteration and refuses to concern himself very much with isocolon or antithesis; then he uses his modified euphuism to lend dignity, formality, and grace to special occasions, such as Duke Robert's proposal to Margaret in Chapter 10.

Thomas of Reading is such an eclectic work, composed of so many different elements, that one naturally wonders how Deloney put them together. Did he learn from Nashe? It is difficult to say; but, opposite as they were temperamentally, their fiction is traceable to many of the same sources—particularly English history, the jest-book, and contemporary daily life. One guesses that Deloney mixed these elements without much help from Nashe; but whether he did or not, the two writers were thinking along the same lines. Both make frequent use of contemporary historians like Holinshed and refer to their own works as "histories." Both also see possibilities in the jestbook form, especially for a scene with colloquial dialogue and boisterous action. *Jack of Newbury* and *The Unfortunate Traveler* are offspring of the jest-biography, but they are superior to it in rendering a concrete sense of reality—of what people actually eat, drink, and wear; of everyday speech rhythms. Unlike Nashe, Deloney confines all boisterous action to minor characters, thus protecting his heroes from unseemly conduct. Nashe, on the other hand, in keeping with his basically anti-heroic conception, plunges his hero-rogue into the center of the most compromising of situations.

To the extent that they communicate a sense of the 1590's, a sense of the Elizabethan "present" in which they live—and through that present, a sense of any present, including ours—Nashe and Deloney are "novelists" (in the same way that Gascoigne is a novelist). Yet "novel" fits *Master F. J.* much better than it does *Thomas of Reading*, which, however, has elements of the novel in it and perhaps should be referred to as a "novel-romance," with emphasis on "romance." In the end, Deloney is not writing about a real present or a real past so much as an ideal future. The real Henry I probably did not watch any carts go by, and the real John Winchcomb probably did not live on so grand a scale as Chapter 3 of *Jack of Newbury* makes out. Deloney idealizes the past, and to make the action "seem real," to make it convincing and believable, he uses a great many "realistic" details from the Elizabethan present. Both historically and in Deloney's romance Jack becomes a wealthy and important citizen. But Holinshed says nothing about Jack's helping the queen at Flodden Field. Deloney invents that action as appropriate to his wonderful hero's versatility, loyalty, and courage; and then he makes the invention easily believable by investing it with a whole network of circumstantial detail (such as the weapons Jack's 150 men carried, the order in which they marched or rode horseback, and what they wore even as to color and material). The result is a new genre, historical romance. The emphasis throughout is on deeds of heroism, and the essential point is that John Winchcomb and Thomas Cole are late sixteenth-century heroic models. They are a new breed of hero—Lancelot brought up to date.

Deloney is not writing escape fiction. The idealized eras of Henry I and Henry VIII are to offer ideal patterns of conduct; all young apprentices should emulate Thomas Cole. Unlike Malory, Deloney is sanguine about the future. Through his vivid scenes he implies that Englishmen can progress almost without limit if only king, executive, and worker will each do his part.

The scene is Deloney's narrative unit. He uses summary and commentary well but sparingly, as in the opening paragraphs of *Thomas*. But in Chapter 1, as a scene starts to unfold and we are gradually brought in fairly close to the action, Deloney seems much surer of himself. Almost anything that he can assimilate at all he can render into sparkling scene. Most of the details in Chapter 5 of *Jack of Newbury* had appeared in a work of expository prose called *The Forest* (1571), by Thomas Fortescue; but in Deloney's hands these same details not only take on a new life but are made strictly relevant to the story-line.[1] In *Thomas* there are short scenes, long scenes, omitted scenes, and contrasting scenes placed back to back. Chapter 10 of *Jack* is all dialogue.[2] Usually the details of a scene are not especially numerous, but they are always apt and significant. They are of just the right number and quality to make us visualize a particular setting—a highway, a field, a bedroom, a dining room, a shop, a tavern.

The dialogue is not easily described because there is virtually every imaginable kind. Much of it is colloquial, as in the scenes with Cole and his fellow clothiers at Gerard's Hall. But for Duke Robert and

---

[1]Hyder E. Rollins was the first to see the relationship between Deloney and Fortescue. See his "Thomas Deloney's Euphuistic Learning and *The Forest*." See also Lawlis, ed., *The Novels of Thomas Deloney*, p. 356. Deloney's sense of relevance may also be illustrated by Chapter 4 of *Jack of Newbury*. At first the episode seems designed only to exemplify Will Sommers' love of fun; the action is pure jest and seems almost completely detached from the rest of the story. But if we attend to all the details, we see the relevance of the episode. The "weaver maidens" take pride in their equipment; their part of the clothing industry (like all the other parts) is run efficiently; they are happy; they speak up freely; they have wit and a sense of humor; and they have no reason to be afraid of the consequences when they give the king's jester a fitting punishment. After Chapter 4, we see no more of Will Sommers; but the suggestions regarding the daily lives of average workers in the clothing industry pervade the whole work.

[2]Compare similar passages in Rabelais' *Gargantua* (1534); see Samuel Putnam's translation, *The Portable Rabelais* (New York, 1946), pp. 60–65.

Margaret there is a formal language, vaguely euphuistic, with a modest amount of alliteration and assonance and with an occasional long monologue like the ones we have observed in Lyly, Greene, and Lodge. But even Deloney's monologues tend to become dramatic monologues; like the poems in that genre by Donne, Marvell, and Browning, the words imply certain contemporaneous actions. Gray's wife notes, in the middle of her apostrophe to the absent Margaret in Chapter 13: "Here, she hath left me my keys."

It is through the dialogue that we first become aware of Deloney's minor characters—the host of businessmen, wives, and servants, many of whom we recognize by an appropriate malapropism, dialect, foreign accent, or exaggerated trait of some kind.[3] Crab, Weasel, Hodgkins, Old Bosom, Sir William Ferris, and Tom Dove come easily to mind from *Thomas of Reading* alone. They remind us more of Dickens than of any writer in the sixteenth century. Like Dickens, but unlike Nashe, Deloney lets his characters grow out of situations inherent in a developing story. Occasionally they emerge almost as part of their environment: just as we remember and associate Miss Havisham of *Great Expectations* with her decaying house, so we remember Old Bosom in the context of his inn and warehouse. In contrast, Zadoch and Dr. Zachary of *The Unfortunate Traveler* remain hazy, indistinct, and unrelated, despite the fact that their dialogue (pp. 534 ff.) is as lively as any sequence of dialogue in Deloney. Nashe's characterization is sharp only when he pauses to etch in a "character," such as the one of Vanderhulk; but usually the character sketch, though brilliantly incisive, is not relevant to the story, which Nashe is perfectly willing to interrupt.

The fact that Deloney nowhere dwells at length on a completely loathsome person, like Vanderhulk, is perhaps significant. Yet every story has its villains—Cardinal Wolsey in *Jack of Newbury;* Dioclesian and Maximinus in *The Gentle Craft, Part I;* the priest who refuses to perform a burial ceremony in *The Gentle Craft, Part II;* and the Jarmans in *Thomas of Reading.* The Jarmans, murderers of Thomas Cole, are by far the worst of the lot; but even they receive little direct attention. They are bad, and they eventually get their comeuppance in a manner as "enjoyable" as Orlick's death in *Great Expectations.* But they are only one part of the total picture. We are to appreciate also the omens; Thomas' premonition of death; his final remarks about family and friends; and then, after the murder, the detective work leading

[3]E. M. Forster's use of the term "flat characters," in a purely descriptive sense rather than a pejorative sense, applies to Deloney as well as to Dickens. See *Aspects of the Novel* (New York, 1927), pp. 105–109.

to the Jarmans' apprehension and subsequent hanging. Throughout the scene we are kept strictly on the outside; all we know, even of Thomas, comes from what we happen to hear and see, for we are given no inner thoughts and feelings.

At one point the focus goes awry: the narrator centers on the Jarmans' many exploits through the years and the secret language they use with each other in reference to their victims; as a consequence, the emphasis begins to turn away from the subject of Chapter 11, Thomas' unfortunate death. For the moment we get a straight journalistic account, in the manner of Deloney's broadside ballads of the 1580's.[4] But on the whole the scene is quite successful, and the objectivity is part of its success; violent and unreasonable action, as Hemingway has shown in "The Killers," can be effectively related in understatement, in quiet and disinterested presentation of the bare action.

A scene about a "churching feast" follows the murder scene. Deloney seems to have learned what Shakespeare also learned, that there are ways of telling a story so that you can have your cake and eat it too. The murder of Duncan in *Macbeth* is followed by the drunken porter's knocking at the gate; the murder of Cole is followed by the amusing gossip of giddy women. Tragedy and farce are not only possible in the same work, but in adjoining scenes; and the main effect is not to cancel out, but to accent. The farcical scene makes us take Cole's death more, rather than less, seriously.[5]

The two contrasting scenes represent a new boldness in Deloney's technique, not observable in his previous three works of prose fiction. He is attempting more in *Thomas* than he had attempted before, particularly in terms of a comprehensive narrative structure. The compression of time, the view of Thomas only at the end of his successful career, requires a structure different from that of *Jack of Newbury*. One feels a breadth of space rather than a passage of time. *Jack* is the biography of a whole adult life; in *Thomas* only four years elapse, but during that time we are to observe not only Thomas Cole but eight other clothiers as well (and the wives and servants of all nine). Deloney divides the action between two separate but interrelated plots, the main plot concentrating on the middle class and the subplot the upper class, with Margaret, the impoverished daughter

[4]Compare Greene's focus on the cony-catchers in *A Notable Discovery*; unlike Deloney, Greene seems to imply a respect for the knaves' prowess and a scorn of the simple-minded cony.

[5]See Kenneth Burke, *Counter Statement* (New York, 1931), p. 158, for a discussion of contrasting scenes.

of the banished Earl of Shrewsbury, appropriately linking the two plots.

To anyone at the time it must have seemed obvious that Deloney had reversed a time-honored formula, especially for romance: in Malory, Sidney, Rich, Greene, and Lodge, upper-class characters are never minor enough to be relegated to a subplot (though, as we have seen, Greene prepared the way for making persons of low birth major characters). But the narrator of *Thomas* never comments on his reversal of plots, never indicates any doubt that his perspective is correct. He calmly and assuredly agrees with Henry I in the first chapter: sensing the dawn of a new era, he gives right of way to a rising middle class. But he does so without showing the strains that one would expect to find; there is no bitterness against the upper class and no bragging on the part of the newly rich. The relationship between Margaret and the Grays of Gloucester is a good example of the tact that the narrator recognizes as necessary if the new order is to be successful. What gives balance to the whole is the vision of an ideal commonwealth, in which king, executives, and workers make agreements that satisfy both individual and national interests. Deloney's technique is equal to his conception, for at the end—despite Thomas' murder, Duke Robert's execution, and Margaret's retirement from the world—the vision of an ideal commonwealth seems so real that if it does not actually exist, it surely will in some future golden age.

Yet the vision is not a single rosy glow of well being. The Grays, as much as they love their former servant and respect her wishes, cannot help expressing their view that her entrance into a convent is a tremendous waste. Deloney typically dramatizes conflict, and the Grays' response forms an integral part of the scene's dialectical movement.

Thomas of Reading

In the days of King Henry the First, who was the first king that instituted the high court of parliament,[6] there lived nine men, which for the trade of clothing were famous throughout all England. Which

[6]*King Henry the First . . . parliament:* This information regarding Henry I (King of England, 1100–1135) Deloney took from Raphael Holinshed's *Chronicles;* see the 1587 edition, III, 38 (sig. D5ᵛ). Much of the background for *Thomas of Reading* comes from Holinshed and Richard Grafton, the leading historians of the time.

art in those days was held in high reputation, both in respect of the great riches that thereby was gotten as also of the benefit it brought to the whole commonwealth. The younger sons of knights and gentlemen, to whom their fathers would leave no lands, were most commonly preferred to learn this trade to the end that thereby they might live in good estate and drive forth their days in prosperity.

Among all crafts this was the only chief, for that it was the greatest merchandise by the which our country became famous through all nations. And it was verily thought that the one half of the people in the land lived in those days thereby, and in such good sort that in the commonwealth there was few or no beggars at all. Poor people, whom God lightly blesseth with most children, did by means of this occupation so order them that by the time that they were come to be six or seven years of age, they were able to get their own bread. Idleness was then banished our coast, so that it was a rare thing to hear of a thief in those days. Therefore it was not without cause that clothiers were then both honored and loved, among whom these nine persons in this king's days were of great credit: *viz.*, Thomas Cole of Reading, Gray of Gloucester, Sutton of Salisbury, Fitzallen of Worcester (commonly called William of Worcester), Tom Dove of Exeter, and Simon of Southampton (alias "Sup-broath"), who were by the king called the six worthy husbands of the west. Then were there three living in the north—that is to say, Cutbert of Kendal, Hodgekins of Halifax, and Martin Byram of Manchester.[7] Every one of these kept a great number of servants at work—spinners, carders, weavers, fullers, dyers, shearmen, and rowers—to the great admiration of all those that came into their houses to behold them.

Now you shall understand, these gallant clothiers, by reason of their dwelling places, separated themselves in three several companies: Gray of Gloucester, William of Worcester, and Thomas of Reading, because their journey to London was all one way, they conversed commonly together; and Dove of Exeter, Sutton of Salisbury, and Simon of Southampton, they in like sort kept company, the one with the other, meeting ever altogether at Bazingstoke; and the three northern clothiers did the like, who commonly did not meet till they came to Bosom's Inn[8] in London.

[7]*Thomas Cole of Reading . . . Martin Byram of Manchester:* Some of these names appear in Holinshed but not in connection with the clothing industry. The alliteration suggests that Deloney may have invented a name to go with a town ("William of Worcester," etc.).

[8]*Bosom's Inn:* apparently the name of a tavern on Laurence Lane, off Cheapside; Deloney seems to have created a character, Old Bosom, to go with the name of the inn. See Sugden, *Topographical Dictionary*, p. 69.

Moreover, for the love and delight that these western men had each in other's company, they did so provide that their wains and themselves would ever meet upon one day in London at Gerard's Hall,[9] surnamed "the Giant," for that he surpassed all other men of that age, both in stature and strength, whose merriments and memorable deeds, I will set down unto you in this following discourse.

Chapter 1

How King Henry Sought the Favor of All His Subjects, Especially of the Clothiers

This King Henry, who for his great learning and wisdom was called "Beauclerk," being the third son to the renowned conquerer, after the death of his brother William Rufus, took upon him the government of this land in the absence of his second brother Robert, Duke of Normandy,[10] who at this time was at wars against the infidels and was chosen King of Jerusalem. The which he, for the love he bore to his own country, refused and with great honor returned from the Holy Land. Of whose coming, when King Henry understood (knowing he would make claim to the crown), sought by all means possible to win the good will of his nobility and to get the favor of the commons by courtesy. For the obtaining whereof he did them many favors, thereby the better to strengthen himself against his brother.

It chanced on a time as he, with one of his sons and divers of his nobility, rode from London towards Wales to appease the fury of the Welshmen, which then began to raise themselves in arms against his authority, that he met with a great number of wains laden with cloth coming to London; and seeing them still drive on one after another so many together, demanded whose they were.

The wainmen answered in this sort: "Cole's of Reading," quoth they.

Then by and by the king asked another, saying, "Whose cloth is all this?"

"Old Cole's," quoth he.

[9]*Gerard's Hall:* a merchant's house in Cheapside, the house named (according to legend) after a giant who used a 40-foot pole for a walking stick.

[10]*Robert, Duke of Normandy:* Henry I's older brother and the eldest son of William the Conqueror; Holinshed and Grafton probably were wrong in saying that he became a ruler of Jerusalem, but it is true that in 1099, with Godfrey of Bouillon and Robert of Flanders, he captured Jerusalem from the Turks. For obvious reasons, Deloney suppresses one bit of information in the chronicles: Robert was short and fat, and that is why his father called him "Robert Curthose."

And again anon, after he asked the same question to other, and still they answered, "Old Cole's."

And it is to be remembered that the king met them in such a place, so narrow and straight, that he with all the rest of his train were fain to stand up close to the hedge, whilest the carts passed by, the which at that time being in number above two hundred, was near hand an hour ere the king could get room to be gone. So that by his long stay he began to be displeased, although the admiration of that sight did much qualify his fury. But breaking out in discontent, by reason of his stay, he said he thought old Cole had got a commission for all the carts in the country to carry his cloth.

"And how if he have?" quoth one of the wainmen. "Doth that grieve you, good sir?"

"Yea, good sir," said our king. "What say you to that?"

The fellow, seeing the king in asking that question to bend his brows, though he knew not what he was, yet being abashed, he answered thus: "Why, sir, if you be angry, nobody can hinder you; for possible, sir, you have anger at commandment."

The king, seeing him in uttering of his words to quiver and quake, laughed heartily at him, as well in respect of his simple answer as at his fear. And so, soon after, the last wain went by, which gave present passage unto him and his nobles; and thereupon entering into communication of the commodity of clothing, the king gave order at his home return to have old Cole brought before his majesty, to the intent he might have conference with him, noting him to be a subject of great ability. But by that time he came within a mile of Staines, he met another company of wains in like sort laden with cloth, whereby the king was driven into a further admiration; and demanding whose they were, answer was made in this sort:

"They be Goodman Sutton's of Salisbury, good sir."

And by that time a score of them were past, he asked again, saying: "Whose are these?"

"Sutton's of Salisbury," quoth they; and so still, as often as the king asked that question, they answered, "Sutton's of Salisbury."

"God send me many such Suttons," said the king.

And thus the farther he traveled westward, more wains and more he met continually; upon which occasion he said to his nobles that it would never grieve a king to die for the defense of a fertile country and faithful subjects.

"I always thought," quoth he, "that England's valor was more than her wealth; yet now I see her wealth sufficient to maintain her valor, which I will seek to cherish in all I may, and with my sword keep myself in possession of that I have. Kings and lovers can brook no partners, and therefore let my brother Robert think that although he was heir to England by birth, yet I am king by possession. All his favorers I must account my foes and will serve them as I did the ungrateful Earl of Shrewsbury, whose lands I have seized, and banished his body."

But now we will leave the king to his journey into Wales and, waiting his home return, in the meantime tell you of the meeting of these jolly clothiers at London.

Chapter 2

How William of Worcester, Gray of Glou-
cester, and Old Cole of Reading Met All
Together at Reading and of Their Communi-
cation by the Way as They Rode to London

When Gray of Gloucester and William of Worcester were come to Reading, according to their custom, they always called old Cole to have his company to London, who also duly attended their coming, having provided a good breakfast for them. And when they had well refreshed themselves, they took their horses and rode on towards the city; and in their journey William of Worcester asked them if they had not heard of the Earl of Moraigne's escape out of the land.[11]

"What, is he fled?" quoth Gray. "I muse much of that matter, being in such great regard with the king as he was."

"But I pray you, do you not know the cause of his going?" quoth Cole.

"The common report," quoth Gray, "is this: that the covetous earl, who through a greedy desire never left begging of the king for one thing or other, and his request being now denied him, of mere obstinacy and willful frowardness hath banished himself out of the land and quite forsaken the country of Cornwall, having made a vow never to set foot within England again. And as report goeth he, with the late banished Earl of Shrewsbury, have joined themselves with Robert, Duke of Normandy, against the king, the which action of theirs hath inflamed the king's wrath, that their ladies with their children are

[11]*Earl of Moraigne's . . . land:* possibly a reference to the Count of Mortain (d. 1091?), who helped Robert in his rebellion against William Rufus in 1088; by 1101, when Robert moved against Henry I, the count probably had died.

quite turned out of doors succorless and friendless, so that, as it is told me, they wander up and down the country like forlorn people; and although many do pity them, yet few do relieve them."

"A lamentable hearing," quoth William of Worcester.

And with that, casting their eyes aside, they espied Tom Dove with the rest of his companions come riding to meet them. Who, as soon as they were come thither, fell into such pleasant discourses as did shorten the way they had to Colebrook, where always at their coming towards London they dined. And being entered into their inn, according to old custom, good cheer was provided for them, for these clothiers were the chiefest guests that traveled along the way. And this was as sure as an act of parliament: that Tom Dove could not digest his meat without music nor drink wine without women. So that his hostess, being a merry wench, would often times call in two or three of her neighbors' wives to keep him company, where, ere they parted, they were made as pleasant as pies. And this being a continual custom amongst them when they came thither, at length the women's husbands began to take exceptions at their wives going thither; whereupon great controversy grew between them, in such sort that when they were most restrained, then they had most desire to work their wills.

"Now, gip," quoth they, "must we be so tied to our task that we may not drink with our friends? Fie, fie, upon these yellow hose;[12] will no other die serve your turn? Have we thus long been your wives, and do you now mistrust us? Verily you eat too much salt, and that makes you grow choleric. Bad livers judge all other the like, but in faith you shall not bridle us so like asses, but we will go to our friends when we are sent for, and do you what you can."

"Well," quoth their husbands, "if you be so headstrong, we will tame you. It is the duty of honest women to obey their husbands' sayings."

"And of honest men," quoth they, "to think well of their wives; but who do sooner impeach their credit than their husbands, charging them if they do but smile, that they are subtle; and if they do but wink, they account them wily; if sad of countenance, then sullen; if they be froward, then are they counted shrews; and sheepish, if they be gentle. If a woman keep her house, then you will say she is melancholy; if she walk abroad, then you call her a gadder; a Puritan, if she be precise; and a wanton, if she be pleasant. So there is

[12]*yellow hose:* a symbol for "jealous men."

no woman in the world that knows how to please you, that we think ourselves accursed to be married wives, living with so many woes. These men, of whose company you forewarn us, are, for aught that ever we saw, both honest and courteous, and in wealth far beyond yourselves. Then what reason is there why we should refrain to visit them? Is their good will so much to be requited with scorn that their cost may not be countervailed with our company? If a woman be disposed to play light of love, alas, alas, do you think that you can prevent her? Nay, we will abide by it, that the restraint of liberty enforceth women to be lewd; for where a woman cannot be trusted, she cannot think herself beloved, and if not beloved, what cause hath she to care for such a one? Therefore, husbands, reform your opinions and do not work your own woes with our discredit. These clothiers, we tell you, are jolly fellows, and but in respect of our courtesy, they would scorn our company."

The men, hearing their wives so well to plead for themselves, knew not how to answer, but said they would put the burden on their consciences if they dealt unjustly with them, and so left them to their own wills. The women, having thus conquered their husbands' conceits, would not leave the favor of their friends for frowns; and as above the rest Tom Dove was the most pleasantest, so was he had in most reputation with the women, who for his sake made this song:

Welcome to town, Tom Dove, Tom Dove,
The merriest man alive;
Thy company still we love, we love,
God grant thee well to thrive;
And never will depart from thee,
For better or worse, my joy,
For thou shalt still have our good will;
God's blessing on my sweet boy.

This song went up and down through the whole country and at length became a dance among the common sort, so that Tom Dove, for his mirth and good fellowship, was famous in every place. Now when they came to London, they were welcome to the host, Gerard the Giant; and as soon as they were alighted, they were saluted by the merchants, who waited their coming thither and always prepared for them a costly supper, where they commonly made their bargain. And upon every bargain made, they still used to send some tokens to the clothiers' wives. The next morning they went to the hall, where they met the northern clothiers, who greeted one another in this sort:

"What, my masters of the west, well met. What cheer? What cheer?"

"Even the best cheer our merchants could make us," quoth Gray.

"Then you could not choose but fare well," quoth Hodgekins.

"And you be weary of our company, adieu," quoth Sutton.

"Not so," said Martin, "but shall we not have a game ere we go?"

"Yes, faith, for a hundred pounds."

"Well said, old Cole," said they; and with that Cole and Gray went to the dice with Martin and Hodgekins; and the dice running on Hodgekins' side, Cole's money began to waste.

"Now, by the mass," quoth Cole, "my money shrinks as bad as northern cloth."[13]

When they had played long, Gray stepped to it and recovered again the money that Cole had lost. But while they were thus playing, the rest being delighted in contrary matters, every man satisfied his own humor.

Tom Dove called for music; William of Worcester for wine; Sutton set his delight in hearing merry tales; Simon of Southampton got him into the kitchen and to the pottage pot he goes, for he esteemed more of a mess of pottage than of a venison pasty.

Now, sir, Cutbert of Kendal was of another mind, for no meat pleased him so well as mutton, such as was laced in a red petticoat. And you shall understand that always when they went to dice, they got into Bosom's Inn, which was so called of his name that kept it. Who, being a foul sloven, went always with his nose in his bosom, and one hand in his pocket, the other on his staff, figuring forth a description of cold winter. For he always wore two coats, two caps, two or three pair of stockings, and a high pair of shoes, over the which he drew on a great pair of lined slippers; and yet he would oft complain of cold. Wherefore of all men generally he was called "Old Bosom," and his house, "Bosom's Inn."

This lump of cold ice had lately married a young wife, who was as wily as she was wanton; and in her company did Cutbert only delight. And the better to make passage to his love, he would often thus commune with her:

"I muse, goodwife—" quoth he.

[13]*money shrinks . . . northern cloth:* We are to be reminded of a proverb (Tilley, (C432): "Like northern cloth, shrunk in the wetting."

"Good wife?" quoth she. "Verily, sir, in mine opinion, there is none good but God, and therefore call me 'mistress.' "[14]

Then said Cutbert, "Fair mistress, I have often mused that you, being so proper a woman, could find in your heart for to match with such a greasy carl as this, an evil-mannered mate, a foul lump of kitchen stuff, and such a one as is indeed a scorn of men. How can you like him that all women mislikes or love such a loathsome creature? Methinks verily it should grieve you to lend him a kiss, much more to lie with him."

"Indeed, sir," quoth she, "I had but hard fortune in this respect, but my friends would have it so, and truly my liking and my love toward him are alike: he never had the one, nor never shall get the other. Yet I may say to you, before I married him, there were divers proper young men that were suitors unto me, who loved me as their lives; and glad was he that could get my company. Those were my golden days, wherein my pleasure abounded, but these are my years of care and grief, wherein my sorrows exceed. Now no man regards me; no man cares for me; and albeit in secret they might bear me good will, yet who dares show it? And this is a double grief. He carries over me so jealous a mind that I cannot look at a man but presently he accuseth me of inconstancy, although (I protest) without cause."

"And in troth," quoth Cutbert, "he should have cause to complain for somewhat, were I as you."

"As sure as I live, and so he shall," quoth she, "if he do not change his bias."

Cutbert, hearing her say so, began to grow further in requesting her favor, wishing he might be her servant and secret friend. And the better to obtain his desire, he gave her divers gifts, insomuch that she began something to listen unto him. And albeit she liked well of his speeches, yet would she blame him and take him up very short sometimes for the same, till in the end Cutbert showed himself to be desperate, saying he would drown himself rather than live in her disdain.

"Oh, my sweetheart, not so," quoth she, "God forbid I should be the death of any man. Comfort thyself, kind Cutbert, and take this

[14]*goodwife . . . Good wife . . . mistress*: A pun seems to be involved (thus beginning a series of puns and ironic statements that continue to the end of the chapter); Cutbert means "goodwife" (Mrs. or mistress, without any sense of good or bad), but Winifred takes him to mean "good wife."

kiss in token of further kindness. And if thou wilt have my favor, thou must be wise and circumspect; and in my husband's sight I would always have thee to find fault with my doings, blame my bad housewifery, dispraise my person, and take exceptions at everything, whereby he will be as well pleased as Simon of Southampton with a mess of pottage."

"Dear mistress," quoth he, "I will fulfill your charge to the uttermost, so that you will not take my jest in earnest."

She answered, "Thy foulest speeches I will esteem the fairest and take every dispraise to be a praise from thee, turning each word to the contrary; and so, for this time, adieu, good Cutbert, for supper time draws near, and it is meet for me to look to my meat."

With that, down comes Old Bosom, calling his wife, saying, "Ho, Winifred, is supper ready? They have done playing above. Therefore let the chamberlain cover the table."

"By and by, husband," quoth she, "it shall be done straight way."

"How now, my masters, who wins?" quoth Cutbert.

"Our money walks to the west," quoth Martin. "Cole hath won forty pounds of me, and Gray hath gotten well."

"The best is," quoth Hodgekins, "they will pay for our supper."

"Then let us have good store of sack," quoth Sutton.

"Content," said Cole, "for I promise you, I strive not to grow rich by dice playing. Therefore call for what you will, I will pay for all."

"Yea!" said Simon. "Chamberlain, I pray thee bring a whole pottle[15] of pottage for me."

Now Tom Dove had all the fiddlers at a beck of his finger, which follow him up and down the city, as diligent as little chickens after a hen, and made a vow that there should want no music. And at that time, here lived in London a musician of great reputation, named Reior, who kept his servants in such costly garments that they might seem to come before any prince. Their coats were all of one color; and it is said that afterward the nobility of this land, noting it for a seemly sight, used in like manner to keep their men all in one livery. This Reior was the most skilfullest musician that lived at that time, whose wealth was very great, so that all the instruments whereon his servants played were richly garnished with studs of silver and some gold. The bows belonging to their violins were all likewise of pure silver. He was also for his wisdom called to great office in the city, who also built, at his own cost, the priory

---

[15]*pottle:* a pot holding half a gallon (usually of wine).

and hospital of St. Bartholomew in Smithfield.[16] His servants, being the best consort in the city, were by Tom Dove appointed to play before the young princes.

Then supper being brought to the board, they all sat down. And by and by after comes up their host, who took his place among them; and anon after, the goodwife, in a red petticoat and waistcoat, comes among them as white as a lily, saying, "My masters, you are welcome; I pray you be merry."

Thus falling close to their meat, when they had well fed, they found leisure to talk one with another. At what time Cutbert began thus to find fault, "Iwis, my host," quoth he, "you have a wise house-wife to your wife. Here is meat dressed of a new fashion. God sends meat, and the devil sends cooks."

"Why, what ails the meat?" quoth she. "Serves it not your turn? Better men than yourself are content withal, but a paltry companion is ever worst to please."

"Away, you sluttish thing," quoth Cutbert. "Your husband hath a sweet jewel of you. I marvel such a grave, ancient man would match himself with such a young giglot[17] that hath as much hand-someness in her as good housewifery, which is just nothing at all."

"Well, sir," said she, "in regard of my husband's presence I am loath to aggravate anger; otherwise I would tell thee thy own."

"Go to, what need all this?" quoth the company. "In good faith, Cutbert, you are to blame; you find fault where none is."

"Tush, I must speak my mind," quoth Cutbert. "I cannot dissemble; I trust the goodman thinks never the worse of me. So I have his good will, what the foul evil care I for his wife's."

"Enough," quoth Tom Dove. "Let us with music remove these brabbles; we mean to be merry and not melancholy."

Then said old Cole, "Now trust me, Cutbert, we will have our hostess and you friends ere we part. Here, woman, I drink to you; and regard not his words, for he is brabbling wheresoever he comes."

Quoth the woman, "Nothing grieves me so much as that he should thus openly check me. If he had found anything amiss, he might have spied a better time to tell me of it than now. Iwis, he need not thrust

---

[16]*Reior . . . skilfullest musician . . . built . . . priory and hospital of St. Bartholomew in Smithfield:* The person is Rahere (d. 1144), a favorite of Henry I's and founder of the priory and hospital in 1123. As for his being a musician, Deloney probably is expanding on this statement from Stow's *Survey:* "Rahere, a pleasant witted Gentleman, and therefore in his time called the kinges Minstrell" (Kingsford's ed., II, 25).

[17]*giglot:* frivolous girl.

my bad housewifery into my husband's head. I live not so quietly with him, God wot." And with that she wept.

"Come, Cutbert," quoth they, "drink to her and shake hands and be friends."

"Come on, you puling baggage," quoth he, "I drink to you. Here, will you pledge me and shake hands?"

"No," quoth she, "I will see thee choked first. Shake hands with thee! I will shake hands with the devil as soon."

"Go to," said her husband, "you shall shake hands with him then. If you will not shake hands, I'll shake you. What, you young huswife!"

"Well, husband," said she, "it becomes a woman to obey her husband; in regard whereof, I drink to him."

"That's well said," quoth the company; and so she took her leave and went down.

And within a while after, they paid the shot and departed thence to Gerard's Hall, where they went to their lodging. And the next day they took their way homeward all together; and coming to Colebrook, they took up their lodging. And it was Cole's custom to deliver his money to the goodwife of the house to keep it till morning, which in the end turned to his utter destruction, as hereafter shall be showed.

Chapter 3

How Gray's Wife of Gloucester, with One or Two More of Her Neighbors, Went to the Fair, Where Servants Came to Be Hired, and How She Took the Earl of Shrewsbury's Daughter into Her Service

It was wont to be an old custom in Gloucestershire that, at a certain time in the year, all such young men and maidens as were out of service resorted to a fair that was kept near Gloucester, there to be ready for any that would come to hire them. The young men stood all on a row on the one side, and the maidens on the other. It came to pass that the Earl of Shrewsbury's daughter,[18] whose father was lately banished, being driven into great distress and weary with travail, as one whose delicate life was never used to such toil, sat her down upon the highway side, making this lamentation:

[18]*Earl of Shrewsbury's daughter:* In Holinshed and Grafton there is no reference to a daughter Margaret, but the earl himself, Robert of Bellême (fl. 1098), was an ally of Duke Robert's against Henry I—though Deloney prefers not to make any point of it.

"Oh, false and deceitful world!" quoth she. "Who is in thee that wishes not to be rid of thee? For thy extremities are great. Thou art deceitful to all and trusty to none. Fortune is thy treasurer, who is like thyself; wavering and unconstant, she setteth up tyrants, beateth down kings, giveth shame to some and renown to others. Fortune giveth these evils, and we see it not; with her hands she toucheth us, and we feel it not; she treads us underfoot, and we know it not; she speaks in our ears, and we hear her not; she cries aloud, and we understand her not. And why? Because we know her not until misery doth make her manifest.

"Ah, my dear father, well mayst thou do. Of all misfortunes it is most unhappy to be fortunate, and by this misfortune came my fall. Was ever good lady brought to this extremity? What is become of my rare jewels, my rich array, my sumptuous fare, my waiting servants, my many friends, and all my vain pleasures? My pleasure is banished by displeasure, my friends fled like foes, my servants gone, my feasting turned to fasting, my rich array consumed to rags, and my jewels deck out my chiefest enemies. Therefore of all things the mean estate is best; poverty with surety is better than honor mixed with fear. Seeing God hath allotted me to this misery of life, I will frame my heart to embrace humility and carry a mind answerable to my misfortunes. Fie on this vain title of "ladyship"; how little doth it avail the distressed! No, no, I must therefore forget my birth and parentage and think no more on my father's house, where I was wont to be served. Now will I learn to serve, and plain "Meg" shall be my name. Good Lord, grant I may get a good service; nay, any service shall serve, where I may have meat, drink, and apparel."

She had no sooner spoke these words, but she espied a couple of maidens more coming towards her who were going to the fair and, bidding her good morrow, asked her if she went to the fair.

"Yea, marry," quoth she, "I am a poor man's child that is out of service, and I hear that at the statute[19] folks do come of purpose to hire servants."

"True it is," said the maidens, "and thither go we for the same purpose, and would be glad of your company."

"With a good will, and I am right glad of yours," said she, "beseeching you good maidens you will do me the favor to tell me what service were best for me; for the more to blame my parents, they would never put me forth to know anything."

[19]*at the statute:* at the fair (which is held at a time fixed by statute or charter).

"Why, what can you do?" quoth the maidens. "Can you brew and bake, make butter and cheese, and reap corn well?"

"No, verily," said Margaret, "but I would be right glad to learn to do anything, whatsoever it be."

"If you could spin or card," said another, "you might do excellent well with a clothier, for they are the best services that I know. There you shall be sure to fare well and to live merrily."

Then Margaret wept, saying, "Alas, what shall I do? I was never brought up to these things."

"What, can you do nothing?" quoth they.

"No, truly," quoth she, "that is good for anything, but I can read and write and sew. Some skill I have in my needle and a little on my lute; but this, I see, will profit me nothing."

"Good Lord," quoth they, "are you bookish? We did never hear of a maid before that could read and write. And although you can do no other thing, yet possibly you may get a service, if you can behave yourself mannerly."

"I pray you," quoth another, "seeing you are bookish, will you do so much as to read a love letter that is sent me? For I was at a friend's of mine with it, and he was not at home; and so I know not what is in it."

"I pray you let me see it," quoth Margaret, "and I will show you." Whereupon she readeth as followeth:

> Oh, Jenny my joy, I die for thy love,
> And now I hear say that thou dost remove;
> And therefore, Jenny, I pray thee recite
> Where I shall meet thee soon at night.
>
> For why, with my master no more will I stay,
> But for thy love I will run away;
> Oh, Jenny, Jenny, thou puttest me to pain,
> That thou no longer wilt here remain.
>
> I will wear out my shoes of neat's leather,[20]
> But thou and I will meet together;
> And in spite of fortune, rat, or mouse,
> We will dwell in one house.
>
> For who doth not esteem of thee,
> Shall have no service done of me;
> Therefore, good Jenny, have a care
> To meet poor Fragment at the fair.

---

[20]*neat's leather:* cowhide.

"Now alas, good soul," quoth Jenny, "I think he be the kindest young man in the world."

The rest answered that he seemed no less.

"And surely it appeareth that he is a pretty witty fellow," quoth one of them. "How finely he hath written his letter in rhyme; trust me, I will give you a good thing, and let me have a copy of it to send to my sweetheart."

"That you shall, with all my heart." And so, coming to the fair, they took up their standing.

Within a while after, Goodwife Gray of Gloucester came thither to store herself of divers commodities; and when she had bought what she would, she told her neighbor she had great need of a maid servant or twain.

"Therefore," quoth she, "good neighbor, go with me, and let me have your opinion."

"With a good will," said her neighbor.

And together they went; and looking and viewing the maidens over, she took special notice of Margaret.

"Believe me," quoth she, "there stands a very proper maiden, and one of a modest and comely countenance."

"Verily," said her neighbor, "so she is, as ever I looked upon."

The maiden, seeing them to view her so well, was so abashed that a scarlet color overspread her lily cheeks. Which, the woman perceiving, came unto her and asked if she were willing to serve.

The maid, with a low curtsy and a most gentle speech, answered it was the only cause of her coming.

"Can you spin or card?" said Goodwife Gray.

"Truly, dame," said she, "though my cunning therein be but small, my good will to learn is great; and I trust my diligence shall content you."

"What wages will you take?" quoth Goodwife Gray.

"I will refer that," said Margaret, "to your conscience and courtesy, desiring no more than what I shall deserve."

Then, asking what coutrywoman she was, the maiden wept, saying, "Ah, good dame, I was untimely born in Shropshire of poor parents, and yet not so needy as unfortunate; but death, having ended their sorrows, hath left me to the cruelty of these envious times, to finish my parents' tragedy with my troubles."

"What, maiden!" quoth her dame. "Have you a care to do your business and to live in God's fear, and you shall have no care to regard fortune's frowns."

And so they went home together.

Now, so soon as the goodman saw her, he asked his wife where she had that maiden.

She said, "At the fair."

"Why, then," quoth he, "thou hast brought all the fair away, and I doubt[21] it were better for us to send the fair to another town, than to keep the fair here."

"Why, man," quoth she, "what mean you by that?"

"Woman, I mean this, that she will prove a loadstone to draw the hearts of all my men after her; and so we shall have wise service done of all sides."

Then said his wife, "I hope, husband, Margaret will have a better care both to her own credit and our commodity than so, and let me alone to look to such matters."

"Is thy name Margaret?" quoth her master. "Proper is thy name to thy person, for thou art a pearl indeed, orient, and rich in beauty."

His wife, hearing him say so, began to change her opinion.

"What, husband," quoth she, "is the wind at that door? Begin you to like your maid so well? I doubt I had most need to look to yourself. Before God, I had rather than an angel I had chosen some other; but hear you, maid, you shall pack hence. I will not nourish a snake in my bosom, and therefore get you gone. I will none of you; provide a service where you may."

The maiden, hearing her say so, fell down on her knees and besought her, saying, "Oh, sweet dame, be not so cruel to me to turn me out of doors now. Alas, I know not where to go or what to do if you forsake me. Oh, let not the fading beauty of my face despoil me of your favor; for rather than that shall hinder my service, this my knife shall soon disfigure my face, and I will banish beauty as my greatest enemy."

And with that her abundant tears stopped her speech, that she could not utter one word more. The woman, seeing this, could not harbor anger longer, nor could her master stay in the room for weeping.

"Well, Margaret," said her dame, little knowing that a lady kneeled before her, "using thyself well, I will keep thee; and thou shalt have my good will, if thou govern thyself with wisdom."

And so she sent her about her business.

---

[21]*I doubt:* correct Elizabethan usage, but confusing today; the sense is "I have no doubt" or "I think."

Her husband, coming to supper, said, "How now! Wife, art thou so doubtful of me that thou hast put away thy maiden?"

"Iwis," quoth she, "you are a wise man, to stand praising of a maid's beauty before her face."

"And you a wise woman," quoth he, "to grow jealous without a cause."

So to supper they went, and because Margaret showed herself of finest behavior above the rest, she was appointed to wait on the table.

And it is to be understood that Gray did never eat his meat alone but still had some of his neighbors with him, before whom he called his maid, saying, "Margaret, come hither."

Now because there was another of the same name in the house, she made answer.

"I call not you, maiden," quoth he, "but Margaret with the lily-white hand." After which time she was ever called so.

Chapter 4

How the King's Majesty Sent for the Clothiers, and of the Sundry Favors Which He Did Them

King Henry, providing for his voyage into France against King Louis and Robert, Duke of Normandy, his own brother, committed the government of the realm in his absence to the Bishop of Salisbury, a man of great wisdom and learning whom the king esteemed highly; and afterward he thought good to send for the chief clothiers of England, who, according to the king's appointment, came to the court. And having license to come before his majesty, he spoke to this effect:

"The strength of a king is the love and friendship of his people, and he governs over his realm most surely that ruleth justice with mercy; for he ought to fear many whom many do fear. Therefore the governors of the commonwealth ought to observe two special precepts: the one is that they so maintain the profit of the commons that whatsoever in their calling they do, they refer it thereunto; the other, that they be always as well careful over the whole commonwealth as over any part thereof, lest while they uphold the one, the other be brought to utter decay.

"And forasmuch as I do understand, and have partly seen, that you, the clothiers of England, are no small benefit to the wealth public, I thought it good to know from your own mouths if there be anything not yet granted that may benefit you or any other thing to be removed that doth hurt you.

"The great desire I have to maintain you in your trades hath moved me hereunto. Therefore, boldly say what you would have in the one thing or the other, and I will grant it you."

With that, they all fell down upon their knees and desired God to save his majesty, and withal requested three days' respite to put in their answer; which was granted. And thereupon they departed.

When the clothiers had well considered of these matters, at length they thought meet to request of his majesty for their first benefit—that all the cloth measures through the land might be of one length (whereas to their great disadvantage before, every good town had a several measure). The difficulty thereof was such that they could not keep them in memory, nor know how to keep their reckonings.

The second thing whereof they found themselves grieved was this: that the people would not take cracked money, though it were never so good silver. Whereupon it came to pass that the clothiers, and divers other receiving great sums of money, do take among it much cracked money; it served them to no use because it would not go current, but lay upon their hands without profit or benefit. Whereof they prayed reformation.

The third was a grief whereof Hodgekins of Halifax complained, and that was that whereas the town of Halifax lived altogether upon clothing and, by the reason of false borderers[22] and other evil-minded persons, they were oft robbed and had their cloths carried out of their fields where they were drying, that it would please his majesty to grant the town this privilege: that whosoever he was that was taken stealing their cloth might presently, without any further trial, be hanged up.

When the day of their appearance approached, the clothiers came before the king and delivered up their petition in writing which his majesty, most graciously perusing, said he was ready to fulfill their request. And therefore for the first point of their petition he called for a staff to be brought him and, measuring thereupon the just length of his own arm, delivered it to the clothiers, saying, "This measure shall be called a yard,[23] and no other measure throughout all the realm

[22]*borderers:* persons who lived near the border between England and Scotland.

[23]*This measure shall be called a yard:* Deloney is dramatizing what he read in Holinshed, III, 28 (sig. C6ᵛ), or in Grafton, *Chronicle,* [ed. Sir Henry Ellis] (London, 1809), I, 179. But actually "yard" did not come into use until the fourteenth century, in the reign of Edward III.

of England shall be used for the same; and by this shall men buy and sell, and we will so provide that whosoever he be that abuseth our subjects by any false measure, that he shall not only pay a fine for the same to the king, but also have his body punished by imprisonment.

"And as concerning the second point of your petition (because of my sudden departure out of the land, I know not better how to ease you of this grief of cracked money) this decree I make because they account cracked money not current: I say, none shall be current but cracked money. And therefore I will give present charge that all the money through the land shall be slit, and so you shall suffer no loss.

"But now for your last request for the town of Halifax, where by thieves your cloths are so often stolen from you, seeing the laws already provided in that case are not sufficient to keep men in awe, it is indeed high time to have sharper punishment for them."

With that, Hodgekins unmannerly interrupted the king, saying in broad northern speech, "Yea, gude faith, mai liedge, the faule eule[24] of mai saule, giff any thing will keep them whiat,[25] till the karles be hangde up by the cragge. What the dule care they for boaring their eyne,[26] sea lang as they may gae groping up and downe the countrey like fause lizar lownes,[27] begging and craking?"

The king, smiling to hear this rough-hewn fellow, made this reply: "Content thee, Hodgekins, for we will have redress for all; and albeit that hanging of men was never seen in England, yet, seeing the corrupt world is grown more bold in all wickedness, I think it not amiss to ordain this death for such malefactors. And peculiarly to the town of Halifax I give this privilege: that whosoever they find stealing their cloth, being taken with the goods, that without further judgment they shall be hanged up.

"Thus," said our king, "have I granted what you request; and if hereafter you find any other thing that may be good for you, it shall

[24]*faule eule:* foul evil, often implying syphilis, but here perhaps not. Hodgekin's speech in this paragraph is exactly as it appears in the 1612 edition (without any attempt at modernization).

[25]*keep them whiat:* keep them quit; "whiat" was a variation of the northern "wheyte."

[26]*boaring their eyne:* "eyne" or "ean" means "lambs," but the intent of the sexual image is not entirely clear; probably the sense is, "What the devil do they care for taking care of their lambs (seeing that they are properly bred, etc.), so long as they . . . ."

[27]*fause lizar lownes:* false loons, of some kind; a "lowne" or "loon" is an aquatic bird with a loud cry; "lizar" seems to be a form of "lizor" or "leasow," meaning "pasture."

be granted; for no longer would I desire to live among you, than I have care for the good of the commonwealth."

At which word ended, the king rose from his royal throne, while the clothiers on their knees prayed for both his health and happy success and showed themselves most thankful for his highness' favor. His majesty, bending his body toward them, said that at his home return he would, by the grace of God, visit them.

Chapter 5

How the Clothiers Had Provided a Sumptuous Feast for the King's Sons, Prince William and Prince Richard, at Gerard's Hall; Showing Also What Chance Befell Cutbert of Kendal at that Same Instant

The clothiers, departing from the court in a merry mind, joyful of their good success, each one to other praised and magnified the king's great wisdom and virtue, commending also his affability and gentle disposition, so that Hodgekins affirmed on his faith that he had rather speak to the king's majesty than to many justices of peace.

"Indeed," said Cole, "he is a most mild and merciful prince, and I pray God he may long reign over us."

"Amen," said the rest.

Then said Cole, "My masters, shall we forget the great courtesy of the king's sons, those sweet and gentle princes, that still showed us favor in our suit? In my opinion it were reason to gratify them in some sort, that we may not utterly be condemned of ingratitude; wherefore, if you think good, we will prepare a banquet for them at our host Gerard's, who, as you know, hath a fair house and goodly rooms. Besides, the man himself is of a most courageous mind and good behavior, sufficient to entertain a prince; his wife also is a dainty fine cook. All which considered, I know not a fitter place in London."

" 'Tis true," quoth Sutton, "and if the rest be content, I am pleased it shall be so."

At this they all answered, "Yea, for," quoth they, "it will not be passing forty shillings apiece, and that we shall recover in our cracked money."

Being thus agreed, the feast was prepared.

"Tom Dove," quoth they, "we will commit the providing of music to thee."

"And I," said Cole, "will invite divers of our merchants and their wives to the same."

"That is well remembered," said Gray.

Upon this they called to their host and hostess, showing their determination, who most willingly said all things should be made ready.

"But I would have two days' liberty," said the goodwife, "to prepare my house and other things."

"Content," said the clothiers, "in the mean space we will bid our guests and dispatch our other affairs."

But Simon of Southampton charged his hostess that in any case she should not forget to make good store of pottage.

"It shall be done," quoth she.

"It is to be remembered that while this preparation was in hand, that Cutbert of Kendal had not forgot his kindness to his hostess of Bosom's Inn. Therefore, finding time convenient when her husband was overseeing his haymakers, he greeted her in this sort:

"Sweet hostess, though I were the last time I was in town overbold with you, yet I hope it was not so offensive to you as you made show for."

"Bold, my Cutbert?" quoth she. "Thou hast vowed thyself my servant; and so being, you are not to be blamed for doing what I willed you. By my honesty, I could not choose but smile to myself, so soon as I was out of their sight, to think how prettily you began your brabble."

"But now," quoth he, "we will change our chidings to kissings, and it vexeth me that these cherry lips should be subject to such a lobcock[28] as thy husband."

"Subject to him!" quoth she. "In faith, sir, no; I will have my lips at as much liberty as my tongue—the one to say what I list, and the other to touch whom I like. In troth, shall I tell thee, Cutbert, the churl's breath smells so strong that I care as much for kissing of him as for looking on him. 'Tis such a misshapen miser and such a bundle of beastliness that I can never think on him without spitting. Fie upon him! I would my friends had carried me to my grave when they went with me to the church to make him my husband."

And so, shedding a few dissembling tears, she stopped.

"What, my sweet mistress," quoth he, "weep you? Nay, sit down by my side, and I will sing thee one of my country jigs to make thee merry."

"Wilt thou, in faith?" quoth she.

[28]*lobcock:* country bumpkin.

"Yes, verily," said Cutbert.

"And in troth," quoth she, "if you fall a-singing, I will sing with you."

"That is well; you can so suddenly change your notes," quoth Cutbert. "Then have at it."

Man.	Long have I lov'd this bonny lass,
	Yet durst not show the same.
Wom.	Therein you prov'd youself an ass,
Man.	I was the more to blame.
	Yet still will I remain to thee,
	Trang dilly do, trang dilly,
	Thy friend and lover secretly.
Wom.	Thou art my own sweet bully.
Man.	But when shall I enjoy thee,
	Delight of thy fair love?
Wom.	Even when thou seest that fortune doth
	All manner lets[29] remove.
Man.	Oh, I will fold thee in my arms,
	Trang dilly do, trang dilly,
	And keep thee so from sudden harms.
Wom.	Thou art my own sweet bully.
Wom.	My husband he is gone from home,
	You know it very well.
Man.	But when will he return again?
Wom.	In troth, I cannot tell.
	If long he keep him out of sight,
	Trang dilly do, trang dilly,
	Be sure thou shalt have thy delight.
Man.	Thou art my bonny lassy.

While they were singing this song, her husband, being on a sudden come home, stood secretly in a corner and heard all. And blessing himself with both his hands, said, "Oh, abominable dissimulation, monstrous hypocrisy! And are you in this humor? Can you brawl together and sing together? Well," quoth he, "I will let them alone and see a little more of their knavery. Never did cat watch mouse so narrowly as I will watch them."

And so, going into the kitchen, he asked his wife if it were not dinner time.

"Even by and by, husband," quoth she, "the meat will be ready."

Presently after comes in Hodgekins and Martin, who straight asked for Cutbert of Kendal. Answer was made that he was in his chamber.

[29]*lets:* hindrances.

So when they had called him, they went to dinner; then they requested that their host and hostess would sit with them.

"Husband," said she, "you may go if you please; but as for me, I will desire pardon."

"Nay, goodwife, go up," said her husband. "What, woman, you must bear with your guests."

"Why, husband," quoth she, "do you think that any can bear the flirts and frumps which that northern tyke gave me the last time he was in town? Now, God forgive me, I had as lief see the devil as see him. Therefore, goodhusband, go up yourself, and let me alone, for, in faith, I shall never abide that jack while I live."

Upon these words away went her husband, and though he said little he thought the more. Now when he came up, his guests bade him welcome.

"I pray you sit down, good mine host," quoth they. "Where is your wife? What, will not she sit with us?"

"No, verily," said he, "the foolish woman hath taken such a displeasure against Cutbert that she swears she will never come in his company."

"Is it so?" said the other. "Then trust me we are well agreed. And I swear by my father's sale,"[30] quoth he, "that were it not more for good will to you than love to her, I would never come to your house more."

"I believe it well," said old Bosom.

And so with other communication they drove out the time, till dinner was ended.

After they were risen, Martin and Hodgekins got them forth about their affairs, but Cutbert took his host by the hand, saying, "My host, I'll go talk with your wife; for my part, I thought we had been friends: but seeing her stomach is so big and her heart so great, I will see what she will say to me. And with that he stepped into the kitchen, saying, "God speed you, hostess."

"It must be when you are away then," said she.

"What is your reason?" said the other.

"Because God never comes where knaves are present."

[30]*sale:* northern dialect for "soul." It is not entirely clear whether "the other" person speaking is Cutbert, Hodgekins, or Martin (all from the north); probably it is Cutbert, though Hodgekins or Martin could be speaking up for him. "Sale" can also mean "great hall," but that sense does not seem to apply here.

"Gip, goody draggletail!" quoth he. "Had I such a wife, I would present her tallow face to the devil for a candle."[31]

With that she bent her brows and, like a fury of hell, began to fly at him, saying, "Why, you gag-toothed jack, you blinking companion, get thee out of my kitchen quickly, or with my powdered beef broth, I will make your pate as bald as a friar's!"

"Get me gone?" quoth he. "Thou shalt not bid me twice. Out, you dirty heels; you will make your husband's hair grow through his hood, I doubt."

And with that he got him into the hall, and sat him down on the bench by his host, to whom he said, " 'Tis pity, my host, that your aged years that loves quietness should be troubled with such a scolding quean."

"Aye, God help me, God help me," quoth the old man; and so went toward the stable; which his wife, watching, suddenly stepped out and gave Cutbert a kiss.

Within an hour after, the old man craftily called for his nag to ride to field; but as soon as he was gone, Cutbert and his hostess were such good friends that they got into one of the warehouses and locked the door to them. But her husband, having set a spy for the purpose, suddenly turned back and called for a capcase[32] which lay in the warehouse. The servant could not find the key by any means. Whereupon he called to have the lock broke open. Which they within, hearing, opened the door of their own accord.

So soon as her husband spied her in that place, with admiration he said, "Oh, the passion of my heart, what do you here? What, you two that cannot abide one another? What makes you so close together? Is your chiding and railing, brabbling and brawling, come to this? Oh, what dissemblers are these!"

"Why, my host," quoth Cutbert, "what need you take the matter so hot? I gave a cheese to my countryman Hodgekins to lay up and delivered it to your wife to be kept; and then is it not reason that she should come and seek me my cheese?"

"Oh," quoth the old man, "belike the door was locked because the cheese should not run away."

[31]*Had I such a wife . . . candle:* Cutbert is not literally repeating a proverb, but he calls to mind several of them; see Tilley, C42: "It is good to set a candle before the devil" and the proverbs comparing wives or women to the devil.

[32]*capcase:* traveling bag, suitcase.

"The door," said his wife, "unknown to us, clapped to itself and, having a spring lock, was presently fast."

"Well, huswife," quoth he, "I will give you as much credit as a crocodile; but as for your companion, I will teach him to come hither to look for cheeses."

And with that he caused his men to take him presently and to bind him hand and foot. Which being done, they drew him up in a basket into the smoky louver[33] of the hall, and there they did let him hang all that night, even till the next day dinner time, when he should have been at the banquet with the princes. For neither Hodgekins nor Martin could entreat their inflamed host to let him down.

And in such a heat was he driven with drawing him up that he was fain to cast off his gowns, his coats, and two pair of his stockings to cool himself, making a vow he should hang there seven years, except the king's sons came in person to beg his pardon. Which, most of all, grieved Cutbert. When Cole and the rest of the western yeomen heard hereof, they could not choose but laugh, to think that he was so taken tardy.

The young princes, having given promise to be with the clothiers, kept their hour. But when all the rest went to give them entertainment, Simon was so busy in supping his pottage that he could not spare so much time. Which, when the princes saw, with a smiling countenance, they said, "Sup, Simon, there's good broth."

"Or else beshrew our hostess," quoth he, never looking behind him to see who spoke till the prince clapped him on the shoulder. But, Good Lord, how blank he was when he spied them, knowing not how to excuse the matter.

Well, the princes having ended their banquet, Gerard comes, and with one of his hands took the table of sixteen feet long quite from the ground over their heads from before the princes and set it on the other side of the hall, to the great admiration of all them that beheld it.

The princes, being then ready to depart, the clothiers moved them in pleasant manner to be good to one of their company that did neither sit, lie, nor stand.

"Then he must needs hang," quoth the princes.

"And so he doth, most excellent princes," quoth they; and therewithal told them the whole matter.

[33]*smoky louver:* the louver or opening in the roof to permit smoke to escape from the hall.

When they heard the story, down to Bosom's Inn they go, where, looking up into the roof, spied poor Cutbert pinned up in a basket and almost smoked to death, who, although he were greatly a-shamed, yet most pitifully desired that they would get him released.

"What is his trespass?" said the prince.

"Nothing, if it shall like your grace," quoth he, "but for looking for a cheese."

"But he could not find it without my wife," said the goodman. "The villain had lately dined with mutton and could not digest his meat without cheese, for which cause I have made him to fast these twenty hours, to the end he may have a better stomach to eat his dinner than to use dalliance."

"Let me entreat you," quoth the prince, "to release him; and if ever hereafter you catch him in the corn, clap him in the pound."

"Your grace shall request or command anything at my hand," said the old man.

And so Cutbert was let down unbound; but when he was loose, he vowed never to come within that house more. And it is said the old man Bosom ordained that, in remembrance of this deed, every year once all such as came thither to ask for cheeses should be so served. Which thing is to this day kept.

Chapter 6

How Simon's Wife of Southampton, Being
Wholly Bent to Pride and Pleasure, Requested
her Husband to See London. Which, Being
Granted, How She Got Goodwife Sutton of
Salisbury to Go with Her. Who Took Crab
to Go Along with Them, and How He
Prophesied of Many Things

The clothiers, being all come from London, Simon's wife of Southampton, who was with her husband very merry and pleasant, broke her mind unto him in this sort:

"Good Lord, husband, will you never be so kind as let me go to London with you? Shall I be penned up in Southampton like a parrot in a cage or a capon in a coop? I would request no more of you in lieu of all my pains, cark, and care,[34] but to have one week's time

---

[34]*cark, and care:* an Elizabethan cliché, the sense of which was "a troubled state of mind" (from "cark," to make or be anxious).

to see that fair city. What is this life if it be not mixed with some delight, and what delight is more pleasing than to see the fashions and manners of unknown places? Therefore, good husband, if thou lovest me, deny not this simple request. You know I am no common gadder, nor have oft troubled you with travel. God knows, this may be the last thing that ever I shall request at your hands."

"Woman," quoth he, "I would willingly satisfy your desire, but you know it is not convenient for both of us to be abroad. Our charge is great, and therefore our care ought not to be small. If you will go yourself, one of my men shall go with you, and money enough you shall have in your purse; but to go with you myself, you see my business will not permit me."

"Husband," said she, "I accept your gentle offer, and it may be I shall entreat my gossip, Sutton, to go along with me."

"I shall be glad," quoth her husband. "Prepare yourself when you will."

When she had obtained this license, she sent her man Weasel to Salisbury, to know of Goodwife Sutton if she would keep her company to London. Sutton's wife, being as willing to go as she was to request, never rested till she had gotten leave of her husband; the which, when she had obtained, casting in her mind their pleasure would be small, being but they twain; thereupon the wily woman sent letters by choleric Crab, her man, both to Gray's wife and Fitzallen's wife, that they would meet them at Reading. Who, liking well of the match, consented and did so provide that they met according to promise at Reading; and from thence, with Cole's wife, they went all together, with each of them a man, to London, each one taking up their lodging with a several friend.

When the merchants of London understood they were in town, they invited them every day home to their own houses, where they had delicate good cheer; and when they went abroad to see the commodities of the city, the merchants' wives ever bore them company, being attired most dainty and fine. Which, when the clothiers' wives did see, it grieved their hearts they had not the like.

Now when they were brought into Cheapside, there with great wonder they beheld the shops of the goldsmiths and, on the other side, the wealthy mercers, whose shops shined of all sorts of colored silks; in Watling Street, they viewed the great number of drapers; in St. Martin's, shoemakers; at St. Nicholas' Church, the flesh shambles;[35] at the end of the Old Change, the fishmongers; in Candlewick

[35]*flesh shambles:* meat stalls (meat market).

Street, the weavers; then came into the Jews' street, where all the Jews did inhabit; then went they to Blackwell Hall, where the country clothiers did use to meet.

Afterward they proceeded and came to St. Paul's Church, whose steeple was so high that it seemed to pierce the clouds; on the top whereof was a great and mighty weathercock of clean silver, the which notwithstanding seemed as small as a sparrow to men's eyes, it stood so exceeding high. The which goodly weathercock was afterwards stolen away by a cunning cripple, who found means one night to climb up to the top of the steeple and took it down; with the which, and a great sum of money which he had got together by begging in his lifetime, he builded a gate on the northwest side of the city, which to this day is called Cripple Gate.

From thence they went to the Tower of London, which was built by Julius Caesar, who was Emperor of Rome. And there they beheld salt and wine, which had lain there ever since the Romans invaded this land, which was many years before our Savior Christ was born; the wine was grown so thick that it might have been cut like a jelly. And in that place also they saw money that was made of leather, which in ancient time went current amongst the people.

When they had to their great contentation[36] beheld all this, they repaired to their lodgings, having also a sumptuous supper ordained for them, with all delight that might be. And you shall understand that when the country weavers, which came up with their dames, saw the weavers of Candlewick Street, they had great desire presently to have some conference with them; and thus one began to challenge th'other for workmanship.

Quoth Weasel, "I'll work with any of you all for a crown. Take it if you dare, and he that makes his yard of cloth soonest shall have it."

"You shall be wrought withal," said the other, "and if it were for ten crowns; but we will make this bargain, that each of us shall wind their own quills."

"Content," quoth Weasel.

And so to work they went, but Weasel lost. Whereupon another of them took the matter in hand, who lost likewise; so that the London weavers triumphed against the country, casting forth divers frumps.

"Alas, poor fellows," quoth they, "your hearts are good, but your hands are ill."

---

[36]*contentation:* satisfaction, contentment.

"Tush, the fault was in their legs," quoth another. "Pray you, friend, were you not born at home?"

"Why do you ask?" quoth Weasel.

"Because," said he, "the biggest place of your leg is next to your shoe."

Crab, hearing this, being choleric of nature, chafed like a man of law at the bar, and he wagers with them four crowns to twain. The others agreed, to work they go; but Crab conquered them all. Whereupon, the London weavers were nipped in the head like birds and had not a word to say.

"Now," saith Crab, "as we have lost nothing, so you have won nothing; and because I know ye cannot be right weavers, except you be good fellows, therefore if you will go with us, we will bestow the ale upon you."

"That is spoken like a good fellow and like a weaver," quoth the other. So along they went as it were to the Sign of the Red Cross.

When they were set down and had drunk well, they began merrily to prattle and to extol Crab to the skies. Whereupon Crab protested that he would come and dwell among them.

"Nay, that must not be," said a London weaver. "The king hath given us privilege, that none shall live among us but such as serve seven years in London."

With that Crab, according to his old manner of prophesying, said thus:

> The day is very near at hand,
> When as a king of this fair land
> Shall privilege you more than so;
> Then weavers shall in scarlet go.
>
> And to one brotherhood be brought,
> The first that is in London wrought,
> When other tradesmen by your fame,
> Shall covet all to do the same.
>
> Then shall you all live wondrous well,
> But this one thing I shall you tell:
> The day will come before the doom,
> In Candlewick Street shall stand no loom,
>
> Nor any weaver dwelling there,
> But men that shall more credit bear;
> For clothing shall be sore decayed,
> And men undone that use that trade.

And yet the day some men shall see,
This trade again shall raised be,
When as bailiff of Sarum Town,
Shall buy and purchase Bishops Down.

When there never man did sow,
Great store of goodly corn shall grow;
And woad, that makes all colors sound,
Shall spring upon that barren ground.

At that same day I tell you plain,
Who so alive doth then remain,
A proper maiden there shall see,
Within the town of Salisbury.

Of favor sweet, of nature kind,
With goodly eyes, and yet stark blind,
This poor blind maiden I do say,
In age shall go in rich array.

And he that takes her to his wife
Shall lead a joyful happy life,
The wealthiest clothier shall he be,
That ever was in that country.

But clothing kept as it hath been
In London never shall be seen;
For weavers then the most shall win,
That work for clothing next the skin.

Till pride the commonwealth doth peel
And causeth housewives leave their wheel.
Then poverty upon each side
Unto those workmen shall betide.

At that time, from an eagle's nest,
That proudly builded in the west,
A sort shall come with cunning hand,
To bring strange weaving in this land.

And by their gains that great will fall,
They shall maintain the weavers' hall:
But long they shall not flourish so,
But folly will them overthrow.

And men shall count it mickle shame,
To bear that kind of weaver's name,
And this as sure will come to pass,
As here is ale within this glass.

When the silly souls that sat about him heard him speak in this sort, they admired and honored Crab for the same.

"Why, my masters," said Weasel, "do you wonder at these words? He will tell you twenty of these tales, for which cause we call him our canvas prophet."[37]

"His attire fits his title," said they, "and we never heard the like in our lives; and if this should be true, it would be strange."

"Doubt not, but it will be true," quoth Weasel, "for I'll tell you what. He did but once see our Nick kiss Nell, and presently he poured out this rhyme:

> That kiss, oh Nell, God give thee joy,
> Will nine months hence breed thee a boy.

"And I'll tell you what; you shall hear. We kept reckoning, and it fell out as just as Joan's buttocks on a close stool; for which cause, our maids durst never kiss a man in his sight."

Upon this, they broke company and went everyone about his business, the London weavers to their frames, and the country fellows to their dames. Who, after their great banqueting and merriment, went everyone home to their own houses, though with less money than they brought out, yet with more pride.

Especially Simon's wife of Southampton, who told the rest of her gossips that she saw no reason but that their husbands should maintain them as well as the merchants did their wives. "For I tell you what," quoth she, "we are as proper women, in my conceit, as the proudest of them all, as handsome of body, as fair of face, our legs as well made, and our feet as fine. Then what reason is there, seeing our husbands are of as good wealth, but we should be as well maintained?"

"You say true, gossip," said Sutton's wife. "Trust me, it made me blush to see them brave it out so gallantly, and we to go so homely."

"But before God," said the other, "I will have my husband to buy me a London gown, or in faith he shall have little quiet."

"So shall mine," said another.

"And mine, too," quoth the third.

And all of them sang the same note, so that when they came home, their husbands had no little to do.

Especially Simon, whose wife daily lay at him for London apparel. To whom he said, "Good woman, be content; let us go ac-

[37]*canvas prophet:* prophet in coarse-spun working clothes (poor man's prophet).

cording to our place and ability. What will the bailiffs think if I should prank thee up like a peacock, and thou in thy attire surpass their wives? They would either think I were mad, or else that I had more money than I could well use. Consider, I pray thee, goodwife, that such as are in their youth wasters, do prove in their age stark beggars.

"Besides that, it is enough to raise me up in the king's books; for, many times, men's coffers are judged by their garments. Why, we are country folks and must keep ourselves in good compass; gray russet and good homespun cloth doth best become us. I tell thee, wife, it were as indecent for us to go like Londoners as it is for Londoners to go like courtiers."

"What a coil keep you!"[38] quoth she. "Are not we God's creatures as well as Londoners? And the king's subjects as well as they? Then, finding our wealth to be as good as theirs, why should we not go as gay as Londoners? No, husband, no, here is the fault; we are kept without it only because our husbands are not so kind as Londoners. Why, man, a cobbler there keeps his wife better than the best clothier in this country! Nay, I will affirm it that the London oyster-wives and the very kitchen stuff criers do exceed us in their Sunday's attire! Nay, more than that I did see the waterbearer's wife, which belongs to one of our merchants, come in with a tankard of water on her shoulder and yet half a dozen gold rings on her fingers!"

"You may then think, wife," quoth he, "she got them not with idleness.

"But, wife, you must consider what London is—the chief and capital city of all the land, a place on the which all strangers cast their eyes. It is, wife, the king's chamber and his majesty's royal seat. To that city repairs all nations under heaven. Therefore it is most meet and convenient that the citizens of such a city should not go in their apparel like peasants, but for the credit of our country wear such seemly habits as do carry gravity and comeliness in the eyes of all beholders."

"But if we of the country went so," quoth she, "were it not as great credit for the land as the other?"

"Woman," quoth her husband, "it is altogether needless, and in divers respects it may not be."

"Why, then, I pray you," quoth she, "let us go dwell at London."

"A word soon spoken," said her husband, "but not so easy to be

---

[38]*What a coil keep you:* What a fuss (to-do) you are making.

performed; therefore, wife, I pray thee hold thy prating, for thy talk is foolish."

"Yea, yea, husband, your old churlish conditions will never be left. You keep me here like a drudge and a droil.[39] And so you may keep your money in your purse; you care not for your credit. But before I will go so like a shepherdess, I will first go naked. And I tell you plain, I scorn it greatly that you should clap a gray gown on my back as if I had not brought you two pence. Before I was married, you swore I should have anything that I requested, but now all is forgotten."

And in saying this, she went in; and soon after she was so sick that needs she must go to bed. And when she was laid, she drove out that night with many grievous groans, sighing and sobbing; and no rest she could take, God wot. And in the morning, when she should rise, the good soul fell down in a swoon, which put her maidens in a great fright, who, running down to their master, cried out, "Alas, alas, our dame is dead! Our dame is dead!"

The goodman, hearing this, ran up in all haste and there fell to rubbing and chafing of her temples, sending for *aqua vita*, and saying, "Ah, my sweetheart, speak to me, good wife. Alack, alack, call in the neighbors, you queans!" quoth he.

With that, she lifted up her head, fetching a great groan, and presently swooned again; and much ado, iwis, he had to keep life in her. But when she was come to herself, "How dost thou, wife?" quoth he. "What wilt thou have? For God's sake, tell me if thou hast a mind to anything; thou shalt have it."

"Away, dissembler," quoth she, "how can I believe thee? Thou hast said as much to me an hundred times and deceived me. It is thy churlishness that hath killed my heart; never was woman matched to so unkind a man."

"Nay, good wife, blame me not without cause; God knoweth how dearly I love thee."

"Love me! No, no, thou didst never carry my love but on the tip of thy tongue," quoth she. "I dare swear thou desirest nothing so much as my death and, for my part, I would to God thou hadst thy desire. But be content, I shall not trouble thee long." And with that, fetching a sigh, she swooned and gave a great groan.

The man, seeing her in this case, was wondrous woe; but so soon

---

[39]*drudge and a droil:* another alliterative cliché, like "cark and care," in which both nouns mean the same thing (a "droil" is a "drudge").

as they had recovered her, he said, "Oh, my dear wife, if any bad conceit hath engendered this sickness, let me know it; or if thou knowest anything that may procure thy health, let me understand thereof, and I protest thou shalt have it if it cost me all that ever I have."

"Oh, husband," quoth she, "how may I credit your words, when for a paltry suit of apparel you denied me?"

"Well, wife," quoth he, "thou shalt have apparel or anything else thou wilt request, if God send thee once health."

"Oh, husband," quoth she, "how may I credit your words, when happiest woman in the world. Thy words have greatly comforted my heart; methinketh if I had it, I could drink a good draught of Rhenish wine."

Well, wine was sent for.

"Oh, Lord," said she, "that I had a piece of a chicken; I feel my stomach desirous of some meat."

"Glad am I of that," said her husband; and so the woman within a few days after was very well.

But you shall understand that her husband was fain to dress her Londonlike ere he could get her quiet; neither would it please her, except the stuff were bought in Cheapside, for out of Cheapside nothing would content her, were it never so good; insomuch, that if she thought a tailor of Cheapside made not her gown, she would swear it was quite spoiled.

And having thus won her husband to her will, when the rest of the clothiers' wives heard thereof, they would be suited in the like sort, too. So that, ever since, the wives of Southampton, Salisbury, of Gloucester, Worcester, and Reading went all as gallant and as brave as any Londoners' wives.

Chapter 7

How the Clothiers Sent the King Aid into
France and How He Overcame his Brother
Robert and Brought Him into England, and
How the Clothiers Feasted His Majesty and
His Son at Reading

The king's majesty, being at the wars in France against Louis, the French king, and Duke Robert of Normandy, sending for divers supplies of soldiers out of England, the clothiers at their own proper cost set out a great number and sent them over to the king.

Which Roger, Bishop of Salisbury, who governed the realm in the king's absence, did always certify the king thereof with his letters written in their commendations.

And afterward it came to pass that God sent his highness victory over his enemies and, having taken his brother prisoner, brought him most joyfully with him into England and appointed him to be kept in Cardiff Castle prisoner. Yet with this favor: that he might hunt and hawk where he would, up and down the country. And in this sort he lived a good while, of whom we will speak more at large hereafter.

The king, being thus come home, after his winter's rest he made his summer's progress into the west country to take a view of all the chief towns. Whereof the clothiers being advertised, they made great preparation against his coming, because he had promised to visit them all.

And when his grace came to Reading, he was entertained and received with great joy and triumph. Thomas Cole being the chief man of regard in all the town, the king honored his house with his princely presence, where, during the king's abode, he and his son and nobles were highly feasted.

There the king beheld the great number of people that was by that one man maintained in work, whose hearty affection and love toward his majesty did well appear, as well by their outward countenances as their gifts presented unto him. But of Cole himself the king was so well persuaded that he committed much trust to him and put him in great authority in the town. Furthermore, the king said that for the love which those people bore to him living that he would lay his bones among them when he was dead.

"For I know not," said he, "where they may be better bestowed, till the blessed day of resurrection, than among these my friends which are like to be happy partakers of the same."

Whereupon his majesty caused there to be built a most goodly and famous abbey, in which he might show his devotion to God, by increasing his service and leave example to other his successors to do the like. Likewise, within the town he after built a fair and goodly castle, in the which he often kept his court, which was a place of his chief residence during his life, saying to the clothiers that, seeing he found them such faithful subjects, he would be their neighbor and dwell among them.

After his majesty's royal feasting at Reading, he proceeded in progress till he had visited the whole west country, being wondrously delighted to see those people so diligent to apply their business; and coming to Salisbury, the bishop received his majesty with great joy, and with triumph attended on his grace to his palace, where his highness lodged.

There Sutton the clothier presented his highness with a broadcloth, of so fine a thread and exceeding good workmanship and therewithal of so fair a color, as his grace gave commendation thereof; and, as it is said, he held it in such high estimation that thereof he made his parliament robes; and the first parliament that ever was in England was graced with the king's person in those robes. In requital whereof his highness afterward yielded Sutton many princely favors.

And it is to be remembered that Simon of Southampton, seeing the king had overpassed the place where he dwelt, came with his wife and servants to Salisbury. And against the king going forth of that city, he caused a most pleasant arbor to be made upon the top of the hill leading to Salisbury, beset all with red and white roses in such sort that not any part of the timber could be seen; within the which sat a maiden attired like a queen, attended on by a fair train of maidens, who at the king's approach presented him with a garland of sweet flowers, yielding him such honor as the ladies of Rome were wont to do to their princes after their victories. Which the king took in gracious part; and for his farewell from that country, they bore him company over part of the plain, with the sound of divers sweet instruments of music. All which, when his grace understood was done at the cost of a clothier, he said he was the most honored by those men, above all the mean subjects in his land. And so his highness passed on to Exeter, having given great rewards to these maidens.

Thomas Dove and the residue of the clothiers, against his grace's coming thither, had ordained divers sumptuous shows. First, there was one that represented the person of Augustus Caesar, the emperor who commanded after the Roman invasion, that their city should be called Augustus after his own name, which beforetime was called Isca, and of latter years, Exeter.

There his majesty was royally feasted seven days together, at the only cost of clothiers; but the divers delights and sundry pastimes, which they made there before the king and his nobles, is too long here to be rehearsed. And therefore I will overpass them to avoid tediousness.

His grace, then coasting along the country, at last came to

Gloucester, an ancient city, which was built by Glou, a British king, who named it after his own name "Gloucester." Here was his majesty entertained by Gray the clothier, who professed himself to be of that ancient family of Grays, whose first original issued out of the ancient and honorable castle and town of Rithin.

Here was the king most bountifully feasted, having in his company his brother Robert, although his prisoner the same time. And his grace, being desirous to see the maidens card and spin, they were of purpose set to their work. Among whom was fair Margaret with the white hand, whose excellent beauty, having pierced the eyes of that amorous duke, it made such an impression in his heart that afterward he could never forget her. And so vehemently was his affection kindled that he could take no rest till by writing he had bewrayed his mind. But of this we will speak more in another place. And the king at his departure said that to gratify them, he would make his son Robert their earl, who was the first earl that ever was in Gloucester.

Now when his grace was come from thence, he went to Worcester, where William Fitzallen made preparation in all honorable sort to receive him. Which man, being born of great parentage, was not to learn how to entertain his majesty, being descended of that famous family, whose patrimony lay about the town of Oswestry, which town his predecessors had enclosed with stately walls of stone.

Although adverse fortune had so grievously frowned on some of them that their children were fain to become tradesmen, whose hands were to them instead of lands, notwithstanding God raised again the fame of this man, both by his great wealth and also in his posterity; whose eldest son, Henry, the king's godson, became afterward the mayor of London, who was the first mayor that ever was in that city, who governed the same twenty-three years; and then his son Roger Fitzallen was the second mayor.

The princely pleasures that in Worcester were shown the king were many and marvelous, and in no place had his majesty received more delight than here; for the which, at his departure he did show himself very thankful. Now when his grace had thus taken view of all his good towns westward and in that progress had visited these clothiers, he returned to London with great joy of all his commons.

Chapter 8

How Hodgekins of Halifax Came to the Court and Complained to the King that His Privilege Was Nothing Worth Because When They Found Any Offender, They Could Not Get a Hangman to Execute Him. And How by a Friar a Gin Was Devised to Chop off Men's Heads of Itself

After that Hodgekins had got the privilege for the town of Halifax to hang up such thieves as stole their cloth in the night, presently, without any further judgment, all the clothiers of the town were exceeding glad and persuaded themselves that now their goods would be safe all night, without watching them at all. So that whereas before the town maintained certain watchmen to keep their cloth by night, they were hereupon dismissed as a thing needless to be done, supposing with themselves that seeing they should be straight hanged that were found faulty in this point, that no man would be so desperate to enterprise any such act. And indeed the matter being noised through the whole country that they were straight to be hanged that did use such thievery, it made any lewd livers to refrain such thievery.

Nevertheless, there was at that same time living a notable thief named Wallace, whom in the north they called "mighty Wallace," in regard of his valor and manhood. This man, being most subtle in such kind of knavery, having heard of this late privilege and therewithal of the town's security, said that once he would venture his neck for a pack of northern cloth; and therefore coming to one or two of his companions, he asked if they would be partners in his adventure.

"And if," quoth he, "you will herein hazard your bodies, you shall be sharers in all our booties."

At length, by many persuasions the men consented; whereupon, late in the night, they got them all to a farrier's shop and called up the folks of the house.

"What the foul ill wald you have," quoth they, "at this time of the night?"

Wallace answered, saying, "Good fellows, we would have you to remove the shoes of our horses' feet and set them on again; and for your pains, you shall be well pleased." The smith at length was persuaded; and when he had plucked off all the shoes from their horses' feet, they would needs have them all set on again, quite contrary, with the caukins[40] forward that should stand backward.

"How fay, fay, man," quoth the smith. "Are you sick fules? What the deel, do you mean to break your crags? Gud faith, I tro the men be wood."

"Not so, smith," quoth they. "Do thou as we bid thee, and thou shalt have thy money, for it is an old proverb:

> Be it better, or be it worse;
> Please you the man that bears the purse.

"Gud faith, and see I sall," quoth the smith, and so did as he was willed.

When Wallace had thus caused their horses to be shod, to Halifax they went, where they without any let loaded their horses with cloth and so departed a contrary way.

In the morning so soon as the clothiers came to the field, they found that they were robbed; whereupon one ran to another to tell these tidings. Now when Hodgekins heard thereof, rising up in haste, he willed his neighbors to mark and see if they could not descry either the footsteps of men or horses. Which being done, they perceived that horses had been there; and seeking to pursue them by their footsteps, they went a clean contrary way, by reason that the horses were shod backward. And when in vain they had long pursued them, they returned, being never the nearer.

Now Wallace used his feat so long that at length he was taken and two more with him; whereupon, according to the privilege of the town, they put halters about the thieves' necks presently to hang them up.

When they were come to the place appointed, Wallace and the rest, being out of all hope to escape death, prepared themselves patiently to suffer the rigor of the law. And there with the rest laying open the lewdness of his life, grievously lamenting for his sins, at length commending their souls to God, they yielded their bodies to the grave, with which sight the people were greatly moved with pity, because they had never seen men come to hanging before.

But when they should have been tied up, Hodgekins willed one of his neighbors to play the hangman's part; who would not by any means do it, although he was a very poor man, who for his pains should have been possessed of all their apparel.

[40]*caukins:* calkins (the turned down ends of a horseshoe which raise the horse's heels off the ground).

When he would not yield to the office, one of those which had his cloth stolen was commanded to do the deed; but he in like manner would not, saying, "When I have the skill to make a man, I will hang a man, if it chance my workmanship do not like me."

And thus from one to another, the office of the hangman was posted off. At last a rogue came by, whom they would have compelled to have done that deed.

"Nay, my masters," quoth he, "not so. But as you have got a privilege for the town, so you were best to procure a commission to make a hangman, or else you are like to be without for me."

"Neighbor Hodgekins," quoth one, "I pray you do this office yourself. You have had most loss, and therefore you should be the most readiest to hang them yourself."

"No, not I," quoth Hodgekins, "though my loss were ten times greater than it is. Notwithstanding, look, which of these thieves will take upon him to hang the other shall have his life saved; otherwise they shall all to prison till I can provide a hangman."

When Wallace saw the matter brought to this pass, he began stoutly to reply, saying, "My masters of the town of Halifax, though your privilege stretch to hang up men presently that are found stealing your goods, yet it gives you no warrant to imprison them till you provide them a hangman. Myself with these my fellows have here yielded ourselves to satisfy the law; and if it be not performed, the fault is yours and not ours. And therefore we humbly take our leave: from the gallows the eighteenth of August."

And with that he leapt from the ladder, and cast the halter at Hodgekins' face.

When the clothiers saw this, they knew not what to say, but taking them by the sleeves, entreated to have their own again.

"Not so," quoth Wallace, "you get not the value of a plack or a bawbee.[41] We have stolen your cloth; then why do you not hang us? Here we have made ourselves ready, and if you will not hang us, choose. A plague on you," quoth he, "you have hindered me God knows what. I made account to dine this day in heaven, and you keep me here on earth where there is not a quarter of that good cheer. The foul evil take you all. I was fully provided to give the gallows a box on the ear, and now God knows when I shall be in so good a mind again."

And so he, with the rest of his companions, departed.

---

[41]*plack or a bawbee:* two small Scottish coins, each worth about a half-penny in English money.

When Hodgekins saw that, notwithstanding their thievery, how they flouted at their lenity, he was much moved in mind. And as he stood in his dumps, chewing his cud, making his dinner with a dish of melancholy, a gray friar reverently saluted him in this sort: "All hail, Goodman Hodgekins, happiness and health be ever with you, and to all suppressors of lewd livers God send everlasting joys.

"I am sorry, Goodman Hodgekins, that the great privilege which our king gave to this town comes to no greater purpose. Better far had it been that it had never been granted, than so lightly regarded. The town hath suffered through their own peevishness an everlasting reproach this day, only because foolish pity hath hindered justice.

"Consider that compassion is not to be had upon thieves and robbers. Pity only appertaineth to the virtuous sort, who are overwhelmed with the waves of misery and mischance. What great cause of boldness have you given to bad livers by letting these fellows thus to escape, and how shall you now keep your goods in safety, seeing you fulfill not the law which should be your defense? Never think that thieves will make any conscience to carry away your goods, when they find themselves in no danger of death, who have more cause to praise your pity than to commend your wisdom. Wherefore, in time seek to prevent the ensuing evil.

"For my own part, I have that care of your good that I would work all good means for your benefit, and yet not so much in respect of your profit as for the desire I have to uphold justice; and seeing I find you and the rest so womanish that you could not find in your hearts to hang a thief, I have devised how to make a gin that shall cut off their heads without man's help, and if the king will allow thereof."

When Hodgekins heard this, he was somewhat comforted in mind and said to the friar that if by his cunning he would perform it, he would once again make suit to the king to have his grant for the same. The friar willed him to have no doubt in him; and so when he had devised it, he got a carpenter to frame it out of hand.

Hodgekins in the meantime posted up to the court and told his majesty that the privilege of Halifax was not worth a pudding.

"Why so?" said our king.

"Because," quoth Hodgekins, "we can get never a hangman to truss our thieves; but if it shall like your good grace," quoth he, "there is a feat friar that will make us a device which shall, without the hand of man, cut off the crags of all such carls, if your majesty will please to allow thereof."

The king, understanding the full effect of the matter, at length granted his petition; whereupon till this day it is observed in Halifax that such as are taken stealing of their cloth have their heads chopped off with the same gin.

Chapter 9

How the Bailiffs of London Could Get No Man to Be a Catchpole, and How Certain Flemings Took That Office upon Them, Whereof Many of Them Were Fled into This Realm, by Reason of Certain Waters That Had Drowned a Great Part of Their Country

The city of London, being at this time governed by bailiffs, it came to pass that in a certain fray two of their catchpoles were killed, for at that time they had not the name of sergeants; and you shall understand that their office was then so much hated and detested of Englishmen that none of them would take it upon him, so that the bailiffs were glad to get any man whatsoever and to give him certain wages to perform that office.

It came to pass, as I said before, that two of their officers, by arresting of a man, were at one instant slain; by means whereof the bailiffs were enforced to seek others to put in their rooms. But by no means could they get any; wherefore, according to their wonted manner, they made proclamation that if there were any man that would present himself before them, he should not only be settled in that office during their lives, but also should have such maintenance and allowance, as for such men was by the city provided; and, notwithstanding that it was an office most necessary in the commonwealth, yet did the poorest wretch despise it, that lived in any estimation among his neighbors.

At last a couple of Flemings which were fled into this land,[42] by reason that their country was drowned with the sea, hearing the proclamation, offered themselves unto the bailiffs to serve in this place. Who were presently received and accepted and according to order had garments given them—which were of two colors, blue and red (their coats, breeches, and stockings)—whereby they were known and discerned from other men.

[42]*a couple of Flemings . . . fled into this land:* taken from Holinshed, III, 34 (sig. D3ᵛ), but the part about the bailiffs and their garments seems to be Deloney's invention.

Within half a year after, it came to pass that Thomas Dove of Exeter came up to London. Who, having by his jollity and good fellowship brought himself greatly behind hand, was in danger to divers men of the city. Among the rest, one of his creditors feed[43] an officer to arrest him. The Dutchman, that had not been long experienced in such matters and hearing how many of his fellows had been killed for attempting to arrest men, stood quivering and quaking in a corner of the street to watch for Tom Dove; and having long waited, at length he spied him. Whereupon he prepared his mace ready and with a pale countenance proceeded to do his office. At what time, coming behind the man, suddenly with his mace he knocked him on the pate, saying, "I arrest you," giving him such a blow that he felled him to the ground.

The catchpole, thinking he had killed the man, he left his mace behind him and ran away. The creditor he ran after him, calling and crying that he should turn again; but the Fleming would not by any means come back, but got him quite out of the city and took sanctuary at Westminster.

Dove, being come to himself, arose, and went to his inn, no man hindering his passage, being not a little glad he so escaped the danger. Yet, nevertheless, at his next coming to London, another catchpole met with him and arrested him in the king's name.

Dove, being dismayed at this mischievous chance, knew not what to do. At last he requested the catchpole that he would not violently cast him in prison, but stay till such time as he could send for a friend to be his surety. And although kindness in a catchpole be rare, yet was he won with fair words to do him this favor; whereupon Dove desired one to go to his host Gerard, who immediately came unto him and offered himself to be Dove's surety.

The officer, who never saw this man before, was much amazed at his sight; for Gerard was a great and a mighty man of body, of countenance grim, and exceeding high of stature, so that the catchpole was wonderfully afraid, asking if he could find never a surety but the devil, most fearfully entreating him to conjure him away, and he would do Dove any favor.

"What, will you not take my word?" quoth Gerard.

"Sir," quoth the catchpole, "if 'twere for any matter in hell, I would take your word as soon as any devil's in that place, but seeing it is for a matter on earth, I would gladly have a surety."

---

[43]*feed:* gave fees to.

"Why, thou whoreson cricket!" quoth Gerard. "Thou magget-a-pie,[44] thou spinner, thou paltry spider! Dost thou take me for a devil? Sirrah, take my word, I charge thee, for this man—or else, goodman butterfly, I'll make thee repent it!"

The officer, while he was in the house, said he was content. But so soon as he came into the street, he cried, saying, "Help, help, good neighbors, or else the devil will carry away my prisoner!"

Notwithstanding, there was not one man would stir to be the catchpole's aid. Which when he saw, he took fast hold on Thomas Dove and would not by any means let him go.

Gerard, seeing this, made no more to do; but coming to the officer, gave him such a fillip on the forehead with his finger that he felled the poor Fleming to the ground. And while he lay in the street stretching his heels, Gerard took Dove under his arm and carried him home, where he thought himself as safe as King Charlemagne in Mount Alban.

The next morning Gerard conveyed Dove out of town. Who afterward kept him in the country, and came no more in the catchpole's claws.

Chapter 10

How Duke Robert Came A-Wooing to Margaret with the White Hand, and How He Appointed to Come and Steal Her Away from Her Masters

The beautiful Margaret, who had now dwelt with her dame the space of four years, was highly regarded and secretly loved of many gallant gentlemen of the country, but of two especially—Duke Robert and Sir William Ferris. It chanced on a time that fair Margaret, with many other of her master's folks, went a-haymaking attired in a red stammel petticoat and a broad straw hat upon her head. She had a hayfork, and in her lap she bore her breakfast. As she went along, Duke Robert, with one or two of his keepers, met with her, whose amiable sight did now anew kindle the secret fire of love which long lay smothering in his heart. Wherefore, meeting her so happily, he saluted her thus friendly:

"Fair maid, good morrow. Are you walking so diligently to your labor? Needs must the weather be fair where the sun shines so clear, and the hay wholesome that is dried with such splendent rays."

[44]*magget-a-pie:* magpie (a bird with a raucous chatter).

"Renowned and most notable duke," quoth she, "poor harvest folks pray for fair weather, and it is the laborers' comfort to see his work prosper; and the more happy may we count the day that is blessed with your princely presence."

"But more happy," said the duke, "are they which are conversant in thy company. But let me entreat thee to turn back to thy master's with me and commit thy fork to some that are fitter for such toil. Trust me, methinks thy dame is too much ill advised in setting thee to such homely business. I muse thou canst endure this vile beseeming servitude, whose delicate limbs were never framed to prove such painful experiments."

"Albeit," quoth she, "it becometh not me to control your judicial thoughts, yet, were you not the duke, I would say your opinion deceived you. Though your fair eyes seem clear, yet I deem them imperfect if they cast before your mind any shadow or spark of beauty in me. But I rather think, because it hath been an old saying that women are proud to hear themselves praised, that you either speak this to drive away the time or to wring from me my too apparent imperfections. But I humbly entreat pardon; too long have I foreslowed my business and shown myself overbold in your presence." And therewith, with a courtly grace, bending her knees to the courteous duke, she went forward to the field, and the duke to the town of Gloucester.

When he came thither, he made his keepers great cheer, entreating them they would give him respite to be a while with old Gray.

"For we twain must have a game or two," quoth he. "And for my safe return, I gage to you my princely word that, as I am a true knight and a gentleman, I will return safe to your charge again."

The keepers being content, the duke departed, and with old Gray goes to the field to peruse the workfolks. Where, while Gray found himself busy in many matters, he took opportunity to talk with Margaret. She, who by his letters before was privy to his purpose, guessed beforehand the cause of his coming. To whom he spoke to this effect:

"Fair maid, I did long since manifest my love to thee by my letter. Tell me, therefore, were it not better to be a duchess than a drudge? A lady of high reputation, than a servant of simple degree? With me thou mightest live in pleasure, where here thou drawest thy days forth in pain. By my love thou shouldst be made lady of great treasures, where now thou art poor and beggarly. All manner of delights should then attend on thee, and whatsoever thy heart desired, thou shouldst have. Wherefore, seeing it lies in thy own choice, make thyself happy by consenting to my suit."

"Sir," quoth she, "I confess your love deserves a lady's favor, your affection a faithful friend, such a one as should make but one heart and mind of two hearts and bodies. But far unfit is it that the turtle should match with the eagle; though her love be never so pure, her wings are unfit to mount so high. While Thales gazed on the stars, he stumbled in a pit. And they that climb unadvisedly catch a fall suddenly. What availeth high dignity in time of adversity? It neither helpeth the sorrow of the heart nor removes the body's misery. As for wealth and treasure, what are they but fortune's baits to bring men in danger? Good for nothing but to make people forget themselves. And whereas you allege poverty to be a hinderer of the heart's comfort, I find it in myself contrary, knowing more surety to rest under a simple habit than a royal robe. And verily there is none in the world poor but they that think themselves poor, for such as are indued with content are rich, having nothing else. But he that is possessed with riches without content is most wretched and miserable. Wherefore, most noble duke, albeit I account my life unworthy of your least favor, yet I would desire you to match your love to your like, and let me rest to my rake and use my fork for my living."

"Consider, fair Margaret," quoth he, "that it lies not in man's power to place his love where he list, being the work of an high deity. A bird was never seen in Pontus, nor true love in a fleeting mind. Never shall I remove the affection of my heart, which in nature resembleth the stone abiston,[45] whose fire can never be cooled. Wherefore, sweet maiden, give not obstinate denial where gentle acceptance ought to be received."

"Fair sir," quoth she, "consider what high displeasure may rise by a rash match, what danger a king's frowns may breed. My worthless matching with your royalty may perhaps regain your liberty and hazard my life; then call to mind how little you should enjoy your love, or I my wedded lord."

The duke at these words made this reply: that if she consented, she should not dread any danger. "The thunder," quoth he, "is driven away by ringing of bells, the lion's wrath qualified by a yielding body. How much more a brother's anger with a brother's entreaty? By me he hath received many favors, and never yet did he requite any one of them. And who is ignorant that the princely crown which adorneth

[45]*abiston:* asbestos; used also in *Euphues* (footnote 50).

his head is my right? All which I am content he shall still enjoy, so he requite my kindness. But if he should not, then would I be like those men that, eating of the tree lotus, forget the country where they were born; and never more should this clime cover my head, but with thee would I live in a strange land, being better content with an egg in thy company than with all the delicates in England."

The maiden, hearing this, who with many other words was long wooed, at last consented; where, yielding to him her heart with her hand, he departed, appointing to certify her from Cardiff Castle what determination he would follow. So, taking his leave of Gray, he went to his keepers and with them posted to Cardiff.

Now it is to be remembered that Sir William Ferris, within a day or two after, came unto Gray's house, as it was his ordinary custom— but not so much, iwis, for Gray's company, as for the mind he had to Margaret, his maid. Who, although he were a married man and had a fair lady to his wife, yet he laid hard siege to the fort of this maiden's chastity, having with many fair words sought to allure her and by the offer of sundry rich gifts to tempt her. But when she saw that by a hundred denials she could not be rid of him, she now chanced on a sudden to give him such an answer as drove him from a deceit into such a conceit as never after that time he troubled her.

Sir William Ferris, being very importunate to have her grant his desire and when, after sundry assaults, she gave him still the repulse, he would needs know the reason why she would not love him.

Quoth he, "If thou didst consider who he is that seeketh thy favor, what pleasure he may do thee by his purse, and what credit by his countenance, thou wouldst never stand on such nice points. If I be thy friend, who dareth be thy foe? And what is he that will once call thy name in question for anything? Therefore, sweet girl, be better advised and refuse not my offer, being so large."

"Truly, Sir William," quoth she, "though there be many reasons to make me deny your suit, yet is there one above the rest that causes me I cannot love you."

"Now, I pray thee, my wench, let me know that," quoth he, "and I will amend it, whatsoever it be."

"Pardon me, sir," said Margaret, "if I should speak my mind, it would possibly offend you and do me no pleasure because it is a defect in nature, which no physic may cure."

Sir William, hearing her say so, being abashed at her speech, said, "Fair Margaret, let me, if I may obtain no more at thy hands, yet entreat thee to know what this defect should be. I am not wry-necked, crook-legged, stub-footed, lame-handed, nor blear-eyed. What can make this mislike? I never knew anybody that took exceptions at my person before."

"And the more sorry am I," quoth she, "that I was so malapert to speak it, but pardon my presumption, good Sir William. I would I had been like the stork, tongueless; then should I never have caused your disquiet."

"Nay, sweet Margaret," quoth he, "tell me, dear love; I commend thy singleness of heart. Good Margaret, speak."

"Good Sir William, let it rest," quoth she. "I know you will not believe it when I have revealed it; neither is it a thing that you can help. And yet such is my foolishness, had it not been for that, I think verily I had granted your suit ere now. But seeing you urge me so much to know what it is, I will tell you. It is, sir, your ill-favored great nose, that hangs sagging so loathsomely to your lips that I cannot find in my heart so much as to kiss you."

"What, my nose?" quoth he. "Is my nose so great and I never knew it? Certainly I thought my nose to be as comely as any man's. But this it is, we are all apt to think well of ourselves and a great deal better than we ought. But let me see. My nose! By the mass, 'tis true; I do now feel it myself. Good Lord, how was I blinded before?"

Hereupon, it is certain that the knight was driven into such a conceit as none could persuade him but his nose was so great indeed. His lady, or any other that spoke to the contrary, he would say they were flatterers and that they lied, insomuch that he would be ready to strike some of them that commended or spoke well of his nose. If they were men of worship or any other that contraried him in his opinion, he would swear they flouted him and be ready to challenge them the field. He became so ashamed of himself that after that day he would never go abroad, whereby Margaret was well rid of his company.

On a time, a wise and grave gentleman, seeing him grounded in his conceit so strongly, gave his lady counsel not to contrary him therein, but rather say that she would seek out some cunning physician to cure him. "For," said he, "as Sir William hath taken this conceit of himself, so is he like never to bear other opinion till his own conceit doth remove it; the which must be wisely wrought to bring it to pass."

Whereupon, the lady, having conferred with a physician that bore a great name in the country, he undertook to remove this fond conceit by his skill. The day being appointed when the physician should come, and the knight being told thereof, for very joy he would go forth to meet him. When a woman of the town saw the knight, having heard what rumor went because of his nose, she looked very steadfastly upon him. The knight, casting his eye upon her, seeing her to gaze so wistly[46] in his face, with an angry countenance said thus to her, "Why, how now, good huswife, can you not get you about your business?"

The woman, being a shrewish quean, answered him cuttedly.

"No, marry, can I not," quoth she.

"No, you drab? What is the cause?" said the knight.

"Because," quoth she, "your nose stands in my way."

Wherewith the knight, being very angry and abashed, went back again to his house.

The physician being come, he had filled a certain bladder with sheep's blood and conveyed it into his sleeve. Where, at the issue of the bladder, he had put in a piece of a swan's quill, through the which the blood should run out of the bladder so close by his hand that he, holding the knight by the nose, it might not be perceived but that it issued thence. All things being prepared, he told the knight that by a foul corrupt blood wherewith the veins of his nose were overcharged, his impediment did grow.

"Therefore," quoth he, "to have redress for this disease, you must have a vein opened in your nose, whence this foul corruption must be taken. Whereupon it will follow that your nose will fall again to his natural proportion, and never shall you be troubled with this grief any more. And thereupon will I gage my life."

"I pray you, master doctor," said the knight, "is my nose so big as you make it?"

"With reverence I may speak it," said the physician. "To tell the truth, and avoid flattery, I never saw a more misshapen nose so foul to sight."

"Lo, you now, madam," quoth the knight. "This is you that said my nose was as well, as handsome, and as comely a nose as any man's."

"Alas, sir," quoth she, "I spoke it, God wot, because you should not grieve at it, nor take my words in ill part; neither did it indeed become me to mislike of your nose."

"All this we will quickly remedy," said the physician. "Have no doubt."

And with that, he very orderly pricked him in the nose, but not in any vein whereby he might bleed. And presently having a trick finely

---

[46]*wistly:* closely attentive.

to unstop the quill, the blood ran into a basin in great abundance; and when the bladder was empty and the basin almost full, the physician seemed to close the vein and asked him how he felt his nose, showing the great quantity of filthy blood which from thence he had taken.

The knight, beholding it with great wonder, said he thought that no man in the world had been troubled with such abundance of corrupt blood in his whole body as lay in his misshapen nose. And therewithal he began to touch and handle his nose, saying that he felt it mightily assuaged. Immediately a glass was brought wherein he might behold himself.

"Yea, marry," quoth he, "now I praise God. I see my nose is come into some reasonable proportion, and I feel myself very well eased of the burden thereof. But if it continue thus, that's all."

"I will warrant your worship," said the physician, "for ever being troubled with the like again."

Whereupon the knight received great joy, and the doctor a high reward.

Chapter 11

How Thomas of Reading Was Murdered at His Hosts' House of Colebrook; Who Also Had Murdered Many Before Him, and How Their Wickedness Was at Length Revealed

Thomas of Reading, having many occasions to come to London, as well about his own affairs as also the king's business, being in a great office under his majesty, it chanced on a time that his host and hostess of Colebrook, who through covetousness had murdered many of their guests, and having every time he came thither great store of his money to lay up, appointed him to be the next fat pig that should be killed. For it is to be understood that when they plotted the murder of any man, this was always their term, the man to his wife and the woman to her husband.

"Wife, there is now a fat pig to be had if you want one."

Whereupon she would answer thus, "I pray you put him in the hogsty till tomorrow."

This was when any man came thither alone without others in his company, and they saw he had great store of money.

This man should be then laid in the chamber right over the kitchen, which was a fair chamber and better set out than any other in the house. The best bedstead therein, though it were little and low, yet was it most cunningly carved and fair to the eye; the feet whereof were fast nailed to the chamber floor in such sort that it could not in any wise fall. The bed that lay therein was fast sewed to the sides of the bedstead. Moreover, that part of the chamber whereupon this bed and bedstead stood was made in such sort that, by the pulling out of two iron pins below in the kitchen, it was to be let down and taken up by a drawbridge, or in manner of a trap door. Moreover, in the kitchen, directly under the place where this should fall, was a mighty great caldron, wherein they used to seethe their liquor when they went to brewing. Now, the men appointed for the slaughter were laid into this bed, and in the dead time of the night when they were sound asleep, by plucking out the foresaid iron pins, down would the man fall out of his bed into the boiling caldron, and all the clothes that were upon him. Where, being suddenly scalded and drowned, he was never able to cry or speak one word.

Then had they a little ladder ever standing ready in the kitchen, by the which they presently mounted into the said chamber and there closely took away the man's apparel, as also his money in his male or capcase. And then lifting up the said falling floor which hung by hinges, they made it fast as before.

The dead body would they take presently out of the caldron and throw it down the river, which ran near unto their house. Whereby they escaped all danger.

Now if in the morning any of the rest of the guests that had talked with the murdered man over eve[47] chanced to ask for him, as having occasion to ride the same way that he should have done, the goodman would answer that he took horse a good while before day and that he himself did set him forward. The horse the goodman would also take out of the stable and convey him to a haybarn of his that stood from his house a mile or two, whereof himself did always keep the keys full charily, and when any hay was to be brought from thence, with his own hands he would deliver it. Then, before the horse should go from thence, he would dismark him, as, if he were a long tail, he would make him curtal, or else crop his ears, or cut his mane, or put out one of his eyes; and by this means, he kept himself a long time unknown.

Now Thomas of Reading, as I said before, being marked and kept

[47]*over eve:* on the previous evening.

for a fat pig, he was laid in the same chamber of death; but by reason Gray of Gloucester chanced also to come that night, he escaped scalding.

The next time he came, he was laid there again, but before he fell asleep or was warm in his bed, one came riding through the town and cried piteously that London was all on afire and that it had burned down Thomas Becket's house in Westcheap, and a great number more in the same street.

"And yet," quoth he, "the fire is not quenched."

Which tidings, when Thomas of Reading heard, he was very sorrowful, for of the same Becket that day had he received a great piece of money and had left in his house many of his writings and some that appertained to the king also.[48] Therefore, there was no nay but he would ride back again to London presently to see how the matter stood; thereupon, making himself ready, he departed. This cross fortune caused his host to frown.

"Nevertheless, the next time," quoth he, "will pay for all."

Notwithstanding, God so wrought that they were prevented then likewise, by reason of a great fray that happened in the house betwixt a couple that fell out at dice, insomuch as the murderers themselves were enforced to call him up, being a man in great authority, that he might set the house in quietness; out of the which, by means of this quarrel, they doubted to lose many things.

Another time when he should have been laid in the same place, he fell so sick that he requested to have somebody to watch with him. Whereby also they could not bring their vile purpose to pass. But hard it is to escape the ill fortunes whereunto a man is allotted. For albeit that the next time that he came to London his horse stumbled and broke one of his legs as he should ride homeward. Yet hired he another to hasten his own death, for there was no remedy but he should go to Colebrook that night. But by the way he was so heavy asleep that he could scant keep himself in the saddle; and when he came near unto the town, his nose burst out suddenly ableeding.

Well, to his inn he came and so heavy was his heart that he could eat no meat. His host and hostess, hearing he was so melancholy, came up to cheer him, saying, "Jesus, Master Cole, what ails you tonight?

[48]*Becket ... the king also:* an example of Deloney's telescoping, in this case the reigns of Henry I and Henry II; by "the king" Deloney means Henry I, at whose death in 1135 the historical Becket was only about seventeen years old.

Never did we see you thus sad before. Will it please you to have a quart of burned sack?"

"With a good will," quoth he. "And would to God Thomas Dove were here. He would surely make me merry, and we should lack no music. But I am sorry for the man with all my heart, that he is come so far behindhand. But, alas, so much can every man say, but what good doth it him? No, no, it is not words can help a man in this case; the man had need of other relief than so. Let me see: I have but one child in the world and that is my daughter, and half that I have is hers, the other half my wife's. What then? Shall I be good to nobody but them? In conscience, my wealth is too much for a couple to possess, and what is our religion without charity? And to whom is charity more to be shown than to decayed householders?

"Good my host, lend me a pen and ink and some paper, for I will write a letter unto the poor man straight, and something I will give him. That alms which a man bestows with his own hands he shall be sure to have delivered, and God knows how long I shall live."

With that, his hostess dissemblingly answered, saying, "Doubt not, Master Cole, you are like enough by the course of nature to live many years."

"God knows," quoth he, "I never found my heart so heavy before."

By this time, pen, ink, and paper was brought; setting himself to writing, as followeth:

In the name of God, Amen, I bequeath my soul to God and my body to the ground, my goods equally between my wife Elenor, and Isabel my daughter.

Item: I give to Thomas Dove of Exeter one hundred pounds—nay, that is too little, I give to Thomas Dove two hundred pounds—in money, to be paid unto him presently upon his demand thereof by my said wife and daughter.

"Ha, how say you, my host?" quoth he. "Is not this well? I pray you read it."

His host, looking thereon, said, "Why, Master Cole, what have you written here? You said you would write a letter, but methinks you have made a will. What need have you to do thus? Thanks be to God, you may live many fair years."

" 'Tis true," quoth Cole, "if it please God, and I trust this writing cannot shorten my days. But let me see, have I made a will? Now I promise you, I did verily purpose to write a letter; notwithstanding, I have written that that God put into my mind. But look once again, my host, is it not written there that Dove shall have two hundred pounds, to be paid when he comes to demand it?"

"Yes, indeed," said his host.

"Well, then, all is well," said Cole. "And it shall go as it is for me. I will not bestow the new writing thereof any more."

Then, folding it up, he sealed it, desiring that his host would send it to Exeter. He promised that he would. Notwithstanding, Cole was not so satisfied but, after some pause, he would needs hire one to carry it. And so, sitting down sadly in his chair again, upon a sudden he burst forth aweeping. They demanding the cause thereof, he spoke as followeth:

"No cause of these tears I know. But it comes now into my mind," said Cole, "when I set toward this my last journey to London, how my daughter took on, what a coil she kept to have me stay. And I could not be rid of the little baggage a long time, she did so hang about me. When her mother by violence took her away, she cried out most mainly, 'Oh, my father, my father, I shall never see him again.'"

"Alas, pretty soul," said his hostess, "this was but mere kindness in the girl, and it seemeth she is very fond of you. But, alas, why should you grieve at this? You must consider that it was but childishness."

"Aye, it is indeed," said Cole, and with that he began to nod.

Then they asked him if he would go to bed.

"No," said he, "although I am heavy, I have no mind to go to bed at all."

With that, certain musicians of the town came to the chamber and, knowing Master Cole was there, drew out their instruments and very solemnly began to play.

"This music comes very well," said Cole. And when he had listened a while thereunto, he said, "Methinks these instruments sound like the ring of St. Mary Overy's bells,[49] but the base drowns all the rest. And in my ear it goes like a bell that rings a forenoon's knell. For God's sake, let them leave off and bear them this simple reward."

The musicians being gone, his host asked if now it would please him to go to bed.

"For," quoth he, "it is well near eleven of the clock."

With that, Cole, beholding his host and hostess earnestly, began to

[49]*St. Mary Overy's bells:* The twelve bells of this church were famous for the beautiful sounds they gave to the Southwark area (but the bell tower dates from the sixteenth century, not the twelfth).

start back, saying, "What ail you to look so like pale death? Good Lord, what have you done, that your hands are thus bloody?"

"What, my hands?" said his host. "Why, you may see they are neither bloody nor foul. Either your eyes do greatly dazzle, or else fancies of a troubled mind do delude you."

"Alas, my host, you may see," said he, "how weak my wits are. I never had my head so idle before. Come, let me drink once more, and then I will to bed and trouble you no longer."

With that he made himself unready, and his hostess was very diligent to warm a kerchief and put it about his head.

"Good Lord," said he, "I am not sick, I praise God, but such an alteration I find in myself as I never did before."

With that the screech owl cried piteously, and anon after the night raven sat croaking hard by his window.

"Jesu have mercy upon me!" quoth he. "What an ill-favored cry do yonder carrion birds make!"

And therewithal he laid him down in his bed, from whence he never rose again.

His host and hostess, that all this while noted his troubled mind, began to commune betwixt themselves thereof. And the man said he knew not what were best to be done.

"By my consent," quoth he, "the matter should pass, for I think it is not best to meddle on him."

"What, man," quoth she, "faint you now? Have you done so many, and do you shrink at this?"

Then, showing him a great deal of gold which Cole had left with her, she said, "Would it not grieve a body's heart to lose this? Hang the old churl, what should he do living any longer? He hath too much, and we have too little. Tut, husband, let the thing be done and then this is our own."

Her wicked counsel was followed, and when they had listened at his chamber door, they heard the man sound asleep.

"All is safe," quoth they.

And down into the kitchen they go, their servants being all in bed; and pulling out the iron pins, down fell the bed, and the man dropped out into the boiling caldron. He being dead, they betwixt them cast his body into the river. His clothes they hid away, and made all things as it should be. But when he came to the stable to convey thence Cole's horse, the stable door being open, the horse had got loose, and with a part of the halter about his neck and straw trussed under his belly (as the hostlers had dressed him o'er eve). He was gone out at the backside, which led into a great field adjoining to the house; and so, leaping divers hedges, being a lusty stond[50] horse, had got into a ground where a mare was grazing. With whom he kept such a coil that they got into the highway, where one of the town meeting them, knew the mare and brought her and the horse to the man that owed[51] her.

In the meanspace the musicians had been at the inn; and in requital of their evening's gift, they intended to give Cole some music in the morning. The goodman told them he took horse before day. Likewise there was a guest in the house that would have borne him company to Reading, unto whom the host also answered that he himself set him upon horseback and that he went long ago.

Anon comes the man that owed the mare, inquiring up and down to know and if none of them missed a horse. Who said no. At last he came to the Sign of the Crane, where Cole lay; and calling the hostlers, he demanded of them if they lacked none. They said no.

"Why, then," said the man, "I perceive my mare is good for something; for if I send her to field single, she will come home double."

Thus it passed on all that day and the night following. But the next day after, Cole's wife, musing that her husband came not home, sent one of her men on horseback to see if he could meet him.

"And if," quoth she, "you meet him not betwixt this and Colebrook, ask for him at the Crane. But if you find him not there, then ride to London; for I doubt he is either sick or else some mischance hath fallen unto him."

The fellow did so, and asking for him at Colebrook, they answered he went homeward from thence such a day. The servant musing what should be become of his master, and making much inquiry in the town for him, at length one told him of a horse that was found on the highway, and no man knew whence he came. He, going to see the horse, knew him presently, and to the Crane he goes with him. The host of the house, perceiving this, was blank, and that night fled secretly away. The fellow, going unto the justice, desired his help; presently after, word was brought that Jarman of the Crane was gone. Then all the men said he had surely made Cole away; and the musicians told what Jarman said to them when they would have given Cole music. Then the woman, being apprehended and examined, confessed the truth. Jarman soon after was taken in Windsor

---

[50]*stond:* stand; a "stond horse" is one kept in a stable. But "stond" also suggests "stoned," a sense borne out by the context, in which the lusty horse is surely a stallion.

[51]*owed:* owned.

Forest. He and his wife were both hanged after they had laid open all these things before expressed. Also, he confessed that he, being a carpenter, made that false falling floor, and how his wife devised it, and how they had murdered by that means sixty persons. And yet notwithstanding all the money which they had gotten thereby, they prospered not, but at their death were found very far in debt.

When the king heard of this murder, he was for the space of seven days so sorrowful and heavy as he would not hear any suit, giving also commandment that the house should quite be consumed with fire wherein Cole was murdered and that no man should ever build upon that cursed ground.

Cole's substance at his death was exceeding great. He had daily in his house an hundred men servants, and forty maids; he maintained, beside, above two or three hundred people, spinners and carders, and a great many other householders. His wife never after married; and at her death she bestowed a mighty sum of money toward the maintaining of the new-built monastery. Her daughter was most richly married to a gentleman of great worship, by whom she had many children. And some say that the river whereinto Cole was cast did ever since carry the name of Cole, being called the river of Cole and the town of Colebrook.

Chapter 12

How Divers of the Clothiers' Wives Went to the Churching of Sutton's Wife of Salisbury, and of Their Merriments

Sutton's wife of Salisbury, which had lately been delivered of a son, against her going to church prepared great cheer. At what time Simon's wife of Southampton came thither, and so did divers other of the clothiers' wives, only to make merry at this churching feast.[52] And whilst there dames sat at the table, Crab, Weasel, and Wren waited on the board; and as the old proverb speaketh, "Many women, many words," so fell it out at that time; for there was such prattling that it passed. Some talked of their husband's frowardness; some showed their maids' sluttishness; othersome deciphered the costliness of their garments; some told many tales of their neighbors. And, to be brief, there was none of them but would have talk for a whole day.

[52]*churching feast:* The full title of this Anglican service, beginning in 1552, was "The Thanksgiving of Women after Childbirth."

But when Crab, Weasel, and Wren saw this, they concluded betwixt themselves that as oft as any of the women had a good bit of meat on their trenchers, they, offering a clean one, should catch that commodity, and so they did. But the women, being busy in talk, marked it not till, at the last, one found leisure to miss her meat. Whereupon she said that their boldness exceeded their diligence.

"Not so, forsooth," said Weasel. "There is an hundred bolder than we."

"Name me one," said the woman, "if you can."

"A flea is bolder," quoth Crab.

"How will you prove that?" said the woman.

"Because," quoth he, "they will creep under your coats, where we dare not come, and now and then bite you by the buttocks as if they were brawn."

"But what becomes of them?" quoth the woman. "Their sweet meat hath sour sauce, and their lustiness doth often cost them their lives; therefore, take heed."

"A good warning of a fair woman," said Wren, "but I had not thought so fine a wit in a fat belly."

The women, seeing their men so merry, said it was a sign there was good ale in the house.

"That's as fit for a churching," quoth Weasel, "as a cudgel for a curst quean."

Thus with pleasant communication and merry quips they drove out the time till the fruit and spice cakes were set on the board. At what time one of them began to ask of the other if they heard not of the cruel murder of Thomas of Reading.

"What," said the rest, "is old Cole murdered? When, I pray you, was the deed done?"

The other answered, "On Friday last."

"Oh, good Lord," said the women, "how was it done? Can you tell?"

"As report goeth," said the other, "he was roasted alive."

"Oh, pitiful! Was he roasted? Indeed, I heard one say a man was murdered at London and that he was sodden[53] at an innholder's house and served in to the guests instead of pork."

"No, neighbor, it was not at London," said another. "I hear say 'twas coming from London, at a place called Colebrook, and it is reported for truth that the innholder made pies of him and penny pasties, yea, and made his own servant eat a piece of him."

[53]*sodden:* boiled.

"But, I pray you, good neighbor, can you tell how it was known? Some say that a horse revealed it."

"Now, by the mass," quoth Gray's wife, "it was told one of my neighbors that a certain horse did speak and told great things."

"That sounds like a lie," said one of them.

"Why," said another, "may not a horse speak as well as Balaam's ass?"

"It may be, but it is unlikely," said the third.

"But where was the horse when he spoke?"

"As some say," quoth she, "he was in the field and had broke out of the stable where he stood fast locked in mighty strong iron fetters, which he burst in pieces, as if they had been straws and broke down the stable door and so got away."

The goodman, coming in at these speeches, asked what that was they talked of.

"Marry," said his wife, "we hear that Cole of Reading is murdered. I pray you, is it true?"

"Aye," said Sutton, "it is true. That vile villain, his host, murdered him, in whose house the man had spent many a pound."

"But did they make pies of him?" said his wife.

"No, no," quoth her husband. "He was scalded to death in a boiling caldron and afterward thrown into a running river that is hard by."

"But, good husband, how was it known?"

"By his horse," quoth he.

"What, did he tell his master was murdered? Could the horse speak English?"

"Jesus, what a foolish woman are you," quoth he, "to ask such a question! But to end this, you are all heartily welcome, good neighbors, and I am sorry you had no better cheer."

So with thanks the women departed. Thus have ye heard the divers tales that will be spread abroad of an evil deed.

Chapter 13

How Duke Robert Deceived His Keepers and
Got from Them; How He Met Fair Margaret
and, in Carrying Her Away, Was Taken; For
the Which He Had His Eyes Put Out

Duke Robert, having, as you heard, obtained the love of fair Margaret, did now cast in his mind how he might delude his keepers and carry her away. In the end he, being fully resolved what to do, sent his letter unto her, wherein he requested that she would be ready to meet him in the forest betwixt Cardiff and Gloucester.

The young lady, having secretly received his message, unknown to her master or dame, in a morning betime made her ready and got forth, walking to the appointed place where her love should meet her.

During her abode there and thinking long ere her love came, she entered into divers passions, which indeed presaged some disaster fortune to follow.

"Oh, my dear love," said she, "how slack art thou in performing thy promise! Why do not thy deeds agree with thy inditing? See, these are thy words: 'Come, my dear Margaret, and with Cupid's swift wings fly to thy friend. Be now as nimble in thy footing as the camels of Bactria that run an hundred miles a day. I will wait and stay for thee, so I stay not too long. There is no country like Austria for ambling horses, and to carry thee I have got one.'"

"Oh, my love," quoth she, "here am I, but where art thou? Oh, why dost thou play the truant with time, who, like the wind, slides away unseen? An ambling jennet of Spain is too slow to serve our turns. A flying horse, for flying lovers, were most meet."

And thus casting many looks through the sylvan shades up and down to espy him, she thought every minute an hour till she might see him. Sometimes she would wish herself a bird that she might fly through the air to meet him, or a pretty squirrel to climb the highest tree to descry his coming. But finding her wishes vain, she began thus to excuse him and persuaded herself, saying:

"How much to blame am I, to find fault with my friend? Alas, men that lack their liberty must come when they can, not when they would. Poor prisoners cannot do what they desire, and then why should I be so hasty? Therefore if safely I may lay me down, I will beguile unquiet thoughts with quiet sleep. It is said that Galino[54] breeds no serpents, nor doth England's forests nourish bears or lions; therefore, without hurt I hope I may rest awhile."

Thus leaving fair Margaret in a sweet slumber, we will return to Duke Robert, who had thus plotted his escape from his keepers.

Having liberty of the king to hawk and hunt, he determined on a day, as he should follow the chase, to leave the hounds to the hart and the hunters to their horns and, being busy in their sport, himself

[54]*Galino:* an unidentified place name, possibly invented by Deloney.

would fly. Which he performed at that time when he appointed Margaret to meet him. And so coming to the place, his horse all on a water and himself in a sweat, finding his love asleep, he awaked her with a kiss, saying, "Arise, fair Margaret, now comes the time wherein thou shalt be made a queen." And presently setting her on horseback, he posted away.

Now when the keepers saw they had lost his company and that at the killing of the game he was not present, they were among themselves in such a mutiny that they were ready one to stab another.

"It was thy fault," said one, "that he thus escaped from us, that hadst more mind of thy pleasure than of thy prisoner; and by this means we are all undone."

The other said as much to him, that he had thought he had followed him in the chase. But leaving at last this contention, the one posted up to the king, while the others coasted up and down the country to search for the duke. Who, having killed his horse in traveling, was most unhappily met on foot with fair Margaret ere he could come to any town, where he might for money have another. But when he spied his keepers come to take him, he desired Margaret to make shift for herself and to seek to escape them. But she, being of a contrary mind, said she would live and die with him.

The duke, seeing himself ready to be surprised, drew out his sword and said he would buy his liberty with his life before he would yield to be any more a prisoner; and thereupon began a great fight betwixt them, insomuch that the duke had killed two of them. But himself, being sore wounded and faint with overmuch bleeding, at length fell down, being not able any longer to stand; and by this means the good duke was taken with his fair love and both of them committed to prison.

But in the meanspace, when Gray's wife had missed her maid and saw she was quite gone, she made great lamentation for her among her neighbors; for she loved her as dearly as any child that ever she bore of her own body.

"Oh, Margaret," quoth she, "what cause hadst thou thus to leave me? If thou didst mislike of anything, why didst thou not tell me? If thy wages were too little, I would have mended it. If thy apparel had been too simple, thou shouldst have had better. If thy work had been too great, I would have had help for thee.

"Farewell, my sweet Meg, the best servant that ever came in any man's house. Many may I have of thy name, but never any of thy nature. Thy diligence is much; in thy hands I laid the whole government of my house and thereby eased myself of that care which now will cumber me.

"Here, she hath left me my keys unto my chests, but my comfort is gone with her presence. Every gentle word that she was wont to speak comes now into my mind. Her courteous behavior shall I never forget. With how sweet and modest a countenance would she qualify my overhasty nature? It repents my heart that ever I spoke foul word unto her. Oh, Meg, wert thou here again, I would never chide thee more; but I was an unworthy dame for such a servant. What will become of me now if I should chance to be sick, seeing she is gone that was wont to be both my apothecary and physician?"

"Well," quoth her neighbors, "there is no remedy now but to rest content. You shall one day hear of her, doubt you not, and think this: that she was not so good, but you may get another as good; and therefore do not take it so heavily."

"Oh, neighbor, blame me not to grieve, seeing I have lost so great a jewel, and sure I am persuaded that scant in a body's lifetime they shall meet with the like.

"I protest I would circuit England round about on my bare feet to meet with her again. Oh, my Meg was surely stole away from me, else would she not have gone in such sort."

Her husband, on the other side, grieved as much and rested not night nor day riding up and down to seek her. But she, poor soul, is fast locked up in prison, and therefore cannot be met withal.

But when the king understood of his brother's escape, he was marvelous wroth, giving great charge and commandment when he was taken that both his eyes should be put out and he kept in prison till his dying day, appointing also that the maid should lose her life for presumption in loving him.

This matter, being rumored over all England, it came to the ears of Gray and his wife. Who, hearing that Margaret also was there in prison appointed to die, the good aged woman never rested till she came to the court. Where, kneeling before the king, with many tears she besought his majesty to spare the maiden's life, saying, "Most royal king, consider, I humbly beseech you, that the duke your brother was able to entice any woman to his love, much more a silly maiden, especially promising her marriage, to make her a lady, a duchess, or a queen. Who would refuse such an offer, when at the instant they might get both a princely husband and a high dignity?

If death be a lover's guerdon, then what is due to hatred? I am in my heart persuaded that, had my poor Margaret thought it would have bred your highness' displeasure, she would never have bought his love so dear. Had your grace made it known to your commons that it was unlawful for any to marry the duke your brother, who would have attempted such an action? If she had wilfully disobeyed your grace's commandment, she might have been thought worthy of death. But seeing ignorantly she offended, I beseech your grace recall the sentence and let me still enjoy my servant, for never will I rise till your majesty have granted my petition."

His highness, who was of nature merciful, beholding the woman's abundant tears, took pity on her and granted her suit. Which, being obtained, she went home with all haste possible. And from thence, she with her husband, taking their journey to Cardiff Castle, they came at that very instant when the maiden was led toward her death. Who went in most joyful sort to the same, saying that they were not worthy to be accounted true lovers that were not willing to die for love.

And so with a smiling countenance she passed on, as if she had eaten *Apium Risus*, which causeth a man to die laughing. But her dame Gray, seeing her, fell about her neck and with many kisses embraced her, saying, "Thou shalt not die, my wench, but go home with me; and for thy delivery, behold here the king's letters."

And with that she delivered them up to the governor of the castle, who, reading them, found these words written: "We pardon the maid's life and grant her liberty, but let her not pass till she see her lover's eyes put out, which we will have you do in such sort that only the sight may perish, but the eye continue fair; for which cause I have sent down Dr. Piero that he may execute the same."

The governor of the castle, having read the king's letter, said thus to the maiden: "The king's majesty hath pardoned thy life and allowed thy liberty, but you must not pass before you see your lover's eyes put out."

"Oh, sir," said the maiden, "mistake not yourself; they are my eyes that must be put out, and not the duke's. As his offense grew by my means, so I, being guilty, ought to receive the punishment."

"The king's commandment must be fulfilled," said the governor.

And therewithal Duke Robert was brought forth. Who, hearing that he must lose his eyes, said thus: "The noble mind is never conquered by grief nor overcome by mischance, but as the hart reneweth his age by eating the serpent, so doth a man lengthen his life with devouring sorrow. My eyes have offended the king, and they must be punished. My heart is in as great fault. Why is not that killed?"

"The king's majesty," said the governor, "spares your life of mere love, and only is content to satisfy the law with the loss of your eyes; wherefore take in good part this punishment and think you have deserved greater than is granted."

With this Margaret cried out, saying, "Oh, my dear love, most gentle prince, well may you wish that I had never been born, who by seeing of me must lose your sight. But happy should I count myself, if it so please the king, that I might redeem thy eyes with my life, or else that, being an equal offender, I might receive equal punishment. Hadst thou sustained this smart for some queen or princess of high blood, it might with the more ease be borne; but to endure it for such a one as I, it must needs cause a treble grief to be increased."

"Content thee, fair Margaret," said the duke, "for honor ought to be given to virtue and not riches; for glory, honor, nobility, and riches without virtue are but cloaks of maliciousness. And now let me take my leave of thy beauty, for never must I behold thy face. Notwithstanding, I account my eyes well lost, in that I do forgo them for so peerless a paragon. Now, fair heavens, farewell; the sun, moon, and stars shall I in this world never behold again. And farewell also the fruitful earth; well may I feel thee, but those poor windows of my body are now denied to view thee any more. And though the world hath ever been my foe, yet will I bid it farewell, too. And farewell, all my friends; whiles I live here in this world, I must suppose to sleep and wake when I come in heaven, where I hope to see you all again. Yet had it pleased the king, I had rather have lost my life than my eyes. Life, why, what is it but a flower, a bubble in the water, a span long, and full of misery? Of such small account is life that every soldier will sell it for six pence. And trust me I do now detest life, worse than a goat doth hate basil."

With that the doctor prepared his instrument and, being ready to set to the duke's eyes, he said, "Oh, stay, master doctor, till I have conveyed my love's countenance down into my heart. Come hither, my sweet, and let me give thee my last kiss, while my eyes may direct me to thy cherry lips."

Then embracing her in his arms, he said, "Oh, that I might give thee a kiss of twenty years long and to satisfy my greedy eyes with thy fair sight. Yet it doth somewhat content me, because thou art present at my punishment, that I may hold thee by the hand, to comfort my heart at the sudden prick of my eye."

This being said, the doctor performed his duty and so put out the crystal sight. At what time Duke Robert started up and, with a most manly courage, said, "I must thank his majesty that, though he depriveth me of my sight, yet he leaveth me eyes to weep for my sins."

But so soon as Margaret beheld the deed, she fell down in a swoon; and much ado her dame had to recover her life. Which when the duke understood, he was wondrous woe, groping for her with his bleeding eyes, saying, "Oh, where is my love? For God's sake have regard to her. And I pray you most heartily, good Goodwife Gray, let her have this favor for my sake, that she may be used kindly."

And with that the keepers led him into the castle, and Margaret was carried away wondrous sick and ill; but her dame was most tender over her and would suffer her to lack nothing. When she was somewhat well recovered, her dame Gray set her on horseback; and at her coming to Gloucester there was no small joy.

Chapter 14

How Tom Dove, Being Fallen to Decay, Was Forsaken of His Friends and Despised of His Servants; and How in the End He Was Raised Again Through the Liberality of the Clothiers

Such as seek the pleasure of this world follow a shadow wherein is no substance; and as the adder *aspis* tickleth a man to death, so doth vain pleasure flatter us till it makes us forget God and consume our substance, as by Tom Dove it is apparent, who had through a free heart and a liberal mind wasted his wealth; and look how his goods, consumed, so his friends fled from him. And albeit he had been of great ability and thereby done good unto many, yet no man regarded him in his poverty; but casting a scornful countenance upon him, they passed by him with slender salutation. Neither would any of his old acquaintance do him good or pleasure him the value of a farthing; his former friendship done to them was quite forgot, and he made of as much account as Job when he sat on the dunghill.

Now when his wicked servants saw him in this disgrace with the world, they on the other side began to disdain him. Notwithstanding that he, to his great cost, had long time brought them up, yet did they nothing regard it, but behind his back in most scornful sort derided him and both in their words and actions greatly abuse him.

Reverence they would do none unto him; but when they spoke, it was in such malapert sort as would grieve an honest mind to hear it.

At last it came to pass that, breaking out into mere contempt, they said they would stay no longer with him and that it was a great discredit to them to serve a person so beggarly; whereupon they thought it convenient to seek for their benefits elsewhere. When the distressed man found the matter so plain, being in great grief, he spoke thus unto them: "Now do I find, to my sorrow, the small trust that is in this false world. Why, my masters," quoth he, "have you so much forgotten my former prosperity that you nothing regard my present necessity? In your wants I forsook you not; in your sickness I left you not; nor despised you in your great poverty. It is not unknown, though you do not consider it, that I took some of you up in the highway; other some from your needy parents; and brought the rest from mere beggary to a house of bounty, where from paltry boys I brought you up to man's estate and have, to my great cost, taught you a trade, whereby you may live like men. And in requital of all my courtesy, cost, and good will, will you now on a sudden forsake me? Is this the best recompense that you can find in your hearts to yield me?

"This is far from the minds of honest servants. The fierce lion is kind to those that do him good; pluck but one thorn out of his foot, and for the same he will show manifold favors. The wild bull will not overthrow his dam; and the very dragons are dutiful to their nourishers. Be better advised and call to mind, I beseech you, that I have not plucked a thorn out of your feet, but drawn your whole bodies out of perils; and when you had no means to help yourselves, I only was your support and he, that, when all other forsook you, did comfort you in all your extremities."

"And what of all this?" quoth one of them. "Because you took us up poor, doth it therefore follow that we must be your slaves? We are young men, and for our parts we are no further to regard your profit than it may stand with our preferment. Why should we lose our benefit to pleasure you? If you taught us our trade, and brought us up from boys to men, you had our service for it, whereby you made no small benefit if you had as·well used it as we got it. But if you be poor, you may thank yourself, being a just scourge for your prodigality; and it is my opinion plain that to stay with you is the next way to make us like you, neither able to help ourselves nor our friends. Therefore, in brief, come pay me my wages, for I will not stay. Let the rest do as they will for I am resolved."

"Well," said his master, "if needs thou wilt be gone, here is part of thy wages in hand, and the rest, so soon as God sends it, thou shalt have it."

And with that, turning to the rest, he said, "Let me yet entreat you to stay and leave me not altogether destitute of help. By your labors must I live, and without you I know not what to do. Consider therefore my need, and regard my great charge. And if for my sake you will do nothing, take compassion on my poor children; stay my sliding foot, and let me not utterly fall through your flying from me."

"Tush," quoth they, "what do you talk to us? We can have better wages and serve a man of credit where our fare shall be far better and our gains greater. Therefore the world might count us right coxcombs if we should forsake our profit to pleasure you. Therefore, adieu; God send you more money, for you are like to have no more men." And thus they departed.

When they were gone, within a while after they met one with another, saying, "What cheer? Are you all come away?"

"In faith, aye, what should we do else?" quoth they. "But hear'st thou, sirrah, hast thou got thy wages?"

"Not yet," saith the other, "but I shall have it, and that is as good. 'Tis but ten shillings."

"Saist thou so?" said he. "Now I see thou art one of God Almighty's idiots."

"Why so?" said the other.

"Because," quoth he, "thou wilt be fed with shales. But I'll tell thee one thing: 'twere best for thee quickly to arrest him, lest some other doing it before and there be nothing left to pay thy debt. Hold thy peace, fair words make fools fain, and it is an old saying, 'One bird in hand is worth two in bush.' If thou dost not arrest him presently, I will not give thee two pence for thy ten shillings."

"How shall I come by him?" quoth the other.

"Give me but two pots of ale, and I'll betray him," saith he.

So they being agreed, this smooth-faced Judas comes to his late master and told him that a friend of his at the door would speak with him. The unmistrusting man, thinking no evil, went to the door, where presently an officer arrested him at his man's suit.

The poor man, seeing this, being stricken into a sudden sorrow, in the grief of his heart spoke to this effect: "Ah, thou lewd fellow, art thou the first man that seeks to augment my misery? Have I thus long given thee bread to breed my overthrow? And nourished thee in thy need to work my destruction? Full little did I think when thou so often didst dip thy false fingers in my dish, that I gave food to my chiefest foe. But what booteth complaints in these extremes? Go, wife," quoth he, "unto my neighbors, and see if thou canst get any of them to be my bail."

But in vain was her pains spent. Then he sent her to his kinsfolks, and they denied him; to his brother, and he would not come at him. So that there was no shift, but to prison he must. But as he was going, a messenger met him with a letter from Master Cole, wherein, as you heard, he had promised him two hundred pounds. Which when the poor man read, he greatly rejoiced; and showing the same to the officer, he was content to take his own word.

Whereupon Tom Dove went presently to Reading, where, at his coming, he found all the rest of the clothiers lamenting Cole's untimely death. Where the woeful widow paid him the money, by which deed all the rest of the clothiers were induced to do something for Dove. And, thereupon, one gave him ten pounds, another twenty, another thirty pounds, to begin the world anew; and by this means, together with the blessing of God, he grew into greater credit than ever he was before.

And riches being thus come upon him, his former friends came fawning unto him; and when he had no need of them, then everyone was ready to proffer him kindness. His wicked servants also, that disdained him in his distress, were after glad to come creeping unto him, entreating with cap and knee for his favor and friendship. And albeit he seemed to forgive their trespasses done against him, yet he would often say he would never trust them for a straw. And thus he ever after lived in great wealth and prosperity, doing much good to the poor and, at his death, left to his children great lands.

Chapter 15

*How Fair Margaret Made Her Estate and
High Birth Known to Her Master and Dame;
and for the Entire Love She Bore to Duke
Robert, Made a Vow Never to Marry, But
Became a Nun in the Abbey at Gloucester*

After fair Margaret was come again to Gloucester, never did she behold the clear day but with a weeping eye; and so great was the sorrow which she conceived for the loss of Duke Robert, her faithful lover, that she utterly despised all the pleasures of this life and at last bewrayed herself in this sort unto her dame:

"Oh, my good master and dame, too long have I dissembled my parentage from you; whom the froward destinies do pursue to deserved punishment. The woeful daughter am I of the unhappy Earl of Shrewsbury, who ever since his banishment have done nothing but drawn mischance after me; wherefore let me entreat you, dear master and dame, to have your good wills to spend the remnant of my life in some blessed monastery."

When Gray and his wife heard this, they wondered greatly, as well at her birth as at her strange demand. Whereupon her dame knew not how to call her, whether maiden or madam, but said, "Oh, good Lord, are you a lady and I knew it not? I am sorry that I knew it not before."

But when the folks of the house heard that Margaret was a lady, there was no small alteration. And moreover her dame said that she had thought to have had a match between her and her son, and by many persuasions did seek to withdraw her from being a nun, saying in this manner: "What, Margaret, thou art young and fair; the world, no doubt, hath better fortune for thee, whereby thou mayst leave an honorable issue behind thee, in whom thou mayst live after death."

These and many other reasons did they allege unto her, but all in vain, she making this reply: "Who knoweth not that this world giveth the pleasure of an hour but the sorrow of many days? For it payeth ever that which it promiseth, which is nothing else but continual trouble and vexation of the mind. Do you think, if I had the offer and choice of the mightiest princes of Christendom, that I could match myself better than to my Lord Jesus? No, no, he is my husband, to whom I yield myself both body and soul, giving to him my heart, my love, and most firm affection. I have overlong loved this vile world; therefore I beseech you further dissuade me not."

When her friends by no means could alter her opinion, the matter was made known to his majesty, who, against the time that she should be received into the monastery, came to Gloucester with most part of his nobility to honor her action with his princely presence.

All things being therefore prepared, the young lady was in most princely wise attired in a gown of pure white satin, her kirtle of the same, embroidered with gold about the skirts in most curious sort. Her head was garnished with gold, pearls, and precious stones, having her hair like threads of burnished gold hanging down behind her, in manner of a princely bride. About her ivory neck jewels of inestimable price were hung, and her handwrists[55] were compassed about with bracelets of bright shining diamonds.

[55]*handwrists:* wrists.

The streets, through the which she should pass, were pleasantly decked with green oaken boughs. Then came the young lady, most like an heavenly angel, out of her master's house. At what time all the bells in Gloucester were solemnly rung, she being led betwixt the king's majesty, having on his royal robes and imperial crown, and the chief bishop, wearing his miter in a cope of cloth of gold; over her head a canopy of white silk, fringed about in princely manner. Before her went an hundred priests singing, and after her all the chief ladies of the land; then all the wives and maidens of Gloucester followed, with an innumerable sort of people on every side standing to behold her. In this sort she passed on to the cathedral church, where she was brought to the nunnery gate.

The lady abbess received her. Where the beautiful maiden, kneeling down, made her prayer in sight of all the people. Then with her own hands she undid her virgin's fair gown and took it off and gave it away to the poor; after that, her kirtle, then her jewels, bracelets, and rings, saying, "Farewell, the pride and vanity of this world." The ornaments of her head were the next she gave away; and then was she led on one side, where she was stripped and, instead of her smock of soft silk, had a smock of rough hair put upon her.

Then came one with a pair of shears and cut off her golden-colored locks, and with dust and ashes all bestrewed her head and face. Which being done, she was brought again into the people's sight, barefoot and barelegged. To whom she said, "Now, farewell, the world; farewell, the pleasures of this life. Farewell, my lord the king, and to the duke's sweet love, farewell. Now shall my eyes weep for my former transgressions, and no more shall my tongue talk of vanity. Farewell, my good master and dame, and farewell, all good people."

With which words she was taken away and never after seen abroad. When Duke Robert heard thereof, he desired that at his death his body might be buried in Gloucester. "In that town," quoth he, "where first my clear eyes beheld the heavenly beauty of my love and where for my sake she forsook the world." Which was performed accordingly.

The king also at his death requested to be buried at Reading, for the great love he bore to that place, amongst those clothiers, who, living, were his heart's comfort. Gray, dying wondrous wealthy, gave land to the monastery whereinto Margaret was taken. William Fitz-allen also died a most rich man, having built many houses for the poor, whose son Henry after was the first mayor that ever was in London.

Sutton of Salisbury did also at his death much good and gave an hundred pounds to be yearly lent to poor weavers of the town, to the world's end. Simon of Southampton gave a most bounteous gift towards the building of a monastery at Winchester. Hodgekins of Halifax did also great good, and so did Cutbert of Kendal, who had married twenty-three couples out of his own house, giving each of them ten pounds to begin the world withal. Martin Byram of Manchester gave toward the building of a free school in Manchester a great mass of money.

And thus, gentle reader, have I finished my story of these worthy men, desiring thee to take my pains in good part. Which will encourage me to greater matters, perceiving this courteously accepted.

Finis

Textual Notes[1]

THE SACKFUL OF NEWS

In 1939 F. P. Wilson wrote that *The Sackful of News* "was entered in the Stationers' Register in 1557/8 and often later; we know that it remained alive, because it is repeatedly referred to in Elizabethan literature; yet the earliest copy which can now be traced is dated 1673" (*HLQ*, II, 121). We can say little more now. The 1673 edition (Wing S223) is still the earliest extant. I have used the Huntington Library copy of it as copytext for the present edition; the only other extant copy, owned by the British Museum, I did not see.

We may presume, with Wilson, that *Sackful* was published several times before 1673, the first time probably in 1558. A good guess is that *Sackful*, like Deloney's four works of prose fiction, was so popular that all the early editions simply were read out of existence—sold out and passed around from one reader to another until copies that normally would have come down to us fell apart and then were thrown away.

The only modern edition is that of W. Carew Hazlitt in *Shakespeare Jest-Books*. Hazlitt omitted tales 20 and 21 as "too gross for publication." In the remaining tales he suggested no textual emendations; nor are any suggested in the present edition. Except for the normalizing and modernizing described in the introduction, the intent has been to copy the 1673 edition exactly. Whether the tales, as printed in 1673, are exactly as they were in 1558, no one can say; but judging from the "internal evidence," there is no reason to suspect drastic changes: *Sackful* has a certain integrity, especially in the narrator's consistently calm and generous attitude toward non-Londoners. George Gascoigne's *A Hundred Sundry Flowers* (1573; STC 11635) is cor-

---

[1] I have seen almost all the copies of the early editions that are referred to in the following notes as owned by the Folger Shakespeare Library. Copies owned by other libraries I have not seen firsthand; instead, I used photostatic reproductions of substantive editions and microfilm reproductions of derivative editions. Recent information regarding early editions I have obtained from the late Professor William A. Jackson and Miss Katharine F. Pantzer, revisers of the *Short-Title Catalogue*.

THE ADVENTURES OF MASTER F. J.

rectly described in the card catalogue of the Folger Library as a quarto in two parts, each part having its own colophon. The first part includes *The Supposes* and *Jocasta; The Adventures of Master F. J.* is the first work in the second part.

I have used as copytext the first of four copies of the 1573 edition owned by the Folger Library.[2] It has been collated with the second edition of 1575 (the first of two Folger copies), with the third edition of 1587 (the Huntington Library copy), and with C. T. Prouty's modern edition of 1942, which is now, unhappily, out of print. The relation between the first two editions will be discussed below. The compositor of the third edition followed the second edition rather closely; collation shows that he did not see the first edition.

Usually the modern editor feels obliged to accept revisions that clearly have been made by the author himself. Since there is no doubt that Gascoigne is responsible for the major changes in the second edition of 1575, several modern editors—W. Carew Hazlitt in his edition of 1869, John W. Cunliffe in 1907, and Robert Ashley and Edwin M. Moseley in 1953—have used the second edition as their copytext. Yet there may be legitimate reasons for using the first edition, as I have done (and Prouty already had done in 1942), as copytext. One reason is that the second edition was not actually "revised"—in the way, for example, *Euphues* was revised—a word changed here, a sentence or paragraph omitted or added there. *Master F. J.* was rewritten; what we have, in effect, are two versions of the same story. The editor must choose one version or the other; there is, I think, no way of incorporating all the changes made in the second edition into the text of the first edition.

Furthermore, in so far as we can reconstruct what happened, the 1575 edition may not have been a rewriting for a literary purpose; it may have been an elaborate expurgation that Gascoigne made after he had been accused of slandering living persons through the characters in the first edition of *Master F. J.* Whatever the reasons were, Gascoigne eliminated the prefaces by A. B., H. W., and G. T.; changed the names of the characters

[2]Copy 3 lacks *Master F. J.;* in copies 1, 2, and 4 I did not see any differences that would indicate corrections in press. The four Folger copies are among more than a dozen extant copies of the first edition scattered over England, Scotland, and the United States. I have seen reproductions of the Harvard and Huntington copies; in the passages that contain the expressions I have listed in the substantive emendations there were no corrections in press. Prouty based his text on the copy owned by Emmanuel College, Cambridge; I see no differences between his text and the Folger copies that would indicate press corrections in the Emmanuel copy.

and places; pretended that a fictitious "Bartello" was the author; and eliminated G. T. as the narrator. Thus Gascoigne radically changed, and in my judgment ruined, his original story.

For these reasons I have used the first edition as copytext, though I have accepted several emendations from the second edition and one from the third. As the following list will show, three of Prouty's emendations have been accepted; I myself have contributed only one.

Substantive Emendations

PAGE	LINE	
40	28	abilities] Prouty; ability 73; *passage om. in* 75, 87
44	22	her hand] his hand 73–87
50	41	pocket] 75, 87; packet 73
51	31	I] 75, 87; *om.* 73
55	32	pleased] 75, 87; please 73
56	5	retire] 75, 87; reitre 73
58	19	folded] 75, 87; unfolded 73
65	38	to gaze] Prouty; to gare 73–87
74	9	inexprimable] 75, 87; inexprivable 73
79	28	received] 75, 87; conceived 73
	38	being] 75, 87; bying 73
88	17	bounds] 87; bonds 73, 75
94	21	as it] 75, 87; at is 73
102	10	imparted] 75, 87; emported 73
103	27	had ever passed] 75, 87; passed 73
106	22	wot] Prouty; wrot 73; woot 75, 87

EUPHUES: THE ANATOMY OF WIT

As explained in footnote 21, the first edition of *Euphues* (STC 17051) probably came out in December, 1578, and the second edition (STC 17052) six months later in June, 1579. The third edition (STC 17053) probably appeared in December, 1579. Before deciding which of these early editions to use as copytext, I considered the reasons R. Warwick Bond gave (I, 98) in 1902 for choosing the first edition: (1) "Arber [has] already given us a most faithful reprint of the third edition, which differs only very slightly from the second"; (2) "there attaches . . . such supreme interest to the first edition of a work so famous as *Euphues* as overrides all other considerations"; and (3) the second edition, "though it has the augmentations, introduces as many errors as it corrects."

Since the third edition derives from the second and probably contains no revisions by the author, there can be no good reason for using it as copytext. In 1868 Edward Arber never dreamed that the edition he used was the third; he thought it was the first.

An "*editio princeps*" tended to elicit from both Arber and Bond a book collector's response. From a strictly editorial point of view, a first edition is still extremely "valuable," though not for the same reasons that it is to a book collector. It is valuable because it is substantive—in this case because it is based on a completed manuscript that Lyly must have handed the bookseller, Gabriel Cawood, sometime before 2 December 1578, when Cawood had it entered in the Stationers' Register (Arber, II, 342). But the second edition is also substantative because—in Bond's judgment as well as mine—it was revised by the author. All the other early editions derive from the first or second.

Bond's judgment that the second edition "introduces as many errors as it corrects" is misleading. The second edition is not careless. It may have its share of turned letters (and other obvious errors that I correct silently); but the short list of substantive emendations, below, reflects my judgment that it is unusually accurate. But the real importance of the second edition has to do with the "augmentations"—the insertion of passages, some of only a sentence, but one of them almost two pages long. There are no less than thirteen such additions in the narrative part of *Euphues*, the part that I have selected for the present volume (and roughly the first half of *Euphues: The Anatomy of Wit* as a whole). My footnotes to the text indicate where these passages were added. That they "bear the stamp of the author's hand," as Bond put it, there can be little doubt. As I have tried to suggest in footnotes 11 and 12, Lyly's revision goes beyond the adding of these thirteen passages; many of the changes may seem insignificant to us, but to Lyly the smallest details were important.

The question, then, in choosing a copytext, is not whether the author revised the second edition, but how the editor is to go about incorporating the revisions. Fundamentally, it is a matter of balancing one difficulty against another. If the editor uses the second edition as copytext, he automatically has the author's revisions; but he must separate out the compositor's mistakes. On the other hand, if he uses the first edition, he automatically gets rid of the compositor's mistakes in the second edition; but he risks missing some of the author's revisions. In the final analysis, I decided that the second difficulty was greater than the first. It seemed to me that the author's revisions are both subtle and extensive. Rather than run the danger of missing some of them, I decided to use the second edition as copytext. Doubtless I have paid the penalty of not catching all the compositor's mistakes, though constant reference to Bond's edition, which is based on the first edition, should have provided a certain amount of protection in that regard.

Except for the fourth and sixth editions,[3] I compared, line by line, the

[3]Although I have not seen the fourth and sixth editions, Bond saw them— and I have used his edition. Fortunately, I was able to return the favor; I collated the editions of 1585 and 1587, both inaccessible to Bond. What I found was that the 1585 edition followed that of 1581 and 1587 followed 1585; there is no evidence of authorial revision, but I have accepted two rather obvious corrections from the 1585 edition.

first thirteen editions—the ones printed for Gabriel Cawood between 1578 and about 1597. In my notes, "1580" or "80" refers to the Folger copy of the fifth edition, and not to the fourth edition (also printed in 1580), the unique copy of which is owned by Robert H. Taylor; "1581" or "81" refers to the Harvard copy of the seventh edition, not to the sixth edition (also printed in 1581), the unique copy of which is owned by the British Museum.

There is no space here to record all my collation notes, but the relation of the editions to each other may be summarized briefly. A great deal of new material and a substantial number of emendations appeared in the second edition, probably printed in June, 1579 (the unique copy of which is owned by the Trinity College Library, Cambridge University). The third edition (for which I used the Bodleian copy) probably was printed in December, 1579, and followed the second edition for the most part, though in one or two instances the compositor may have had access to the first edition of 1578 (for which I used the British Museum copy; I did not see the only other extant copy owned by Trinity College, Cambridge). I did not collate the fourth edition. The fifth edition (1580) probably followed the fourth or the third, though there are two passages that seem to have been printed from the 1578 edition. I have not seen the sixth edition. The seventh (1581) probably followed the sixth or fifth. The eighth (1585: the Huntington copy) followed the seventh. The ninth (1587: the Folger copy) followed the eighth. The tenth (1590?: the Folger copy) followed the ninth, though at least in one instance the compositor glanced at an earlier edition, probably that of 1585. The eleventh (1592: the Newberry copy) followed the tenth very closely, even in obvious mistakes. The twelfth (1593?: the Folger copy) also followed the tenth, while occasionally going all the way back to the first. The thirteenth (1597? the Folger copy) used both the twelfth and the tenth.

Substantive Emendations

(In the following list, "79¹" refers to the second edition and "79²" to the third edition; "79," without a raised numeral, indicates that the two 1579 editions are in agreement.)

Page	Line	
123	12	six months] three months 78–97 *(see footnote 21)*
132	32	thy heart] 85–97; heart 78–81
138	30	they cry] 78, 79²; the cry 79¹
148	17	thus abruptly] 85–97; this abruptly 78–81
	33	whose courteous] 78, 80–97; most courteous 79
149	4–5	thy countryman] 78, 79²; the countryman 79¹
153	1	chained] 78; changed 79
159	10	Philautus] Bond; Euphues 78–97
174	6	parson's] 78; person's 79

OF APOLONIUS AND SILLA

Farewell to the Military Profession (1581; STC 20996), by Barnaby Rich, is a quarto that includes three dedications by Rich, two introductory poems commending the author, a poem by the printer addressed to the reader, eight *novelle*, and "The Conclusion." "Of Apolonius and Silla" is the second of the eight *novelle*.

For "Apolonius" I have used as my copytext the first edition of 1581, the unique copy of which is owned by the Bodleian Library. It has been collated with the second edition of 1583 (two unique fragments owned by the Folger Library), with the third edition of 1594 (the unique copy in the Folger Library), and with the fourth edition of 1606 (the Folger copy). The second edition follows the first rather closely. The third follows the second—though, unhappily, not in accidentals (many commas in the second edition have been omitted, and a good many commas and colons have been substituted for periods and question marks). In the early part of "Apolonius" the fourth edition follows the third very closely; later it follows the first edition (but never the second).

Thomas M. Cranfill's introduction and notes were very helpful in a number of ways, but since his text is a facsimile edition, I did not collate the 1581 edition with it. Cranfill's suggestion (p. lxxiv) that Rich himself was the "discreet reviser" of the fourth edition may be correct, though Rich seems to have done little, if any, revising of the prefatory matter or of the second *novella*, "Of Apolonius and Silla." One could argue that "the Scots by custom" (mentioned in footnote 33) was removed by the author. But after the Scotsman James I succeeded Elizabeth in 1603, one suspects that there was a marked decrease in slighting references to Scotsmen and that printers and typesetters occasionally took their red pencils in hand, without so much as a sir-reverence to authors.

Substantive Emendations

PAGE	LINE	
195	28	tale] 83–06; tall 81
196	24	sped] 94, 06; speed 81, 83
199	28	of office] 83–06; to office 81
216	34	Silvio] 83, 94; Salvano 81, 06
217	11	whom she] 83, 94; whom he 81, 06

PANDOSTO

Since Robert Greene died in 1592, no edition after that date contains revisions by the author. The only question is whether the second edition, printed in the year of his death, contains any such revisions. Collation shows that it does not. I have therefore used as copytext the first edition (the unique British Museum copy) of 1588 (STC 12285), in which, however, sig. B is missing. For sig. B, I used as copytext the unique Folger copy of the 1592 edition. Except for sig. B, only the 1588 edition is substantive; the next seven editions derive from it.

In the following description of the relationships of the early editions, the copy referred to in parentheses in each case happens to be the only extant copy. The 1592 edition (Folger) follows the 1588 (British Museum) closely—not line by line, but so literally as to copy a number of obvious mistakes; the third edition of 1595 (Huntington) follows the second closely, frequently line by line; the fourth edition of 1607 (Bodleian) follows the third, often line by line, though it introduces a number of single-word emendations; the fifth edition of 1609 (Folger) follows the fourth, though occasionally it has access to an earlier edition, probably that of 1595; the sixth edition of 1614 (British Museum) follows the fifth; and the seventh edition of 1619 (Huntington) also follows the fifth; the eighth edition of 1629 (Bodleian) follows the seventh, though very carelessly.

The fourth edition of 1607 and the fifth edition of 1609 were set by alert compositors. Their emendations, however, are not usually so valuable in correcting the text as they are in indicating how the meanings of words changed between 1588 and 1607–09. I have accepted four emendations from the 1607 edition, but one of them is dubious: if Greene actually wrote "not only . . . and," the emendation "not only . . . but" is an illegitimate substantive emendation.

I have collated only one modern edition of *Pandosto*, that by James Winny (1957); but I have consulted the editions by J. Payne Collier (1843), W. Carew Hazlitt (1875), and Alexander B. Grosart (1881–83).

Substantive Emendations

PAGE	LINE	
239	28	treachery of] 95–09; treachery 92; *this section lacking in 88*
240	21	low for fortune. Thou] Collier; low. For fortune, thou 92–09; *lacking in 88*
252	13–14	not only . . . but] 07, 09; not only . . . and 88–95
254	13	of other] 07, 09; at other 88–95
258	21–22	Which sudden] 07, 09; With sudden 88–95
261	2	that] 07, 09; then 88–95

ROSALIND

Although Thomas Lodge lived until 1625, he probably was not responsible for any of the changes one notes in comparing the first six editions. In my judgment the first edition of 1590 (STC 16664) is the only authoritative edition; the others derive from it. There are two extant copies of the first edition. I used as copytext the perfect copy owned by the Carl H. Pforzheimer Library. The Folger copy lacks sig. R; but, unlike the Pforzheimer copy, it was corrected in press. All substantive corrections from the Folger copy have been accepted in the present edition.

There are a number of changes in the second edition of 1592 (the British Museum copy), but it is doubtful whether the author made any of them. "Thy" has been changed inconsistently to "your'"; there are a number of whimsically synonymous substitutions, like "exceed" for "surpass," and a few omissions of word or phrase, sometimes fatal to the sense. But as the list of emendations, below, will indicate, the 1592 edition contributes a few corrections of the 1590 edition; and, most importantly, it adds a "Schedule" after the prefatory material (see footnote 11).

The 1592 edition follows an uncorrected copy of the 1590 edition. The third edition of 1596 (Huntington copy) follows the second edition; the fourth edition of 1598 (Huntington copy) follows the third; the fifth edition of 1604 (Huntington copy) follows the fourth; and the sixth edition of 1609 (Folger copy) follows the fifth, though in a few instances it seems to have access to the second edition of 1592.

I have also collated W. W. Greg's edition of 1907, obtaining from it one valuable emendation and a number of helpful suggestions for the footnotes; unfortunately, Greg used as his copytext the Hunterian Club edition of 1878, in which there were several copying errors, such as "cutting" for "entering" (sig. I2 of the first edition) and "hart" for "part" (sig. L3ᵛ).

Substantive Emendations

(In the following list, "F" stands for "Folger" and "Pf" for "Pforzheimer"; "90," without the "F" or "Pf," means that the two copies of the 1590 edition are in agreement.)

PAGE	LINE	
292	33	sons] 92; son 90
	39	sons] 92; son 90
295	35	hast thou] 98; thou hast 90–96
317	21	you are of] 04; you of 90–98
338	8	Rosader] 04; Ganymede 90–98
339	26	their excuse] 92; there excuse 90
342	2	sighed] 96; sight 90, 92
343	15	am I] Greg; and I 90–09
349	15	thou be] 92; thou 90
350	18	lying] 92; lie 90
359	17–18	their cates] 96; there cates 90, 92
361	12	and disdain] 96; at disdain 90, 92
367	20	full of] 90F, 92; full 90Pf
368	17	you] 96; youth 90, 92

A NOTABLE DISCOVERY OF COZENAGE

The earliest entry of *A Notable Discovery of Cozenage* in the Stationers' Register was 13 December 1591 (Arber, II, 600), when *The Second Part of Cony-Catching* was also entered. *A Notable Discovery* had already been published and was being reissued along with *The Second Part,* which probably was written to take advantage of a popular demand. It seems fairly clear now that there were at least three separate editions of *A Notable Discovery* in 1591 and a fourth edition in 1592.

Alexander B. Grosart in 1881, G. B. Harrison in 1923, and A. V. Judges in 1930 thought they were using "the first edition of 1591" as copytext. But they all used what in all probability was the third edition. The Bodleian Library and the Huntington Library now possess unique copies of earlier editions; the Bodleian is the earliest now extant, presumably the first edition, while the Huntington copy is the next earliest, presumably the second. That apparently relegates the British Museum copy used by Grosart, Harrison, and Judges to being the unique copy of the third edition.

The second edition follows the first rather closely, especially toward the beginning; it follows the first edition in a few obvious errors. But it also corrects a few errors, all of them rather obvious except one—the change of "brawling" in the first edition to "broking," which may indicate a revision by Greene himself, or perhaps only a return to the manuscript. The third edition follows the second fairly closely except for a tendency to omit words not necessary to the general sense; "a pint of wine" in the first and second editions becomes "the wine," and "gentle fool" becomes "fool." The fourth edition (usually following the third edition, though toward the end it seems to have access to the second) makes a number of changes; most of them are insignificant ("stoppeth" to "stop"), but a few are "improvements" in grammar, idiom, or clarity.

There is a possibility that Greene had a hand in some of these emendations. Although in my judgment he probably did not, I have given in the footnotes the most significant changes made in the second through the fourth editions.

I used the first edition as copytext; but since there is one leaf missing at the end (as explained in note 94), I have used the second edition as copy-text for the missing part.

Substantive Emendations

(In the following list, 91¹ refers to the first edition, 91² to the second, and 91³ to the third, all published in 1591; "91," without the raised numeral, means that all three editions are in agreement.)

PAGE	LINE	
400	6	Aristippus] 91², 91³, 92; Chrisippus 91¹
401	15	two. So their] 91², 91³, 92; two their 91¹
	28	that] 91², 91³, 92; *om.* 91¹
402	8	side] 91², 91³, 92; *om.* 91¹
403	6–7	carry you . . . with him] 91², 91³ 92; carry him . . . with them 91¹
404	21	broking] 91², 91³, 92; brawling 91¹
	23	pickpocket] pickpockets 91, 92
407	19	*nisi*] 91³, 92; *mihi* 91¹, 91²
413	23	they are] he is 91, 92
414	21	but] 92; *om.* 91
	21–22	because they] 91², 91³, 92; because he 91¹
416	26	travel] 92; travail 91
420	11	be spoken] 91², 91³, 92; spoken 91¹

THE UNFORTUNATE TRAVELER

Thomas Nashe's *The Unfortunate Traveler* was entered in the Stationers' Register by J. Wolf on 17 September 1593 (Arber, II, 636), and then in 1594 there were two separate editions of it (STC 18380 and 18381).[4] Surprisingly enough, there were no other early editions.

For the reasons that McKerrow gives in his edition of Nashe (II, 192–193), the second edition probably was set from the first and not from manuscript. We may be sure that some of the alterations introduced in the second edition were not made by Nashe. The difficulty lies in determining whether he was involved in any of the alterations—and, if so, how and to what extent. In seeking answers to these questions I have compared the two editions; the main differences seem to fall into five separate categories.

[4]For the first edition I used the copy owned by the Huntington Library (hereafter referred to as "HN"). I did not collate the British Museum copy of the first edition; but McKerrow collated it, and I have collated his edition. Like McKerrow, I used the Bodleian copy of the second edition (hereafter referred to as "O") and did not see the other three extant copies at the British Museum, Christ Church, and Corpus Christi College.

1. The second edition contains two short passages that were omitted in the first edition—"carousing a whole health to the duke's arms" (McKerrow, II, 247, lines 21–22) and "The name of the place I remember not, but it is as one goes to St. Paul's Church, not far from the iemmes Piazza" (McKerrow, II, 280, lines 18–20). My footnotes 112 and 165 pinpoint these additions in the present volume. McKerrow may be right that the passages were added by Nashe; they were, he says, "more likely to have been inserted by the author than by any one else" (II, 196). Nashe was more likely than the compositor, who, one hopes, would never have taken such liberties with the author's manuscript. But there is the possibility of an intermediate person, connected with the printing house, a person whom today we would call an editor. McKerrow's judgments (IV, 273) that the first insertion ("carousing a whole health," etc.) is necessary to the sense and that it constitutes "almost certain proof of revision by the author" are both open to question. As to the authorship, McKerrow apparently meant that the passage did not originally make sense and that only the author could have made sense of it by supplying the correct insertion. But the original passage makes sense; the insertion, if I understand it, leaves the old sense and adds a new one. The second insertion ("The name of the place," etc.) is an aside, contributing nothing to the sense but adding a little something to the casual and yet seemingly knowledgeable tone of the context. It is in Jack's off-hand manner. Even the obscurity of it, rising possibly from Nashe's ignorance of Rome, may argue for, at least as well as it argues against, Nashe's authorship.

2. As McKerrow notes (II, 192), three complete sentences, each about one line in length, appear in HN but are omitted in O. I agree that these omissions are inadvertent errors on the part of the compositor of the second edition.

3. There are, however, a number of other omissions in O that seem to be deliberate: "humble-spirited" is omitted in the expression "too few such humble-spirited noblemen" (McKerrow, II, 212, line 6); "to heaven" in "mine host and I should part to heaven" (214.10; *p. 449*);[5] and "simple" in "his former simple request" (216.29; *p. 451*). McKerrow (II, 194) interprets these omissions as attempts on Nashe's part to make his style more concise. But it is difficult to believe that Nashe could have done anything so futile. His style is naturally full and emphatic, and there are literally dozens of such passages left unrevised in O. Surely the author, of all people, would have been aware of the magnitude of the task before ever undertaking it. In any case, the person responsible for the omissions did not follow through; we are left with Nashe's style comparatively untouched by this particular kind of revision.

4. Offsetting these omissions is a contrary tendency to add a word or phrase. In the following examples the expression added in O appears in

[5]"214.10" is a reference to McKerrow, II, 214, line 10; "*p. 449*," in italics. is a page reference to the present edition.

brackets: "which [God knows] they had not" (246.28; *p. 479*); "came [hastily] bustling down the stairs" (304.7; *p. 527*). One could argue that some of the additions, through unnecessary to the sense, contribute precision: "your honor's [poor] suppliant" (215.33; *p. 451*); "my [silly] jailer" (263.33; *p. 494*); "pitched or [rather] set up his rest" (234.3; *p. 468*).

5. Finally, there are many changes, by far the most numerous kind, that may be described as merely whimsical: "in no wise" in O for "not" in HN; "the calf of the leg" for "the calf of my leg"; "further" for "farther"; "murther" for "murder"; "these" for "those"; "this" for "that"; "fall in" for "fall out"; "with a trice" for "in a trice"; "tale tellers" for "telltales." It would seem that whoever made these changes in O was amusing himself with what he regarded as verbal equivalents for expressions in HN; but in the last two examples—which may be found on 224.25 (*p. 458*) and 215.28 (*p. 450*)—he spoils perfectly idiomatic expressions.

One is impressed by the insignificance, the pettiness even, of many of the changes in the second edition. It is of course possible that Nashe idled away a few hours at such petty revisions, but it does not seem very likely. The likeliest, it seems to me, are the additions in 4; the next likeliest are the insertions in 1. But it seems to me highly doubtful that Nashe had anything to do with the changes in 2, 3, and 5. He had great facility; a rewriting of whole pages or sections would have been more in his vein than any of the changes one actually finds in O.

After making the above analysis of the two early editions, I decided to use the first edition as my copytext and then take up the alterations in the second edition one by one as I came to them. In the list below, 19 emendations are from the second edition; Nashe may have been responsible for the one mentioned in note 46, but the others probably were made by the compositor. Of the remaining emendations, two are from Grosart, four from McKerrow (who used the second edition as his copytext), and two from Ashley and Moseley. I contributed four emendations and, for the convenience of teachers and students, divided the text into eight sections. The result is a "conservative," as opposed to an "eclectic," text.

Substantive Emendations

(The 18 corrections listed on the *errata* page (sig. A3) of the first edition have been accepted in the text and of course are not included in the following list.)

PAGE	LINE	
445	6	palatine] O; palaine HN
449	6–7	the pissing] pissing HN, O
451	22–23	his highness] O; highness HN
455	19	likely] lightly HN, O
456	34	begged] O; bedgd HN
	39	three] O; ten HN

PAGE	LINE	
460	10	their clean] O; they clean HN
461	25	angle] McKerrow (IV, 264); ankle HN, O
478	16	procuring] O; precuring HN
484	6	bitch] O; hitch HN
490	12	named), I,] named I) HN, O
495	7	a poinard] O; poinard HN
	18	heard] O; hard HN
496	28	his days] O; days HN
501	28	inbent] O; imbent HN
502	32	wandering] Ashley and Moseley; wondering HN, O
503	5	harnessed] O; harnished HN
	6	gilt ... gilt] guilt ... guilt HN; guilt ... gilt O
505	31	gold] O; God HN
508	14	the monstrost] McKerrow (IV, 283); the monstrous HN, O
510	17	it out] Grosart; out it HN, O
516	29	fellows who] McKerrow (IV, 286); fellows HN, O
518	4	till it] O; till HN
521	13	lighted] O; light HN
	30	Travel ... travail] Ashley and Moseley; Travail ... travail HN, O
523	16	it is] Grosart; is HN; is it O
	27	*Quasque*] O; *Quasq* HN
525	7	misers] O; misons HN
531	27	from drinking] McKerrow; for drinking HN, O
543	5	when I] O; when he HN
546	24	forgive] O; forgive it HN

THOMAS OF READING

The earliest entry in the Stationers' Register for *Thomas of Reading* is 19 April 1602 (Arber, III, 204). But we may never know whether an edition was published that year or what edition it was. All we know, with reasonable certainty, is that Deloney died in 1600 and that the earliest extant edition of *Thomas* was published in 1612 (STC 6569). There seems to be no reason to doubt the statement on the title page that it is the fourth edition. The first edition probably appeared before 1600, the second in 1602 (sometime after 19 April), and the third between 1602 and 1612. Other extant editions appeared in 1623, 1632, and 1636. For my edition of Deloney in 1961, I collated these three editions with the 1612 edition; needless to say, I have not done all that work again. I did, however, check every word of the 1961 text with the 1612 copytext, with the result that two errors turned up in the 1961 text: "I well" on page 283, line 28, should be changed to "I will"; and "faith" on page 297, line 1, should be changed to "saith."

Of the two extant copies of the 1612 edition, the British Museum copy was corrected in press; when substantive, these corrections have been accepted in the text. I used the Huntington copy as copytext.

Collation shows that the four early editions have, for the most part, a falling domino relationship with each other: the 1623 edition probably was set from a corrected copy of the 1612 edition, 1632 from 1623, and 1636 from 1632. Most of the substantive emendations listed below are "23–36"; once the 1623 edition made a change, the 1632 and 1636 editions tended to follow it, though the 1636 edition made nine independent emendations of a substantive nature that I have accepted. F. O. Mann in his 1912 edition made four emendations that I have accepted; I have made two.

The 1612 edition is casual with regard to making such expressions as "good wife" and "goodwife" interchangeable. Other examples are "good man" and "goodman," "country man" and "countryman." In each case I have tried to make a distinction, making the expression one word or two according to the sense. Incidentally, the problem arises in part because of Deloney's interest in double meanings. See note 14.

If the *Thomas of Reading* text is more eclectic than any of the others in this volume, the reason is that the copytext is the fourth edition—not the first or second, as is usually the case—and the fourth edition was somewhat carelessly printed. Usually I would not have accepted the 1632 emendation "His wife never after married" for "His wife after never married" in the 1612 edition. It is not the editor's business to be an accomplice in improving the author's grammar or idiom. But although the 1612 edition is all we have as a substantive text, it is careless enough for us to suspect that some of the awkward expressions are not Deloney's. There is always the possibility that the 1623, the 1632, or the 1636 compositor had access to one of the three editions earlier than 1612. But the nature of the corrections in the three later editions would seem to indicate simply (and commendably) an attentiveness to the story and common sense.

Substantive Emendations

Page	Line	
559	22	be so] 23–36; so be 12
	25	too much] 23–26; two much 12
562	2	good but God] 23–36; good but good 12
563	12	look to] 36; look for 12–32
564	24	to blame] 32; too blame 12, 23, 36
571	18	do take] 23–36; to take 12
572	21	made] Mann; make 12–36
574	13	to be] 23–36; be to 12
576	22	to you] 23–36; o you 12
577	27	makes] make 12–36
578	5	look for] look 12–36
579	30	Simon's] Mann; Sutton's 12–36

|

A Select Bibliography

GENERAL[1]

Arber, Edward. *A Transcript of the Registers of the Company of Stationers of London, 1554–1640.* London: [publisher not given] 1875–77.

Ashley, Robert, and Edwin M. Moseley, eds. *Elizabethan Fiction.* New York: Holt, Rinehart and Winston, 1953.

Baker, Ernest A. *The History of the English Novel,* vols. I and II. London: Witherby, 1924 and 1929.

Booth, Wayne C. *The Rhetoric of Fiction.* Chicago: Univ. of Chicago Press, 1961.

Dunlop, John Colin. *History of Prose Fiction,* vol. II. London: Bell, 1888.

Frye, Northrop. *Anatomy of Criticism: Four Essays.* Princeton, N.J.: Princeton Univ. Press, 1957.

Hugo, Howard E. *Aspects of Fiction: A Handbook.* Boston: Little, Brown, 1962.

Judges, A. V., ed. *The Elizabethan Underworld: A Collection of Tudor and Early Stuart Tracts and Balladry . . . .* London: Routledge, 1930.

Miller, Edwin H. *The Professional Writer in Elizabethan England.* Cambridge, Mass.: Harvard Univ. Press, 1959.

Mish, Charles C. *English Prose Fiction, 1600–1700: A Chronological Checklist.* Charlottesville, Va.: Bibliographical Society of the Univ. of Virginia, 1952.

O'Dell, Sterg. *A Chronological Checklist of Prose Fiction in English, Printed in England and Other Countries, 1475–1640.* Cambridge, Mass.: The Technology Press of M. I. T., 1954.

Pollard, A. W., and G. R. Redgrave. *Short-Title Catalogue . . . 1475–1640.* London: Bibliographical Society, 1926.

Raleigh, Sir Walter, *et al. Shakespeare's England: An Account of the Life and Manners of His Age.* 2 vols. Oxford: Clarendon Press, 1916.

Schlauch, Margaret. *Antecedents of the English Novel, 1400–1600 (from Chaucer to Deloney).* Warsaw: PWN, Polish Scientific Publishers; London: Oxford Univ. Press, 1963.

---

[1]A few works not especially relevant to a study of prose fiction are included here to permit shortened references to them in the footnotes and textual notes.

Scholes, Robert, ed. *Approaches to the Novel: Materials for a Poetics*. San Francisco: Chandler, 1961.

Tilley, Morris Palmer. *A Dictionary of the Proverbs in England in the Sixteenth and Seventeenth Centuries*. Ann Arbor, Mich.: Univ. of Michigan Press, 1950.

THE JESTBOOK

Hazlitt, W. Carew, ed. *Shakespeare Jest-Books*. 3 vols. London: Willis and Sotheran, 1864.

Schultz, Ernst. *Die englischen Schwankbücher bis herab zu "Dobson's Drie Bobs" (1607)*, in *Palaestra*, CXVII. Berlin: Mayer and Müller, 1912.

Wilson, F. P. "The English Jestbooks of the Sixteenth and Early Seventeenth Centuries." *HLQ*, II (1939), 121–158.

Zall, P. M., ed. *A Hundred Merry Tales and Other English Jestbooks of the Fifteenth and Sixteenth Centuries*. Lincoln, Nebr.: Univ. of Nebraska Press, 1963.

GASCOIGNE

Adams, Robert P. "Gascoigne's 'Master F. J.' as Original Fiction." *PMLA*, LXIII (1958), 315–326.

Bradner, Leicester. "Point of View in George Gascoigne's Fiction." *SSF*, III (1965), 16–22.

Fieler, Frank B. "Gascoigne's Use of Courtly Love Conventions in 'The Adventures Passed by Master F. J.'" *SSF*, I (1963), 26–32.

Prouty, C. T. *George Gascoigne: Elizabethan Courtier, Soldier, and Poet*. New York: Columbia Univ. Press, 1942.

————, ed. *George Gascoigne's A Hundreth Sundrie Flowres*. Vol. XVII, *The University of Missouri Studies*, No. 2, 1942.

LYLY

Barish, Jonas A. "The Prose Style of John Lyly." *ELH*, XXIII (1956), 14–35.

Bond, R. Warwick, ed. *The Complete Works of John Lyly*. 3 vols. Oxford: Clarendon Press, 1902.

Croll, Morris W., and Harry Clemons, eds. *Euphues: The Anatomy of Wit, and Euphues and His England, by John Lyly*. London: Routledge, 1916.

Hunter, G. K. *John Lyly: The Humanist as Courtier*. London: Routledge and Kegan Paul, 1962.

King, Walter N. "John Lyly and Elizabethan Rhetoric." *SP*, LII (1955), 149–161.

Parks, George B. "Before *Euphues*," pp. 475–493 in *Joseph Quincy Adams Memorial Studies*, James G. McManaway, Giles E. Dawson, and Edwin E. Willoughby, eds. Washington, D.C.: The Folger Shakespeare Library, 1948.

Ringler, William, ed., and Walter Allen, Jr., trans. *Oratorio in Laudem Artis Poeticae, by John Rainolds*. Princeton, N.J.: Princeton Univ. Press, 1940.

Turner, Robert Y. "Some Dialogues of Love in Lyly's Comedies." *ELH*, XXIX (1962), 276–288.

RICH

Cranfill, Thomas M., and Dorothy Hart Bruce. *Barnaby Rich: A Short Biography*. Austin, Texas: Univ. of Texas Press, 1953.

Cranfill, Thomas M., ed. *Rich's Farewell to Military Profession (1581)*. Austin, Texas: Univ. of Texas Press, 1959.

Wolf, Melvin H., ed. *Rich's Faultes Faults, and Nothing Else But Faultes (1606)*. Gainesville, Fla.: Scholars' Facsimiles & Reprints, 1965.

GREENE

Ellis-Fermor, Una. "Marlowe and Greene: A Note on Their Relations as Dramatic Artists," pp. 136–149 in *Studies in Honor of T. W. Baldwin*, Don Cameron Allen, ed. Urbana, Ill.: Univ. of Illinois Press, 1958.

Esler, Anthony. "Robert Greene and the Spanish Armada." *ELH*, XXXII (1965), 314–332.

Lawlor, John. "*Pandosto* and the Nature of Dramatic Romance." *PQ*, XLI (1962), 96–113.

Miller, Edwin H. "The Relationship of Robert Greene and Thomas Nashe (1588–1592)." *PQ*, XXXIII (1954), 353–367.

LODGE

Greg, W. W., ed. *Lodge's 'Rosalynde'*. London: Humphrey Milford, 1907. (The appendi, pp. 187–209, is W. G. Stone's "Shakspeare's *As You Like It* and Lodge's *Rosalynde* Compared.")

Mincoff, Marco. "What Shakespeare Did to *Rosalynde*." *SJ*, XCVI (1961), 78–89.

Paradise, N. Burton. *Thomas Lodge*. New Haven, Conn.: Yale Univ. Press, 1931.

Sisson, Charles J., ed. *Thomas Lodge and Other Elizabethans*. Cambridge, Mass.: Harvard Univ. Press, 1933.

NASHE

Bowers, Fredson T. "Thomas Nashe and the Picaresque Novel." *Univ. of Virginia Studies*, I (1941), 12–27.

Croston, A. K. "The Use of Imagery in Nashe's *The Unfortunate Traveller*." *RES*, XXIV (1948), 90–101.

Hibbard, G. R. *Thomas Nashe: A Critical Introduction*. Cambridge, Mass.: Harvard Univ. Press, 1962.

Latham, Agnes M. C. "Satire on Literary Themes and Modes in Nashe's 'The Unfortunate Traveller,'" pp. 85–100 in *English Essays and Studies 1948, Being Volume One of the New Series of Essays and Studies Collected for the English Association by F. P. Wilson*. London: Murray, 1948.

McKerrow, Ronald B., ed. *The Works of Thomas Nashe*. 5 vols. London: Bullen, 1904–1910. Reprinted, Oxford: Blackwell, 1957, with corrections and supplementary notes by F. P. Wilson.

Summersgill, Travis L. "The Influence of the Marprelate Controversy upon the Style of Thomas Nashe." *SP*, XLVIII (1951), 145–160.

DELONEY

Chevalley, Abel. *Thomas Deloney: le roman des métiers au temps de Shakespeare*. Paris: Nouvelle Revue française, 1926.

Hablützel, Margrit Elisabeth. *Die Bildwelt Thomas Deloneys*. Bern: Francke, 1946.

Lange, Alexis F., ed. *The Gentle Craft* [both parts] *by Thomas Deloney*. *Palaestra*, XVIII. Berlin: Mayer and Müller, 1903.

Lawlis, Merritt E. *Apology for the Middle Class: The Dramatic Novels of Thomas Deloney*. Bloomington, Ind.: Indiana Univ. Press, 1960.

———, ed. *The Novels of Thomas Deloney*. Bloomington, Ind.: Indiana Univ. Press, 1961.

Mann, Francis Oscar, ed. *The Works of Thomas Deloney*. Oxford: Clarendon Press, 1912.

Reuter, Ole. "Some Aspects of Thomas Deloney's Prose Style." *Neuphilologische Mitteilungen*, XL (1939), 23–72.

Rollins, Hyder E. "Thomas Deloney's Euphuistic Learning and *The Forest*." *PMLA*, L (1935), 679–686.

Biographical Sketches

DELONEY, THOMAS (d. 1600). When and where he was born and who his parents were we do not know; in fact, we know less about him than any of the other Elizabethan writers of prose fiction. He was living in London by 1586, when a son was born in October and buried in December; according to Nashe, he was a silk weaver. By the standards of such "university wits" as Nashe, Deloney was unlearned; but he knew Latin and probably knew French. His first published work was a translation in 1583 of three letters, all in Latin, between Gebhardt, the Archbishop of Cologne, and Pope Gregory XIII. In the same year a "T. D.," probably Deloney, translated Bonaventure Des Périers' collection of comic *novelle* from French; the English title was *The Mirror of Mirth*. Within the last three or four years of his life Deloney wrote four works of prose fiction—*Jack of Newbury; The Gentle Craft, Part I; The Gentle Craft, Part II;* and *Thomas of Reading,* probably in that order. Chapter VI of *Jack* seems to reflect his own experiences. In 1595 Deloney and a few other freemen were jailed for drawing up a complaint about foreigners immigrating to London and not observing the rules laid down by the Weavers' Company regarding apprenticeship. After petitioning the Lord Chief Justice, the freemen were released from jail. But in the following year Deloney got into trouble again by writing a ballad in which he complained of the scarcity of grain. He seems never to have been apprehended, probably because he was constantly running from the authorities. Beginning in 1592, Deloney was occasionally referred to as the principal writer of ballads in England, succeeding William Elderton, who died in 1592. A number of Deloney's ballads were printed individually as broadside ballads, which in some ways were the Elizabethan equivalent of modern newspapers and reflect Elizabethan interests and attitudes. Two collections of Deloney's ballads were published—*The Garland of Good Will,* existing only in a 1631 edition but probably published as early as 1596, and *Strange Histories,* extant in 1602 but possibly published once earlier. Will Kemp, the comic actor, in *Nine Days' Wonder* (1600) noted that Deloney had recently died and was "honestly buried."

GASCOIGNE, GEORGE (c. 1539-1577). His father was a Catholic, a country squire, a justice of the peace, and a member of parliament representing Bedford; his mother was related to Sir Martin Frobisher, the famous voyager. Gascoigne was a student at Trinity College, Cambridge, though he seems to have been too restless to stay long enough for a degree. Nor did he take a law degree, though he studied at Gray's Inn in 1555 and again later. Somewhere he learned four languages—Latin, French, Italian, and Dutch. A sonnet, published in 1566, was his first venture in print. At about the same time he had both a comedy and a tragedy acted on the stage, probably at Gray's Inn. The comedy, *The Supposes*, was a translation and adaptation in prose of Ariosto's *I Suppositi*. The tragedy, *Jocasta*, written in collaboration with Francis Kinwelmarshe, was in blank verse; it was a translation and adaptation of Lodovico Dolce's *Giocasta*, an Italian version of Euripides' *The Phoenissae*. Between May of 1572 and the autumn of 1574 Gascoigne made at least one trip to Holland, where he took part in the war with Spain; he distinguished himself at the siege of Middleburgh and was captured by the Spanish and held prisoner for four months. In "Dulce Bellum Inexpertis" and *The Spoil of Antwerp* he reported his war adventures. *A Hundred Sundry Flowers*, containing the novel *Master F. J.* and the narrative poem "Dan Bartholomew of Bath," appeared in 1573. But for the 1575 edition *Master F. J.* was rewritten. The reason, according to C. T. Prouty (*Gascoigne*, pp. 193 ff.), is that F. J., the hero of the story, is in reality Gascoigne himself; in recounting a chapter from his own life Gascoigne libels other living persons. According to that theory, the 1575 edition is an attempt to remedy the libelous situation. But to some critics, notably Robert P. Adams, the evidence is not entirely conclusive; Adams doubts that the first edition is autobiographical. Gascoigne's final years were productive. *Certain Notes of Instruction*, a work of criticism, appeared in 1575 with the rewritten *Master F. J.; The Steel Glass*, a satire, was published in 1576; and *The Grief of Joy*, a collection of elegies, Gascoigne presented to Queen Elizabeth in manuscript not long before his death in 1577. All in all, he was poet, playwright, novelist, satirist, linguist, scholar, soldier, and courtier—a good representative, English style, of the "Renaissance man" in the 1560's and 1570's. From time to time critics have claimed for him a good many "firsts": first English novel, first English treatise on prosody, first English comedy written in prose, first (or almost first) true satire in England. Whether these claims are justifiable or not, Gascoigne had an original mind and was one of the two or three most versatile writers of the entire century.

GREENE, ROBERT (1558-1592). He was probably the son of a saddler in Norwich (according to Edwin H. Miller, *Professional Writer in Elizabethan England*, p. 8). In 1575 he entered Cambridge; by 1588 he had obtained the M.A. from Oxford as well as Cambridge and referred to himself as

"Master of Arts in both universities." The few available facts of his life need to be reassessed. He seems to have married a girl of gentle birth, squandered her dowry, deserted her and their child, and ended up penniless in the gutter at age thirty-four; but why he thus burned himself out no one seems to know. He possessed charm and wit in abundance; and although he wrote fast and carelessly, he had a great deal of talent. *Mamillia* (1583) was his first romance and first published work; *Pandosto* (1588) and *Menaphon* (1589) were perhaps the best of fifteen or so romances written in the 1580's. In addition, he wrote at least six plays, including *Friar Bacon and Friar Bungay* (c. 1591), and at least a dozen pamphlets. *A Notable Discovery of Cozenage* (1591) was the first of several pamphlets on the subject of crime in the Elizabethan underworld, which Greene seems to have known firsthand. But the self-castigation in the seemingly autobiographical pamphlets—*Greene's Mourning Garment, Greene's Farewell to Folly, Greene's Groatsworth of Wit, The Repentance of Robert Greene,* and *Greene's Vision*—should not be taken as literally as it has been on occasion. One critic affirms that in *Groatsworth of Wit* Greene "dropped the pretense of fiction" and wrote autobiographically. But the "Greene" who emerges from the pamphlets may be just as much of a creation as a character in one of the romances. Tucker Brooke observed (*Literary History of England,* [New York, 1948], p. 428) that Greene in one respect may be compared to Bunyan in *Grace Abounding:* like Bunyan, he gives such an orderly analysis of his allegedly disordered life that it is difficult to believe in his moral ruin. Brooke probably is right—even if Greene was guilty of something more than Bunyan's furtive ringing of the church bell.

LODGE, THOMAS (1558–1625). His father was like a character in one of Deloney's romances; the elder Thomas Lodge began as an apprentice grocer, became wealthy, rose to the highest civic offices—alderman, sheriff, and mayor of London. The son went to the Merchant Taylor's School in London and then to Trinity College, Oxford, where he took the A.B. in 1577. He entered Lincoln's Inn to study law the following year; but although he lived there off and on for the next seventeen years as "gentleman in chambers" (acording to E. A. Tenney, *Lodge* [Ithaca, N.Y., 1935], p. 64), he never took a law degree. His first published work was *Defense of Plays* (1580), a response to Stephen Gosson's *School of Abuse. Rosalind* (1590) was the most popular (and best) of half a dozen romances. In them and in *Phillis* (1593), a sonnet cycle, he followed trends; but with *Scilla's Metamorphosis* (1589), a long narrative poem in the manner of Shakespeare's *Venus and Adonis,* and *A Fig for Momus* (1595), a verse satire, he helped start new trends. His desire to be active and his need for money seem to have prompted his going on a privateering expedition with Captain Clarke in 1586 to the Azores and Canaries. In 1591 he accompanied Sir Thomas Cavendish on a voyage that was supposed to go round the world and bring back riches from South America and the Orient. But the expedition was a failure in a number of ways; and when Lodge returned to London a year and a half later, he was without money and his friend Robert Greene had died. Later he studied medicine (earning M.D. degrees from both Avignon and Oxford), turned Catholic, married, practiced medicine in London, and translated Seneca. In *A Treatise of the Plague* Dr. Lodge showed what a literary man with a medical degree could do in analyzing the terrible plague of 1603 (that "wonderful year" when Queen Elizabeth died and the Tudor dynasty came to an end.)

LYLY, JOHN (1554?–1606). His grandfather was William Lyly, friend of Colet and Erasmus and author of the Latin grammar used in Elizabethan schools. His father was a minor ecclesiastical official. Lyly himself took the A.B. at Magdalen College, Oxford, in 1573 and the M.A. two years later. His first published work, *Euphues: The Anatomy of Wit* (1578), was one of the most popular works of the age; there were no less than twenty editions of it by 1636. A sequel, *Euphues and His England* (1580) was not quite so popular. As G. K. Hunter has shown (*Lyly*, pp. 68 ff.) Lyly's patron and employer during his most creative period was the Earl of Oxford, son-in-law of Burghley, to whom Lyly also owed some allegiance. In the summer of 1589 the bishops enlisted Lyly to defend their cause against "Martin Marprelate," the pseudonym used by one or more anonymous Puritan writers who attacked the bishops in a lively and idiomatic invective. Lyly's only performance was *Pap with a Hatchet* (1589), in which he showed that he had no gift for polemic or satire. His gift was for the language of *Euphues*, which we call "euphuism" and which carried over into the well-chiseled dialogue of seven plays, all comedies, beginning with *Campaspe* (1584); all seven were in prose except *The Woman in the Moon* (*c.* 1589), which was in blank verse. *Endymion* and *Gallathea* are perhaps the favorites today. With his last play, *Mother Bombie* (1590), he faded out of the literary picture—except in his tremendous influence, which may be seen in Shakespeare's *Love's Labor's Lost*, Lodge's *Rosalind*, and many another play and work of prose fiction through the 1590's.

NASHE, THOMAS (1567–1601). Of his family, background, and early years practically nothing is known. After graduating from St. John's College, Cambridge, in 1586, he continued studying at the university for a while and then began writing in London for a living. His first published work was a preface to Greene's *Menaphon* (1589). As McKerrow suggests (*Works of Thomas Nashe*, V, 15), Nashe may have achieved a local reputation as a wit, even without having published anything yet, "for otherwise it is hard to understand his being asked to introduce the work of so well known a writer as Robert Greene." Yet he was Greene's friend, which probably also was a factor. In the same year he seems to have been employed (as was Lyly) by the bishops to help answer the Puritans who were writing the anonymous tracts signed "Martin Marprelate." But what

Nashe actually contributed we are not sure, though it is possible that he wrote the anti-Martinist pamphlet called *An Almond for a Parrot*. The other great controversy that he entered has long been called the "Harvey–Nashe Quarrel." Gabriel Harvey, more than a dozen years older than Nashe, was considerably more learned but not nearly so clever and witty. *Pierce Penniless* (1592), *Strange News* (1593), and *Have with You to Saffron Waldon* (1596) show Nashe's genius for satire. All his writings have elements of satire in them, including *The Unfortunate Traveler* (1594), his only work of prose fiction, and a play, now lost, called *The Isle of Dogs* (1597), probably written in collaboration with Ben Jonson. Apparently the satire in the play was so strong that Jonson was imprisoned and Nashe would have been if he had not fled to Yarmouth to lie low for six weeks. Unlike Gascoigne, Greene, and Lodge, he was not versatile; but he probably was the best satirist the age produced. Unlike Lodge, he seems to have done little traveling, and probably none outside England. In *The Unfortunate Traveler* he occasionally gives the impression of having traveled; but verisimilitude is part of his job as a storyteller. Privately he may have agreed with the "banished English earl" that everything people claim they get from travel "we may read in books, and a great deal more, too, without stirring our feet out of a warm study" (p. 523).

RICH, BARNABY (1542–1617). Nothing is known of Rich's parents or early life. He referred to himself as a gentleman, but at one point he asserts that "every ordinary soldier that hath served seven years without reproach ought to be accounted a gentleman" (Cranfill and Bruce, *Rich*, pp. 14–15). By that criterion Rich was indeed a gentleman, though he may have been one also by the strict criterion that he also mentions: "a gentleman born ... must be descended from three degrees of gentry, both by father and mother." He did not attend either university. His military career began in 1562 when he served under the Earl of Warwick at Le Havre. By 1570 he was serving in Ireland; and within a few years he was soldiering in Holland, about which he writes in *Alarm to England* (1578). His first publication, however, had been *A Right Excellent and Pleasant Dialogue between Mercury and an English Soldier* (1574). Later he wrote *A Pathway to Military Practice* (1587), a military handbook. But although Rich was primarily a soldier, and in his writings usually dealt with public affairs relating to his military service, he also attempted romances—notably *Don Simonides* (1581, with a sequel in 1584), *Farewell to the Military Profession* (1581), a collection of eight *novelle*, and *The Adventures of Brusanus* (1592).